KIPLING

A Selection of His Stories and Poems

VOLUME II

KIPLING

A Selection of His Stories and Poems

ed BY JOHN BEECROFT

ILLUSTRATED BY RICHARD M. POWERS

Doubleday & Company, Inc., Garden City, New York

CONTENTS

VOLUME II

STORIES

STORIES

'THE FINEST STORY IN THE WORLD'

'Or ever the knightly years were gone
With the old world to the grave,
I was a king in Babylon
And you were a Christian slave.'

W. E. HENLEY

HIS name was Charlie Mears; he was the only son of his mother who was a widow, and he lived in the north of London, coming into the City every day to work in a bank. He was twenty years old and suffered from aspirations. I met him in a public billiard-saloon where the marker called him by his first name, and he called the marker 'Bullseyes.' Charlie explained, a little nervously, that he had only come to the place to look on, and since looking on at games of skill is not a cheap amusement for the young, I suggested that Charlie should go back to his mother.

That was our first step towards better acquaintance. He would call on me sometimes in the evenings instead of running about London with his fellow-clerks; and before long, speaking of himself as a young man must, he told me of his aspirations, which were all literary. He desired to make himself an undying name chiefly through verse, though he was not above sending stories of love and death to the penny-in-the-slot journals. It was my fate to sit still while Charlie read me poems of many hundred lines, and bulky fragments of plays that would surely shake the world. My reward was his unreserved confidence, and the self-revelations and troubles of a young man are almost as holy as those of a maiden. Charlie had never fallen in love, but was anxious to do so at the first opportunity; he believed in all things good and all things honourable, but at the same time, was curiously careful to let me see that he knew his way about the world as befitted a bank-clerk on twenty-five shillings a week. He rhymed 'dove' with 'love' and 'moon' with 'June,' and devoutly believed that they had never so been rhymed before. The long lame gaps in his plays he filled up with hasty words of apology and description and swept on, seeing all that he intended to do so clearly that he esteemed it already done, and turned to me for applause.

I fancy that his mother did not encourage his aspirations, and I know that his writing-table at home was the edge of his washstand. This he told me almost at the outset of our acquaintance; when he was ravaging my bookshelves, and a little before I was implored to speak the truth as to his chances of 'writing something really great, you know.' Maybe I encouraged him too much, for, one night, he called on me, his eyes flaming with excitement, and said breathlessly:—

'Do you mind—can you let me stay here and write all this evening? I won't interrupt you, I won't really. There's no place for me to write in at my mother's.'

'What's the trouble?' I said, knowing well what that trouble was.

'I've a notion in my head that would make the most splendid story that was ever written. Do let me write it out here. It's *such* a notion!'

There was no resisting the appeal. I set him a table; he hardly thanked me, but plunged into the work at once. For half an hour the pen scratched without stopping. Then Charlie sighed and tugged his hair. The scratching grew slower; there were more erasures; and at last ceased. The finest story in the world would not come forth.

'It looks such awful rot now,' he said mournfully. 'And yet it seemed so good when I was thinking about it. What's wrong?'

I could not dishearten him by saying the truth. So I answered: 'Perhaps you don't feel in the mood for writing.'

'Yes, I do—except when I look at this stuff. Ugh!'

'Read me what you've done,' I said.

He read, and it was wondrous bad, and he paused at all the specially turgid sentences, expecting a little approval; for he was proud of those sentences, as I knew he would be.

'It needs compression,' I suggested cautiously.

'I hate cutting my things down. I don't think you could alter a word here without spoiling the sense. It reads better aloud than when I was writing it.'

'Charlie, you're suffering from an alarming disease afflicting a numerous class. Put the thing by, and tackle it again in a week.'

'I want to do it at once. What do you think of it?'

'How can I judge from a half-written tale? Tell me the story as it lies in your head.'

Charlie told, and in the telling there was everything that his ignorance had so carefully prevented from escaping into the written word. I looked at him, wondering whether it were possible that he did not know the originality, the power of the notion that had come in his way? It was distinctly a Notion among notions. Men had been puffed up with pride by ideas not a tithe as excellent and practicable. But Charlie babbled on serenely, interrupting the current of pure fancy with samples of horrible sentences that he purposed to use. I heard him out to the end. It would be folly to allow his thought to remain in his own inept hands, when I could do so much with it. Not all that could be done indeed; but, oh so much!

'What do you think?' he said at last. 'I fancy I shall call it "The Story of a Ship."'

'I think the idea is pretty good; but you won't be able to handle it for ever so long. Now I——'

'Would it be of any use to you? Would you care to take it? I should be proud,' said Charlie promptly.

There are few things sweeter in this world than the guileless, hot-headed, intemperate, open admiration of a junior. Even a woman in her blindest devotion does not fall into the gait of the man she adores, tilt her bonnet to the angle at which he wears his hat, or interlard her speech with his pet oaths. And Charlie did all these things. Still it was necessary to salve my conscience before I possessed myself of Charlie's thought.

'Let's make a bargain. I'll give you a fiver for the notion,' I said.

Charlie became a bank-clerk at once.

'Oh, that's impossible. Between two pals, you know, if I may call you so, and speaking as a man of the world, I couldn't. Take the notion if it's any use to you. I've heaps more.'

He had—none knew this better than I—but they were the notions of other men.

'Look at it as a matter of business—between men of the world,' I returned. 'Five pounds will buy you any number of poetry-books. Business is business, and you may be sure I shouldn't give that price unless——'

'Oh, if you put it *that* way,' said Charlie, visibly moved by the thought of the books. The bargain was clinched with an agreement that he should at unstated intervals come to me with all the notions that he possessed, should have a table of his own to write at, and unquestioned right to inflict upon me all his poems and fragments of poems. Then I said, 'Now tell me how you came by this idea.'

'It came by itself.' Charlie's eyes opened a little.

'Yes, but you told me a great deal about the hero that you must have read before somewhere.'

'I haven't any time for reading, except when you let me sit here, and on Sundays I'm on my bicycle or down the river all day. There's nothing wrong about the hero, is there?'

'Tell me again and I shall understand clearly. You say that your hero went pirating. How did he live?'

'He was on the lower deck of this ship-thing that I was telling you about.'

'What sort of ship?'

'It was the kind rowed with oars, and the sea spurts through the oar-holes and the men row sitting up to their knees in water. Then there's a bench running down between the two lines of oars and an overseer with a whip walks up and down the bench to make the men work.'

'How do you know that?'

'It's in the tale. There's a rope running overhead, looped to the upper deck, for the overseer to catch hold of when the ship rolls. When the over-seer misses the rope once and falls among the rowers, remember the hero laughs at him and gets licked for it. He's chained to his oar of course—the hero.'

'How is he chained?'

'With an iron band round his waist fixed to the bench he sits on, and a sort of handcuff on his left wrist chaining him to the oar. He's on the lower deck where the worst men are sent, and the only light comes from the hatch-ways and through the oar-holes. Can't you imagine the sunlight just squeez-ing through between the handle and the hole and wobbling about as the ship rolls?'

'I can, but I can't imagine your imagining it.'

'How could it be any other way? Now you listen to me. The long oars on the upper deck are managed by four men to each bench, the lower ones by three, and the lowest of all by two. Remember it's quite dark on the lowest deck and all the men there go mad. When a man dies at his oar on that deck he isn't thrown overboard, but cut up in his chains and stuffed through the oar-hole in little pieces.'

'Why?' I demanded amazed, not so much at the information as the tone of command in which it was flung out.

'To save trouble and to frighten the others. It needs two overseers to drag a man's body up to the top deck; and if the men at the lower-deck oars were left alone, of course they'd stop rowing and try to pull up the benches by all standing up together in their chains.'

'You've a most provident imagination. Where have you been reading about galleys and galley-slaves?'

'Nowhere that I remember. I row a little when I get the chance. But, perhaps, if you say so, I may have read something.'

He went away shortly afterwards to deal with booksellers, and I won-dered how a bank-clerk aged twenty could put into my hands with a profligate abundance of detail, all given with absolute assurance, the story of extrava-gant and bloodthirsty adventure, riot, piracy, and death in unnamed seas. He had led his hero a desperate dance through revolt against the overseers, to command of a ship of his own, and the ultimate establishment of a king-dom on an island 'somewhere in the sea, you know;' and, delighted with my paltry five pounds, had gone out to buy the notions of other men, that these might teach him how to write. I had the consolation of knowing that this notion was mine by right of purchase; and I thought that I could make something of it.

When next he came to me he was drunk—royally drunk—on many poets for the first time revealed to him. His pupils were dilated, his words tumbled over each other, and he wrapped himself in quotations—as a beggar would enfold himself in the purple of Emperors. Most of all was he drunk with Longfellow.

'Isn't it splendid? Isn't it superb?' he cried, after hasty greetings. 'Listen to this—

> ' "Wouldst thou,"—so the helmsman answered,
>   "Know the secret of the sea?
> Only those who brave its dangers
> Comprehend its mystery."

By gum!

> ' "Only those who brave its dangers
>   Comprehend its mystery." '

he repeated twenty times, walking up and down the room and forgetting me. 'But I can understand it too,' he said to himself. 'I don't know how to thank you for that fiver. And this; listen—

> ' "I remember the black wharves and the slips
>   And the sea-tides tossing free;
> And the Spanish sailors with bearded lips,
> And the beauty and mystery of the ships,
> And the magic of the sea."

I haven't braved any dangers, but I feel as if I knew all about it.'

'You certainly seem to have a grip of the sea. Have you ever seen it?'

'When I was a little chap I went to Brighton once; we used to live in Coventry, though, before we came to London. I never saw it,

> ' "When descends on the Atlantic
>   The gigantic
> Storm-wind of the Equinox." '

He shook me by the shoulder to make me understand the passion that was shaking himself.

'When that storm comes,' he continued, 'I think that all the oars in the ship that I was talking about get broken, and the rowers have their chests smashed in by the oar-heads bucking. By the way, have you done anything with that notion of mine, yet?'

'No. I was waiting to hear more of it from you. Tell me how in the world you're so certain about the fittings of the ship. You know nothing of ships.'

'I don't know. It's as real as anything to me until I try to write it down. I was thinking about it only last night in bed, after you had lent me *Treasure Island*; and I made up a whole lot of new things to go into the story.'

'What sort of things?'

'About the food the men ate; rotten figs and black beans and wine in a skin-bag, passed from bench to bench.'

'Was the ship built so long ago as *that*?'

'As what? I don't know whether it was long ago or not. It's only a notion, but sometimes it seems just as real as if it was true. Do I bother you with talking about it?'

'Not in the least. Did you make up anything else?'

'Yes, but it's nonsense.' Charlie flushed a little.

'Never mind; let's hear about it.'

'Well, I was thinking over the story, and after awhile I got out of bed and wrote down on a piece of paper the sort of stuff the men might be supposed to scratch on their oars with the edges of their handcuffs. It seemed to make the thing more life-like. It *is* so real to me, y'know.'

'Have you the paper on you?'

'Ye—es, but what's the use of showing it? It's only a lot of scratches. All the same, we might have 'em reproduced in the book on the front page.'

'I'll attend to those details. Show me what your men wrote.'

He pulled out of his pocket a sheet of notepaper, with a single line of scratches upon it, and I put this carefully away.

'What is it supposed to mean in English?' I said.

'Oh, I don't know. I mean it to mean "I'm beastly tired." It's great nonsense,' he repeated, 'but all those men in the ship seem as real as real people to me. Do do something to the notion soon; I should like to see it written and printed.'

'But all you've told me would make a long book.'

'Make it then. You've only to sit down and write it out.'

'Give me a little time. Have you any more notions?'

'Not just now. I'm reading all the books I've bought. They're splendid.'

When he had left I looked at the sheet of notepaper with the inscription upon it. Then I took my head tenderly between both hands, to make certain that it was not coming off or turning around. Then . . . but there seemed to be no interval between leaving my rooms and finding myself arguing with a policeman outside a door marked *Private* in a corridor of the British Museum. All I demanded, as politely as possible, was 'the Greek antiquity man.' The policeman knew nothing except the rules of the Museum, and it became necessary to forage through all the houses and offices inside the gates. An elderly gentleman called away from his lunch put an end to my search by holding the notepaper between finger and thumb and sniffing at it scornfully.

'What does this mean? H'mm,' said he. 'So far as I can ascertain it is an attempt to write extremely corrupt Greek on the part'—here he glared at me with intention—'of an extremely illiterate—ah—person.' He read slowly from the paper, '*Pollock, Erckmann, Tauchnitz, Henniker*'—four names familiar to me.

'Can you tell me what the corruption is supposed to mean—the gist of the thing?' I asked.

'I have been—many times—overcome with weariness in this particular employment. That is the meaning.' He returned me the paper, and I fled without a word of thanks, explanation, or apology.

I might have been excused for forgetting much. To me of all men had been given the chance to write the most marvellous tale in the world, nothing less than the story of a Greek galley-slave, as told by himself. Small wonder that his dreaming had seemed real to Charlie. The Fates that are so careful to shut the doors of each successive life behind us had, in this case, been neglectful, and Charlie was looking, though that he did not know, where never man had been permitted to look with full knowledge since Time began. Above all, he was absolutely ignorant of the knowledge sold to me for five pounds; and he would retain that ignorance; for bank-clerks do not understand metempsychosis, and a sound commercial education does not include Greek. He would supply me—here I capered among the dumb gods of Egypt and laughed in their battered faces—with material to make my tale sure—so sure that the world would hail it as an impudent and vamped fiction. And I—I alone would know that it was absolutely and literally true. I—I alone held this jewel to my hand for the cutting and polishing. Therefore I danced again among the gods of the Egyptian court, till a policeman saw me and took steps in my direction.

It remained now only to encourage Charlie to talk, and here there was no difficulty. But I had forgotten those accursed books of poetry. He came to me time after time, as useless as a surcharged phonograph—drunk on Byron, Shelley, or Keats. Knowing now what the boy had been in his past lives, and desperately anxious not to lose one word of his babble, I could not hide from him my respect and interest. He misconstrued both into respect for the present soul of Charlie Mears, to whom life was as new as it was to Adam, and interest in his readings: he stretched my patience to breaking point by reciting poetry—not his own now, but that of others. I wished every English poet blotted out of the memory of mankind. I blasphemed the mightiest names of song because they had drawn Charlie from the path of direct narrative, and would, later, spur him to imitate them; but I choked down my impatience until the first flood of enthusiasm should have spent itself and the boy returned to his dreams.

'What's the use of my telling you what I think, when these chaps wrote things for the angels to read?' he growled, one evening. 'Why don't you write something like theirs?'

'I don't think you're treating me quite fairly,' I said, speaking under strong restraint.

'I've given you the story,' he said shortly, replunging into 'Lara.'

'But I want the details.'

'The things I make up about that damned ship that you call a galley? They're quite easy. You can just make 'em up for yourself. Turn up the gas a little, I want to go on reading.'

I could have broken the gas-globe over his head for his amazing stupidity. I could indeed make up things for myself did I only know what Charlie did not know that he knew. But since the doors were shut behind me I could only wait his youthful pleasure and strive to keep him in good temper. One minute's want of guard might spoil a priceless revelation: now and again he would toss his books aside—he kept them in my rooms, for his mother would have been shocked at the waste of good money had she seen them—and launched into his sea dreams. Again I cursed all the poets of England. The plastic mind of the bank-clerk had been overlaid, coloured, and distorted by that which he had read, and the result as delivered was a confused tangle of other voices most like the mutter and hum through a City telephone in the busiest part of the day.

He talked of the galley—his own galley had he but known it—with illustrations borrowed from the 'Bride of Abydos.' He pointed the experiences of his hero with quotations from 'The Corsair,' and threw in deep and desperate moral reflections from 'Cain' and 'Manfred,' expecting me to use them all. Only when the talk turned on Longfellow were the jarring cross-currents dumb, and I knew that Charlie was speaking the truth as he remembered it.

'What do you think of this?' I said one evening, as soon as I understood the medium in which his memory worked best, and, before he could expostulate, read him nearly the whole of 'The Saga of King Olaf.'

He listened open-mouthed, flushed, his hands drumming on the back of the sofa where he lay, till I came to the Song of Einar Tamberskelver and the verse:—

> ' "Einar then, the arrow taking
> From the loosened string,
> Answered, "That was Norway breaking
> 'Neath thy hand, O King." ' '

He gasped with pure delight of sound.

'That's better than Byron, a little?' I ventured.

'Better! Why it's *true!* How could he have known?'

I went back and repeated:—

> ' "What was that?" said Olaf, standing
> On the quarter-deck,
> "Something heard I like the stranding
> Of a shattered wreck." ' '

'How could he have known how the ships crash and the oars rip out and go z-zzp all along the line? Why only the other night . . . But go back please and read "The Skerry of Shrieks" again.'

'No, I'm tired. Let's talk. What happened the other night?'

'I had an awful dream about that galley of ours. I dreamed I was drowned in a fight. You see we ran alongside another ship in harbour. The water was dead still except where our oars whipped it up. You know where I always sit in the galley?' He spoke haltingly at first, under the fine English fear of being laughed at.

'No. That's news to me,' I answered meekly, my heart beginning to beat.

'On the fourth oar from the bow on the right side on the upper deck. There were four of us at that oar, all chained. I remember watching the water and trying to get my handcuffs off before the row began. Then we closed up on the other ship, and all their fighting men jumped over our bulwarks, and my bench broke and I was pinned down with the three other fellows on top of me, and the big oar jammed across our backs.'

'Well?' Charlie's eyes were alive and alight. He was looking at the wall behind my chair.

'I don't know how we fought. The men were trampling all over my back, and I lay low. Then our rowers on the left side—tied to their oars, you know—began to yell and back water. I could hear the water sizzle, and we spun round like a cock-chafer and I knew, lying where I was, that there was a galley coming up bow-on, to ram us on the left side. I could just lift my head and see her sail over the bulwarks. We wanted to meet her bow to bow, but it was too late. We could only turn a little bit because the galley on our right had hooked herself on to us and stopped our moving. Then, by gum! there was a crash! Our left oars began to break as the other galley, the moving one y'know, stuck her nose into them. Then the lower-deck oars shot up through the deck planking, butt first, and one of them jumped clear up into the air and came down again close at my head.'

'How was that managed?'

'The moving galley's bow was plunking them back through their own oar-holes, and I could hear no end of a shindy in the decks below. Then her nose caught us nearly in the middle, and we tilted sideways, and the fellows in the right-hand galley unhitched their hooks and ropes, and threw things on to our upper deck—arrows, and hot pitch or something that stung, and we went up and up on the left side, and the right side dipped, and I twisted my head round and saw the water stand still as it topped the right bulwarks; and then it curled over and crashed down on the whole lot of us on the right side, and I felt it hit my back, and I woke.'

'One minute, Charlie. When the sea topped the bulwarks, what did it look like?' I had my reasons for asking. A man of my acquaintance had once gone down with a leaking ship in a still sea, and had seen the water-level pause for an instant ere it fell on the dock.

'It looked just like a banjo-string drawn tight, and it seemed to stay there for years,' said Charlie.

Exactly! The other man had said: 'It looked like a silver wire laid down along the bulwarks, and I thought it was never going to break.' He had paid everything except the bare life for this little valueless piece of knowledge, and I had travelled ten thousand weary miles to meet him and take his knowledge at second hand. But Charlie, the bank-clerk on twenty-five shillings a week, who had never been out of sight of a made road, knew it all. It was no consolation to me that once in his lives he had been forced to die for his gains. I also must have died scores of times, but behind me, because I could have used my knowledge, the doors were shut!

'And then?' I said, trying to put away the devil of envy.

'The funny thing was, though, in all the row I didn't feel a bit astonished or frightened. It seemed as if I'd been in a good many fights, because I told my next man so when the row began. But that cad of an overseer on my deck wouldn't unloose our chains and give us a chance. He always said that we'd all be set free after a battle, but we never were; we never were.' Charlie shook his head mournfully.

'What a scoundrel!'

'I should say he was. He never gave us enough to eat, and sometimes we were so thirsty that we used to drink salt-water. I can taste that salt-water still.'

'Now tell me something about the harbour where the fight was fought.'

'I didn't dream about that. I know it was a harbour though; because we were tied up to a ring on a white wall and all the face of the stone under water was covered with wood to prevent our ram getting chipped when the tide made us rock.'

'That's curious. Our hero commanded the galley, didn't he?'

'Didn't he just! He stood by the bows and shouted like a good 'un. He was the man who killed the overseer.'

'But you were all drowned together, Charlie, weren't you?'

'I can't make that fit quite,' he said, with a puzzled look. 'The galley must have gone down with all hands, and yet I fancy that the hero went on living afterwards. Perhaps he climbed into the attacking ship. I wouldn't see that, of course. I was dead, you know.'

He shivered slightly and protested that he could remember no more.

I did not press him further, but to satisfy myself that he lay in ignorance of the workings of his own mind, deliberately introduced him to Mortimer Collins's *Transmigration*, and gave him a sketch of the plot before he opened the pages.

'What rot it all is!' he said frankly, at the end of an hour. 'I don't understand his nonsense about the Red Planet Mars and the King, and the rest of it. Chuck me the Longfellow again.'

I handed him the book and wrote out as much as I could remember of his description of the sea-fight, appealing to him from time to time for confirmation of fact or detail. He would answer without raising his eyes from the book, as assuredly as though all his knowledge lay before him on the printed page. I spoke under the normal key of my voice that the current might not be broken, and I know that he was not aware of what he was saying, for his thoughts were out on the sea with Longfellow.

'Charlie,' I asked, 'when the rowers on the galleys mutinied how did they kill their overseers?'

'Tore up the benches and brained 'em. That happened when a heavy sea was running. An overseer on the lower deck slipped from the centre plank and fell among the rowers. They choked him to death against the side of the ship with their chained hands quite quietly, and it was too dark for the other overseer to see what had happened. When he asked he was pulled down too and choked, and the lower deck fought their way up deck by deck, with the pieces of the broken benches banging behind 'em. How they howled!'

'And what happened after that?'

'I don't know. The hero went away—red hair and red beard and all. That was after he had captured our galley, I think.'

The sound of my voice irritated him, and he motioned slightly with his left hand as a man does when interruption jars.

'You never told me he was red-headed before, or that he captured your galley,' I said, after a discreet interval.

Charlie did not raise his eyes.

'He was as red as a red bear,' said he abstractedly. 'He came from the north; they said so in the galley when he looked for rowers—not for slaves, but free men. Afterwards—years and years afterwards—news came from another ship, or else he came back——'

His lips moved in silence. He was rapturously retasting some poem before him.

'Where had he been, then?' I was almost whispering that the sentence might come gently to whichever section of Charlie's brain that was working on my behalf.

'To the Beaches—the Long and Wonderful Beaches!' was the reply after a minute of silence.

'To Furdurstrandi?' I asked, tingling from head to foot.

'Yes, to Furdurstrandi,' he pronounced the word in a new fashion. 'And I too saw——' The voice failed.

'Do you know what you have said?' I shouted incautiously.

He lifted his eyes, fully roused now. 'No!' he snapped. 'I wish you'd let a chap go on reading. Hark to this:—

' "But Othere, the old sea-captain,
    He neither paused nor stirred
      Till the king listened, and then
      Once more took up his pen
    And wrote down every word.

' "And to the King of the Saxons
    In witness of the truth,
      Raising his noble head,
      He stretched his brown hand and said,
  'Behold this walrus tooth.' "

By Jove, what chaps those must have been, to go sailing all over the shop never knowing where they'd fetch the land! Hah!'

'Charlie,' I pleaded, 'if you'll only be sensible for a minute or two I'll make our hero in our tale every inch as good as Othere.'

'Umph! Longfellow wrote that poem. I don't care about writing things any more. I want to read.' He was thoroughly out of tune now, and raging over my own ill-luck, I left him.

Conceive yourself at the door of the world's treasure-house guarded by a child—an idle irresponsible child playing knuckle-bones—on whose favour depends the gift of the key, and you will imagine one-half my torment. Till that evening Charlie had spoken nothing that might not lie within the experiences of a Greek galley-slave. But now, or there was no virtue in books, he had talked of some desperate adventure of the Vikings, of Thorfin Karlsefne's sailing to Wineland, which is America, in the ninth or tenth century. The battle in the harbour he had seen; and his own death he had described. But this was a much more startling plunge into the past. Was it possible that he had skipped half a dozen lives and was then dimly remembering some episode of a thousand years later? It was a maddening jumble, and the worst of it was that Charlie Mears in his normal condition was the last person in the world to clear it up. I could only wait and watch, but I went to bed that night full of the wildest imaginings. There was nothing that was not possible if Charlie's detestable memory only held good.

I might rewrite the Saga of Thorfin Karlsefne as it had never been written before, might tell the story of the first discovery of America, myself the discoverer. But I was entirely at Charlie's mercy, and so long as there was a three-and-sixpenny Bohn volume within his reach Charlie would not tell. I dared not curse him openly; I hardly dared jog his memory, for I was dealing with the experiences of a thousand years ago, told through the mouth of a boy of to-day; and a boy of to-day is affected by every change of tone and gust of opinion, so that he must lie even when he most desires to speak the truth.

I saw no more of Charlie for nearly a week. When next I met him it was in Gracechurch Street with a bill-book chained to his waist. Business took him over London Bridge, and I accompanied him. He was very full of the importance of that book and magnified it. As we passed over the Thames we paused to look at a steamer unloading great slabs of white and brown marble. A barge drifted under the steamer's stern and a lonely ship's cow in that barge bellowed. Charlie's face changed from the face of the bank-clerk to that of an unknown and—though he would not have believed this—a much shrewder man. He flung out his arm across the parapet of the bridge and laughing very loudly, said:—

'When they heard *our* bulls bellow the Skrœlings ran away!'

I waited only for an instant, but the barge and the cow had disappeared under the bows of the steamer before I answered.

'Charlie, what do you suppose are Skrœlings?'

'Never heard of 'em before. They sound like a new kind of sea-gull. What a chap you are for asking questions!' he replied. 'I have to go to the cashier of the Omnibus Company yonder. Will you wait for me and we can lunch somewhere together? I've a notion for a poem.'

'No, thanks. I'm off. You're sure you know nothing about Skrœlings?'

'Not unless he's been entered for the Liverpool Handicap.' He nodded and disappeared in the crowd.

Now it is written in the Saga of Eric the Red or that of Thorfin Karl-sefne, that nine hundred years ago when Karlsefne's galleys came to Leif's booths, which Leif had erected in the unknown land called Markland, which may or may not have been Rhode Island, the Skrœlings—and the Lord He knows who these may or may not have been—came to trade with the Vikings, and ran away because they were frightened at the bellowing of the cattle which Thorfin had brought with him in the ships. But what in the world could a Greek slave know of that affair? I wandered up and down among the streets trying to unravel the mystery, and the more I considered it, the more baffling it grew. One thing only seemed certain, and that certainty took away my breath for the moment. If I came to full knowledge of anything at all, it would not be one life of the soul in Charlie Mears's body; but half a dozen —half a dozen several and separate existences spent on blue water in the morning of the world!

Then I walked round the situation.

Obviously if I used my knowledge I should stand alone and unapproachable until all men were as wise as myself. That would be something, but manlike I was ungrateful. It seemed bitterly unfair that Charlie's memory should fail me when I needed it most. Great Powers above—I looked up at them through the fog smoke—did the Lords of Life and Death know what this meant to me? Nothing less than eternal fame of the best kind, that comes from One, and is shared by one alone. I would be content—remembering Clive, I stood astounded at my own moderation,—with the mere right to tell one story, to work out one little contribution to the light literature of the day. If Charlie were permitted full recollection for one hour—for sixty short minutes—of existences that had extended over a thousand years— I would forego all profit and honour from all that I should make of his speech. I would take no share in the commotion that would follow throughout the particular corner of the earth that calls itself 'the world.' The thing should be put forth anonymously. Nay, I would make other men believe that they had written it. They would hire bull-hided self-advertising Englishmen to bellow it abroad. Preachers would found a fresh conduct of life upon it, swearing that it was new and that they had lifted the fear of death from all mankind. Every Orientalist in Europe would patronise it discursively with Sanskrit and Pali texts. Terrible women would invent unclean variants of the men's belief for the elevation of their sisters. Churches and religions would war over it. Between the hailing and re-starting of an omnibus I foresaw the scuffles that would arise among half a dozen denominations all professing 'the doctrine of the True Metempsychosis as applied to the world and the New Era;' and saw, too, the respectable English newspapers shying, like frightened kine over the beautiful simplicity of the tale. The mind leaped forward a hundred—two hundred—a thousand years. I saw with sorrow that men would mutilate and garble the story; that rival creeds would turn it upside down till, at last, the western world which clings to the dread of death more closely than the hope of life, would set it aside as an interesting superstition and stampede after some faith so long forgotten that it seemed altogether new. Upon this I changed the terms of the bargain that I would make with the Lords of Life and Death. Only let me know, let me write, the story with sure knowledge that I wrote the truth, and I would burn the manuscript as a solemn sacrifice. Five minutes after the last line was written I would destroy it all. But I must be allowed to write it with absolute certainty.

There was no answer. The flaming colours of an Aquarium poster caught my eye, and I wondered whether it would be wise or prudent to lure Charlie into the hands of the professional mesmerist there, and whether, if he were under his power, he would speak of his past lives. If he did, and if people believed him . . . but Charlie would be frightened and fluttered, or made conceited by the interviews. In either case he would begin to lie, through fear or vanity. He was safest in my own hands.

'They are very funny fools, your English,' said a voice at my elbow, and turning round I recognised a casual acquaintance, a young Bengali law student, called Grish Chunder, whose father had sent him to England to become civilised. The old man was a retired native official, and on an income of five pounds a month contrived to allow his son two hundred pounds a year, and the run of his teeth in a city where he could pretend to be the cadet of a royal house, and tell stories of the brutal Indian bureaucrats who ground the faces of the poor.

Grish Chunder was a young, fat, full-bodied Bengali, dressed with scrupulous care in frock-coat, tall hat, light trousers, and tan gloves. But I had known him in the days when the brutal Indian Government paid for his university education, and he contributed cheap sedition to *Sachi Durpan*, and intrigued with the wives of his fourteen-year-old schoolmates.

'That is very funny and very foolish,' he said nodding at the poster. 'I am going down to the Northbrook Club. Will you come too?'

I walked with him for some time. 'You are not well,' he said. 'What is there on your mind? You do not talk.'

'Grish Chunder, you've been too well educated to believe in a God, haven't you?'

'Oah, yes, *here!* But when I go home I must conciliate popular superstition, and make ceremonies of purification, and my women will anoint idols.'

'And hang up *tulsi* and feast the *purohit*, and take you back into caste again and make a good *khuttri* of you again, you advanced social Free-thinker. And you'll eat *desi* food, and like it all, from the smell in the court-yard to the mustard oil over you.'

'I shall very much like it,' said Grish Chunder unguardedly. 'Once a Hindu—always a Hindu. But I like to know what the English think they know.'

'I'll tell you something that one Englishman knows. It's an old tale to you.'

I began to tell the story of Charlie in English, but Grish Chunder put a question in the vernacular, and the history went forward naturally in the tongue best suited for its telling. After all, it could never have been told in English. Grish Chunder heard me, nodding from time to time, and then came up to my rooms, where I finished the tale.

'Beshak,' he said philosophically. 'Lekin darwaza band hai. (Without doubt, but the door is shut.) I have heard of this remembering of previous existences among my people. It is of course an old tale with us, but, to happen to an Englishman—a cow-fed Mlechh—an outcast. By Jove, that is most peculiar!'

'Outcast yourself, Grish Chunder! You eat cow-beef every day. Let's think the thing over. The boy remembers his incarnations.'

'Does he know that?' said Grish Chunder quietly, swinging his legs as he sat on my table. He was speaking in his English now.

'He does not know anything. Would I speak to you if he did? Go on!'

'There is no going on at all. If you tell that to your friends they will say you are mad and put it in the papers. Suppose, now, you prosecute for libel.'

'Let's leave that out of the question entirely. Is there any chance of his being made to speak?'

'There is a chance. Oah, yess! But if he spoke it would mean that all this world would end now—instanto—fall down on your head. These things are not allowed, you know. As I said, the door is shut.'

'Not a ghost of a chance?'

'How can there be? You are a Christi-án, and it is forbidden to eat, in your books, of the Tree of Life, or else you would never die. How shall you all fear death if you all know what your friend does not know that he knows? I am afraid to be kicked, but I am not afraid to die, because I know what I know. You are not afraid to be kicked, but you are afraid to die. If you were not, by God! you English would be all over the shop in an hour, upsetting the balances of power, and making commotions. It would not be good. But no fear. He will remember a little and a little less, and he will call it dreams. Then he will forget altogether. When I passed my First Arts Examination in Calcutta that was all in the cram-book on Wordsworth. "Trailing clouds of glory," you know.'

'This seems to be an exception to the rule.'

'There are no exceptions to rules. Some are not so hard-looking as others, but they are all the same when you touch. If this friend of yours said so-and-so and so-and-so, indicating that he remembered all his lost lives, or one piece of a lost life, he would not be in the bank another hour. He would be what you called sack because he was mad, and they would send him to an asylum for lunatics. You can see that, my friend.'

'Of course I can, but I wasn't thinking of him. His name need never appear in the story.'

'Ah! I see. That story will never be written. You can try.'

'I am going to.'

'For your own credit and for the sake of money, of course?'

'No. For the sake of writing the story. On my honour that will be all.'

'Even then there is no chance. You cannot play with the Gods. It is a very pretty story now. As they say, Let it go on that—I mean at that. Be quick; he will not last long.'

'How do you mean?'

'What I say. He has never, so far, thought about a woman.'

'Hasn't he, though!' I remembered some of Charlie's confidences.

'I mean no woman has thought about him. When that comes; bus—hogya—all up! I know. There are millions of women here. Housemaids, for instance. They kiss you behind doors.'

I winced at the thought of my story being ruined by a housemaid. And yet nothing was more probable.

Grish Chunder grinned.

'Yes—also pretty girls—cousins of his house, and perhaps not of his house. One kiss that he gives back again and remembers will cure all this nonsense, or else——'

'Or else what? Remember he does not know that he knows.'

'I know that. Or else, if nothing happens he will become immersed in the trade and the financial speculations like the rest. It must be so. You can see that it must be so. But the woman will come first, I think.'

There was a rap at the door, and Charlie charged in impetuously. He had been released from office; and by the look in his eyes I could see that he had come over for a long talk; most probably with poems in his pockets. Charlie's poems were very wearying, but sometimes they led him to talk about the galley.

Grish Chunder looked at him keenly for a minute.

'I beg your pardon,' Charlie said uneasily; 'I didn't know you had any one with you.'

'I am going,' said Grish Chunder.

He drew me into the lobby as he departed.

'That is your man,' he said quickly. 'I tell you he will never speak all you wish. That is rot—bosh! But he would be most good to make to see things. Suppose now we pretend that it was only play'—I had never seen Grish Chunder so excited—'and pour the ink-pool into his hand. Eh, what do you think? I tell you that he could see anything that a man could see. Let me get the ink and the camphor. He is a seer and he will tell us very many things.'

'He may be all you say, but I'm not going to trust him to your gods and devils.'

'They will not hurt him. He will only feel a little stupid and dull when he wakes up. You have seen boys look into the ink-pool before.'

'That is the reason why I am not going to see it any more. You'd better go, Grish Chunder.'

He went, insisting far down the staircase that it was throwing away my only chance of looking into the future.

This left me unmoved, for I was concerned for the past, and no peering of hypnotised boys into mirrors and ink-pools would help me to that. But I recognised Grish Chunder's point of view and sympathised with it.

'What a big black brute that was!' said Charlie, when I returned to him. 'Well, look here, I've just done a poem; did it instead of playing dominoes after lunch. May I read it?'

'Let me read it to myself.'

'Then you miss the proper expression. Besides, you always make my things sound as if the rhymes were all wrong.'

'Read it aloud, then. You're like the rest of 'em.'

Charlie mouthed me his poem, and it was not much worse than the average of his verses. He had been reading his books faithfully, but he was not pleased when I told him that I preferred my Longfellow undiluted with Charlie.

Then we began to go through the MS. line by line; Charlie parrying every objection and correction with:

'Yes, that may be better, but you don't catch what I'm driving at.'

Charlie was, in one way at least, very like one kind of poet.

There was a pencil scrawl at the back of the paper and 'What's that?' I said.

'Oh, that's not poetry at all. It's some rot I wrote last night before I went to bed, and it was too much bother to hunt for rhymes; so I made it a sort of blank verse instead.'

Here is Charlie's 'blank verse':—

'We pulled for you when the wind was against us and the sails were low.
　　　Will you never let us go?
We ate bread and onions when you took towns or ran aboard quickly when you were beaten back by the foe,
The captains walked up and down the deck in fair weather singing songs, but we were below,
We fainted with our chins on the oars and you did not see that we were idle for we still swung to and fro.
　　　Will you never let us go?
The salt made the oar-handles like shark-skin; our knees were cut to the bone with salt cracks; our hair was stuck to our foreheads; and our lips were cut to our gums and you whipped us because we could not row.
　　　Will you never let us go?
But in a little time we shall run out of the portholes as the water runs

along the oar-blade, and though you tell the others to row after us you will never catch us till you catch the oar-thresh and tie up the winds in the belly of the sail. Aho!

   Will you never let us go?'

'H'm. What's oar-thresh, Charlie?'

'The water washed up by the oars. That's the sort of song they might sing in the galley y'know. Aren't you ever going to finish that story and give me some of the profits?'

'It depends on yourself. If you had only told me more about your hero in the first instance it might have been finished by now. You're so hazy in your notions.'

'I only want to give you the general notion of it—the knocking about from place to place and the fighting and all that. Can't you fill in the rest yourself? Make the hero save a girl on a pirate-galley and marry her or do something.'

'You're a really helpful collaborator. I suppose the hero went through some few adventures before he married.'

'Well, then, make him a very artful card—a low sort of man—a sort of political man who went about making treaties and breaking them—a black-haired chap who hid behind the mast when the fighting began.'

'But you said the other day that he was red-haired.'

'I couldn't have. Make him black-haired of course. You've no imagination.'

Seeing that I had just discovered the entire principles upon which our half-memory falsely called imagination is based, I felt entitled to laugh, but forbore, for the sake of the tale.

'You're right. *You're* the man with imagination. A black-haired chap in a decked ship,' I said.

'No, an open ship—like a big boat.'

This was maddening.

'Your ship has been built and designed, closed and decked in; you said so yourself,' I protested.

'No, no, not that ship. That was open or half-decked because—— By Jove you're right! You made me think of the hero as a red-haired chap. Of course if he were red, the ship would be an open one with painted sails.'

Surely, I thought, he would remember now that he had served in two galleys at least—in a three-decked Greek one under the black-haired 'political man,' and again in a Viking's open sea-serpent under the man 'red as a red bear' who went to Markland. My devil prompted me to speak.

'Why, "of course," Charlie?' said I.

'I don't know. Are you making fun of me?'

The current was broken for the time being. I took up a note-book and pretended to make many entries in it.

'It's a pleasure to work with an imaginative chap like yourself,' I said, after a pause. 'The way that you've brought out the character of the hero is simply wonderful.'

'Do you think so?' he answered with a pleased flush. 'I often tell myself that there's more in me than my mo—— than people think.'

'There's an enormous amount in you.'

'Then, won't you let me send an essay on The Ways of Bank-Clerks to *Tit-Bits*, and get the guinea prize?'

'That wasn't exactly what I meant, old fellow: perhaps it would be better to wait a little and go ahead with the galley-story.'

'Ah, but I sha'n't get the credit of that. *Tit-Bits* would publish my name and address if I win. What are you grinning at? They *would*.'

'I know it. Suppose you go for a walk. I want to look through my notes about our story.'

Now this reprehensible youth who left me, a little hurt and put back, might for aught he or I knew have been one of the crew of the Argo—had been certainly slave or comrade to Thorfin Karlsefne. Therefore he was deeply interested in guinea competitions. Remembering what Grish Chunder had said I laughed aloud. The Lords of Life and Death would never allow Charlie Mears to speak with full knowledge of his pasts; and I must even piece out what he had told me with my own poor inventions while Charlie wrote of the ways of bank-clerks.

I got together and placed on one file all my notes; and the net result was not cheering. I read them a second time. There was nothing that might not have been compiled at second-hand from other people's books—except, perhaps, the story of the fight in the harbour. The adventures of a Viking had been written many times before; the history of a Greek galley-slave was no new thing, and though I wrote both, who could challenge or confirm the accuracy of my details? I might as well tell a tale of two thousand years hence. The Lords of Life and Death were as cunning as Grish Chunder had hinted. They would allow nothing to escape that might trouble or make easy the minds of men. Though I was convinced of this, yet I could not leave the tale alone. Exaltation followed reaction, not once, but twenty times in the next few weeks. My moods varied with the March sunlight and flying clouds. By night or in the beauty of a spring morning I perceived that I could write that tale and shift continents thereby. In the wet windy afternoons, I saw that the tale might indeed be written, but would be nothing more than a faked, false-varnished, sham-rusted piece of Wardour Street work at the end. Then I blessed Charlie in many ways—though it was no fault of his. He seemed to be busy with prize competitions, and I saw less and less of him as the weeks went by and the earth cracked and grew ripe to spring, and the buds swelled in their sheaths. He did not care to read or talk of what he had read, and there was a new ring of self-assertion in his voice. I hardly cared to remind him of the galley when we met; but Charlie alluded to it on every occasion, always as a story from which money was to be made.

'I think I deserve twenty-five per cent, don't I, at least,' he said, with beautiful frankness. 'I supplied all the ideas, didn't I?'

This greediness for silver was a new side in his nature. I assumed that it had been developed in the City, where Charlie was picking up the curious nasal drawl of the underbred City man.

'When the thing's done we'll talk about it. I can't make anything of it at present. Red-haired or black-haired hero are equally difficult.'

He was sitting by the fire staring at the red coals. 'I can't understand what you find so difficult. It's all as clear as mud to me,' he replied. A jet of gas puffed out between the bars, took light, and whistled softly. 'Suppose we take the red-haired hero's adventures first, from the time that he came south to my galley and captured it and sailed to the Beaches.'

I knew better now than to interrupt Charlie. I was out of reach of pen and paper, and dared not move to get them lest I should break the current. The gas-jet puffed and whinnied, Charlie's voice dropped almost to a whisper, and he told a tale of the sailing of an open galley to Furdurstrandi, of sunsets on the open sea, seen under the curve of the one sail evening after evening when the galley's beak was notched into the centre of the sinking disc, and 'we sailed by that for we had no other guide,' quoth Charlie. He spoke of a landing on an island and explorations in its woods, where the crew killed three men whom they found asleep under the pines. Their ghosts, Charlie said, followed the galley, swimming and choking in the water, and the crew cast lots and threw one of their number overboard as a sacrifice to the strange gods whom they had offended. Then they ate seaweed when their provisions failed, and their legs swelled, and their leader, the red-haired man, killed two rowers who mutinied, and after a year spent among the woods they set sail for their own country, and a wind that never failed carried them back so safely that they all slept at night. This, and much more Charlie told. Sometimes the voice fell so low that I could not catch the words, though every nerve was on the strain. He spoke of their leader, the red-haired man, as a pagan speaks of his God; for it was he who cheered them and slew them impartially as he thought best for their needs; and it was he who steered them for three days among floating ice, each floe crowded with strange beasts that 'tried to sail with us,' said Charlie, 'and we beat them back with the handles of the oars.'

The gas-jet went out, a burnt coal gave way, and the fire settled with a tiny crash to the bottom of the grate. Charlie ceased speaking, and I said no word.

'By Jove!' he said at last, shaking his head. 'I've been staring at the fire till I'm dizzy. What was I going to say?'

'Something about the galley-book.'

'I remember now. It's a quarter of the profits, isn't it?'

'It's anything you like when I've done the tale.'

'I wanted to be sure of that. I must go now. I've—I've an appointment.' And he left me.

Had not my eyes been held I might have known that that broken muttering over the fire was the swan-song of Charlie Mears. But I thought it the prelude to fuller revelation. At last and at last I should cheat the Lords of Life and Death!

When next Charlie came to me I received him with rapture. He was nervous and embarrassed, but his eyes were very full of light, and his lips a little parted.

'I've done a poem,' he said; and then, quickly: 'its the best I've ever done. Read it.' He thrust it into my hand and retreated to the window.

I groaned inwardly. It would be the work of half an hour to criticise— that is to say praise—the poem sufficiently to please Charlie. Then I had good reason to groan, for Charlie, discarding his favourite centipede metres, had launched into shorter and choppier verse, and verse with a motive at the back of it. This is what I read:—

'The day is most fair, the cheery wind
  Halloos behind the hill
Where he bends the wood as seemeth good,
  And the sapling to his will!
Riot O wind; there is that in my blood
  That would not have thee still!

'She gave me herself, O Earth, O Sky;
  Gray sea, she is mine alone!
Let the sullen boulders hear my cry,
  And rejoice tho' they be but stone!

'Mine! I have won her, O good brown earth,
  Make merry! 'Tis hard on Spring;
Make merry; my love is doubly worth
  All worship your fields can bring!
Let the hind that tills you feel my mirth
  At the early harrowing.'

'Yes, it's the early harrowing, past a doubt,' I said, with a dread at my heart. Charlie smiled, but did not answer.

'Red cloud of the sunset, tell it abroad;
  I am victor. Greet me, O Sun,
Dominant master and absolute lord
  Over the soul of one!'

'Well?' said Charlie, looking over my shoulder.

I thought it far from well, and very evil indeed, when he silently laid a photograph on the paper—the photograph of a girl with a curly head, and a foolish slack mouth.

'Isn't it—isn't it wonderful?' he whispered, pink to the tips of his ears, wrapped in the rosy mystery of first love. 'I didn't know; I didn't think—it came like a thunderclap.'

'Yes. It comes like a thunderclap. Are you very happy, Charlie?'

'My God—she—she loves me!' He sat down repeating the last words to himself. I looked at the hairless face, the narrow shoulders already bowed by desk-work, and wondered when, where, and how he had loved in his past lives.

'What will your mother say?' I asked cheerfully.

'I don't care a damn what she says.'

At twenty the things for which one does not care a damn should, properly, be many, but one must not include mothers in the list. I told him this gently; and he described Her, even as Adam must have described to the newly-named beasts the glory and tenderness and beauty of Eve. Incidentally I learned that She was a tobacconist's assistant with a weakness for pretty dress, and had told him four or five times already that She had never been kissed by a man before.

Charlie spoke on and on, and on; while I, separated from him by thousands of years, was considering the beginnings of things. Now I understood why the Lords of Life and Death shut the doors so carefully behind us. It is that we may not remember our first and most beautiful wooings. Were it not so, our world would be without inhabitants in a hundred years.

'Now, about that galley-story,' I said still more cheerfully, in a pause in the rush of the speech.

Charlie looked up as though he had been hit. 'The galley—what galley? Good heavens, don't joke, man! This is serious! You don't know how serious it is!'

Grish Chunder was right. Charlie had tasted the love of woman that kills remembrance, and the finest story in the world would never be written.

A MATTER OF FACT

And if ye doubt the tale I tell,
Steer through the South Pacific swell;
Go where the branching coral hives
Unending strife of endless lives,
Where, leagued about the 'wildered boat,
The rainbow jellies fill and float;
And, lilting where the laver lingers,
The starfish trips on all her fingers;
Where, 'neath his myriad spines ashock,
The sea-egg ripples down the rock;
An orange wonder dimly guessed,
From darkness where the cuttles rest,
Moored o'er the darker deeps that hide
The blind white Sea-snake and his bride;
Who, drowsing, nose the long-lost ships
Let down through darkness to their lips.
                                    —THE PALMS

❦ ONCE a priest always a priest; once a Mason always a Mason; but once a journalist always and for ever a journalist.

There were three of us, all newspaper men, the only passengers on a little tramp-steamer that ran where her owners told her to go. She had once been in the Bilbao iron ore business, had been lent to the Spanish Government for service at Manilla; and was ending her days in the Cape Town coolie-trade, with occasional trips to Madagascar and even as far as England. We found her going to Southampton in ballast, and shipped in her because the fares were nominal. There was Keller, of an American paper, on his way back to the States from palace executions in Madagascar; there was a burly half Dutchman, called Zuyland, who owned and edited a paper up country near Johannesburg; and there was myself, who had solemnly put away all journalism, vowing to forget that I had ever known the difference between an imprint and a stereo advertisement.

Three minutes after Keller spoke to me, as the *Rathmines* cleared Cape Town, I had forgotten the aloofness I desired to feign, and was in heated discussion on the immorality of expanding telegrams beyond a certain fixed point. Then Zuyland came out of his state-room, and we were all at home instantly, because we were men of the same profession needing no introduction. We annexed the boat formally, broke open the passengers' bathroom door—on the Manilla lines the Dons do not wash—cleaned out the orange-peel and cigar-ends at the bottom of the bath, hired a Lascar to shave us throughout the voyage, and then asked each other's names.

Three ordinary men would have quarrelled through sheer boredom before they reached Southampton. We, by virtue of our craft, were anything but ordinary men. A large percentage of the tales of the world, the thirty-nine that cannot be told to ladies and the one that can, are common property coming of a common stock. We told them all, as a matter of form, with all their local and specific variants which are surprising. Then came, in the intervals of steady card-play, more personal histories of adventure and things seen and reported; panics among white folk, when the blind terror ran from man to man on the Brooklyn Bridge, and the people crushed each other to death they knew not why; fires, and faces that opened and shut their mouths horribly at red-hot window-frames; wrecks in frost and snow, reported from the sleet-sheathed rescue tug at the risk of frost-bite; long rides after diamond thieves; skirmishes on the veldt and in municipal committees with the Boers; glimpses of lazy, tangled Cape politics and the mule-rule in the Transvaal; card-tales, horse-tales, woman-tales by the score and the half hundred; till the first mate, who had seen more than us all put together, but lacked words to clothes his tales with, sat open-mouthed far into the dawn.

When the tales were done we picked up cards till a curious hand or a chance remark made one or other of us say, 'That reminds me of a man who—or a business which—' and the anecdotes would continue while the *Rathmines* kicked her way northward through the warm water.

In the morning of one specially warm night we three were sitting immediately in front of the wheel-house where an old Swedish boatswain whom we called 'Frithiof the Dane' was at the wheel pretending that he could not hear our stories. Once or twice Frithiof spun the spokes curiously, and Keller lifted his head from a long chair to ask, 'What is it? Can't you get any pull on her?'

'There is a feel in the water,' said Frithiof, 'that I cannot understand. I think that we run downhills or somethings. She steers bad this morning.'

Nobody seems to know the laws that govern the pulse of the big waters. Sometimes even a landsman can tell that the solid ocean is a-tilt, and that the ship is working herself up a long unseen slope; and sometimes the captain says, when neither full steam nor fair wind justify the length of a day's run, that the ship is sagging downhill; but how these ups and downs come about has not yet been settled authoritatively.

'No, it is a following sea,' said Frithiof; 'and with a following sea you shall not get good steerage way.'

The sea was as smooth as a duck-pond, except for a regular oily swell. As I looked over the side to see where it might be following us from, the sun rose in a perfectly clear sky and struck the water with its light so sharply that it seemed as though the sea should clang like a burnished gong. The wake of the screw and the little white streak cut by the log-line hanging over the stern were the only marks on the water as far as eye could reach.

Keller rolled out of his chair and went aft to get a pine-apple from the ripening stock that were hung inside the after awning.

'Frithiof, the log-line has got tired of swimming. It's coming home,' he drawled.

'What?' said Frithiof, his voice jumping several octaves.

'Coming home,' Keller repeated, leaning over the stern. I ran to his side and saw the log-line, which till then had been drawn tense over the stern railing, slacken, loop, and come up off the port quarter. Frithiof called up the speaking-tube to the bridge, and the bridge answered, 'Yes, nine knots.' Then Frithiof spoke again, and the answer was, 'What do you want of the skipper?' and Frithiof bellowed, 'Call him up.'

By this time Zuyland, Keller, and myself had caught something of Frithiof's excitement, for any emotion on shipboard is most contagious. The captain ran out of his cabin, spoke to Frithiof, looked at the log-line, jumped on the bridge, and in a minute we felt the steamer swing round as Frithiof turned her.

'Going back to Cape Town?' said Keller.

Frithiof did not answer, but tore away at the wheel. Then he beckoned us three to help, and we held the wheel down till the *Rathmines* answered it, and we found ourselves looking into the white of our own wake, with the still oily sea tearing past our bows, though we were not going more than half steam ahead.

The captain stretched out his arm from the bridge and shouted. A minute later I would have given a great deal to have shouted too, for one-half of the sea seemed to shoulder itself above the other half, and came on in the shape of a hill. There was neither crest, comb, nor curl-over to it; nothing but black water with little waves chasing each other about the flanks. I saw it stream past and on a level with the *Rathmine's* bow-plates before the steamer made up her mind to rise, and I argued that this would be the last of all earthly voyages for me. Then we rose for ever and ever and ever, till I heard Keller saying in my ear, 'The bowels of the deep, good Lord!' and the *Rathmines* stood poised, her screw racing and drumming on the slope of a hollow that stretched downwards for a good half-mile.

We went down that hollow, nose under for the most part, and the air smelt wet and muddy, like that of an emptied aquarium. There was a second hill to climb; I saw that much: but the water came aboard and carried me aft till it jammed me against the smoking-room door, and before I could catch breath or clear my eyes again we were rolling to and fro in torn water, with the scuppers pouring like eaves in a thunderstorm.

'There were three waves,' said Keller; 'and the stoke-hold's flooded.'

The firemen were on deck waiting, apparently, to be drowned. The engineer came and dragged them below, and the crew, gasping, began to work the clumsy Board of Trade pump. That showed nothing serious, and when I understood that the *Rathmines* was really on the water, and not beneath it, I asked what had happened.

'The captain says it was a blow-up under the sea—a volcano,' said Keller.

'It hasn't warmed anything,' I said. I was feeling bitterly cold, and cold was almost unknown in those waters. I went below to change my clothes, and when I came up everything was wiped out by clinging white fog.

'Are there going to be any more surprises?' said Keller to the captain.

'I don't know. Be thankful you're alive, gentlemen. That's a tidal wave thrown up by a volcano. Probably the bottom of the sea has been lifted a few feet somewhere or other. I can't quite understand this cold spell. Our sea-thermometer says the surface water is 44°, and it should be 68°, at least.'

'It's abominable,' said Keller, shivering. 'But hadn't you better attend to the fog-horn? It seems to me that I heard something.'

'Heard! Good heavens!' said the captain from the bridge, 'I should think you did.' He pulled the string of our fog-horn, which was a weak one. It sputtered and choked, because the stoke-hold was full of water and the fires were half-drowned, and at last gave out a moan. It was answered from the fog by one of the most appalling steam-sirens I have ever heard. Keller turned as white as I did, for the fog, the cold fog, was upon us, and any man may be forgiven for fearing the death he cannot see.

'Give her steam there!' said the captain to the engine-room. 'Steam for the whistle, if we have to go dead slow.'

We bellowed again, and the damp dripped off the awnings to the deck as we listened for the reply. It seemed to be astern this time, but much nearer than before.

'The *Pembroke Castle*, by gum!' said Keller, and then, viciously, 'Well, thank God, we shall sink her too.'

'It's a side-wheel steamer,' I whispered. 'Can't you hear the paddles?'

This time we whistled and roared till the steam gave out, and the answer nearly deafened us. There was a sound of frantic threshing in the water, apparently about fifty yards away, and something shot past in the whiteness that looked as though it were gray and red.

'The *Pembroke Castle* bottom up,' said Keller, who, being a journalist, always sought for explanations. 'That's the colours of a Castle liner. We're in for a big thing.'

'The sea is bewitched,' said Frithiof from the wheel-house. 'There are two steamers.'

Another siren sounded on our bow, and the little steamer rolled in the wash of something that had passed unseen.

'We're evidently in the middle of a fleet,' said Keller quietly. 'If one doesn't run us down, the other will. Phew! What in creation is that?'

I sniffed for there was a poisonous rank smell in the cold air—a smell that I had smelt before.

'If I was on land I should say that it was an alligator. It smells like musk,' I answered.

'Not ten thousand alligators could make that smell,' said Zuyland; 'I have smelt them.'

'Bewitched! Bewitched!' said Frithiof. 'The sea she is turned upside down, and we are walking along the bottom.'

Again the *Rathmines* rolled in the wash of some unseen ship, and a silver-gray wave broke over the bow, leaving on the deck a sheet of sediment —the gray broth that has its place in the fathomless deeps of the sea. A sprinkling of the wave fell on my face, and it was so cold that it stung as boiling water stings. The dead and most untouched deep water of the sea had been heaved to the top by the submarine volcano—the chill, still water that kills all life and smells of desolation and emptiness. We did not need either the blinding fog or that indescribable smell of musk to make us unhappy—we were shivering with cold and wretchedness where we stood.

'The hot air on the cold water makes this fog,' said the captain. 'It ought to clear in a little time.'

'Whistle, oh! whistle, and let's get out of it,' said Keller.

The captain whistled again, and far and far astern the invisible twin steam-sirens answered us. Their blasting shriek grew louder, till at last it seemed to tear out of the fog just above our quarter, and I cowered while the *Rathmines* plunged bows-under on a double swell that crossed.

'No more,' said Frithiof, 'it is not good any more. Let us get away, in the name of God.'

'Now if a torpedo-boat with a *City of Paris* siren went mad and broke her moorings and hired a friend to help her, it's just conceivable that we might be carried as we are now. Otherwise this thing is——'

The last words died on Keller's lips, his eyes began to start from his head, and his jaw fell. Some six or seven feet above the port bulwarks, framed in fog, and as utterly unsupported as the full moon, hung a Face. It was not human, and it certainly was not animal, for it did not belong to this earth as known to man. The mouth was open, revealing a ridiculously tiny tongue —as absurd as the tongue of an elephant; there were tense wrinkles of white skin at the angles of the drawn lips; white feelers like those of a barbel sprang from the lower jaw, and there was no sign of teeth within the mouth. But the horror of the face lay in the eyes, for those were sightless—white, in sockets as white as scraped bone, and blind. Yet for all this the face, wrinkled as the mask of a lion is drawn in Assyrian sculpture, was alive with rage and terror. One long white feeler touched our bulwarks. Then the face disappeared with the swiftness of a blind worm popping into its burrow, and the next thing that I remember is my own voice in my own ears, saying gravely to the mainmast, 'But the air-bladder ought to have been forced out of its mouth, you know.'

Keller came up to me, ashy white. He put his hand into his pocket, took a cigar, bit it, dropped it, thrust his shaking thumb into his mouth and mumbled, 'The giant gooseberry and the raining frogs! Gimme a light— gimme a light! I say, gimme a light.' A little bead of blood dropped from his thumbnail.

I respected the motive, though the manifestation was absurd. 'Stop, you'll bite your thumb off,' I said, and Keller laughed brokenly as he picked up his cigar. Only Zuyland, leaning over the port bulwarks, seemed self-possessed. He declared later that he was very sick.

'We've seen it,' he said, turning round. 'That is it.'

'What?' said Keller, chewing the unlighted cigar.

As he spoke the fog was blown into shreds, and we saw the sea, gray with mud, rolling on every side of us and empty of all life. Then in one spot it bubbled and became like the pot of ointment that the Bible speaks of. From that wide-ringed trouble a Thing came up—a gray and red Thing with a neck—a Thing that bellowed and writhed in pain. Frithiof drew in his breath and held it till the red letters of the ship's name, woven across his jersey, straggled and opened out as though they had been type badly set. Then he said with a little cluck in his throat, 'Ah, me! It is blind. *Hur illa!* That Thing is blind,' and a murmur of pity went through us all, for we could see that the Thing on the water was blind and in pain. Something had gashed and cut the great sides cruelly and the blood was spurting out. The gray ooze of the undermost sea lay in the monstrous wrinkles of the back and poured away in sluices. The blind white head flung back and battered the wounds, and the body in its torment rose clear of the red and gray waves till we saw a pair of quivering shoulders streaked with weed and rough with shells, but as white in the clear spaces as the hairless, nameless, blind, toothless head. Afterwards came a dot on the horizon and the sound of a shrill scream, and it was as though a shuttle shot all across the sea in one breath, and a second head and neck tore through the levels, driving a whispering wall of water to right and left. The two Things met—the one untouched and the other in its death throe—male and female, we said, the female coming to the male. She circled round him bellowing, and laid her neck across the curve of his great turtle-back, and he disappeared under water for an instant, but flung up again, grunting in agony while the blood ran. Once the entire head and neck shot clear of the water and stiffened, and I heard Keller saying, as though he was watching a street accident, 'Give him air. For God's sake give him air!' Then the death struggle began, with crampings and twistings and jerkings of the white bulk to and fro, till our little steamer rolled again, and each gray wave coated her plates with the gray slime. The sun was clear, there was no wind, and we watched, the whole crew, stokers and all, in wonder and pity, but chiefly pity. The Thing was so helpless, and, save for his mate, so alone. No human eye should have beheld him; it was monstrous and indecent to exhibit him there in trade waters between atlas degrees of latitude. He had been spewed up, mangled and dying from his rest on the sea-floor, where he might have lived till the Judgment Day, and we saw the tides of his life go from him as an angry tide goes out across rocks in the teeth of a landward gale. The mate lay rocking on the water a little distance off, bellowing continually, and the smell of musk came down upon the ship making us cough.

At last the battle for life ended, in a batter of coloured seas. We saw the writhing neck fall like a flail, the carcase turn sideways, showing the glint of a white belly and the inset of a gigantic hind-leg or flapper. Then all sank, and sea boiled over it, while the mate swam round and round, darting her blind head in every direction. Though we might have feared that she would attack the steamer, no power on earth could have drawn any one of us from our places that hour. We watched, holding our breaths. The mate paused in her search; we could hear the wash beating along her sides; reared her neck as high as she could reach, blind and lonely in all that loneliness of the sea, and sent one desperate bellow booming across the swells, as an oyster shell skips across a pond. Then she made off to the westward, the sun shining on the white head and the wake behind it, till nothing was left to see but a little pin point of silver on the horizon. We stood on our course again, and the *Rathmines*, coated with the sea-sediment, from bow to stern, looked like a ship made gray with terror.

*   *   *   *   *

'We must pool our notes,' was the first coherent remark from Keller. 'We're three trained journalists—we hold absolutely the biggest scoop on record. Start fair.'

I objected to this. Nothing is gained by collaboration in journalism when all deal with the same facts, so we went to work each according to his own lights. Keller triple-headed his account, talked about our 'gallant captain,' and wound up with an allusion to American enterprise in that it was a citizen of Dayton, Ohio, that had seen the sea-serpent. This sort of thing would have discredited the Creation, much more a mere sea tale, but as a specimen of the picture-writing of a half-civilised people it was very interesting. Zuyland took a heavy column and a half, giving approximate lengths and breadths and the whole list of the crew whom he had sworn on oath to testify to his facts. There was nothing fantastic or flamboyant in Zuyland. I wrote three-quarters of a leaded bourgeois column, roughly speaking, and refrained from putting any journalese into it for reasons that had begun to appear to me.

Keller was insolent with joy. He was going to cable from Southampton to the New York *World*, mail his account to America on the same day, paralyse London with his three columns of loosely knitted headlines, and generally efface the earth. 'You'll see how I work a big scoop when I get it,' he said.

'Is this your first visit to England?' I asked.

'Yes,' said he. 'You don't seem to appreciate the beauty of our scoop. It's pyramidal—the death of the sea-serpent! Good heavens alive man, it's the biggest thing ever vouchsafed to a paper!'

'Curious to think that it will never appear in any paper, isn't it?' I said. Zuyland was near me, and he nodded quickly.

'What do you mean?' said Keller. 'If you're enough of a Britisher to throw this thing away, I sha'n't. I thought you were a newspaper man.

'I am. That's why I know. Don't be an ass, Keller. Remember, I'm seven hundred years your senior, and what your grandchildren may learn five hundred years hence, I learned from my grandfathers about five hundred years ago. You won't do it, because you can't.'

This conversation was held in open sea, where everything seems possible, some hundred miles from Southampton. We passed the Needles Light at dawn, and the lifting day showed the stucco villas on the green and the awful orderliness of England—line upon line, wall upon wall, solid stone dock and monolithic pier. We waited an hour in the Customs shed, and there was ample time for the effect to soak in.

'Now, Keller, you face the music. The *Havel* goes out to-day. Mail by her, and I'll take you to the telegraph office,' I said.

I heard Keller gasp as the influence of the land closed about him, cowing him as they say Newmarket Heath cows a young horse unused to open country.

'I want to retouch my stuff. Suppose we wait till we get to London?' he said.

Zuyland, by the way, had torn up his account and thrown it overboard that morning early. His reasons were my reasons.

In the train Keller began to revise his copy, and every time that he looked at the trim little fields, the red villas, and the embankments of the line, the blue pencil plunged remorselessly through the slips. He appeared to have dredged the dictionary for adjectives. I could think of none that he had not used. Yet he was a perfectly sound poker player and never showed more cards than were sufficient to take the pool.

'Aren't you going to leave him a single bellow?' I asked sympathetically. 'Remember, everything goes in the States, from a trouser-button to a double eagle.'

'That's just the curse of it,' said Keller below his breath. 'We've played 'em for suckers so often that when it comes to the golden truth—I'd like to try this on a London paper. You have first call there, though.'

'Not in the least. I'm not touching the thing in the papers. I shall be happy to leave 'em all to you; but surely you'll cable it home?'

'No. Not if I can make the scoop here and see the Britishers sit up.'

'You won't do it with three columns of slushy headline, believe me. They don't sit up as quickly as some people.'

'I'm beginning to think that too. Does *nothing* make any difference in this country?' he said, looking out of the window. 'How old is that farmhouse?'

'New. It can't be more than two hundred years at the most.'

'Um. Fields, too?'

'That hedge there must have been clipped for about eighty years.'

'Labour cheap—eh?'

'Pretty much. Well, I suppose you'd like to try the *Times* wouldn't you?'

'No,' said Keller, looking at Winchester Cathedral. 'Might as well try to electrify a hay-rick. And to think that the *World* would take three columns and ask for more—with illustrations too! It's sickening.'

'But the *Times* might,' I began.

Keller flung his paper across the carriage, and it opened in its austere majesty of solid type—opened with the crackle of an encyclopædia.

'Might! You *might* work your way through the bow-plates of a cruiser. Look at that first page!'

'It strikes you that way, does it?' I said. 'Then I'd recommend you to try a light and frivolous journal.'

'With a thing like this of mine—of ours? It's sacred history!'

I showed him a paper which I conceived would be after his own heart, in that it was modelled on American lines.

'That's homey,' he said, 'but it's not the real thing. Now, I should like one of these fat old *Times*' columns. Probably there'd be a bishop in the office, though.'

When we reached London Keller disappeared in the direction of the Strand. What his experiences may have been I cannot tell, but it seems that he invaded the office of an evening paper at 11.45 a. m. (I told him English editors were most idle at that hour), and mentioned my name as that of a witness to the truth of his story.

'I was nearly fired out,' he said furiously at lunch. 'As soon as I mentioned you, the old man said that I was to tell you that they didn't want any more of your practical jokes, and that you knew the hours to call if you had anything to sell, and that they'd see you condemned before they helped to puff one of your infernal yarns in advance. Say, what record do you hold for truth in this city, anyway?'

'A beauty. You ran up against it, that's all. Why don't you leave the English papers alone and cable to New York? Everything goes over there.'

'Can't you see that's just why?' he repeated.

'I saw it a long time ago. You don't intend to cable, then?'

'Yes, I do,' he answered, in the over-emphatic voice of one who does not know his own mind.

That afternoon I walked him abroad and about, over the streets that run between the pavements like channels of grooved and tongued lava, over the bridges that are made of enduring stone, through subways floored and sided with yard-thick concrete, between houses that are never rebuilt, and by river steps hewn to the eye from the living rock. A black fog chased us into Westminster Abbey, and, standing there in the darkness, I could hear the wings of the dead centuries circling round the head of Litchfield A. Keller, journalist, of Dayton, Ohio, U. S. A., whose mission it was to make the Britishers sit up.

He stumbled gasping into the thick gloom, and the roar of the traffic came to his bewildered ears.

'Let's go to the telegraph office and cable,' I said. 'Can't you hear the New York *World* crying for news of the great sea-serpent, blind, white, and smelling of musk, stricken to death by a submarine volcano, assisted by his loving wife to die in mid-ocean, as visualised by an independent American citizen, a breezy, newsy, brainy newspaper man of Dayton, Ohio? 'Rah for the Buckeye State. Step lively! Both gates! Szz! Boom—ah!' Keller was a Princeton man, and he seemed to need encouragement.

'You've got me on your own ground,' said he, tugging at his overcoat pocket. He pulled out his copy, with the cable forms—for he had written out his telegram—and put them all into my hand, groaning, 'I pass. If I hadn't come to your cursed country—if I'd sent it off at Southampton—if I ever get you west of the Alleghenies, if——'

'Never mind, Keller. It isn't your fault. It's the fault of your country. If you had been seven hundred years older you'd have done what I'm going to do.'

'What are you going to do?'

'Tell it as a lie.'

'Fiction?' This with the full-blooded disgust of a journalist for the illegitimate branch of the profession.

'You can call it that if you like. I shall call it a lie.'

And a lie it has become, for Truth is a naked lady, and if by accident she is drawn up from the bottom of the sea, it behoves a gentleman either to give her a print petticoat or to turn his face to the wall, and vow that he did not see.

BEYOND THE PALE

Love heeds not caste nor sleep a broken bed. I went in search of love and lost myself.

—HINDU PROVERB

A MAN should, whatever happens, keep to his own caste, race and breed. Let the White go to the White and the Black to the Black. Then, whatever trouble falls is in the ordinary course of things—neither sudden, alien nor unexpected.

This is the story of a man who wilfully stepped beyond the safe limits of decent everyday society, and paid for it heavily.

He knew too much in the first instance; and he saw too much in the second. He took too deep an interest in native life; but he will never do so again.

Deep away in the heart of the City, behind Jitha Megji's *bustee*, lies Amir Nath's Gully, which ends in a dead-wall pierced by one grated window. At the head of the Gully is a big cowbyre, and the walls on either side of the Gully are without windows. Neither Suchet Singh nor Gaur Chand approve of their women-folk looking into the world. If Durga Charan had been of their opinion, he would have been a happier man to-day, and little Bisesa would have been able to knead her own bread. Her room looked out through the grated window into the narrow dark Gully where the sun never came and where the buffaloes wallowed in the blue slime. She was a widow, fifteen years old, and she prayed the Gods, day and night, to send her a lover; for she did not approve of living alone.

One day, the man—Trejago was his name—came into Amir Nath's Gully on a wandering; and, after he had passed the buffaloes, stumbled over a big heap of cattle-food.

Then he saw that the Gully ended in a trap, and heard a little laugh from behind the grated window. It was a pretty little laugh, and Trejago, knowing that, for all practical purposes, the old *Arabian Nights* are good guides, went forward to the window, and whispered that verse of 'The Love Song of Har Dyal' which begins:—

Can a man stand upright in the face of the naked Sun; or a Lover in the Presence of his Beloved?

If my feet fail me, O Heart of my Heart, am I to blame, being blinded by the glimpse of your beauty?

There came the faint *tchink* of a woman's bracelets from behind the grating, and a little voice went on with the song at the fifth verse:—

Alas! alas! Can the Moon tell the Lotus of her love when the Gate of Heaven is shut and the clouds gather for the rains?

They have taken my Beloved, and driven her with the pack-horses to the North.

There are iron chains on the feet that were set on my heart.

Call to the bowmen to make ready——

The voice stopped suddenly, and Trejago walked out of Amir Nath's Gully, wondering who in the world could have capped 'The Love Song of Har Dyal' so neatly.

Next morning, as he was driving to office, an old woman threw a packet into his dogcart. In the packet was the half of a broken glass-bangle, one flower of the blood-red *dhak*, a pinch of *bhusa* or cattle-food, and eleven cardamoms. That packet was a letter—not a clumsy compromising letter, but an innocent unintelligible lover's epistle.

Trejago knew far too much about these things, as I have said. No Englishman should be able to translate object-letters. But Trejago spread all the trifles on the lid of his office-box and began to puzzle them out.

A broken glass-bangle stands for a Hindu widow all India over; because, when her husband dies, a woman's bracelets are broken on her wrists. Trejago saw the meaning of the little bit of the glass. The flower of the *dhak* means diversely 'desire,' 'come,' 'write,' or 'danger,' according to the other things with it. One cardamom means 'jealousy'; but when any article is duplicated in an object-letter, it loses its symbolic meaning and stands merely for one of a number indicating time, or, if incense, curds, or saffron be sent also, place. The message ran then—'A widow—*dhak* flower and *bhusa*,—at eleven o'clock.' The pinch of *bhusa* enlightened Trejago. He saw—this kind of letter leaves much to instinctive knowledge—that the *bhusa* referred to the big heap of cattle-food over which he had fallen in Amir Nath's Gully, and that the message must come from the person behind the grating; she being a widow. So the message ran then—'A widow, in the Gully in which is the heap of *bhusa*, desires you to come at eleven o'clock.'

Trejago threw all the rubbish into the fireplace and laughed. He knew that men in the East do not make love under windows at eleven in the forenoon, nor do women fix appointments a week in advance. So he went, that very night at eleven, into Amir Nath's Gully, clad in a *boorka*, which cloaks a man as well as a woman. Directly the gongs of the City made the hour, the little voice behind the grating took up 'The Love Song of Har Dyal' at the verse where the Panthan girl calls upon Har Dyal to return. The song is really pretty in the Vernacular. In English you miss the wail of it. It runs something like this—

> Alone upon the housetops, to the North
> I turn and watch the lightning in the sky,—
> The glamour of thy footsteps in the North,
> *Come back to me, Beloved or I die!*

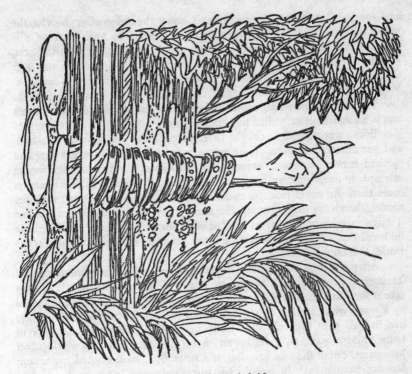

Below my feet the still bazar is laid,
　　Far, far, below the weary camels lie,—
The camels and the captives of thy raid.
　　Come back to me, Beloved or I die!

My father's wife is old and harsh with years,
　　And drudge of all my father's house am I.—
My bread is sorrow and my drink is tears,
　　Come back to me, Beloved or I die!

As the song stopped, Trejago stepped up under the grating and whispered—'I am here.'

Bisesa was good to look upon.

That night was the beginning of many strange things, and of a double life so wild that Trejago to-day sometimes wonders if it were not all a dream. Bisesa, or her old handmaiden who had thrown the object-letter, had detached the heavy grating from the brick-work of the wall; so that the window slid inside, leaving only a square of raw masonry into which an active man might climb.

In the day-time, Trejago drove through his routine of office-work, or put on his calling-clothes and called on the ladies of the Station; wondering how long they would know him if they knew of poor little Bisesa. At night, when all the City was still, came the walk under the evil-smelling *boorka*, the patrol through Jitha Megji's *bustee*, the quick turn into Amir Nath's Gully between the sleeping cattle and the dead walls, and then, last of all, Bisesa, and the deep, even breathing of the old woman who slept outside the door of the bare little room that Durga Charan allotted to his sister's daughter. Who or what Durga Charan was, Trejago never inquired; and why in the world he was not discovered and knifed never occurred to him till his madness was over, and Bisesa . . . But this comes later.

Bisesa was an endless delight to Trejago. She was as ignorant as a bird; and her distorted versions of the rumours from the outside world that had reached her in her room, amused Trejago almost as much as her lisping attempts to pronounce his name—'Christopher.' The first syllable was always more than she could manage, and she made funny little gestures with her roseleaf hands, as one throwing the name away, and then, kneeling before Trejago asked him, exactly as an Englishwoman would do, if he were sure he loved her. Trejago swore that he loved her more than any one else in the world. Which was true.

After a month of this folly, the exigencies of his other life compelled Trejago to be especially attentive to a lady of his acquaintance. You may take it for a fact that anything of this kind is not only noticed and discussed by a man's own race but by some hundred and fifty natives as well. Trejago had to walk with this lady and talk to her at the Band stand, and once or twice to drive with her; never for an instant dreaming that this would affect his dearer, out-of-the-way life. But the news flew, in the usual mysterious fashion, from mouth to mouth, till Bisesa's duenna heard of it and told Bisesa. The child was so troubled that she did the household work evilly, and was beaten by Durga Charan's wife in consequence.

A week later, Bisesa taxed Trejago with the flirtation. She understood no gradations and spoke openly. Trejago laughed and Bisesa stamped her little feet—little feet, light as marigold flowers, that could lie in the palm of a man's one hand.

Much that is written about Oriental passion and impulsiveness is exaggerated and compiled at secondhand, but a little of it is true; and when an Englishman finds that little, it is quite as startling as any passion in his own proper life. Bisesa raged and stormed, and finally threatened to kill herself if Trejago did not at once drop the alien *Memsahib* who had come between them. Trejago tried to explain, and to show her that she did not understand these things from a Western standpoint. Bisesa drew herself up, and said simply—

'I do not. I know only this—it is not good that I should have made you dearer than my own heart to me, *Sahib*. You are an Englishman. I am only a black girl'—she was fairer than bar-gold in the Mint,—'and the widow of a black man.'

Then she sobbed and said—'But on my soul and my Mother's soul, I love you. There shall no harm come to you, whatever happens to me.'

Trejago argued with the child, and tried to soothe her, but she seemed quite unreasonably disturbed. Nothing would satisfy her save that all relations between them should end. He was to go away at once. And he went. As he dropped out of the window, she kissed his forehead twice, and he walked home wondering.

A week, and then three weeks, passed without a sign from Bisesa. Trejago, thinking that the rupture had lasted quite long enough, went down to Amir Nath's Gully for the fifth time in the three weeks, hoping that his rap at the sill of the shifting grating would be answered. He was not disappointed.

There was a young moon, and one stream of light fell down into Amir Nath's Gully, and struck the grating which was drawn away as he knocked. From the black dark, Bisesa held out her arms into the moonlight. Both hands had been cut off at the wrists, and the stumps were nearly healed.

Then, as Bisesa bowed her head between her arms and sobbed, some one in the room grunted like a wild beast, and something sharp—knife, sword, or spear—thrust at Trejago in his *boorka*. The stroke missed his body, but cut into one of the muscles of the groin, and he limped slightly from the wound for the rest of his days.

The grating slid into its place. There was no sign whatever from inside the house,—nothing but the moonlight strip on the high wall, and the blackness of Amir Nath's Gully behind.

The next thing Trejago remembers, after raging and shouting like a madman between those pitiless walls, is that he found himself near the river as the dawn was breaking, threw away his *boorka* and went home bareheaded.

*   *   *   *   *

What was the tragedy—whether Bisesa had, in a fit of causeless despair, told everything, or the intrigue had been discovered and she tortured to tell; whether Durga Charan knew his name and what became of Bisesa—Trejago does not know to this day. Something horrible had happened, and the thought of what it must have been, comes upon Trejago in the night now and again, and keeps him company till the morning. One special feature of the case is that he does not know where lies the front of Durga Charan's house. It may open on to a courtyard common to two or more houses, or it may lie behind any one of the gates of Jitha Megji's *bustee*. Trejago cannot tell. He cannot get Bisesa—poor little Bisesa—back again. He has lost her in the City where each man's house is as guarded and as unknowable as the grave; and the grating that opens into Amir Nath's Gully has been walled up.

But Trejago pays his calls regularly, and is reckoned a very decent sort of man.

There is nothing peculiar about him, except a slight stiffness, caused by a riding-strain, in the right leg.

A BANK FRAUD

He drank strong waters and his speech was coarse;
 He purchased raiment and forbore to pay;
He stuck a trusting junior with a horse,
 And won Gymkhanas in a doubtful way.
Then, 'twixt a vice and folly, turned aside
To do good deeds and straight to cloak them, lied.
—THE MESS ROOM

IF REGGIE BURKE were in India now, he would resent this tale being told; but as he is in Hongkong and won't see it, the telling is safe. He was the man who worked the big fraud on the Sind and Sialkote Bank. He was manager of an up-country Branch, and a sound practical man with a large experience of native loan and insurance work. He could combine the frivolities of ordinary life with his work, and yet do well. Reggie Burke rode anything that would let him get up, danced as neatly as he rode, and was wanted for every sort of amusement in the Station.

As he said himself, and as many men found out rather to their surprise, there were two Burkes, both very much at your service. 'Reggie Burke,' between four and ten, ready for anything from a hot-weather gymkhana to a riding-picnic, and, between ten and four, 'Mr. Reginald Burke, Manager of the Sind and Sialkote Branch Bank.' You might play polo with him one afternoon and hear him express his opinions when a man crossed; and you might call on him next morning to raise a two-thousand-rupee loan on a five-hundred-pound insurance policy, eighty pounds paid in premiums. He would recognise you, but you would have some trouble in recognising him.

The Directors of the Bank—it had its headquarters in Calcutta and its General Manager's word carried weight with the Government—picked their men well. They had tested Reggie up to a fairly severe breaking-strain. They trusted him just as much as Directors ever trust Managers. You must see for yourself whether their trust was misplaced.

Reggie's Branch was in a big Station, and worked with the usual staff—one Manager, one Accountant, both English, a Cashier, and a horde of native clerks; besides the Police patrol at nights outside. The bulk of its work, for it was in a thriving district, was *hoondi* and accommodation of all kinds. A fool has no grip of this sort of business, and a clever man who does not go about among his clients, and know more than a little of their affairs, is worse than a fool. Reggie was young-looking, clean-shaved, with a twinkle in his eye, and a head that nothing short of a gallon of the Gunners' Madeira could make any impression on.

One day, at a big dinner, he announced casually that the Directors had shifted on to him a Natural Curiosity, from England, in the Accountant line. He was perfectly correct. Mr. Silas Riley, Accountant, was a most curious animal—a long, gawky, rawboned Yorkshireman, full of the savage self-conceit that blossoms only in the best county in England. Arrogance was a mild word for the mental attitude of Mr. S. Riley. He had worked himself up, after seven years, to a Cashier's position in a Huddersfield Bank; and all his experience lay among the factories of the North. Perhaps he would have done better on the Bombay side, where they are happy with one-half per cent profits, and money is cheap. He was useless for Upper India and a wheat Province, where a man wants a large head and a touch of imagination if he is to turn out a satisfactory balance-sheet.

He was wonderfully narrow-minded in business, and, being new to the country, had no notion that Indian banking is totally distinct from Home work. Like most clever self-made men, he had much simplicity in his nature; and, somehow or other, had construed the ordinarily polite terms of his letter of engagement into a belief that the Directors had chosen him on account of his special and brilliant talents, and that they set great store by him. This notion grew and crystallised; thus adding to his natural North-country conceit. Further, he was delicate, suffered from some trouble in his chest, and was short in his temper.

You will admit that Reggie had reason to call his new Accountant a Natural Curiosity. The two men failed to hit it off at all. Riley considered Reggie a wild, feather-headed idiot, given to Heaven only knew what dissipation in low places called 'Messes,' and totally unfit for the serious and solemn vocation of banking. He could never get over Reggie's look of youth and 'you-be-damned' air; and he couldn't understand Reggie's friends—clean-built, careless men in the Army—who rode over to big Sunday breakfasts at the Bank, and told sultry stories till Riley got up and left the room. Riley was always showing Reggie how the business ought to be conducted, and Reggie had more than once to remind him that seven years' limited experience between Huddersfield and Beverley did not qualify a man to steer a big up-country business. Then Riley sulked, and referred to himself as a pillar of the Bank and a cherished friend of the Directors, and Reggie tore his hair. If a man's English subordinates fail him in India, he comes to a hard time indeed, for native help has strict limitations. In the winter Riley went sick for weeks at a time with his lung complaint, and this threw more work on Reggie. But he preferred it to the everlasting friction when Riley was well.

One of the Travelling Inspectors of the Bank discovered these collapses and reported them to the Directors. Now Riley had been foisted on the Bank by an M.P., who wanted the support of Riley's father, who, again, was anxious to get his son out to a warmer climate because of those lungs. The M.P. had interest in the Bank; but one of the Directors wanted to advance a nominee of his own; and, after Riley's father had died, he made the rest of the Board see that an Accountant who was sick for half the year had better give place to a healthy man. If Riley had known the real story of his appointment, he might have behaved better; but, knowing nothing, his stretches of sickness alternated with restless, persistent, meddling irritation of Reggie, and all the hundred ways in which conceit in a subordinate situation can find play. Reggie used to call him striking and hair-curling names behind his back as a relief to his own feelings; but he never abused him to his face, because he said, 'Riley is such a frail beast that half of his loathsome conceit is due to pains in the chest.'

Late one April, Riley went very sick indeed. The Doctor punched and thumped him, and told him he would be better before long. Then the Doctor went to Reggie and said—'Do you know how sick your Accountant is?'—'No!' said Reggie—'The worse the better, confound him! He's a nuisance when he's well. I'll let you take away the Bank Safe if you can keep him quiet through this hot weather.'

But the Doctor did not laugh—'Man, I'm not joking,' he said. 'I'll give him another three months in his bed and a week or so more to die in. On my honour and reputation that's all the grace he has in this world. Consumption has hold of him to the marrow.'

Reggie's face changed at once into the face of 'Mr. Reginald Burke,' and he answered, 'What can I do?'—'Nothing,' said the Doctor. 'For all practical purposes the man is dead already. Keep him quiet and cheerful, and tell him he's going to recover. That's all. I'll look after him to the end, of course.'

The Doctor went away, and Reggie sat down to open the evening mail. His first letter was one from the Directors, intimating for his information that Mr. Riley was to resign, under a month's notice, by the terms of his agreement, telling Reggie that their letter to Riley would follow, and advising Reggie of the coming of a new Accountant, a man whom Reggie knew and liked.

Reggie lit a cheroot, and, before he had finished smoking, he had sketched the outline of a fraud. He put away—burked—the Directors' letter, and went in to talk to Riley, who was as ungracious as usual, and fretting himself over the way the Bank would run during his illness. He never thought of the extra work on Reggie's shoulders, but solely of the damage to his own prospects of advancement. Then Reggie assured him that everything would be well, and that he, Reggie, would confer with Riley daily on the management of the Bank. Riley was a little soothed, but he hinted in as many words that he did not think much of Reggie's business capacity. Reggie was humble. And he had letters in his desk from the Directors that a Gilbarte or a Hardie might have been proud of!

The days passed in the big darkened house, and the Directors' letter of dismissal to Riley came and was put away by Reggie, who, every evening, brought the books to Riley's room, and showed him what had been going forward, while Riley snarled. Reggie did his best to make statements pleasing to Riley, but the Accountant was sure that the Bank was going to rack and ruin without him. In June, as the lying in bed told on his spirit, he asked whether his absence had been noted by the Directors, and Reggie said that they had written most sympathetic letters, hoping that he would be able to resume his valuable services before long. He showed Riley the letters; and Riley said that the Directors ought to have written to him direct. A few days later, Reggie opened Riley's mail in the half-light of the room, and gave him the sheet—not the envelope—of a letter to Riley from the Directors. Riley said he would thank Reggie not to interfere with his private papers, specially as Reggie knew he was too weak to open his own letters. Reggie apologised.

Then Riley's mood changed, and he lectured Reggie on his evil ways: his horses and his bad friends. 'Of course lying here, on my back, Mr. Burke, I can't keep you straight; but when I'm well, I *do* hope you'll pay some heed to my words.' Reggie, who had dropped polo, and dinners, and tennis and all, to attend to Riley, said that he was penitent and settled Riley's head on the pillow and heard him fret and contradict in hard, dry, hacking whispers, without a sign of impatience. This, at the end of a heavy day's office work, doing double duty, in the latter half of June.

When the new Accountant came, Reggie told him the facts of the case, and announced to Riley that he had a guest staying with him. Riley said that he might have had more consideration than to entertain his 'doubtful friends' at such a time. Reggie made Carron, the new Accountant, sleep at the Club in consequence. Carron's arrival took some of the heavy work off his shoulders, and he had time to attend to Riley's exactions—to explain, soothe, invent, and settle and re-settle the poor wretch in bed, and to forge complimentary letters from Calcutta. At the end of the first month Riley wished to send some money home to his mother. Reggie sent the draft. At the end of the second month Riley's salary came in just the same. Reggie paid it out of his own pocket, and, with it, wrote Riley a beautiful letter from the Directors.

Riley was very ill indeed, but the flame of his life burnt unsteadily. Now and then he would be cheerful and confident about the future, sketching plans for going Home and seeing his mother. Reggie listened patiently when the office-work was over, and encouraged him.

At other times Riley insisted on Reggie reading the Bible and grim 'Methody' tracts to him. Out of these tracts he pointed morals directed at his Manager. But he always found time to worry Reggie about the working of the Bank, and to show him where the weak points lay.

This indoor, sickroom life and constant strains wore Reggie down a good deal, and shook his nerves, and lowered his billiard play by forty points. But the business of the Bank, and the business of the sickroom, had to go on, though the glass was 116° in the shade.

At the end of the third month Riley was sinking fast, and had begun to realise that he was very sick. But the conceit that made him worry Reggie kept him from believing the worst. 'He wants some sort of mental stimulant if he is to drag on,' said the Doctor. 'Keep him interested in life if you care about his living.' So Riley, contrary to all the laws of business and the finance, received a 25-per-cent rise of salary from the Directors. The 'mental stimulant' succeeded beautifully. Riley was happy and cheerful, and, as is often the case in consumption, healthiest in mind when the body was weakest. He lingered for a full month, snarling and fretting about the Bank, talking of the future, hearing the Bible read, lecturing Reggie on sin, and wondering when he would be able to move abroad.

But at the end of September, one mercilessly hot evening, he rose up in his bed with a little gasp, and said quickly to Reggie—'Mr. Burke, I am going to die. I know it in myself. My chest is all hollow inside, and there's nothing to breathe with. To the best of my knowledge I have done nowt'— he was returning to the talk of his boyhood—'to lie heavy on my conscience. God be thanked, I have been preserved from the grosser forms of sin; and I counsel *you*, Mr. Burke . . .'

Here his voice died down, and Reggie stooped over him.

'Send my salary for September to my Mother . . . done great things with the Bank if I had been spared . . . mistaken policy . . . no fault of mine. . . .'

Then he turned his face to the wall and died.

Reggie drew the sheet over Its face, and went out into the verandah, with his last 'mental stimulant'—a letter of condolence and sympathy from the Directors—unused in his pocket.

'If I'd been only ten minutes earlier,' thought Reggie, 'I might have heartened him up to pull through another day.'

THE DAUGHTER OF THE REGIMENT

Jain 'Ardin' was a Sarjint's wife,
  A Sarjint's wife wus she.
She married of 'im in Orldershort
  An' comed acrost the sea.
(Chorus) 'Ave you never 'eard tell o' Jain 'Ardin'?
                  Jain 'Ardin'?
                  Jain 'Ardin'?
   'Ave you never 'eard tell o' Jain 'Ardin'?
The pride o' the Companee?
                —OLD BARRACK-ROOM BALLAD

'A GENTLEMAN who doesn't know the Circasian Circle ought not to stand up for it—puttin' everybody out.' That was what Miss McKenna said, and the Sergeant who was my *vis-à-vis* looked the same thing. I was afraid of Miss McKenna. She was six feet high, all yellow freckles and red hair, and was simply clad in white satin shoes, a pink muslin dress, an apple-green stuff sash, and black silk gloves, with yellow roses in her hair. Wherefore I fled from Miss McKenna and sought my friend Private Mulvaney, who was at the cant—refreshment-table.

'So you've been dancin' with little Jhansi McKenna, Sǫrr—she that's goin' to marry Corp'ril Slane? Whin you next conversh wid your lorruds an' your ladies, tell thim you've danced wid little Jhansi. 'Tis a thing to be proud av.'

But I wasn't proud. I was humble. I saw a story in Private Mulvaney's eye; and besides, if he stayed too long at the bar, he would, I knew, qualify for more pack-drill. Now to meet an esteemed friend doing pack-drill outside the guard-room is embarrassing, especially if you happen to be walking with his Commanding Officer.

'Come on to the parade-ground, Mulvaney, it's cooler there, and tell me about Miss McKenna. What is she, and who is she, and why is she called "Jhansi"?'

'D'ye mane to say you've niver heard av Ould Pummeloe's daughter? An' you thinkin' you know things! I'm wid ye in a minut' whin me poipe's lit.'

We came out under the stars. Mulvaney sat down on one of the artillery bridges, and began in the usual way: his pipe between his teeth, his big hands clasped and dropped between his knees, and his cap well on the back of his head—

'Whin Mrs. Mulvaney, that is, was Miss Shad, that was, you were a dale younger than you are now, an' the Army was dif'rint in sev'ril e-senshuls. Bhoys have no call for to marry nowadays, an' that's why the Army has so few rale, good, honust, swearin', strapagin', tinder-hearted, heavy-futted wives as ut used to have whin I was a Corp'ril. I was rejuced aftherwards—but no matther—I was a Corp'ril wanst. In thim times, a man lived *an'* died wid his regiment; an' by natur', he married whin he was a *man*. Whin I was Corp'ril —Mother av Hivin, how the rigimint has died an' been borrun since that day!—my Colour-Sar'jint was Ould McKenna, an' a married man tu. An' his woife—his first woife, for he married three times did McKenna—was Bridget McKenna, from Portarlington, like mesilf. I've misremembered fwhat her first name was; but in B Comp'ny we called her "Ould Pummeloe," by reason av her figure, which was entirely cir-cum-fe-renshill. Like the big dhrum! Now that woman—God rock her sowl to rest in glory!—was for everlastin' havin' childher; an' McKenna, whin the fifth or sixth come squallin' on to the musther-roll, swore he wud number thim off in future. But Ould Pummeloe she prayed av him to christen them after the names av the stations they was borrun in. So there was Colaba McKenna, an' Muttra McKenna, an' a whole Presidincy av other McKennas, an' little Jhansi, dancin' over yonder. Whin the childher wasn't bornin', they was dyin'; for, av our childher die like sheep in these days, they died like flies thin. I lost me own little Shad—but no matter. 'Tis long ago, and Mrs. Mulvaney niver had another.

'I'm digresshin. Wan divil's hot summer, there come an order from some mad ijjit, whose name I misremember, for the rigimint to go up-country. Maybe they wanted to know how the new rail carried throops. They knew! On me sowl, they knew before they was done! Old Pummeloe had just buried Muttra McKenna; an', the season bein' onwholesim, only little Jhansi McKenna, who was four year ould thin, was left on hand.

'Five children gone in fourteen months. 'Twas harrd, wasn't ut?

'So we wint up to our new station in that blazin' heat—may the curse av Saint Lawrence conshume the man who gave the ordher! Will I iver forget that move? They gave us two wake thrains to the rigimint; an' we was eight hundher' and sivinty strong. There was A, B, C, an' D Companies in the secon' thrain, wid twelve women, no orficers' ladies, an' thirteen childher. We was to go six hundher' miles, an' railways was new in thim days. Whin we had been a night in the belly av the thrain—the men ragin' in their shirts an' dhrinkin' anything they cud find, an' eatin' bad fruit-stuff whin they cud, for we cudn't stop 'em—I was a Corp'ril thin—the cholera bruk out wid the dawnin' av the day.

'Pray to the Saints, you may niver see cholera in a throop-thrain! 'Tis like the judgmint av God hittin' down from the nakid sky! We run into a rest-camp—as ut might have been Ludianny, but not by any means so com-fortable. The Orficer Commandin' sent a telegrapt up the line, three hundher' mile up, askin' for help. Faith, we wanted ut, for ivry sowl av the followers ran for the dear life as soon as the thrain stopped; an' by the time that telegrapt was writ, there wasn't a naygur in the station exceptin' the telegrapt-clerk—an' he only bekaze he was held down to his chair by the scruff av his

sneakin' black neck. Thin the day began wid the noise in the carr'ges, an' the rattle av the men on the platform fallin' over, arms an' all, as they stud for to answer the Comp'ny muster-roll before goin' over to the camp. 'Tisn't for me to say what like the cholera was like. Maybe the Doctor cud ha' tould, av he hadn't dropped on to the platform from the door av a carriage where we was takin' out the dead. He died wid the rest. Some bhoys had died in the night. We tuk out siven, and twenty more was sickenin' as we tuk thim. The women was huddled up anyways, screamin' wid fear.

'Sez the Commandin' Orficer whose name I misremember, "Take the women over to that tope av trees yonder. Get thim out av the camp. 'Tis no place for thim."

'Ould Pummeloe was sittin' on her beddin'-rowl, thryin' to kape little Jhansi quiet. "Go off to that tope!" sez the Orficer. "Go out av the men's way!"

' "Be damned av I do!" sez Ould Pummeloe, an' little Jhansi, squattin' by her mother's side, squeaks out, "Be damned av I do," tu. Thin Ould Pummeloe turns to the women an' she sez, "Are you goin' to let the bhoys die while you're picnickin', ye sluts?" sez she. " 'Tis wather they want. Come on an' help."

'Wid that, she turns up her sleeves an' steps out for a well behind the rest-camp—little Jhansi trottin' behind wid a *lotah* an' string, an' the other women followin' like lambs, wid horse-buckets and cookin' pots. Whin all the things was full, Ould Pummeloe marches back into camp—'twas like a battlefield wid all the glory missin'—at the hid av the rigimint av women.

'"McKenna, me man!" she sez, wid a voice on her like grand-roun's challenge, "tell the bhoys to be quiet. Ould Pummeloe's comin' to look afther thim—wid free dhrinks."

'Thin we cheered, an' the cheerin' in the lines was louder than the noise av the poor divils wid the sickness on thim. But not much.

'You see, we was a new an' raw rigimint in those days, an' we cud make neither head nor tail av the sickness; an' so we was useless. The men was goin' roun' an' about like dumb sheep, waitin' for the nex' man to fall over, an' sayin' undher their spache, "Fwhat is ut? In the name av God, *fwhat* is ut?" 'Twas horrible. But through ut all, up an' down, an' down an' up, wint Ould Pummeloe an' little Jhansi—all we cud see av the baby, undher a dead man's helmut wid the chin-strap swingin' about her little stummick—up an' down wid the wather an' fwhat brandy there was.

'Now an' thin Ould Pummeloe, the tears runnin' down her fat, red face, sez, "Me bhoys, me poor, dead, darlin' bhoys!" But, for the most, she was thryin' to put heart into the men an' kape thim stiddy; and little Jhansi was tellin' thim all they wud be "betther in the mornin'." 'Twas a thrick she'd picked up from hearin' Ould Pummeloe whin Muttra was burnin' out wid fever. In the mornin'! 'Twas the iverlastin' mornin' at St. Pether's Gate was the mornin' for seven-an'-twenty good men; and twenty more was sick to the death in that bitter, burnin' sun. But the women worked like angils as I've said, an' the men like divils, till two doctors come down from above, and we was rescued.

'But, just before that, Ould Pummeloe, on her knees over a bhoy in my squad—right-cot man to me he was in the barrick—tellin' him the worrud av the Church that niver failed a man yet, sez, "Hould me up, bhoys! I'm feelin' bloody sick!" 'Twas the sun, not the cholera, did ut. She misremembered she was only wearin' her old black bonnet, an' she died wid "McKenna, me man," houldin' her up, an' the bhoys howled whin they buried her.

'That night, a big wind blew, an' blew, an' blew, an' blew the tents flat. But it blew the cholera away an' niver another case there was all the while we was waitin'—ten days in quarantin'. Av you will belave me, the thrack av the sickness in the camp was for all the wurruld the thrack av a man walkin' four times in a figur-av-eight through the tents. They say 'tis the Wandherin' Jew takes the cholera wid him. I belave ut.

'An *that*,' said Mulvaney, illogically, 'is the cause why little Jhansi McKenna is fwhat she is. She was brought up by the Quartermaster Sergeant's wife whin McKenna died, but she b'longs to B Comp'ny; and this tale I'm tellin' you—*wid* a proper appreciashin av Jhansi McKenna—I've belted into ivry recruity av the Comp'ny as he was drafted. 'Faith, 'twas me belted Corp'ril Slane into askin' the girl!'

'Not really?'

'Man, I did! She's no beauty to look at, but she's Ould Pummeloe's daughter, an' 'tis my juty to provide for her. Just before Slane got his promotion I sez to him, "Slane," sez I, "to-morrow 'twill be insubordinashin av me to chastise you; but, by the sowl av Ould Pummeloe, who is now in glory, av you don't give me your wurrud to ask Jhansi McKenna at wanst, I'll peel the flesh off yer bones wid a brass huk to-night. 'Tis a dishgrace to B Comp'ny she's been single so long!" sez I. Was I goin' to let a three-year-ould preshume to discoorse wid me—my will bein' set? No! Slane wint an' asked her. He's a good bhoy is Slane. Wan av these days he'll get into the Com'ssariat an' dhrive a buggy wid his—savin's. So I provided for Ould Pummeloe's daughter; an' now you go along an' dance agin wid her.'

And I did.

I felt a respect for Miss Jhansi McKenna; and I went to her wedding later on.

Perhaps I will tell you about that one of these days.

THE ROUT OF THE WHITE HUSSARS

It was not in the open fight
 We threw away the sword,
But in the lonely watching
 In the darkness by the ford.
The waters lapped, the night-wind blew,
Full-armed the Fear was born and grew,
And we were flying ere we knew
 From panic in the night.

—BEONI BAR

SOME people hold that an English Cavalry regiment cannot run. This is a mistake. I have seen four hundred and thirty-seven sabres flying over the face of the country in abject terror—have seen the best Regiment that ever drew bridle wiped off the Army List for the space of two hours. If you repeat this tale to the White Hussars they will, in all probability, treat you severely. They are not proud of the incident.

You may know the White Hussars by their 'side,' which is greater than that of all the Cavalry Regiments on the roster. If this is not a sufficient mark, you may know them by their old brandy. It has been sixty years in the Mess and is worth going far to taste. Ask for the 'McGaire' old brandy, and see that you get it. If the Mess Sergeant thinks that you are uneducated, and that the genuine article will be lost on you, he will treat you accordingly. He is a good man. But, when you are at Mess, you must never talk to your hosts about forced marches or long-distance rides. The Mess are very sensitive; and, if they think that you are laughing at them, will tell you so.

As the White Hussars say, it was all the Colonel's fault. He was a new man, and he ought never to have taken the Command. He said that the Regiment was not smart enough. This to the White Hussars, who knew that they could walk round any Horse and through any Guns and over any Foot on the face of the earth! That insult was the first cause of offence.

Then the Colonel cast the Drum-Horse—the Drum-Horse of the White Hussars! Perhaps you do not see what an unspeakable crime he had committed. I will try to make it clear. The soul of the Regiment lives in the Drum-Horse who carries the silver kettle-drums. He is nearly always a big piebald Waler. That is a point of honour; and a Regiment will spend anything you please on a piebald. He is beyond the ordinary laws of casting. His work is very light, and he only manœuvres at a footpace. Wherefore, so long as he can step out and look handsome, his wellbeing is assured. He knows more about the Regiment than the Adjutant, and could not make a mistake if he tried.

The Drum-Horse of the White Hussars was only eighteen years old, and perfectly equal to his duties. He had at least six years' more work in him, and carried himself with all the pomp and dignity of a Drum-Major of the Guards. The Regiment had paid Rs.1200 for him.

But the Colonel said that he must go, and he was cast in due form and replaced by a washy, bay beast, as ugly as a mule, with a ewe-neck, rat-tail, and cow-hocks. The Drummer detested that animal, and the best of the Band-horses put back their ears and showed the whites of their eyes at the very sight of him. They knew him for an upstart and no gentleman. I fancy that the Colonel's ideas of smartness extended to the Band, and that he wanted to make it take part in the regular parade movements. A Cavalry Band is a sacred thing. It only turns out for Commanding Officers' parades, and the Band Master is one degree more important than the Colonel. He is a High Priest and the 'Keel Row' is his holy song. The 'Keel Row' is the Cavalry Trot; and the man who has never heard that tune rising above the rattle of the Regiment going past the saluting-base, has something yet to understand.

When the Colonel cast the Drum-Horse of the White Hussars, there was nearly a mutiny.

The officers were angry, the Regiment were furious, and the Bandsmen swore—like troopers. The Drum-Horse was going to be put up to auction— public auction—to be bought, perhaps, by a Parsee and put into a cart! It was worse than exposing the inner life of the Regiment to the whole world, or selling the Mess Plate to a Jew—a Black Jew.

The Colonel was a mean man and a bully. He knew what the Regiment thought about his action; and, when the troopers offered to buy the Drum-Horse, he said that their offer was mutinous and forbidden by the Regulations.

But one of the Subalterns—Hogan-Yale, an Irishman—bought the Drum-Horse for Rs.160 at the sale: and the Colonel was wroth. Yale professed repentance—he was unnaturally submissive—and said that, as he had only made the purchase to save the horse from possible ill-treatment and starvation, he would now shoot him and end the business. This appeared to soothe the Colonel, for he wanted the Drum-Horse disposed of. He felt that he had made a mistake, and could not of course acknowledge it. Meantime, the presence of the Drum-Horse was an annoyance to him.

Yale took to himself a glass of the old brandy, three cheroots, and his friend Martyn; and they all left the Mess together. Yale and Martyn conferred for two hours in Yale's quarters; but only the bull-terrier who keeps watch over Yale's boot-trees knows what they said. A horse, hooded and sheeted to his ears, left Yale's stables and was taken, very unwillingly, into the Civil Lines. Yale's groom went with him. Two men broke into the Regimental Theatre and took several paint-pots and some large scenery-brushes. Then night fell over the Cantonments, and there was a noise as of a horse kicking his loose-box to pieces in Yale's stables. Yale had a big, old, white Waler trap-horse.

The next day was a Thursday, and the men, hearing that Yale was going to shoot the Drum-Horse in the evening, determined to give the beast a regular regimental funeral—a finer one than they would have given the Colonel had he died just then. They got a bullock-cart and some sacking, and mounds and mounds of roses, and the body, under sacking, was carried out to the place where the anthrax cases were cremated; two-thirds of the Regiment following. There was no Band, but they all sang 'The Place where the old Horse died' as something respectful and appropriate to the occasion. When the corpse was dumped into the grave and the men began throwing down armfuls of roses to cover it, the Farrier-Sergeant ripped out an oath and said aloud, 'Why, it ain't the Drum-Horse any more than it's me!' The Troop-Sergeant-Majors asked him whether he had left his head in the Canteen. The Farrier-Sergeant said that he knew the Drum-Horse's feet as well as he knew his own; but he was silenced when he saw the regimental number burnt in on the poor stiff, upturned near-fore.

Thus was the Drum-Horse of the White Hussars buried; the Farrier-Sergeant grumbling. The sacking that covered the corpse was smeared in places with black paint; and the Farrier-Sergeant drew attention to this fact. But the Troop-Sergeant-Major of E Troop kicked him severely on the shin, and told him that he was undoubtedly drunk.

On the Monday following the burial, the Colonel sought revenge on the White Hussars. Unfortunately, being at that time temporarily in Command of the Station, he ordered a Brigade field-day. He said that he wished to make the Regiment 'sweat for their damned insolence,' and he carried out his notion thoroughly. That Monday was one of the hardest days in the memory of the White Hussars. They were thrown against a skeleton-enemy, and pushed forward, and withdrawn, and dismounted, and 'scientifically handled' in every possible fashion over dusty country, till they sweated profusely. Their only amusement came late in the day when they fell upon the battery of Horse Artillery and chased it for two miles. This was a personal question, and most of the troopers had money on the event; the Gunners saying openly that they had the legs of the White Hussars. They were wrong. A march-past concluded the campaign, and when the Regiment got back to their Lines, the men were coated with dirt from spur to chin-strap.

The White Hussars have one great and peculiar privilege. They won it at Fontenoy, I think.

Many Regiments possess special rights such as wearing collars with undress uniform, or a bow of riband between the shoulders, or red and white roses in their helmets on certain days of the year. Some rights are connected with regimental saints, and some with regimental successes. All are valued highly; but none so highly as the right of the White Hussars to have the Band playing when their horses are being watered in the Lines. Only one tune is played, and that tune never varies. I don't know its real name, but the

White Hussars call it, 'Take me to London again.' It sounds very pretty. The Regiment would sooner be struck off the roster than forego their distinction.

After the 'dismiss' was sounded, the officers rode off home to prepare for stables; and the men filed into the lines riding easy. That is to say, they opened their tight buttons, shifted their helmets, and began to joke or to swear as the humour took them; the more careful slipping off and easing girths and curbs. A good trooper values his mount exactly as much as he values himself, and believes, or should believe, that the two together are irresistible where women or men, girls or guns, are concerned.

Then the Orderly-Officer gave the order, 'Water horses,' and the Regiment loafed off to the squadron-troughs which were in rear of the stables and between these and the barracks. There were four huge troughs, one for each squadron, arranged *en échelon*, so that the whole Regiment could water in ten minutes if it liked. But it lingered for seventeen, as a rule, while the Band played.

The Band struck up as the squadrons filed off to the troughs, and the men slipped their feet out of the stirrups and chaffed each other. The sun was just setting in a big, hot bed of red cloud, and the road to the Civil Lines seemed to run straight into the sun's eye. There was a little dot on the road. It grew and grew till it showed as a horse, with a sort of gridiron-thing on his back. The red cloud glared through the bars of the gridiron. Some of the troopers shaded their eyes with their hands and said—'What the mischief 'as that there 'orse got on 'im?'

In another minute they heard a neigh that every soul—horse and man— in the Regiment knew, and saw, heading straight towards the Band, the dead Drum-Horse of the White Hussars!

On his withers banged and bumped the kettle-drums draped in crape, and on his back, very stiff and soldierly, sat a bareheaded skeleton.

The Band stopped playing, and, for a moment, there was a hush.

Then some one in E Troop—men said it was the Troop-Sergeant-Major —swung his horse round and yelled. No one can account exactly for what happened afterwards; but it seems that, at least, one man in each troop set an example of panic, and the rest followed like sheep. The horses that had barely put their muzzles into the troughs reared and capered; but as soon as the Band broke, which it did when the ghost of the Drum-Horse was about a furlong distant, all hooves followed suit, and the clatter of the stampede— quite different from the orderly throb and roar of a movement on parade, or the rough horse-play of watering in camp—made them only more terrified. They felt that the men on their backs were afraid of something. When horses once know that, all is over except the butchery.

Troop after troop turned from the troughs and ran—anywhere and everywhere—like spilt quicksilver. It was a most extraordinary spectacle, for men and horses were in all stages of easiness, and the carbine-buckets flopping against their sides urged the horses on. Men were shouting and cursing, and trying to pull clear of the Band which was being chased by the Drum-Horse, whose rider had fallen forward and seemed to be spurring for a wager.

The Colonel had gone over to the Mess for a drink. Most of the officers were with him, and the Subaltern of the Day was preparing to go down to the Lines, and receive the watering reports from the Troop-Sergeant-Majors. When 'Take me to London again' stopped, after twenty bars, every one in the Mess said, 'What on earth has happened?' A minute later, they heard unmilitary noises, and saw, far across the plain, the White Hussars scattered, and broken, and flying.

The Colonel was speechless with rage, for he thought that the Regiment had risen against him or was unanimously drunk. The Band, a dis-organised mob, tore past, and at its heels laboured the Drum-Horse—the dead and buried Drum-Horse—with the jolting, clattering skeleton. Hogan-Yale whispered softly to Martyn—'No wire will stand that treatment,' and the Band, which had doubled like a hare, came back again. But the rest of the Regiment was gone, was rioting all over the Province, for the dusk had shut in and each man was howling to his neighbour that the Drum-Horse was on his flank. Troop-horses are far too tenderly treated as a rule. They can, on emergencies, do a great deal, even with seventeen stone on their backs. As the troopers found out.

How long this panic lasted I cannot say. I believe that when the moon rose the men saw they had nothing to fear, and, by two and threes and half-troops, crept back into Cantonments very much ashamed of themselves. Meantime, the Drum-Horse, disgusted at his treatment by old friends, pulled up, wheeled round, and trotted up to the Mess verandah-steps for bread. No one liked to run; but no one cared to go forward till the Colonel made a movement and laid hold of the skeleton's foot. The Band had halted some distance away, and now came back slowly. The Colonel called it, individually and collectively, every evil name that occurred to him at the time; for he had set his hand on the bosom of the Drum-Horse and found flesh and blood. Then he beat the kettle-drums with his clenched fist, and discovered that they were but made of silvered paper and bamboo. Next, still swearing, he tried to drag the skeleton out of the saddle, but found that it had been wired into the cantle. The sight of the Colonel, with his arms round the skeleton's pelvis and his knee in the old Drum-Horse's stomach, was striking. Not to say amusing. He worried the thing off in a minute or two, and threw it down on the ground, saying to the Band—'Here, you curs, that's what you're afraid of.' The skeleton did not look pretty in the twilight. The Band-Sergeant seemed to recognise it, for he began to chuckle and choke. 'Shall I take it away, sir?' said the Band-Sergeant. 'Yes,' said the Colonel, 'take it to Hell, and ride there yourselves!'

The Band-Sergeant saluted, hoisted the skeleton across his saddle-bow, and led off to the stables. Then the Colonel began to make inquiries for the rest of the Regiment, and the language he used was wonderful. He would disband the Regiment—he would courtmartial every soul in it—he would not command such a set of rabble, and so on, and so on. As the men dropped in, his language grew wilder, until at last it exceeded the utmost limits of free speech allowed even to a Colonel of Horse.

Martyn took Hogan-Yale aside and suggested compulsory retirement from the Service as a necessity when all was discovered. Martyn was the weaker man of the two. Hogan-Yale put up his eyebrows and remarked, firstly, that he was the son of a Lord, and, secondly, that he was as innocent as the babe unborn of the theatrical resurrection of the Drum-Horse.

'My instructions,' said Yale, with a singularly sweet smile, 'were that the Drum-Horse should be sent back as impressively as possible. I ask you, *am* I responsible if a mule-headed friend sends him back in such a manner as to disturb the peace of mind of a regiment of Her Majesty's Cavalry?'

Martyn said, 'You are a great man, and will in time become a General; but I'd give my chance of a troop to be safe out of this affair.'

Providence saved Martyn and Hogan-Yale. The Second-in-Command led the Colonel away to the little curtained alcove wherein the Subalterns of the White Hussars were accustomed to play poker of nights; and there, after many oaths on the Colonel's part, they talked together in low tones. I fancy that the Second-in-Command must have represented the scare as the work of some trooper whom it would be hopeless to detect; and I know that he dwelt upon the sin and the shame of making a public laughing-stock of the scare.

'They will call us,' said the Second-in-Command, who had a fine imagination—'they will call us the "Fly-by-Nights"; they will call us the "Ghost Hunters"; they will nickname us from one end of the Army List to the other. All the explanation in the world won't make outsiders understand that the officers were away when the panic began. For the honour of the Regiment and for your own sake keep this thing quiet.'

The Colonel was so exhausted with anger that soothing him down came easier than might be imagined. He was made to see, gently and by degrees, that it was obviously impossible to court-martial the whole Regiment, and equally impossible to proceed against any subaltern who, in his belief, had any concern in the hoax.

'But the beast's alive! He's never been shot at all!' shouted the Colonel. 'It's flat flagrant disobedience! I've known a man broke for less—dam' sight less. They're mocking me, I tell you, Mutman! They're mocking me!'

Once more, the Second-in-Command set himself to soothe the Colonel, and wrestled with him for half an hour. At the end of that time, the Regimental Sergeant-Major reported himself. The situation was rather novel to him; but he was not a man to be put out by circumstances. He saluted and said, 'Regiment all come back, Sir.' Then, to propitiate the Colonel—'An' none of the 'orses any the worse, Sir.'

The Colonel only snorted and answered—'You'd better tuck the men into their cots, then, and see that they don't wake up and cry in the night.' The Sergeant withdrew.

His little stroke of humour pleased the Colonel, and, further, he felt slightly ashamed of the language he had been using. The Second-in-Command worried him again, and the two sat talking far into the night.

Next day but one, there was a Commanding Officer's parade, and the Colonel harangued the White Hussars vigorously. The pitch of his speech was that, since the Drum-Horse in his old age had proved himself capable of cutting up the whole Regiment, he should return to his post of pride at the head of the Band, *but* the Regiment were a set of ruffians with bad consciences.

The White Hussars shouted, and threw everything movable about them into the air, and when the parade was over, they cheered the Colonel till they couldn't speak. No cheers were put up for Lieutenant Hogan-Yale, who smiled very sweetly in the background.

Said the Second-in-Command to the Colonel, unofficially—

'These little things ensure popularity, and do not the least affect discipline.'

'But I went back on my word,' said the Colonel.

'Never mind,' said the Second-in-Command. 'The White Hussars will follow you anywhere from to-day. Regiments are just like women. They will do anything for trinketry.'

A week later, Hogan-Yale received an extraordinary letter from some one who signed himself 'Secretary, *Charity and Zeal*, 3709, E. C.,' and asked for 'the return of our skeleton which we have reason to believe is in your possession.'

'Who the deuce is this lunatic who trades in bones?' said Hogan-Yale.

'Beg your pardon, Sir,' said the Band-Sergeant, 'but the skelton is with me, an' I'll return it if you'll pay the carriage into the Civil Lines. There's a coffin with it, Sir.'

Hogan-Yale smiled and handed two rupees to the Band-Sergeant, saying, 'Write the date on the skull, will you?'

If you doubt this story, and know where to go, you can see the date on the skeleton. But don't mention the matter to the White Hussars.

I happen to know something about it, because I prepared the Drum-Horse for his resurrection. He did not take kindly to the skeleton at all.

AT THE PIT'S MOUTH

Men say it was a stolen tide—
    The Lord that sent it he knows all,
But in mine ear will aye abide
    The message that the bells let fall,
And awesome bells they were to me,
That in the dark rang, 'Enderby.'
                                    JEAN INGELOW

ONCE upon a time there was a Man and his Wife and a Tertium Quid. All three were unwise, but the Wife was the unwisest. The Man should have looked after his Wife, who should have avoided the Tertium Quid, who, again, should have married a wife of his own, after clean and open flirtations, to which nobody can possibly object, round Jakko or Observatory Hill. When you see a young man with his pony in a white lather, and his hat on the back of his head flying down-hill at fifteen miles an hour to meet a girl who will be properly surprised to meet him, you naturally approve of that young man, and wish him Staff appointments, and take an interest in his welfare, and, as the proper time comes, give them sugar-tongs or side-saddles according to your means and generosity.

The Tertium Quid flew down-hill on horseback, but it was to meet the Man's Wife; and when he flew up-hill it was for the same end. The Man was in the Plains, earning money for his Wife to spend on dresses and four-hundred-rupee bracelets, and inexpensive luxuries of that kind. He worked very hard, and sent her a letter or a post-card daily. She also wrote to him daily, and said that she was longing for him to come up to Simla. The Tertium Quid used to lean over her shoulder and laugh as she wrote the notes. Then the two would ride to the Post-office together.

Now, Simla is a strange place and its customs are peculiar; nor is any man who has not spent at least ten seasons there qualified to pass judgment on circumstantial evidence, which is the most untrustworthy in the Courts. For these reasons, and for others which need not appear, I decline to state positively whether there was anything irretrievably wrong in the relations between the Man's Wife and the Tertium Quid. If there was, and hereon you must form your own opinion, it was the Man's Wife's fault. She was kittenish in her manners, wearing generally an air of soft and fluffy innocence. But she was deadlily learned and evil-instructed; and, now and again, when the mask dropped, men saw this, shuddered and—almost drew back. Men are occasionally particular, and the least particular men are always the most exacting.

Simla is eccentric in its fashion of treating friendships. Certain attachments which have set and crystallised through half a dozen seasons acquire almost the sanctity of the marriage bond, and are revered as such. Again, certain attachments equally old, and, to all appearance, equally venerable, never seem to win any recognised official status; while a chance-sprung acquaintance, not two months born, steps into the place which by right belongs to the senior. There is no law reducible to print which regulates these affairs.

Some people have a gift which secures them infinite toleration, and others have not. The Man's Wife had not. If she looked over the garden wall, for instance, women taxed her with stealing their husbands. She complained pathetically that she was not allowed to choose her own friends. When she put up her big white muff to her lips, and gazed over it and under her eyebrows at you as she said this thing, you felt that she had been infamously misjudged, and that all the other women's instincts were all wrong; which was absurd. She was not allowed to own the Tertium Quid in peace; and was so strangely constructed that she would not have enjoyed peace had she been so permitted. She preferred some semblance of intrigue to cloak even her most commonplace actions.

After two months of riding, first round Jakko, then Elysium, then Summer Hill, then Observatory Hill, then under Jutogh, and lastly up and down the Cart Road as far as the Tara Devi gap in the dusk, she said to the Tertium Quid, 'Frank, people say we are too much together, and people are so horrid.'

The Tertium Quid pulled his moustache, and replied that horrid people were unworthy of the consideration of nice people.

'But they have done more than talk—they have written—written to my hubby—I'm sure of it,' said the Man's Wife, and she pulled a letter from her husband out of her saddle-pocket and gave it to the Tertium Quid.

It was an honest letter, written by an honest man, then stewing in the Plains on two hundred rupees a month (for he allowed his wife eight hundred and fifty), and in a silk banian and cotton trousers. It is said that, perhaps, she had not thought of the unwisdom of allowing her name to be so generally coupled with the Tertium Quid's; that she was too much of a child to understand the dangers of that sort of thing; that he, her husband, was the last man in the world to interfere jealously with her little amusements and interests, but that it would be better were she to drop the Tertium Quid quietly and for her husband's sake. The letter was sweetened with many pretty little pet names, and it amused the Tertium Quid considerably. He and She laughed over it, so that you, fifty yards away, could see their shoulders shaking while the horses slouched along side by side.

Their conversation was not worth reporting. The upshot of it was that, next day, no one saw the Man's Wife and the Tertium Quid together. They had both gone down to the Cemetery, which, as a rule, is only visited officially by the inhabitants of Simla.

A Simla funeral with the clergyman riding, the mourners riding, and the coffin creaking as it swings between the bearers, is one of the most depressing things on this earth, particularly when the procession passes under the wet, dank dip beneath the Rockcliffe Hotel, where the sun is shut out, and all the hill streams are wailing and weeping together as they go down the valleys.

Occasionally, folk tend the graves, but we in India shift and are transferred so often that, at the end of the second year, the Dead have no friends —only acquaintances who are far too busy amusing themselves up the hill to attend to old partners. The idea of using a Cemetery as a rendezvous is distinctly a feminine one. A man would have said simply, 'Let people talk. We'll go down the Mall.' A woman is made differently, especially if she be such a woman as the Man's Wife. She and the Tertium Quid enjoyed each other's society among the graves of men and women whom they had known and danced with aforetime.

They used to take a big horse-blanket and sit on the grass a little to the left of the lower end, where there is a dip in the ground, and where the occupied graves stop short and the ready-made ones are not ready. Each well-regulated Indian Cemetery keeps half a dozen graves permanently open for contingencies and incidental wear and tear. In the Hills these are more usually baby's size, because children who come up weakened and sick from the Plains often succumb to the effects of the Rains in the Hills or get pneumonia from their *ayahs* taking them through damp pine-woods after the sun has set. In Cantonments, of course, the man's size is more in request; these arrangements varying with the climate and population.

One day when the Man's Wife and the Tertium Quid had just arrived in the Cemetery, they saw some coolies breaking ground. They had marked out a full-size grave, and the Tertium Quid asked them whether any *Sahib* was sick. They said that they did not know; but it was an order that they should dig a *Sahib's* grave.

'Work away,' said the Tertium Quid, 'and let's see how it's done.'

The coolies worked away, and the Man's Wife and the Tertium Quid watched and talked for a couple of hours while the grave was being deepened. Then a coolie, taking the earth in baskets as it was thrown up, jumped over the grave.

'That's queer,' said the Tertium Quid. 'Where's my ulster?'

'What's queer?' said the Man's Wife.

'I have got a chill down my back—just as if a goose had walked over my grave.'

'Why do you look at the thing, then?' said the Man's Wife. 'Let us go.'

The Tertium Quid stood at the head of the grave, and stared without answering for a space. Then he said, dropping a pebble down, 'It is nasty—and cold: horribly cold. I don't think I shall come to the Cemetery any more. I don't think grave-digging is cheerful.'

The two talked and agreed that the Cemetery was depressing. They also arranged for a ride next day out from the Cemetery through the Mashobra Tunnel up to Fagoo and back, because all the world was going to a garden-party at Viceregal Lodge, and all the people of Mashobra would go too.

Coming up the Cemetery road, the Tertium Quid's horse tried to bolt up-hill, being tired with standing so long, and managed to strain a back sinew.

'I shall have to take the mare to-morrow,' said the Tertium Quid, 'and she will stand nothing heavier than a snaffle.'

They made their arrangements to meet in the Cemetery, after allowing all the Mashobra people time to pass into Simla. That night it rained heavily, and, next day, when the Tertium Quid came to the trysting-place, he saw that the new grave had a foot of water in it, the ground being a tough and sour clay.

' 'Jove! That looks beastly,' said the Tertium Quid. 'Fancy being boarded up and dropped into that well!'

They then started off to Fagoo, the mare playing with the snaffle and picking her way as though she were shod with satin, and the sun shining divinely. The road below Mashobra to Fagoo is officially styled the Hima-layan-Thibet Road; but in spite of its name it is not much more than six feet wide in most places, and the drop into the valley below may be anything between one and two thousand feet.

'Now we're going to Thibet,' said the Man's Wife merrily, as the horses drew near to Fagoo. She was riding on the cliff-side.

'Into Thibet,' said the Tertium Quid, 'ever so far from people who say horrid things, and hubbies who write stupid letters. With you—to the end of the world!'

A coolie carrying a log of wood came round a corner, and the mare went wide to avoid him—forefeet in and haunches out, as a sensible mare should go.

'To the world's end,' said the Man's Wife, and looked unspeakable things over her near shoulder at the Tertium Quid.

He was smiling, but, while she looked, the smile froze stiff as it were on his face, and changed to a nervous grin—the sort of grin men wear when they are not quite easy in their saddles. The mare seemed to be sinking by the stern, and her nostrils cracked while she was trying to realise what was happening. The rain of the night before had rotted the drop-side of the Himalayan-Thibet Road, and it was giving way under her. 'What are you doing?' said the Man's Wife. The Tertium Quid gave no answer. He grinned nervously and set his spurs into the mare, who rapped with her forefeet on the road, and the struggle began. The Man's Wife screamed, 'Oh, Frank, get off!'

But the Tertium Quid was glued to the saddle—his face blue and white —and he looked into the Man's Wife's eyes. Then the Man's Wife clutched at the mare's head and caught her by the nose instead of the bridle. The brute threw up her head and went down with a scream, the Tertium Quid upon her, and the nervous grin still set on his face.

The Man's Wife heard the tinkle-tinkle of little stones and loose earth falling off the roadway, and the sliding roar of the man and horse going down. Then everything was quiet, and she called on Frank to leave his mare and walk up. But Frank did not answer. He was underneath the mare, nine hundred feet below, spoiling a patch of Indian corn.

As the revellers came back from Viceregal Lodge in the mists of the evening, they met a temporarily insane woman, on a temporarily mad horse, swinging round the corners, with her eyes and her mouth open, and her head like the head of a Medusa. She was stopped by a man at the risk of his life, and taken out of the saddle, a limp heap, and put on the bank to explain herself. This wasted twenty minutes, and then she was sent home in a lady's 'rickshaw, still with her mouth open and her hands picking at her riding-gloves.

She was in bed through the following three days, which were rainy; so she missed attending the funeral of the Tertium Quid, who was lowered into eighteen inches of water, instead of the twelve to which he had first objected.

A SECOND-RATE WOMAN

Est fuga, volvitur rota,
    On we drift: where looms the dim port?
One Two Three Four Five contribute their quota:
    Something is gained if one caught but the import,
Show it us, Hugues of Saxe-Gotha.
                                    MASTER HUGUES OF SAXE-GOTHA

❧ 'DRESSED! Don't tell me that woman ever dressed in her life. She stood in the middle of the room while her *ayah*—no, her husband—it *must* have been a man—threw her clothes at her. She then did her hair with her fingers, and rubbed her bonnet in the flue under the bed. I *know* she did, as well as if I had assisted at the orgie. Who is she?' said Mrs. Hauksbee.

'Don't!' said Mrs. Mallowe feebly. 'You make my head ache. I'm miserable to-day. Stay me with *fondants*, comfort me with chocolates, for I am——Did you bring anything from Peliti's?'

'Questions to begin with. You shall have the sweets when you have answered them. Who and what is the creature? There were at least half a dozen men round her, and she appeared to be going to sleep in their midst.'

'Delville,' said Mrs. Mallowe, ' "Shady" Delville, to distinguish her from Mrs. Jim of that ilk. She dances as untidily as she dresses, I believe, and her husband is somewhere in Madras. Go and call, if you are so interested.'

'What have I to do with Shigramitish women? She merely caught my attention for a minute, and I wondered at the attraction that a dowd has for a certain type of man. I expected to see her walk out of her clothes—until I looked at her eyes.'

'Hooks and eyes, surely,' drawled Mrs. Mallowe.

'Don't be clever, Polly. You make my head ache. And round this hayrick stood a crowd of men—a positive crowd!'

'Perhaps *they* also expected——'

'Polly, don't be Rabelaisian!'

Mrs. Mallowe curled herself up comfortably on the sofa, and turned her attention to the sweets. She and Mrs. Hauksbee shared the same house at Simla; and these things befell two seasons after the matter of Otis Yeere, which has been already recorded.

Mrs. Hauksbee stepped into the veranda and looked down upon the Mall, her forehead puckered with thought.

'Hah!' said Mrs. Hauksbee shortly. 'Indeed!'

'What is it?' said Mrs. Mallowe sleepily.

'That dowd and The Dancing Master—to whom I object.'

'Why to The Dancing Master? He is a middle-aged gentleman, of reprobate and romantic tendencies, and tries to be a friend of mine.'

'Then make up your mind to lose him. Dowds cling by nature, and I should imagine that this animal—how terrible her bonnet looks from above! —is specially clingsome.'

'She is welcome to The Dancing Master so far as I am concerned. I never could take an interest in a monotonous liar. The frustrated aim of his life is to persuade people that he is a bachelor.'

'O-oh! I think I've met that sort of man before. And isn't he?'

'No. He confided that to me a few days ago. Ugh! Some men ought to be killed.'

'What happened then?'

'He posed as the horror of horrors—a misunderstood man. Heaven knows the *femme incomprise* is sad enough and bad enough—but the other thing!'

'And so fat too! I should have laughed in his face. Men seldom confide in me. How is it they come to you?'

'For the sake of impressing me with their careers in the past. Protect me from men with confidences!'

'And yet you encourage them?'

'What can I do? They talk, I listen, and they vow that I am sympathetic. I know I always profess astonishment even when the plot is—of the most old possible.'

'Yes. Men are so unblushingly explicit if they are once allowed to talk, whereas women's confidences are full of reservations and fibs, except——'

'When they go mad and babble of the Unutterabilities after a week's acquaintance. Really, if you come to consider, we know a great deal more of men than of our own sex.'

'And the extraordinary thing is that men will never believe it. They say we are trying to hide something.'

'They are generally doing that on their own account. Alas! These chocolates pall upon me, and I haven't eaten more than a dozen. I think I shall go to sleep.'

'Then you'll get fat, dear. If you took more exercise and a more intelligent interest in your neighbours you would——'

'Be as much loved as Mrs. Hauksbee. You're a darling in many ways and I like you—you are not a woman's woman—but *why* do you trouble yourself about mere human beings?'

'Because in the absence of angels, who I am sure would be horribly dull, men and women are the most fascinating things in the whole wide world, lazy one. I am interested in The Dowd—I am interested in The Dancing Master—I am interested in the Hawley Boy—and I am interested in *you*.'

'Why couple me with the Hawley Boy? He is your property.'

'Yes, and in his own guileless speech, I'm making a good thing out of him. When he is slightly more reformed, and has passed his Higher Standard, or whatever the authorities think fit to exact from him, I shall select a pretty little girl, the Holt girl, I think, and'—here she waved her hands airily —' "whom Mrs. Hauksbee hath joined together let no man put asunder." That's all.'

'And when you have yoked May Holt with the most notorious detrimental in Simla, and earned the undying hatred of Mamma Holt, what will you do with me, Dispenser of the Destinies of the Universe?'

Mrs. Hauksbee dropped into a low chair in front of the fire, and, chin in hand, gazed long and steadfastly at Mrs. Mallowe.

'I do not know,' she said, shaking her head, '*what* I shall do with you, dear. It's obviously impossible to marry you to some one else—your husband would object and the experiment might not be successful after all. I think I shall begin by preventing you from—what is it?—"sleeping on ale-house benches and snoring in the sun." '

'Don't! I don't like your quotations. They are so rude. Go the Library and bring me new books.'

'While you sleep? No! If you don't come with me, I shall spread your newest frock on my '*rickshaw*-bow, and when any one asks me what I am doing, I shall say that I am going to Phelps's to get it let out. I shall take care that Mrs. MacNamara sees me. Put your things on, there's a good girl.'

Mrs. Mallowe groaned and obeyed, and the two went off to the Library, where they found Mrs. Delville and the man who went by the nickname of The Dancing Master. By that time Mrs. Mallowe was awake and eloquent.

'That is the Creature!' said Mrs. Hauksbee, with the air of one pointing out a slug in the road.

'No,' said Mrs. Mallowe. 'The man is the Creature. Ugh! Good-evening, Mr. Bent. I thought you were coming to tea this evening.'

'Surely it was for to-morrow, was it not?' answered The Dancing Master. 'I understood . . . I fancied . . . I'm so sorry . . . How very unfortunate!' . . .

But Mrs. Mallowe had passed on.

'For the practised equivocator you said he was,' murmured Mrs. Hauksbee, 'he strikes *me* as a failure. Now wherefore should he have preferred a walk with The Dowd to tea with us? Elective affinities, I suppose—both grubby. Polly, I'd never forgive that woman as long as the world rolls.'

'I forgive every woman everything,' said Mrs. Mallowe. 'He will be a sufficient punishment for her. What a common voice she has!'

Mrs. Delville's voice was not pretty, her carriage was even less lovely, and her raiment was strikingly neglected. All these things Mrs. Mallowe noticed over the top of a magazine.

'Now *what* is there in her?' said Mrs. Hauksbee. 'Do you see what I meant about the clothes falling off? If I were a man I would perish sooner than be seen with that rag-bag. And yet, she has good eyes, but— Oh!'

'What is it?'

'She doesn't know how to use them! On my Honour, she does not. Look! Oh look! Untidiness I can endure, but ignorance never! The woman's a fool.'

'Hsh! She'll hear you.'

'All the women in Simla are fools. She'll think I mean some one else. Now she's going out. What a thoroughly objectionable couple she and The Dancing Master make! Which reminds me. Do you suppose they'll ever dance together?'

'Wait and see. I don't envy her the conversation of The Dancing Master —loathly man! His wife ought to be up here before long.'

'Do you know anything about him?'

'Only what he told me. It may be all a fiction. He married a girl bred in the country, I think, and, being an honourable, chivalrous soul, told me that he repented his bargain and sent her to her mother as often as possible— a person who has lived in the Doon since the memory of man and goes to Mussoorie when other people go Home. The wife is with her at present. So he says.'

'Babies?'

'One only, but he talks of his wife in a revolting way. I hated him for it. *He* thought he was being epigrammatic and brilliant.'

'That is a vice peculiar to men. I dislike him because he is generally in the wake of some girl, disappointing the Eligibles. He will persecute May Holt no more, unless I am much mistaken.'

'No. I think Mrs. Delville may occupy his attention for a while.'

'Do you suppose she knows that he is the head of a family?'

'Not from his lips. He swore me to eternal secrecy. Wherefore I tell you. Don't you know that type of man?'

'Not intimately, thank goodness! As a general rule, when a man begins to abuse his wife to me, I find that the Lord gives me wherewith to answer him according to his folly; and we part with a coolness between us. I laugh.'

'I'm different. I've no sense of humour.'

'Cultivate it, then. It has been my mainstay for more years than I care to think about. A well-educated sense of Humour will save a woman when Religion, Training, and Home influences fail; and we may all need salvation sometimes.'

'Do you suppose that the Delville woman has humour?'

'Her dress bewrays her. How can a Thing who wears her *supplément* under her left arm have any notion of the fitness of things—much less their folly? If she discards The Dancing Master after having once seen him dance, I may respect her. Otherwise——'

'But are we not both assuming a great deal too much, dear? You saw the woman at Peliti's—half an hour later you saw her walking with The Dancing Master—an hour later you met her here at the Library.'

'Still with The Dancing Master, remember.'

'Still with The Dancing Master, I admit, but why on the strength of that should you imagine——'

'I imagine nothing. I have no imagination. I am only convinced that The Dancing Master is attracted to The Dowd because he is objectionable in every way and she in every other. If I know the man as you have described him, he holds his wife in slavery at present.'

'She is twenty years younger than he.'

'Poor wretch! And, in the end, after he has posed and swaggered and lied—he has a mouth under that ragged moustache simply made for lies—he will be rewarded according to his merits.'

'I wonder what those really are,' said Mrs. Mallowe.

But Mrs. Hauksbee, her face close to the shelf of the new books, was humming softly: *'What shall he have who killed the Deer!'* She was a lady of unfettered speech.

One month later, she announced her intention of calling upon Mrs. Delville. Both Mrs. Hauksbee and Mrs. Mallowe were in morning wrappers, and there was a great peace in the land.

'I should go as I was,' said Mrs. Mallowe. 'It would be a delicate compliment to her style.'

Mrs. Hauksbee studied herself in the glass.

'Assuming for a moment that she ever darkened these doors, I should put on this robe, after all the others, to show her what a morning wrapper ought to be. It might enliven her. As it is, I shall go in the dove-coloured—sweet emblem of youth and innocence—and shall put on my new gloves.'

'If you really are going, dirty tan would be too good; and you know that dove-colour spots with the rain.'

'I care not. I may make her envious. At least I shall try, though one cannot expect very much from a woman who puts a lace tucker into her habit.'

'Just Heavens! When did she do that?'

'Yesterday—riding with The Dancing Master. I met them at the back of Jakko, and the rain had made the lace lie down. To complete the effect, she was wearing an unclean *terai* with the elastic under her chin. I felt almost too well content to take the trouble to despise her.'

'The Hawley Boy was riding with you. What did he think?'

'Does a boy ever notice these things? Should I like him if he did? He stared in the rudest way, and just when I thought he had seen the elastic, he said, "There's something very taking about that face." I rebuked him on the spot. I don't approve of boys being taken by faces.'

'Other than your own. I shouldn't be in the least surprised if the Hawley Boy immediately went to call.'

'I forbade him. Let her be satisfied with The Dancing Master, and his wife when she comes up. I'm rather curious to see Mrs. Bent and the Delville woman together.'

Mrs. Hauksbee departed and, at the end of an hour, returned slightly flushed.

'There is no limit to the treachery of youth! I *ordered* the Hawley Boy, as he valued my patronage, not to call. The first person I stumble over

—literally stumble over—in her poky, dark, little drawing-room is, of course, the Hawley Boy. She kept us waiting ten minutes, and then emerged as though she had been tipped out of the dirty-clothes basket. You know my way, dear, when I am at all put out. I was Superior, *crrrrushingly* Superior! 'Lifted my eyes to Heaven, and had heard of nothing—'dropped my eyes on the carpet and "really didn't know"—'played with my card-case and "supposed so." The Hawley Boy giggled like a girl, and I had to freeze him with scowls between the sentences.'

'And she?'

'She sat in a heap on the edge of a couch, and managed to convey the impression that she was suffering from stomach-ache, at the very least. It was all I could do not to ask after her symptoms. When I rose, she grunted just like a buffalo in the water—too lazy to move.'

'Are you certain?——'

'Am I blind, Polly? Laziness, sheer laziness, nothing else—or her garments were only constructed for sitting down in. I stayed for a quarter of an hour trying to penetrate the gloom, to guess what her surroundings were like, while she stuck out her tongue.'

'Lu—*cy!*'

'Well—I'll withdraw the tongue, though I'm sure if she didn't do it when I was in the room, she did the minute I was outside. At any rate, she lay in a lump and grunted. Ask the Hawley Boy, dear. I believe the grunts were meant for sentences, but she spoke so indistinctly that I can't swear to it.'

'You are incorrigible, simply.'

'I am *not!* Treat me civilly, give me peace with honour, don't put the only available seat facing the window, and a child may eat jam in my lap before Church. But I resent being grunted at. Wouldn't you? Do you suppose that she communicates her views on life and love to The Dancing Master in a set of modulated "Grmphs"?'

'You attach too much importance to The Dancing Master.'

'He came as we went, and The Dowd grew almost cordial at the sight of him. He smiled greasily, and moved about that darkened dog-kennel in a suspiciously familiar way.'

'Don't be uncharitable. Any sin but that I'll forgive.'

'Listen to the voice of History. I am only describing what I saw. He entered, the heap on the sofa revived slightly, and the Hawley Boy and I came away together. *He* is disillusioned, but I felt it my duty to lecture him severely for going there. And that's all.'

'Now for Pity's sake leave the wretched creature and The Dancing Master alone. They never did you any harm.'

'No harm? To dress as an example and a stumbling-block for half Simla, and then to find this Person who is dressed by the hand of God— not that I wish to disparage *Him* for a moment, but you know the *tikka dhurzie* way He attires those lilies of the field—this Person draws the eyes of men—and some of them nice men? It's almost enough to make one discard clothing. I told the Hawley Boy so.'

'And what did that sweet youth do?'

'Turned shell-pink and looked across the far blue hills like a distressed cherub. *Am* I talking wildly, Polly? Let me say my say, and I shall be calm. Otherwise I may go abroad and disturb Simla with a few original reflections. Excepting always your own sweet self, there isn't a single woman in the land who understands me when I am—what's the word?'

'*Tête-fêlée*,' suggested Mrs. Mallowe.

'Exactly! And now let us have tiffin. The demands of Society are exhausting, and as Mrs. Delville says——' Here Mrs. Hauksbee, to the horror of the *khitmatgars*, lapsed into a series of grunts, while Mrs. Mallowe stared in lazy surprise.

' "God gie us a gude conceit of oorselves." ' said Mrs. Hauksbee piously, returning to her natural speech. 'Now, in any other woman that would have been vulgar. I am consumed with curiosity to see Mrs. Bent. I expect complications.'

'Woman of one idea,' said Mrs. Mallowe shortly; 'all complications are as old as the hills! I have lived through or near all—*all*—ALL!'

'And yet do not understand that men and women never behave twice alike. I am old who was young—if ever I put my head in your lap, you dear, big sceptic, you will learn that my parting is gauze—but never, no never, have I lost my interest in men and women. Polly, I shall see this business out to the bitter end.'

'I am going to sleep,' said Mrs. Mallowe calmly. 'I never interfere with men or women unless I am compelled,' and she retired with dignity to her own room.

Mrs. Hauksbee's curiosity was not long left ungratified, for Mrs. Bent came up to Simla a few days after the conversation faithfully reported above, and pervaded the Mall by her husband's side.

'Behold!' said Mrs. Hauksbee, thoughtfully rubbing her nose. 'That is the last link of the chain, if we omit the husband of the Delville, whoever he may be. Let me consider. The Bents and the Delvilles inhabit the same hotel; and the Delville is detested by the Waddy—do you know the Waddy? —who is almost as big a dowd. The Waddy also abominates the male Bent, for which, if her other sins do not weigh too heavily, she will eventually go to Heaven.'

'Don't be irreverent,' said Mrs. Mallowe, 'I like Mrs. Bent's face.'

'I am discussing the Waddy,' returned Mrs. Hauksbee loftily. 'The Waddy will take the female Bent apart, after having borrowed—yes!— everything that she can, from hairpins to babies' bottles. Such, my dear, is life in a hotel. The Waddy will tell the female Bent facts and fictions about The Dancing Master and The Dowd.'

'Lucy, I should like you better if you were not always looking into people's back-bedrooms.'

'Anybody can look into their front drawing-rooms; and remember whatever I do, and whatever I look, I never talk—as the Waddy will. Let us hope that The Dancing Master's greasy smile and manner of the pedagogue will soften the heart of that cow, his wife. If mouths speak truth, I should think that little Mrs. Bent could get very angry on occasion.'

'But what reason has she for being angry?'

'What reason! The Dancing Master in himself is a reason. How does it go? "If in his life some trivial errors fall, Look in his face and you'll believe them all." I am prepared to credit *any* evil of The Dancing Master, because I hate him so. And The Dowd is so disgustingly badly dressed——'

'That she, too, is capable of every iniquity? I always prefer to believe the best of everybody. It saves so much trouble.'

'Very good. I prefer to believe the worst. It saves useless expenditure of sympathy. And you may be quite certain that the Waddy believes with me.'

Mrs. Mallowe sighed and made no answer.

The conversation was holden after dinner while Mrs. Hauksbee was dressing for a dance.

'I am too tired to go,' pleaded Mrs. Mallowe, and Mrs. Hauksbee left her in peace till two in the morning, when she was aware of emphatic knocking at her door.

'Don't be *very* angry, dear,' said Mrs. Hauksbee. 'My idiot of an *ayah* has gone home, and, as I hope to sleep to-night, there isn't a soul in the place to unlace me.'

'Oh, this is too bad!' said Mrs. Mallowe sulkily.

' 'Can't help it. I'm a lone, lorn grass-widow, dear, but I will *not* sleep in my stays. And such news too! Oh, *do* unlace me, there's a darling! The Dowd—The Dancing Master—I and the Hawley Boy—You know the North veranda?'

'How can I do anything if you spin round like this?' protested Mrs. Mallowe, fumbling with the knot of the laces.

'Oh, I forget. I must tell my tale without the aid of your eyes. Do you know you've lovely eyes, dear? Well, to begin with, I took the Hawley Boy to a *kala juggah*.'

'Did he want much taking?'

'Lots! There was an arrangement of loose-boxes in *kanats*, and *she* was in the next one talking to *him*.'

'Which? How? Explain.'

'You know what I mean—The Dowd and The Dancing Master. We could hear every word, and we listened shamelessly—'specially the Hawley Boy. Polly, I quite love that woman!'

'This is interesting. There! Now turn round. What happened?'

'One moment. Ah—h! Blessed relief. I've been looking forward to taking them off for the last half-hour—which is ominous at my time of life. But, as I was saying, we listened and heard The Dowd drawl worse than ever. She drops her final g's like a barmaid or a blue-blooded Aide-de-Camp. "Look he-ere, you're gettin' too fond o' me," she said, and The Dancing Master owned it was so in language that nearly made me ill. The Dowd reflected for a while. Then we heard her say, "Look he-ere, Mister Bent, why are you such an aw-ful liar?" I nearly exploded while The Dancing Master denied the charge. It seems that he never told her he was a married man.'

'I said he wouldn't.'

'And she had taken this to heart, on personal grounds, I suppose. She drawled along for five minutes, reproaching him with his perfidy and grew quite motherly. "Now you've got a nice little wife of your own—you have," she said. "She's ten times too good for a fat old man like you, and, look he-ere, you never told me a word about her, and I've been thinkin' about it a good deal, and I think you're a liar." Wasn't that delicious? The Dancing Master maundered and raved till the Hawley Boy suggested that he should burst in and beat him. His voice runs up into an impassioned squeak when he is afraid. The Dowd must be an extraordinary woman. She explained that had he been a bachelor she might not have objected to his devotion; but since he was a married man and the father of a very nice baby, she considered him a hypocrite, and this she repeated twice. She wound up her drawl with: "An' I'm tellin' you this because your wife is angry with me, an' I hate quarrellin' with any other woman, an' I like your wife. You know how you have behaved for the last six weeks. You shouldn't have done it, indeed you shouldn't. You're too old an' too fat." Can't you imagine how The Dancing Master would wince at that! "Now go away," she said. "I don't want to tell you what I think of you, because I think you are not nice. I'll stay he-ere till the next dance begins." Did you think that the creature had so much in her?'

'I never studied her as closely as you did. It sounds unnatural. What happened?'

'The Dancing Master attempted blandishment, reproof, jocularity, and the style of the Lord High Warden, and I had almost to pinch the Hawley Boy to make him keep quiet. She grunted at the end of each sentence and, in the end, *he* went away swearing to himself, quite like a man in a novel. He looked more objectionable than ever. I laughed. I love that woman—in spite of her clothes. And now I'm going to bed. What do you think of it?'

'I shan't begin to think till the morning,' said Mrs. Mallowe yawning. 'Perhaps she spoke the truth. They do fly into it by accident sometimes.'

Mrs. Hauksbee's account of her eavesdropping was an ornate one but truthful in the main. For reasons best known to herself, Mrs. 'Shady' Delville had turned upon Mr. Bent and rent him limb from limb, casting him away limp and disconcerted ere she withdrew the light of her eyes from him permanently. Being a man of resource, and anything but pleased in that he had been called both old and fat, he gave Mrs. Bent to understand that he had, during her absence in the Doon, been the victim of unceasing persecution at the hands of Mrs. Delville, and he told the tale so often and with such eloquence that he ended in believing it, while his wife marvelled at the manners and customs of 'some women.' When the situation showed signs of languishing, Mrs. Waddy was always on hand to wake the smouldering fires of suspicion in Mrs. Bent's bosom and to contribute generally to the peace and comfort of the hotel. Mr. Bent's life was not a happy one, for if Mrs. Waddy's story were true, he was, argued his wife, untrustworthy to the last degree. If his own statement was true, his charms of manner and conversation were so great that he needed constant surveillance. And he received it, till he repented genuinely of his marriage and neglected his personal appearance. Mrs. Delville alone in the hotel was unchanged. She removed her chair some six paces towards the head of the table, and occasionally in the twilight ventured on timid overtures of friendship to Mrs. Bent, which were repulsed.

'She does it for my sake,' hinted the virtuous Bent.

'A dangerous and designing woman,' purred Mrs. Waddy.

Worst of all, every other hotel in Simla was full!

*   *   *   *   *

'Polly, are you afraid of diphtheria?'

'Of nothing in the world except smallpox. Diphtheria kills, but it doesn't disfigure. Why do you ask?'

'Because the Bent baby has got it, and the whole hotel is upside down in consequence. The Waddy has "set her five young on the rail" and fled. The Dancing Master fears for his precious throat, and that miserable little woman, his wife, has no notion of what ought to be done. She wanted to put it into a mustard bath—for croup!'

'Where did you learn all this?'

'Just now, on the Mall. Dr. Howlen told me. The Manager of the hotel is abusing the Bents, and the Bents are abusing the manager. They *are* a feckless couple.'

'Well. What's on your mind?'

'This; and I know it's a grave thing to ask. Would you seriously object to my bringing the child over here, with its mother?'

'On the most strict understanding that we see nothing of The Dancing Master.'

'He will be only too glad to stay away. Polly, you're an angel. The woman really is at her wits' end.'

'And you know nothing about her, careless, and would hold her up to public scorn if it gave you a minute's amusement. Therefore you risk your life for the sake of her brat. No, Loo, *I'm* not the angel. I shall keep to my rooms and avoid her. But do as you please—only tell me why you do it.'

Mrs. Hauksbee's eyes softened; she looked out of the window and back into Mrs. Mallowe's face.

'I don't know,' said Mrs. Hauksbee simply.

'You dear!'

'Polly!—and for aught you knew you might have taken my fringe off. Never do that again without warning. Now we'll get the rooms ready. I don't suppose I shall be allowed to circulate in society for a month.'

'And I also. Thank goodness I shall at last get all the sleep I want.'

Much to Mrs. Bent's surprise she and the baby were brought over to the house almost before she knew where she was. Bent was devoutly and undisguisedly thankful, for he was afraid of the infection, and also hoped that a few weeks in the hotel alone with Mrs. Delville might lead to explanations. Mrs. Bent had thrown her jealousy to the winds in her fear for her child's life.

'We can give you good milk,' said Mrs. Hauksbee to her, 'and our house is much nearer to the Doctor's than the hotel, and you won't feel as though you were living in a hostile camp. Where is the dear Mrs. Waddy? She seemed to be a particular friend of yours.'

'They've all left me,' said Mrs. Bent bitterly. 'Mrs. Waddy went first. She said I ought to be ashamed of myself for introducing diseases there, and I am *sure* it wasn't my fault that little Dora——'

'How nice!' cooed Mrs. Hauksbee. 'The Waddy is an infectious disease herself—"more quickly caught than the plague and the taker runs presently mad." I lived next door to her at the Elysium, three years ago. Now see, you won't give us the *least* trouble, and I've ornamented all the house with sheets soaked in carbolic. It smells comforting, doesn't it? Remember I'm always in call, and my *ayah's* at your service when yours goes to her meals and—and—if you cry I'll *never* forgive you.'

Dora Bent occupied her mother's unprofitable attention through the day and the night. The Doctor called thrice in the twenty-four hours, and the house reeked with the smell of the Condy's Fluid, chlorine-water, and carbolic acid washes. Mrs. Mallowe kept to her own rooms—she considered that she had made sufficient concessions in the cause of humanity—and Mrs. Hauksbee was more esteemed by the Doctor as a help in the sick-room than the half-distraught mother.

'I know nothing of illness,' said Mrs. Hauksbee to the Doctor. 'Only tell me what to do, and I'll do it.'

'Keep that crazy woman from kissing the child, and let her have as little to do with the nursing as you possibly can,' said the Doctor; 'I'd turn her out of the sick-room, but that I honestly believe she'd die of anxiety. She is less than no good, and I depend on you and the *ayahs*, remember.'

Mrs. Hauksbee accepted the responsibility, though it painted olive hollows under her eyes and forced her to her oldest dresses. Mrs. Bent clung to her with more than childlike faith.

'I *know* you'll make Dora well, won't you?' she said at least twenty times a day; and twenty times a day Mrs. Hauksbee answered valiantly, 'Of course I will.'

But Dora did not improve, and the Doctor seemed to be always in the house.

'There's some danger of the thing taking a bad turn,' he said; 'I'll come over between three and four in the morning to-morrow.'

'Good gracious!' said Mrs. Hauksbee. 'He never told me what the turn would be! My education has been horribly neglected; and I have only this foolish mother-woman to fall back upon.'

The night wore through slowly, and Mrs. Hauksbee dozed in a chair by the fire. There was a dance at the Viceregal Lodge, and she dreamed of it till she was aware of Mrs. Bent's anxious eyes staring into her own.

'Wake up! Wake up! Do something!' cried Mrs. Bent piteously. 'Dora's choking to death! Do you mean to let her die?'

Mrs. Hauksbee jumped to her feet and bent over the bed. The child was fighting for breath, while the mother wrung her hands despairing.

'Oh, what can I do? What can you do? She won't stay still! I can't hold her. Why didn't the Doctor say this was coming?' screamed Mrs. Bent. 'Won't you help me? She's dying!'

'I—I've never seen a child die before!' stammered Mrs. Hauksbee feebly, and then—let none blame her weakness after the strain of long watching— she broke down, and covered her face with her hands. The *ayahs* on the threshold snored peacefully.

There was a rattle of '*rickshaw* wheels below, the clash of an opening door, a heavy step on the stairs, and Mrs. Delville entered to find Mrs. Bent screaming for the Doctor as she ran round the room. Mrs. Hauksbee, her hands to her ears, and her face buried in the chintz of a chair, was quivering with pain at each cry from the bed, and murmuring, 'Thank God, I never bore a child! Oh! thank God, I never bore a child!'

Mrs. Delville looked at the bed for an instant, took Mrs. Bent by the shoulders, and said quietly, 'Get me some caustic. Be quick.'

The mother obeyed mechanically. Mrs. Delville had thrown herself down by the side of the child and was opening its mouth.

'Oh, you're killing her!' cried Mrs. Bent. 'Where's the Doctor? Leave her alone!'

Mrs. Delville made no reply for a minute, but busied herself with the child.

'Now the caustic, and hold a lamp behind my shoulder. Will you do as you are told? The acid-bottle, if you don't know what I mean,' she said.

A second time Mrs. Delville bent over the child. Mrs. Hauksbee, her face still hidden, sobbed and shivered. One of the *ayahs* staggered sleepily into the room, yawning: 'Doctor Sahib come.'

Mrs. Delville turned her head.

'You're only just in time,' she said. 'It was chokin' her when I came an' I've burnt it.'

'There was no sign of the membrane getting to the air-passages after the last steaming. It was the general weakness, I feared,' said the Doctor half to himself, and he whispered as he looked, 'You've done what I should have been afraid to do without consultation.'

'She was dyin',' said Mrs. Delville, under her breath. 'Can you do anythin'? What a mercy it was I went to the dance!'

Mrs. Hauksbee raised her head.

'Is it all over?' she gasped. 'I'm useless—I'm worse than useless! What are *you* doing here?'

She stared at Mrs. Delville, and Mrs. Bent, realising for the first time who was the Goddess from the Machine, stared also.

Then Mrs. Delville made explanation, putting on a dirty long glove and smoothing a crumpled and ill-fitting ball-dress.

'I was at the dance, an' the Doctor was tellin' me about your baby bein' so ill. So I came away early, an' your door was open, an' I—I—lost my boy this way six months ago, an' I've been tryin' to forget it ever since, an' I—I— I am very sorry for intrudin' an' anythin' that has happened.'

Mrs. Bent was putting out the Doctor's eye with a lamp as he stooped over Dora.

'Take it away,' said the Doctor, 'I think the child will do, thanks to you, Mrs. Delville. I should have come too late, but, I assure you'—he was addressing himself to Mrs. Delville—'I had not the faintest reason to expect *this*. The membrane must have grown like a mushroom. Will one of you help me, please?'

He had reason for the last sentence. Mrs. Hauksbee had thrown herself into Mrs. Delville's arms, where she was weeping bitterly, and Mrs. Bent was unpicturesquely mixed up with both, while from the tangle came the sound of many sobs and much promiscuous kissing.

'Good gracious! I've spoilt all your beautiful roses!' said Mrs. Hauksbee, lifting her head from the lump of crushed gum and calico atrocities on Mrs. Delville's shoulder and hurrying to the Doctor.

Mrs. Delville picked up her shawl, and slouched out of the room, mopping her eyes with the glove that she had not put on.

'I always said she was more than a woman,' sobbed Mrs. Hauksbee hysterically, 'and *that* proves it!'

*   *   *   *   *

Six weeks later, Mrs. Bent and Dora had returned to the hotel. Mrs. Hauksbee had come out of the Valley of Humiliation, had ceased to reproach herself for her collapse in an hour of need, and was even beginning to direct the affairs of the world as before.

'So nobody died, and everything went off as it should, and I kissed The Dowd, Polly. I feel so old. Does it show in my face?'

'Kisses don't as a rule, do they? Of course you know what the result of The Dowd's providential arrival has been.'

'They ought to build her a statue—only no sculptor dare copy those skirts.'

'Ah!' said Mrs. Mallowe quietly. 'She has found another reward. The Dancing Master has been smirking through Simla, giving every one to understand that she came because of her undying love for him—for him—to save *his* child, and all Simla naturally believes this.'

'But Mrs. Bent——'

'Mrs. Bent believes it more than any one else. She won't speak to The Dowd now. *Isn't* The Dancing Master an angel?'

Mrs. Hauksbee lifted up her voice and raged till bedtime. The doors of the two rooms stood open.

'Polly,' said a voice from the darkness, 'what did that American-heiress-globe-trotter girl say last season when she was tipped out of her *'rickshaw* turning a corner? Some absurd adjective that made the man who picked her up explode.'

' "Paltry," ' said Mrs. Mallowe. 'Through her nose—like this—"Ha-ow pahltry!" '

'Exactly,' said the voice. 'Ha-ow pahltry it all is!'

'Which?'

'Everything. Babies, Diphtheria, Mrs. Bent and The Dancing Master, I whooping in a chair, and The Dowd dropping in from the clouds. I wonder what the motive was—*all* the motives.'

'Um!'

'What do *you* think?'

'Don't ask me. Go to sleep.'

THE PHANTOM 'RICKSHAW

May no ill dreams disturb my rest,
Nor Powers of Darkness me molest.
EVENING HYMN

❧ ONE of the few advantages that India has over England is a great
Knowability. After five years' service a man is directly or indirectly acquainted
with the two or three hundred Civilians in his Province, all the Messes of
ten or twelve Regiments and Batteries, and some fifteen hundred other
people of the non-official caste. In ten years his knowledge should be doubled, and at the end of twenty he knows, or knows something about, every
Englishman in the Empire, and may travel anywhere and everywhere without paying hotel-bills.

Globe-trotters who expect entertainment as a right, have, even within
my memory, blunted this open-heartedness, but none the less to-day, if you
belong to the Inner Circle and are neither a Bear nor a Black Sheep, all
houses are open to you, and our small world is very, very kind and helpful.

Rickett of Kamartha stayed with Polder of Kumaon some fifteen years
ago. He meant to stay two nights, but was knocked down by rheumatic
fever, and for six weeks disorganised Polder's establishment, stopped Polder's
work, and nearly died in Polder's bedroom. Polder behaves as though he
had been placed under eternal obligation by Rickett, and yearly sends the
little Ricketts a box of presents and toys. It is the same everywhere. The
men who do not take the trouble to conceal from you their opinion that
you are an incompetent ass, and the women who blacken your character
and misunderstand your wife's amusements, will work themselves to the
bone in your behalf if you fall sick or into serious trouble.

Heatherlegh, the Doctor, kept, in addition to his regular practice, a
hospital on his private account—an arrangement of loose boxes for Incur-
ables, his friend called it—but it was really a sort of fitting-up shed for
craft that had been damaged by stress of weather. The weather in India is
often sultry, and since the tale of bricks is always a fixed quantity, and the
only liberty allowed is permission to work overtime and get no thanks, men
occasionally break down and become as mixed as the metaphors in this
sentence.

Heatherlegh is the dearest doctor that ever was, and his invariable prescription to all his patients is, 'Lie low, go slow, and keep cool.' He says
that more men are killed by overwork than the importance of this world
justifies. He maintains that overwork slew Pansay, who died under his hands
about three years ago. He has, of course, the right to speak authoritatively,

and he laughs at my theory that there was a crack in Pansay's head and a little bit of the Dark World came through and pressed him to death. 'Pansay went off the handle,' says Heatherlegh, 'after the stimulus of long leave at Home. He may or he may not have behaved like a blackguard to Mrs. Keith-Wessington. My notion is that the work of the Katabundi Settlement ran him off his legs, and that he took to brooding and making much of an ordinary P. & O. flirtation. He certainly was engaged to Miss Mannering, and she certainly broke off the engagement. Then he took a feverish chill and all that nonsense about ghosts developed. Overwork started his illness, kept it alight, and killed him, poor devil. Write him off to the System that uses one man to do the work of two and a half men.'

I do not believe this. I used to sit up with Pansay sometimes when Heatherlegh was called out to patients and I happened to be within claim. The man would make me most unhappy by describing in a low, even voice, the procession that was always passing at the bottom of his bed. He had a sick man's command of language. When he recovered I suggested that he should write out the whole affair from beginning to end, knowing that ink might assist him to ease his mind.

He was in a high fever while he was writing, and the blood-and-thunder Magazine diction he adopted did not calm him. Two months afterwards he was reported fit for duty, but, in spite of the fact that he was urgently needed to help an undermanned Commission stagger through a deficit, he preferred to die; vowing at the last that he was hag-ridden. I got his manuscript before he died, and this is his version of the affair, dated 1885, exactly as he wrote it:—

My doctor tells me that I need rest and change of air. It is not improbable that I shall get both ere long—rest that neither the red-coated messenger nor the mid-day gun can break, and change of air far beyond that which any homeward-bound steamer can give me. In the meantime I am resolved to stay where I am; and, in flat defiance of my doctor's orders, to take all the world into my confidence. You shall learn for yourselves the precise nature of my malady, and shall, too, judge for yourselves whether any man born of woman on this weary earth was ever so tormented as I.

Speaking now as a condemned criminal might speak ere the drop-bolts are drawn, my story, wild and hideously improbable as it may appear, demands at least attention. That it will ever receive credence I utterly disbelieve. Two months ago I should have scouted as mad or drunk the man who had dared tell me the like. Two months ago I was the happiest man in India. To-day, from Peshawar to the sea, there is no one more wretched. My doctor and I are the only two who know this. His explanation is, that my brain, digestion, and eyesight are all slightly affected; giving rise to my frequent and persistent 'delusions.' Delusions, indeed I call him a fool; but he attends me still with the same unwearied smile, the same bland professional manner, the same neatly-trimmed red whiskers, till I begin to suspect that I am an ungrateful, evil-tempered invalid. But you shall judge for yourselves.

Three years ago it was my fortune—my great misfortune—to sail from Gravesend to Bombay, on return from long leave, with one Agnes Keith-Wessington, wife of an officer on the Bombay side. It does not in the least concern you to know what manner of woman she was. Be content with the knowledge that, ere the voyage had ended, both she and I were desperately and unreasoningly in love with one another. Heaven knows that I can make the admission now without one particle of vanity. In matters of this sort there is always one who gives and another who accepts. From the first day of our ill-omened attachment, I was conscious that Agnes's passion was a stronger, a more dominant, and—if I may use the expression—a purer sentiment than mine. Whether she recognised the fact then, I do not know. Afterwards it was bitterly plain to both of us.

Arrived at Bombay in the spring of the year, we went our respective ways, to meet no more for the next three or four months, when my leave and her love took us both to Simla. There we spent the season together; and there my fire of straw burnt itself out to a pitiful end with the closing year. I attempt no excuse. I make no apology. Mrs. Wessington had given up much for my sake, and was prepared to give up all. From my own lips, in August 1882, she learnt that I was sick of her presence, tired of her company, and weary of the sound of her voice. Ninety-nine women out of a hundred would wearied of me as I wearied of them; seventy-five of that number would have promptly avenged themselves by active and obtrusive flirtation with other men. Mrs. Wessington was the hundredth. On her neither my openly-expressed aversion nor the cutting brutalities with which I garnished our interviews had the least effect.

'Jack, darling!' was her one eternal cuckoo cry: 'I'm sure it's all a mistake—a hideous mistake; and we'll be good friends again some day. *Please* forgive me, Jack, dear.'

I was the offender, and I knew it. That knowledge transformed my pity into passive endurance, and, eventually, into blind hate—the same instinct, I suppose, which prompts a man to savagely stamp on the spider he has but half killed. And with this hate in my bosom the season of 1882 came to an end.

Next year we met again at Simla—she with her monotonous face and timid attempts at reconciliation, and I with loathing of her in every fibre of my frame. Several times I could not avoid meeting her alone; and on each occasion her words were identically the same. Still the unreasoning wail that it was all a 'mistake'; and still the hope of eventually 'making friends.' I might have seen, had I cared to look, that that hope only was keeping her alive. She grew more wan and thin month by month. You will agree with me, at least, that such conduct would have driven any one to despair. It was uncalled for; childish; unwomanly. I maintain that she was much to blame. And again, sometimes, in the black, fever-stricken night-watches,

I have begun to think that I might have been a little kinder to her. But that really *is* a 'delusion.' I could not have continued pretending to love her when I didn't; could I? It would have been unfair to us both.

Last year we met again—on the same terms as before. The same weary appeals, and the same curt answers from my lips. At least I would make her see how wholly wrong and hopeless were her attempts at resuming the old relationship. As the season wore on, we fell apart—that is to say, she found it difficult to meet me, for I had other and more absorbing interests to attend to. When I think it over quietly in my sickroom, the season of 1884 seems a confused nightmare wherein light and shade were fantastically intermingled —my courtship of little Kitty Mannering; my hopes, doubts, and fears; our long rides together; my trembling avowal of attachment; her reply; and now and again a vision of a white face flitting by in the 'rickshaw with the black and white liveries I once watched for so earnestly; the wave of Mrs. Wessington's gloved hand; and, when she met me alone, which was but seldom, the irksome monotony of her appeal. I loved Kitty Mannering; honestly, heartily loved her, and with my love for her grew my hatred for Agnes. In August Kitty and I were engaged. The next day I met those accursed 'magpie' *jhampanies* at the back of Jakko, and, moved by some passing sentiment of pity, stopped to tell Mrs. Wessington everything. She knew it already.

'So I hear you're engaged, Jack dear.' Then, without a moment's pause: 'I'm sure it's all a mistake—a hideous mistake. We shall be as good friends some day, Jack, as we ever were.'

My answer might have made even a man wince. It cut the dying woman before me like the blow of a whip. 'Please forgive me, Jack; I didn't mean to make you angry; but it's true, it's true!'

And Mrs. Wessington broke down completely. I turned away and left her to finish her journey in peace, feeling, but only for a moment or two, that I had been an unutterably mean hound. I looked back, and saw that she had turned her 'rickshaw with the idea, I suppose, of overtaking me.

The scene and its surroundings were photographed on my memory. The rain-swept sky (we were at the end of the wet weather), the sodden, dingy pines, the muddy road, and the black powder-riven cliffs formed a gloomy background against which the black and white liveries of the *jhampanies*, the yellow-panelled 'rickshaw and Mrs. Wessington's down-bowed golden head stood out clearly. She was holding her handkerchief in her left hand and was leaning back exhausted against the 'rickshaw cushions. I turned my horse up a bypath near the Sanjowlie Reservoir and literally ran away. Once I fancied I heard a faint call of 'Jack!' This may have been imagination. I never stopped to verify it. Ten minutes later I came across Kitty on horseback; and, in the delight of a long ride with her, forgot all about the interview.

A week later Mrs. Wessington died, and the inexpressible burden of her existence was removed from my life. I went Plainsward perfectly happy. Before three months were over I had forgotten all about her, except that at times the discovery of some of her old letters reminded me unpleasantly of our bygone relationship. By January I had disinterred what was left of our correspondence from among my scattered belongings and had burnt it. At the beginning of April of this year, 1885, I was at Simla—semi-deserted Simla—once more, and was deep in lover's talks and walks with Kitty. It was decided that we should be married at the end of June. You will understand, therefore, that, loving Kitty as I did, I am not saying too much when I pronounce myself to have been, at that time, the happiest man in India.

Fourteen delightful days passed almost before I noticed their flight. Then, aroused to the sense of what was proper among mortals circumstanced as we were, I pointed out to Kitty that an engagement ring was the outward and visible sign of her dignity as an engaged girl; and that she must forthwith come to Hamilton's to be measured for one. Up to that moment, I give you my word, we had completely forgotten so trivial a matter. To Hamilton's we accordingly went on the 15th of April 1885. Remember that—whatever my doctor may say to the contrary—I was then in perfect health, enjoying a well-balanced mind and an *absolutely* tranquil spirit. Kitty and I entered Hamilton's shop together, and there, regardless of the order of affairs, I measured Kitty for the ring in the presence of the amused assistant. The ring was a sapphire with two diamonds. We then rode out down the slope that leads to the Combermere Bridge and Peliti's shop.

While my Waler was cautiously feeling his way over the loose shale, and Kitty was laughing and chattering at my side—while all Simla, that is to say as much of it as had then come from the Plains, was grouped round the Reading-room and Peliti's veranda,—I was aware that some one, apparently at a vast distance, was calling me by my Christian name. It struck me that I had heard the voice before, but when and where I could not at once determine. In the short space it took to cover the road between the path from Hamilton's shop and the first plank of the Combermere Bridge I had thought over half a dozen people who might have committed such a solecism, and had eventually decided that it must have been some singing in my ears. Immediately opposite Peliti's shop my eye was arrested by the sight of four *jhampanies* in 'mag-pie' livery, pulling a yellow-panelled, cheap, bazar 'rickshaw. In a moment my mind flew back to the previous season and Mrs. Wessington with a sense of irritation and disgust. Was it not enough that the woman was dead and done with, without her black and white servitors reappearing to spoil the day's happiness? Whoever employed them now I thought I would call upon, and ask as a personal favour to change her *jhampanies'* livery. I would hire the men myself, and, if necessary, buy their coats from off their backs. It is impossible to say here what a flood of undesirable memories their presence evoked.

'Kitty,' I cried, 'there are poor Mrs. Wessington's *jhampanies* turned up again! I wonder who has them now?'

Kitty had known Mrs. Wessington slightly last season, and had always been interested in the sickly woman.

'What? Where?' she asked. 'I can't see them anywhere.'

Even as she spoke, her horse, swerving from a laden mule, threw himself directly in front of the advancing 'rickshaw. I had scarcely time to utter a word of warning when to my unutterable horror, horse and rider passed *through* men and carriage as if they had been thin air.

'What's the matter?' cried Kitty; 'what made you call out so foolishly, Jack? If I *am* engaged I don't want all creation to know about it. There was lots of space between the mule and the veranda; and, if you think I can't ride—— There!'

Whereupon wilful Kitty set off, her dainty little head in the air, at a hand-gallop in the direction of the Band-stand; fully expecting, as she herself afterwards told me, that I should follow her. What was the matter? Nothing indeed. Either that I was mad or drunk, or that Simla was haunted with devils. I reined in my impatient cob, and turned round. The 'rickshaw had turned too, and now stood immediately facing me, near the left railing of the Combermere Bridge.

'Jack! Jack, darling!' (There was no mistake about the words this time: they rang through my brain as if they had been shouted in my ear.) 'It's some hideous mistake, I'm sure. *Please* forgive me, Jack, and let's be friends again.'

The 'rickshaw-hood had fallen back, and inside, as I hope and pray daily for the death I dread by night, sat Mrs. Keith-Wessington, handkerchief in hand, and golden head bowed on her breast.

How long I stared motionless I do not know. Finally, I was aroused by my syce taking the Waler's bridle and asking whether I was ill. From the horrible to the commonplace is but a step. I tumbled off my horse and dashed, half fainting, into Peliti's for a glass of cherry-brandy. There two or three couples were gathered round the coffee-tables discussing the gossip of the day. Their trivialities were more comforting to me just then than the consolations of religion could have been. I plunged into the midst of the conversation at once; chatted, laughed, and jested with a face (when I caught a glimpse of it in a mirror) as white and drawn as that of a corpse. Three or four men noticed my condition; and, evidently setting it down to the results of over-many pegs, charitably endeavoured to draw me apart from the rest of the loungers. But I refused to be led away. I wanted the company of my kind—as a child rushes into the midst of the dinner-party after a fright in the dark. I must have talked for about ten minutes or so, though it seemed an eternity to me, when I heard Kitty's clear voice outside enquiring for me. In another minute she had entered the shop, prepared to upbraid me for failing so signally in my duties. Something in my face stopped her.

'Why, Jack,' she cried, 'what *have* you been doing? What *has* happened? Are you ill?' Thus driven into a direct lie, I said that the sun had been a little too much for me. It was close upon five o'clock of a cloudy April afternoon, and the sun had been hidden all day. I saw my mistake as soon as the words were out of my mouth: attempted to recover it; blundered hopelessly and followed Kitty, in a regal rage, out of doors, amid the smiles of my acquaintances. I made some excuse (I have forgotten what) on the score of my feeling faint; and cantered away to my hotel, leaving Kitty to finish the ride by herself.

In my room I sat down and tried calmly to reason out the matter. Here was I, Theobald Jack Pansay, a well-educated Bengal Civilian in the year of grace 1885, presumably sane, certainly healthy, driven in terror from my sweetheart's side by the apparition of a woman who had been dead and buried eight months ago. These were facts that I could not blink. Nothing was further from my thought than any memory of Mrs. Wessington when Kitty and I left Hamilton's shop. Nothing was more utterly commonplace than the stretch of wall opposite Peliti's. It was broad daylight. The road was full of people; and yet here, look you, in defiance of every law of probability, in direct outrage of Nature's ordinance, there had appeared to me a face from the grave.

Kitty's Arab had gone *through* the 'rickshaw: so that my first hope that some woman marvellously like Mrs. Wessington had hired the carriage and the coolies with their old livery was lost. Again and again I went round this treadmill of thought; and again and again gave up baffled and in despair. The voice was as inexplicable as the apparition. I had originally some wild notion of confiding it all to Kitty; of begging her to marry me at once; and in her arms defying the ghostly occupant of the 'rickshaw. 'After all,' I argued, 'the presence of the 'rickshaw is in itself enough to prove the existence of a spectral illusion. One may see ghosts of men and women, but surely never coolies and carriages. The whole thing is absurd. Fancy the ghost of a hillman!'

Next morning I sent a penitent note to Kitty, imploring her to overlook my strange conduct of the previous afternoon. My Divinity was still very wroth, and a personal apology was necessary. I explained, with a fluency born of night-long pondering over a falsehood, that I had been attacked with a sudden palpitation of the heart—the result of indigestion. This eminently practical solution had its effect: and Kitty and I rode out that afternoon with the shadow of my first lie dividing us.

Nothing would please her save a canter round Jakko. With my nerves still unstrung from the previous night I feebly protested against the notion, suggesting Observatory Hill, Jutogh, the Boileaugunge road—anything rather than the Jakko round. Kitty was angry and a little hurt; so I yielded from fear of provoking further misunderstanding, and we set out together towards Chota Simla. We walked a greater part of the way, and, according to our custom, cantered from a mile or so below the Convent to the stretch of level road by the Sanjowlie Reservoir. The wretched horses appeared to fly, and my heart beat quicker and quicker as we neared the crest of the ascent. My mind had been full of Mrs. Wessington all the afternoon; and every inch of the Jakko road bore witness to our old-time walks and talks. The bowlders were full of it; the pines sang it aloud overhead; the rain-fed torrents giggled and chuckled unseen over the shameful story; and the wind in my ears chanted the iniquity aloud.

As a fitting climax, in the middle of the level men call the Ladies' Mile the Horror was awaiting me. No other 'rickshaw was in sight—only the four black and white *jhampanies*, the yellow-panelled carriage, and the golden head of the woman within—all apparently just as I had left them eight months and one fortnight ago! For an instant I fancied that Kitty *must* see what I saw—we were so marvellously sympathetic in all things. Her next words undeceived me—'Not a soul in sight! Come along, Jack, and I'll race you to the Reservoir buildings!' Her wiry little Arab was off like a bird, my Waler following close behind, and in this order we dashed under the cliffs. Half a minute brought us within fifty yards of the 'rickshaw. I pulled my Waler and fell back a little. The 'rickshaw was directly in the middle of the road; and once more the Arab passed through it, my horse following. 'Jack! Jack dear! *Please* forgive me,' rang with a wail in my ears, and, after an interval: 'It's all a mistake, a hideous mistake!'

I spurred my horse like a man possessed. When I turned my head at the Reservoir works, the black and white liveries were still waiting—patiently waiting—under the gray hillside, and the wind brought me a mocking echo of the words I had just heard. Kitty bantered me a good deal on my silence throughout the remainder of the ride. I had been talking up till then wildly and at random. To save my life I could not speak afterwards naturally, and from Sanjowlie to the Church wisely held my tongue.

I was to dine with the Mannerings that night, and had barely time to canter home to dress. On the road to Elysium Hill I overheard two men talking together in the dusk.—'It's a curious thing,' said one, 'how completely all trace of it disappeared. You know my wife was insanely fond of the woman (never could see anything in her myself), and wanted me to pick up her old 'rickshaw and coolies if they were to be got for love or money. Morbid sort of fancy I call it; but I've got to do what the *Memsahib* tells me. Would you believe that the man she hired it from tells me that all four of the men—they were brothers—died of cholera on the way to Hardwar, poor devils; and the 'rickshaw has been broken up by the man himself. 'Told me he never used a dead *Memsahib's* 'rickshaw. 'Spoilt his luck. Queer notion, wasn't it? Fancy poor little Mrs. Wessington spoiling any one's luck except her own!' I laughed aloud at this point; and my laugh jarred on me as I uttered it. So there *were* ghosts of 'rickshaws after all, and ghostly employments in the other world! How much did Mrs. Wessington give her men? What were their hours? Where did they go?

And for visible answer to my last question I saw the infernal Thing blocking my path in the twilight. The dead travel fast, and by short cuts unknown to ordinary coolies. I laughed aloud a second time and checked my laughter suddenly, for I was afraid I was going mad. Mad to a certain extent I must have been, for I recollect that I reined in my horse at the head of the 'rickshaw, and politely wished Mrs. Wessington 'Good-evening.' Her answer was one I knew only too well. I listened to the end; and replied that I had heard it all before, but should be delighted if she had anything further to say. Some malignant devil stronger than I must have entered into me that evening, for I have a dim recollection of talking the commonplaces of the day for five minutes to the Thing in front of me.

'Mad as a hatter, poor devil—or drunk. Max, try and get him to come home.'

Surely *that* was not Mrs. Wessington's voice! The two men had overheard me speaking to the empty air, and had returned to look after me. They were very kind and considerate, and from their words evidently gathered that I was extremely drunk. I thanked them confusedly and cantered away to my hotel, there changed, and arrived at the Mannerings' ten minutes late. I pleaded the darkness of the night as an excuse; was rebuked by Kitty for my unlover-like tardiness; and sat down.

The conversation had already become general; and under cover of it, I was addressing some tender small talk to my sweetheart when I was aware that at the further end of the table a short red-whiskered man was describing, with much broidery, his encounter with a mad unknown that evening.

A few sentences convinced me that he was repeating the incident of half an hour ago. In the middle of the story he looked round for applause, as professional story-tellers do, caught my eye, and straightway collapsed. There was a moment's awkward silence, and the red-whiskered man muttered something to the effect that he had 'forgotten the rest,' thereby sacrificing a reputation as a good story-teller which he had built up for six seasons past. I blessed him from the bottom of my heart, and—went on with my fish.

In the fulness of time that dinner came to an end; and with genuine regret I tore myself away from Kitty—as certain as I was of my own existence that It would be waiting for me outside the door. The red-whiskered man, who had been introduced to me as Dr. Heatherlegh of Simla, volunteered to bear me company as far as our roads lay together. I accepted his offer with gratitude.

My instinct had not deceived me. It lay in readiness in the Mall, and, in what seemed devilish mockery of our ways, with a lighted head-lamp. The red-whiskered man went to the point at once, in a manner that showed he had been thinking over it all dinner-time.

'I say, Pansay, what the deuce was the matter with you this evening on the Elysium Road?' The suddenness of the question wrenched an answer from me before I was aware.

'That!' said I, pointing to It.

'That may be either D. T. or Eyes for aught I know. Now you don't liquor. I saw as much at dinner, so it can't be D. T. There's nothing whatever where you're pointing, though you're sweating and trembling with fright, like a scared pony. Therefore, I conclude that it's Eyes. And I ought to understand all about them. Come along home with me. I'm on the Blessington lower road.'

To my intense delight the 'rickshaw instead of waiting for us kept about twenty yards ahead—and this, too, whether we walked, trotted, or cantered. In the course of that long night ride I had told my companion almost as much as I have told you here.

'Well, you've spoilt one of the best tales I've ever laid tongue to,' said he, 'but I'll forgive you for the sake of what you've gone through. Now come home and do what I tell you; and when I've cured you, young man, let this be a lesson to you to steer clear of women and indigestible food till the day of your death.'

The 'rickshaw kept steady in front; and my red-whiskered friend seemed to derive great pleasure from my account of its exact whereabouts.

'Eyes, Pansay—all Eyes, Brain, and Stomach. And the greatest of these three is Stomach. You've too much conceited Brain, too little Stomach, and thoroughly unhealthy Eyes. Get your Stomach straight and the rest follows. And all that's French for a liver pill. I'll take sole medical charge of you from this hour! for you're too interesting a phenomenon to be passed over.'

By this time we were deep in the shadow of the Blessington lower road and the 'rickshaw came to a dead stop under a pine-clad, overhanging shale cliff. Instinctively I halted too, giving my reason. Heatherlegh rapped out an oath.

'Now, if you think I'm going to spend a cold night on the hillside for the sake of a Stomach-*cum*-Brain-*cum*-Eye illusion—— Lord, ha' mercy! What's that?'

There was a muffled report, a blinding smother of dust just in front of us, a crack, the noise of rent boughs, and about ten yards of the cliff-side—pines, undergrowth, and all—slid down into the road below, completely blocking it up. The uprooted trees swayed and tottered for a moment like drunken giants in the gloom, and then fell prone among their fellows with a thunderous crash. Our two horses stood motionless and sweating with fear. As soon as the rattle of falling earth and stone had subsided, my companion muttered: 'Man, if we'd gone forward we should have been ten feet deep in our graves by now. "There are more things in heaven and earth" . . . Come home, Pansay, and thank God. I want a peg badly.'

We retraced our way over the Church Ridge, and I arrived at Dr. Heatherlegh's house shortly after midnight.

His attempts towards my cure commenced almost immediately, and for a week I never left his sight. Many a time in the course of that week did I bless the good-fortune which had thrown me in contact with Simla's best and kindest doctor. Day by day my spirits grew lighter and more equable. Day by day, too, I became more and more inclined to fall in with Heatherlegh's 'spectral illusion' theory, implicating eyes, brain, and stomach. I wrote to Kitty, telling her that a slight sprain caused by a fall from my horse kept me indoors for a few days; and that I should be recovered before she had time to regret my absence.

Heatherlegh's treatment was simple to a degree. It consisted of liver pills, cold-water baths, and strong exercise, taken in the dusk or at early dawn—for, as he sagely observed: 'A man with a sprained ankle doesn't walk a dozen miles a day, and your young woman might be wondering if she saw you.'

At the end of the week, after much examination of pupil and pulse, and strict injunctions as to diet and pedestrianism, Heatherlegh dismissed me as brusquely as he had taken charge of me. Here is his parting benediction: 'Man, I certify to your mental cure, and that's as much as to say I've cured most of your bodily ailments. Now, get your traps out of this as soon as you can; and be off to make love to Miss Kitty.'

I was endeavouring to express my thanks for his kindness. He cut me short.

'Don't think I did this because I like you. I gather that you've behaved like a blackguard all through. But, all the same, you're a phenomenon, and as queer a phenomenon as you are a blackguard. No!'—checking me a second time—'not a rupee, please. Go out and see if you can find the eyes-brain-and-stomach business again. I'll give you a lakh for each time you see it.'

Half an hour later I was in the Mannerings' drawing-room with Kitty— drunk with the intoxication of present happiness and the foreknowledge that I should never more be troubled with Its hideous presence. Strong in the sense of my new-found security, I proposed a ride at once; and, by preference, a canter round Jakko.

Never had I felt so well, so overladen with vitality and mere animal spirits, as I did on the afternoon of the 30th of April. Kitty was delighted at the change in my appearance, and complimented me on it in her delightfully frank and outspoken manner. We left the Mannerings' house together, laughing and talking, and cantered along the Chota Simla road as of old.

I was in haste to reach the Sanjowlie Reservoir and there make my assurance doubly sure. The horses did their best, but seemed all too slow to my impatient mind. Kitty was astonished at my boisterousness. 'Why, Jack!' she cried at last, 'you are behaving like a child. What are you doing?'

We were just below the Convent, and from sheer wantonness I was making my Waler plunge and curvet across the road as I tickled it with the loop of my riding-whip.

'Doing?' I answered; 'nothing, dear. That's just it. If you'd been doing nothing for a week except lie up, you'd be as riotous as I.

> 'Singing and murmuring in your feastful mirth,
>   Joying to feel yourself alive;
> Lord over Nature, Lord of the visible Earth,
>   Lord of the senses five.'

My quotation was hardly out of my lips before we had rounded the corner above the Convent; and a few yards further on could see across to Sanjowlie. In the centre of the level road stood the black and white liveries, the yellow-panelled 'rickshaw, and Mrs. Keith-Wessington. I pulled up, looked, rubbed my eyes, and, I believe, must have said something. The next thing I knew was that I was lying face downward on the road, with Kitty kneeling above me in tears.

'Has it gone, child?' I gasped. Kitty only wept more bitterly.

'Has what gone, Jack dear? what does it all mean? There must be a mistake somewhere, Jack. A hideous mistake.' Her last words brought me to my feet—mad—raving for the time being.

'Yes, there *is* a mistake somewhere,' I repeated, 'a hideous mistake. Come and look at It.'

I have an indistinct idea that I dragged Kitty by the wrist along the road up to where It stood, and implored her for pity's sake to speak to It; to tell It that we were betrothed; that neither Death nor Hell could break the tie between us: and Kitty only knows how much more to the same effect. Now and again I appealed passionately to the Terror in the 'rickshaw to bear witness to all I had said, and to release me from a torture that was killing me. As I talked I suppose I must have told Kitty of my old relations with Mrs. Wessington, for I saw her listen intently with white face and blazing eyes.

'Thank you, Mr. Pansay,' she said, 'that's *quite* enough. *Syce ghora láo.*'

The syces, impassive as Orientals always are, had come up with the recaptured horses; and as Kitty sprang into her saddle I caught hold of her bridle, entreating her to hear me out and forgive. My answer was the cut of her riding-whip across my face from mouth to eye, and a word or two of farewell that even now I cannot write down. So I judged and judged rightly, that Kitty knew all; and I staggered back to the side of the 'rickshaw. My face was cut and bleeding, and the blow of the riding-whip had raised a livid blue wheal on it. I had no self-respect. Just then, Heatherlegh, who must have been following Kitty and me at a distance, cantered up.

'Doctor,' I said, pointing to my face, 'here's Miss Mannering's signature to my order of dismissal and—— I'll thank you for that lakh as soon as convenient.'

Heatherlegh's face, even in my abject misery, moved me to laughter. 'I'll stake my professional reputation——' he began.

'Don't be a fool,' I whispered. 'I've lost my life's happiness and you'd better take me home.'

As I spoke the 'rickshaw was gone. Then I lost all knowledge of what was passing. The crest of Jakko seemed to heave and roll like the crest of a cloud and fall in upon me.

Seven days later (on the 7th of May, that is to say) I was aware that I was lying in Heatherlegh's room as weak as a little child. Heatherlegh was watching me intently from behind the papers on his writing-table. His first words were not encouraging; but I was too far spent to be much moved by them.

'Here's Miss Kitty has sent back your letters. You corresponded a good deal, you young people. Here's a packet that looks like a ring and a cheerful sort of a note from Mannering Papa, which I've taken the liberty of reading and burning. The old gentleman's not pleased with you.'

'And Kitty?' I asked dully.

'Rather more drawn than her father from what she says. By the same token you must have been letting out any number of queer reminiscences just before I met you. 'Says that a man who would have behaved to a woman as you did to Mrs. Wessington ought to kill himself out of sheer pity for his kind. She's a hot-headed little virago, your mash. 'Will have it too that you were suffering from D. T. when that row on the Jakko road turned up. 'Says she'll die before she ever speaks to you again.'

I groaned and turned over on the other side.

'Now you've got your choice, my friend. This engagement has to be broken off; and the Mannerings don't want to be too hard on you. Was it broken through D. T. or epileptic fits? Sorry I can't offer you a better exchange unless you'd prefer hereditary insanity. Say the word and I'll tell 'em it's fits. All Simla knows about that scene on the Ladies' Mile. Come! I'll give you five minutes to think over it.'

During those five minutes I believe that I explored thoroughly the lowest circles of the Inferno which it is permitted man to tread on earth. And at the same time I myself was watching myself faltering through the dark labyrinths of doubt, misery, and utter despair. I wondered, as Heatherlegh in his chair might have wondered, which dreadful alternative I should adopt. Presently I heard myself answering in a voice that I hardly recognised—

'They're confoundedly particular about morality in these parts. Give 'em fits, Heatherlegh, and my love. Now let me sleep a bit longer.'

Then my two selves joined, and it was only I (half crazed, devil-driven I) that tossed in my bed tracing step by step the history of the past month.

'But I am in Simla,' I kept repeating to myself. 'I, Jack Pansay, am in

Simla, and there are no ghosts here. It's unreasonable of that woman to pretend there are. Why couldn't Agnes have left me alone? I never did her any harm. It might just as well have been me as Agnes. Only I'd never have come back on purpose to kill *her*. Why can't I be left alone—left alone and happy?'

It was high noon when I first awoke: and the sun was low in the sky before I slept—slept as the tortured criminal sleeps on his rack, too worn to feel further pain.

Next day I could not leave my bed. Heatherlegh told me in the morning that he had received an answer from Mr. Mannering, and that, thanks to his (Heatherlegh's) friendly offices, the story of my affliction had travelled through the length and breadth of Simla, where I was on all sides much pitied.

'And that's rather more than you deserve,' he concluded pleasantly, 'though the Lord knows you've been going through a pretty severe mill. Never mind; we'll cure you yet, you perverse phenomenon.'

I declined firmly to be cured. 'You've been much too good to me already, old man,' said I; 'but I don't think I need trouble you further.'

In my heart I knew that nothing Heatherlegh could do would lighten the burden that had been laid upon me.

With that knowledge came also a sense of hopeless, impotent rebellion against the unreasonableness of it all. There were scores of men no better than I whose punishments had at least been reserved for another world; and I felt that it was bitterly, cruelly unfair that I alone should have been singled out for so hideous a fate. This mood would in time give place to another where it seemed that the 'rickshaw and I were the only realities in a world of shadows; that Kitty was a ghost; that Mannering, Heatherlegh, and all the other men and women I knew were all ghosts; and the great, gray hills themselves but vain shadows devised to torture me. From mood to mood I tossed backwards and forwards for seven weary days; my body growing daily stronger and stronger, until the bedroom looking-glass told me that I had returned to every-day life, and was as other men once more. Curiously enough my face showed no signs of the struggle I had gone through. It was pale indeed, but as expressionless and commonplace as ever. I had expected some permanent alteration—visible evidence of the disease that was eating me away. I found nothing.

On the 15th of May I left Heatherlegh's house at eleven o'clock in the morning; and the instinct of the bachelor drove me to the Club. There I found that every man knew my story as told by Heatherlegh, and was, in clumsy fashion, abnormally kind and attentive. Nevertheless I recognised that for the rest of my natural life I should be among but not of my fellows; and I envied very bitterly indeed the laughing coolies on the Mall below. I lunched at the Club, and at four o'clock wandered aimlessly down the Mall in the vague hope of meeting Kitty. Close to the Band-stand the black and white liveries joined me; and I heard Mrs. Wessington's old appeal at my side. I had been expecting this ever since I came out; and was only surprised at her delay. The phantom 'rickshaw and I went side by side along the Chota Simla road in silence. Close to the bazar, Kitty and a man on horseback overtook and passed us. For any sign she gave I might have been a dog in the road. She did not even pay me the compliment of quickening her pace; though the rainy afternoon had served for an excuse.

So Kitty and her companion, and I and my ghostly Light-o'-Love, crept round Jakko in couples. The road was streaming with water; the pines dripped like roof-pipes on the rocks below, and the air was full of fine, driving rain. Two or three times I found myself saying to myself almost aloud: 'I'm Jack Pansay on leave at Simla—*at Simla!* Every-day, ordinary Simla. I mustn't forget that—I mustn't forget that.' Then I would try to recollect some of the gossip I had heard at the Club: the prices of So-and-So's horses—any-thing, in fact, that related to the work-a-day Anglo-Indian world I knew so well. I even repeated the multiplication-table rapidly to myself, to make quite sure that I was not taking leave of my senses. It gave me much com-fort; and must have prevented my hearing Mrs. Wessington for a time.

Once more I wearily climbed the Convent slope and entered the level road. Here Kitty and the man started off at a canter, and I was left alone with Mrs. Wessington. 'Agnes,' said I, 'will you put back your hood and tell me what it all means?' The hood dropped noiselessly, and I was face to face with my dead and buried mistress. She was wearing the dress in which I had last seen her alive; carried the same tiny handkerchief in her right hand; and the same card-case in her left. (A woman eight months dead with a card-case!) I had to pin myself down to the multiplication-table, and to set both hands on the stone parapet of the road, to assure myself that that at least was real.

'Agnes,' I repeated, 'for pity's sake tell me what it all means.' Mrs. Wessington leaned forward, with that odd, quick turn of the head I used to know so well, and spoke.

If my story had not already so madly overleaped the bounds of all human belief I should apologise to you now. As I know that no one—no, not even Kitty, for whom it is written as some sort of justification of my conduct—will believe me, I will go on. Mrs. Wessington spoke and I walked with her from the Sanjowlie road to the turning below the Com-mander-in-Chief's house as I might walk by the side of any living woman's 'rickshaw, deep in conversation. The second and most tormenting of my moods of sickness had suddenly laid hold upon me, and like the Prince in Tennyson's poem, 'I seemed to move amid a world of ghosts.' There had been a garden-party at the Commander-in-Chief's, and we two joined the crowd of homeward-bound folk. As I saw them it seemed that *they* were the shadows—impalpable fantastic shadows—that divided for Mrs. Wes-sington's 'rickshaw to pass through. What we said during the course of that weird interview I cannot—indeed, I dare not—tell. Heatherlegh's com-ment would have been a short laugh and a remark that I had been 'mashing a brain-eye-and-stomach chimera.' It was a ghastly and yet in some indefinable way a marvellously dear experience. Could it be possible, I wondered, that I was in this life to woo a second time the woman I had killed by my own neglect and cruelty?

I met Kitty on the homeward road—a shadow among shadows.

If I were to describe all the incidents of the next fortnight in their order, my story would never come to an end; and your patience would be exhausted. Morning after morning and evening after evening the ghostly 'rickshaw and I used to wander through Simla together. Wherever I went there the four black and white liveries followed me and bore me company to and from my hotel. At the Theatre I found them amid the crowd of yelling *jhampanies*; outside the Club veranda, after a long evening of whist; at the Birthday Ball, waiting patiently for my reappearance; and in broad daylight when I went calling. Save that it cast no shadow, the 'rickshaw was in every respect as real to look upon as one of wood and iron. More than once, indeed, I have had to check myself from warning some hard-riding friend against cantering over it. More than once I have walked down the Mall deep in conversation with Mrs. Wessington to the unspeakable amazement of the passers-by.

Before I had been out and about a week I learned that the 'fit' theory had been discarded in favour of insanity. However, I made no change in my mode of life. I called, rode, and dined out as freely as ever. I had a passion for the society of my kind which I had never felt before; I hungered to be among the realities of life; and at the same time I felt vaguely unhappy when I had been separated too long from my ghostly companion. It would be almost impossible to describe my varying moods from the 15th of May up to to-day.

The presence of the 'rickshaw filled me by turns with horror, blind fear, a dim sort of pleasure, and utter despair. I dared not leave Simla; and I knew that my stay there was killing me. I knew, moreover, that it was my destiny to die slowly and a little every day. My only anxiety was to get the penance over as quietly as might be. Alternately I hungered for a sight of Kitty and watched her outrageous flirtations with my successor—to speak more accurately, my successors—with amused interest. She was as much out of my life as I was out of hers. By day I wandered with Mrs. Wessington almost content. By night I implored Heaven to let me return to the world as I used to know it. Above all these varying moods lay the sensation of dull, numbing wonder that the seen and the Unseen should mingle so strangely on this earth to hound one poor soul to its grave.

*   *   *   *   *

August 27.—Heatherlegh has been indefatigable in his attendance on me; and only yesterday told me that I ought to send in an application for sick leave. An application to escape the company of a phantom! A request that the Government would graciously permit me to get rid of five ghosts and an airy 'rickshaw by going to England! Heatherlegh's proposition moved me to almost hysterical laughter. I told him that I should await the end quietly at Simla; and I am sure that the end is not far off. Believe me that I dread its advent more than any word can say; and I torture myself nightly with a thousand speculations as to the manner of my death.

Shall I die in my bed decently and as an English gentleman should die; or, in one last walk on the Mall, will my soul be wrenched from me to take its place for ever and ever by the side of that ghastly phantasm? Shall I return to my old lost allegiance in the next world, or shall I meet Agnes loathing her and bound to her side through all eternity? Shall we two hover over the scene of our lives till the end of Time? As the day of my death draws nearer, the intense horror that all living flesh feels toward escaped spirits from beyond the grave grows more and more powerful. It is an awful thing to go down quick among the dead with scarcely one-half of your life completed. It is a thousand times more awful to wait as I do in your midst, for I know not what unimaginable terror. Pity me, at least on the score of my 'delusion,' for I know you will never believe what I have written here. Yet as surely as ever a man was done to death by the Powers of Darkness, I am that man.

In justice, too, pity her. For as surely as ever woman was killed by man, I killed Mrs. Wessington. And the last portion of my punishment is even now upon me.

MY OWN TRUE GHOST STORY

As I came through the Desert thus it was—
As I came through the Desert.
                THE CITY OF DREADFUL NIGHT

◄§ THIS story deals entirely with ghosts. There are, in India, ghosts who take the form of fat, cold, pobby corpses, and hide in trees near the roadside till a traveller passes. Then they drop upon his neck and remain. There are also terrible ghosts of women who have died in childbed. These wander along the pathways at dusk, or hide in the crops near a village, and call seductively. But to answer their call is death in this world and the next. Their feet are turned backwards that all sober men may recognise them. There are ghosts of little children who have been thrown into wells. These haunt well-curbs and the fringes of jungles, and wail under the stars, or catch women by the wrist and beg to be taken up and carried. These and the corpse-ghosts, however, are only vernacular articles and do not attack Sahibs. No native ghost has yet been authentically reported to have frightened an Englishman; but many English ghosts have scared the life out of both white and black.

Nearly every other Station owns a ghost. There are said to be two at Simla, not counting the woman who blows the bellows at Syree dâk-bungalow on the Old Road; Mussoorie has a house haunted by a very lively Thing; a White Lady is supposed to do night-watchman round a house in Lahore; Dalhousie says that one of her houses 'repeats' on autumn evenings all the incidents of a horrible horse-and-precipice accident; Murree has a merry ghost, and, now that she has been swept by cholera, will have room for a sorrowful one; there are Officers' Quarters in Mian Mir whose doors open without reason, and whose furniture is guaranteed to creak, not with the heat of June but with the weight of Invisibles who come to lounge in the chairs; Peshawur possesses houses that none will willingly rent; and there is something—not fever—wrong with a big bungalow in Allahabad. The older Provinces simply bristle with haunted houses, and march phantom armies along their main thoroughfares.

Some of the dâk-bungalows on the Grand Trunk Road have handy little cemeteries in their compound—witnesses to the 'changes and chances of this mortal life' in the days when men drove from Calcutta to the North-west. These bungalows are objectionable places to put up in. They are generally very old, always dirty, while the *khansamah* is as ancient as the bungalow. He either chatters senilely, or falls into the long trances of age. In both moods he is useless. If you get angry with him, he refers to some

Sahib dead and buried these thirty years, and says that when he was in that Sahib's service not a *khansamah* in the Province could touch him. Then he jabbers and mows and trembles and fidgets among the dishes, and you repent of your irritation.

Not long ago it was my business to live in dâk-bungalows. I never inhabited the same house for three nights running, and grew to be learned in the breed. I lived in Government-built ones with red brick walls and rail ceilings, an inventory of the furniture posted in every room, and an excited cobra on the threshold to give welcome. I lived in 'converted' ones—old houses officiating as dâk-bungalows—where nothing was in its proper place and there was not even a fowl for dinner. I lived in second-hand palaces where the wind blew through open-work marble tracery just as uncomfortably as through a broken pane. I lived in dâk-bungalows where the last entry in the visitors' book was fifteen months old, and where they slashed off the curry-kid's head with a sword. It was my good-luck to meet all sorts of men, from sober travelling missionaries and deserters flying from British Regiments, to drunken loafers who threw whiskey bottles at all who passed; and my still greater good-fortune just to escape a maternity case. Seeing that a fair proportion of the tragedy of our lives in India acted itself in dâk-bungalows, I wondered that I had met no ghosts. A ghost that would voluntarily hang about a dâk-bungalow would be mad of course; but so many men have died mad in dâk-bungalows that there must be a fair percentage of lunatic ghosts.

In due time I found my ghost, or ghosts rather, for there were two of them.

We will call the bungalow Katmal dâk-bungalow; but *that* was the smallest part of the horror. A man with a sensitive hide has no right to sleep in dâk-bungalows. He should marry. Katmal dâk-bungalow was old and rotten and unrepaired. The floor was of worn brick, the walls were filthy, and the windows were nearly black with grime. It stood on a bypath largely used by native Sub-Deputy Assistants of all kinds, from Finance to Forests; but real Sahibs were rare. The *khansamah*, who was nearly bent double with old age, said so.

When I arrived, there was a fitful, undecided rain on the face of the land, accompanied by a restless wind, and every gust made a noise like the rattling of dry bones in the stiff toddy-palms outside. The *khansamah* completely lost his head on my arrival. He had served a Sahib once. Did I know that Sahib? He gave me the name of a well-known man who has been buried for more than a quarter of a century, and showed me an ancient daguerreotype of that man in his prehistoric youth. I had seen a steel engraving of him at the head of a double volume of Memoirs a month before, and I felt ancient beyond telling.

The day shut in and the *khansamah* went to get me food. He did not go through the pretence of calling it 'khana,'—man's victuals. He said 'ratub,' and that means, among other things, 'grub'—dog's rations. There

was no insult in his choice of the term. He had forgotten the other word,
I suppose.

While he was cutting up the dead bodies of animals, I settled myself
down, after exploring the dâk-bungalow. There were three rooms, beside
my own, which was a corner kennel, each giving into the other through
dingy white doors fastened with long iron bars. The bungalow was a very
solid one, but the partition-walls of the rooms were almost jerry-built in
their flimsiness. Every step or bang of a trunk echoed from my room down
the other three, and every footfall came back tremulously from the far walls.
For this reason I shut the door. There were no lamps—only candles in long
glass shades. An oil wick was set in the bathroom.

For bleak, unadulterated misery that dâk-bungalow was the worst of
the many that I had ever set foot in. There was no fireplace, and the windows would not open; so a brazier of charcoal would have been useless. The
rain and the wind splashed and gurgled and moaned round the house, and
the toddy-palms rattled and roared. Half a dozen jackals went through the
compound singing, and a hyena stood afar off and mocked them. A hyena
would convince a Sadducee of the Resurrection of the Dead—the worst
sort of Dead. Then came the *ratub*—a curious meal, half native and half
English in composition—with the old *khansamah* babbling behind my chair
about dead and gone English people, and the wind-blown candles playing
shadow-bo-peep with the bed and the mosquito-curtains. It was just the sort
of dinner and evening to make a man think of every single one of his past
sins, and of all the others that he intended to commit if he lived.

Sleep, for several hundred reasons, was not easy. The lamp in the bath-
room threw the most absurd shadows into the room, and the wind was
beginning to talk nonsense.

Just when the reasons were drowsy with blood-sucking I heard the
regular—'Let-us-take-and-heave-him-over' grunt of doolie-bearers in the compound. First one doolie came in, then a second, and then a third. I heard
the doolies dumped on the ground, and the shutter in front of my door
shook.

'That's some one trying to come in,' I said. But no one spoke, and I
persuaded myself that it was the gusty wind. The shutter of the room next
to mine was attacked, flung back, and the inner door opened. 'That's some
Sub-Deputy Assistant,' I said, 'and he has brought his friends with him. Now
they'll talk and spit and smoke for an hour.'

But there were no voices and no footsteps. No one was putting his luggage into the next room. The door shut, and I thanked Providence that I
was to be left in peace. But I was curious to know where the doolies had
gone. I got out of bed and looked into the darkness. There was never a
sign of a doolie. Just as I was getting into bed again, I heard, in the next
room, the sound that no man in his senses can possibly mistake—the whir
of a billiard ball down the length of the slate when the striker is stringing
for break. No other sound is like it. A minute afterwards there was another

whir, and I got into bed. I was not frightened—indeed I was not. I was very curious to know what had become of the doolies. I jumped into bed for that reason.

Next minute I heard the double click of a cannon, and my hair sat up. It is a mistake to say that hair stands up. The skin of the head tightens and you can feel a faint, prickly bristling all over the scalp. That is the hair sitting up.

There was a whir and a click, and both sounds could only have been made by one thing—a billiard ball. I argued the matter out at great length with myself; and the more I argued the less probable it seemed that one bed, one table, and two chairs—all the furniture of the room next to mine—could so exactly duplicate the sounds of a game of billiards. After another cannon, a three-cushion one to judge by the whir, I argued no more. I had found my ghost and would have given worlds to have escaped from that dâk-bungalow. I listened, and with each listen the game grew clearer. There was whir on whir and click on click. Sometimes there was a double click and a whir and another click. Beyond any sort of doubt, people were playing billiards in the next room. And the next room was not big enough to hold a billiard table!

Between the pauses of the wind I heard the game go forward—stroke after stroke. I tried to believe that I could not hear voices; but that attempt was a failure.

Do you know what fear is? Not ordinary fear of insult, injury, or death, but abject, quivering dread of something that you cannot see—fear that dries the inside of the mouth and half of the throat—fear that makes you sweat on the palms of the hands, and gulp in order to keep the uvula at work? This is a fine Fear—a great cowardice, and must be felt to be appreciated. The very improbability of billiards in a dâk-bungalow proved the reality of the thing. No man—drunk or sober—could imagine a game at billiards, or invent the spitting crack of a 'screw cannon.'

A severe course of dâk-bungalows has this disadvantage—it breeds infinite credulity. If a man said to a confirmed dâk-bungalow-haunter: 'There is a corpse in the next room, and there's a mad girl in the next one, and the woman and man on that camel have just eloped from a place sixty miles away,' the hearer would not disbelieve because he would know that nothing is too wild, grotesque, or horrible to happen in a dâk-bungalow.

This credulity, unfortunately, extends to ghosts. A rational person fresh from his own house would have turned on his side and slept. I did not. So surely as I was given up for a dry carcass by the scores of things in the bed, because the bulk of my blood was in my heart, so surely did I hear every stroke of a long game at billiards played in the echoing room behind the iron-barred door. My dominant fear was that the players might want a marker. It was an absurd fear; because creatures who could play in the dark would be above such superfluities. I only know that that was my terror; and it was real.

After a long, long while, the game stopped, and the door banged. I slept because I was dead tired. Otherwise I should have preferred to have kept awake. Not for everything in Asia would I have dropped the door-bar and peered into the dark of the next room.

When the morning came, I considered that I had done well and wisely, and enquired for the means of departure.

'By the way, *khansamah*,' I said, 'what were those three doolies doing in my compound in the night?'

'There were no doolies,' said the *khansamah*.

I went into the next room, and the daylight streamed through the open door. I was immensely brave. I would, at that hour, have played Black Pool with the owner of the big Black Pool down below.

'Has this place always been a dâk-bungalow?' I asked.

'No,' said the *khansamah*. 'Ten or twenty years ago, I have forgotten how long, it was a billiard-room.'

'A what?'

'A billiard-room for the Sahibs who built the Railway. I was *khansamah* then in the big house where all the Railway-Sahibs lived, and I used to come across with brandy-*shrab*. These three rooms were all one, and they held a big table on which the Sahibs played every evening. But the Sahibs are all dead now, and the Railway runs, you say, nearly to Kabul.'

'Do you remember anything about the Sahibs?'

'It is long ago, but I remember that one Sahib, a fat man, and always angry, was playing here one night, and he said to me: "Mangal Khan, brandy-*pani do*," and I filled the glass, and he bent over the table to strike, and his head fell lower and lower till it hit the table, and his spectacles came off, and when we—the Sahibs and I myself—ran to lift him he was dead. I helped to carry him out. Aha, he was a strong Sahib! But he is dead, and I, old Mangal Khan, am still living, by your favour.'

That was more than enough! I had my ghost—a first-hand, authenticated article. I would write to the Society for Psychical Research—I would paralyse the Empire with the news! But I would, first of all, put eighty miles of assessed crop-land between myself and that dâk-bungalow before nightfall. The Society might send their regular agent to investigate later on.

I went into my own room and prepared to pack, after noting down the facts of the case. As I smoked I heard the game begin again,—with a miss in balk this time, for the whir was a short one.

The door was open, and I could see into the room. *Click—click!* That was a cannon. I entered the room without fear, for there was sunlight within and a fresh breeze without. The unseen game was going on at a tremendous rate. And well it might, when a restless little rat was running to and fro inside the dingy ceiling-cloth, and a piece of loose window-sash was making fifty breaks off the window-bolt as it shook in the breeze!

Impossible to mistake the sound of billiard balls! Impossible to mistake the whir of a ball over the slate! But I was to be excused. Even when I shut my enlightened eyes the sound was marvellously like that of a fast game.

Entered angrily the faithful partner of my sorrows, Kadir Baksh.

'This bungalow is very bad and low-caste! No wonder the Presence was disturbed and is speckled. Three sets of doolie-bearers came to the bungalow late last night when I was sleeping outside, and said that it was their custom to rest in the rooms set apart for the English people! What honour has the *khansamah?* They tried to enter, but I told them to go. No wonder, if these *Oorias* have been here, that the Presence is sorely spotted. It is shame, and the work of a dirty man!'

Kadir Baksh did not say that he had taken from each gang two annas for rent in advance, and then, beyond my earshot, had beaten them with the big green umbrella whose use I could never before divine. But Kadir Baksh has no notions of morality.

There was an interview with the *khansamah*, but as he promptly lost his head, wrath gave place to pity, and pity led to a long conversation, in the course of which he put the fat Engineer-Sahib's tragic death in three separate stations—two of them fifty miles away. The third shift was to Calcutta, and there the Sahib died while driving a dog-cart.

I did not go away as soon as I intended. I stayed for the night, while the wind and the rat and the sash and the window-bolt played a ding-dong 'hundred and fifty up.' Then the wind ran out and the billiards stopped, and I felt that I had ruined my one genuine ghost story.

Had I only ceased investigating at the proper time, I could have made *anything* out of it.

That was the bitterest thought of all!

THE STRANGE RIDE OF MORROWBIE JUKES

Alive or dead—there is no other way.
—NATIVE PROVERB

✍§ THERE is no invention about this tale. Jukes by accident stumbled upon a village that is well known to exist, though he is the only Englishman who has been there. A somewhat similar institution used to flourish on the outskirts of Calcutta, and there is a story that if you go into the heart of Bikanir, which is in the heart of the Great Indian Desert, you shall come across not a village but a town where the Dead who did not die but may not live have established their headquarters. And, since it is perfectly true that in the same Desert is a wonderful city where all the rich money-lenders retreat after they have made their fortunes (fortunes so vast that the owners cannot trust even the strong hand of the Government to protect them, but take refuge in the waterless sands), and drive sumptuous C-spring barouches, and buy beautiful girls and decorate their palaces with gold and ivory and Minton tiles and mother-o'-pearl, I do not see why Jukes's tale should not be true. He is a Civil Engineer, with a head for plans and distances and things of that kind, and he certainly would not take the trouble to invent imaginary traps. He could earn more by doing his legitimate work. He never varies the tale in the telling, and grows very hot and indignant when he thinks of the disrespectful treatment he received. He wrote this quite straightforwardly at first, but he has touched it up in places and introduced Moral Reflections: thus:—

In the beginning it all arose from a slight attack of fever. My work necessitated my being in camp for some months between Pakpattan and Mubarakpur—a desolate sandy stretch of country as every one who has had the misfortune to go there may know. My coolies were neither more nor less exasperating than other gangs, and my work demanded sufficient attention to keep me from moping, had I been inclined to so unmanly a weakness.

On the 23rd December 1884, I felt a little feverish. There was a full moon at the time, and, in consequence, every dog near my tent was baying it. The brutes assembled in twos and threes and drove me frantic. A few days previously I had shot one loud-mouthed singer and suspended his carcass *in terrorem* about fifty yards from my tent-door, but his friends fell upon, fought for, and ultimately devoured the body: and, as it seemed to me, sang their hymns of thanksgiving afterwards with renewed energy.

The light-headedness which accompanies fever acts differently on different men. My irritation gave way, after a short time, to a fixed determination to slaughter one huge black and white beast who had been foremost in song and first in flight throughout the evening. Thanks to a shaking hand and a giddy head I had already missed him twice with both barrels of my shotgun, when it struck me that my best plan would be to ride him down in the open and finish him off with a hog-spear. This, of course, was merely the semi-delirious notion of a fever-patient; but I remember that it struck me at the time as being eminently practical and feasible.

I therefore ordered my groom to saddle Pornic and bring him round quietly to the rear of my tent. When the pony was ready, I stood at his head prepared to mount and dash out as soon as the dog should again lift up his voice. Pornic, by the way, had not been out of his pickets for a couple of days; the night air was crisp and chilly; and I was armed with a specially long and sharp pair of persuaders with which I had been rousing a sluggish cob that afternoon. You will easily believe, then, that when he was let go he went quickly. In one moment, for the brute bolted as straight as a die, the tent was left far behind, and we were flying over the smooth sandy soil at racing speed. In another we had passed the wretched dog, and I had almost forgotten why it was that I had taken horse and hog-spear.

The delirium of fever and the excitement of rapid motion through the air must have taken away the remnant of my senses. I have a faint recollection of standing upright in my stirrups, and of brandishing my hog-spear at the great white Moon that looked down so calmly on my mad gallop; and of shouting challenges to the camelthorn bushes as they whizzed past. Once or twice, I believe, I swayed forward on Pornic's neck, and literally hung on by my spurs—as the marks next morning showed.

The wretched beast went forward like a thing possessed, over what seemed to be a limitless expanse of moonlit sand. Next, I remember, the ground rose suddenly in front of us, and as we topped the ascent I saw the waters of the Sutlej shining like a silver bar below. Then Pornic blundered heavily on his nose, and we rolled together down some unseen slope.

I must have lost consciousness, for when I recovered I was lying on my stomach in a heap of soft white sand, and the dawn was beginning to break dimly over the edge of the slope down which I had fallen. As the light grew stronger I saw I was at the bottom of a horseshoe-shaped crater of sand, opening on one side directly on to the shoals of the Sutlej. My fever had altogether left me, and, with the exception of a slight dizziness in the head, I felt no bad effects from the fall over night.

Pornic, who was standing a few yards away, was naturally a good deal exhausted, but had not hurt himself in the least. His saddle, a favourite polo one, was much knocked about, and had been twisted under his belly. It took me some time to put him to rights, and in the meantime I had ample opportunities of observing the spot into which I had so foolishly dropped.

At the risk of being considered tedious, I must describe it at length; inasmuch as an accurate mental picture of its peculiarities will be of material assistance in enabling the reader to understand what follows.

Imagine then, as I have said before, a horseshoe-shaped crater of sand with steeply-graded sand walls about thirty-five feet high. (The slope, I fancy, must have been about 65°.) This crater enclosed a level piece of ground about fifty yards long by thirty at its broadest part, with a rude well in the centre. Round the bottom of the crater, about three feet from the level of the ground proper, ran a series of eighty-three semicircular, ovoid, square, and multilateral holes, all about three feet at the mouth. Each hole on inspection showed that it was carefully shored internally with drift-wood and bamboos, and over the mouth a wooden drip-board projected, like the peak of a jockey's cap, for two feet. No sign of life was visible in these tunnels, but a most sickening stench pervaded the entire amphitheatre—a stench fouler than any which my wanderings in Indian villages have introduced me to.

Having remounted Pornic, who was as anxious as I to get back to camp, I rode round the base of the horseshoe to find some place whence an exit would be practicable. The inhabitants, whoever they might be, had not thought fit to put in an appearance, so I was left to my own devices. My first attempt to 'rush' Pornic up the steep sand-banks showed me that I had fallen into a trap exactly on the same model as that which the ant-lion sets for its prey. At each step the shifting sand poured down from above in tons, and rattled on the drip-boards of the holes like small shot. A couple of ineffectual charges sent us both rolling down to the bottom, half choked with the torrents of sand; and I was constrained to turn my attention to the river-bank.

Here everything seemed easy enough. The sand hills ran down to the river edge, it is true, but there were plenty of shoals and shallows across which I could gallop Pornic, and find my way back to *terra firma* by turning sharply to the right or the left. As I led Pornic over the sands I was startled by the faint pop of a rifle across the river; and at the same moment a bullet dropped with a sharp '*whit*' close to Pornic's head.

There was no mistaking the nature of the missile—a regulation Martini-Henry 'picket.' About five hundred yards away a country-boat was anchored in midstream; and a jet of smoke drifting away from its bows in the still morning air showed me whence the delicate attention had come. Was ever a respectable gentleman in such an *impasse?* The treacherous sand slope allowed no escape from a spot which I had visited most involuntarily, and a promenade on the river frontage was the signal for a bombardment from some insane native in a boat. I'm afraid that I lost my temper very much indeed.

Another bullet reminded me that I had better save my breath to cool my porridge; and I retreated hastily up the sands and back to the horseshoe, where I saw that the noise of the rifle had drawn sixty-five human beings from the badger-holes which I had up till that point supposed to be untenanted. I found myself in the midst of a crowd of spectators—about forty men, twenty women, and one child who could not have been more than five years old. They were all scantily clothed in that salmon coloured cloth which one associates with Hindu mendicants, and, at first sight, gave me the impression of a band of loathsome *fakirs*. The filth and repulsiveness of the assembly were beyond all description, and I shuddered to think what their life in the badger-holes must be.

Even in these days, when local self-government has destroyed the greater part of a native's respect for a Sahib, I have been accustomed to a certain amount of civility from my inferiors, and on approaching the crowd naturally expected that there would be some recognition of my presence. As a matter of fact there was; but it was by no means what I had looked for.

The ragged crew actually laughed at me—such laughter I hope I may never hear again. They cackled, yelled, whistled, and howled as I walked into their midst; some of them literally throwing themselves down on the ground in convulsions of unholy mirth. In a moment I had let go Pornic's head, and, irritated beyond expression at the morning's adventure, commenced cuffing those nearest to me with all the force I could. The wretches dropped under my blows like nine-pins, and the laughter gave place to wails for mercy; while those yet untouched clasped me round the knees, imploring me in all sorts of uncouth tongues to spare them.

In the tumult, and just when I was feeling very much ashamed of myself for having thus easily given way to my temper, a thin, high voice murmured in English from behind my shoulder: 'Sahib! Sahib! Do you not know me? Sahib, it is Gunga Dass, the telegraph-master.'

I spun round quickly and faced the speaker.

Gunga Dass (I have, of course, no hesitation in mentioning the man's real name) I had known four years before as a Deccanee Brahmin lent by the Punjab Government to one of the Khalsia States. He was in charge of a branch telegraph-office there, and when I had last met him was a jovial, full-stomached, portly Government servant with a marvellous capacity for making bad puns in English—a peculiarity which made me remember him long after I had forgotten his services to me in his official capacity. It is seldom that a Hindu makes English puns.

Now, however, the man was changed beyond all recognition. Caste-mark, stomach, slate-coloured continuations, and unctuous speech were all gone. I looked at a withered skeleton, turbanless and almost naked, with long matted hair and deep-set codfish-eyes. But for a crescent-shaped scar on the left cheek—the result of an accident for which I was responsible—I should never have known him. But it was indubitably Gunga Dass, and—for this I was thankful—an English-speaking native who might at least tell me the meaning of all that I had gone through that day.

The crowd retreated to some distance as I turned towards the miserable figure, and ordered him to show me some method of escaping from the crater. He held a freshly-plucked crow in his hand, and in reply to my question climbed slowly on a platform of sand which ran in front of the holes, and commenced lighting a fire there in silence. Dried bents, sand-poppies, and drift-wood burn quickly; and I derived much consolation from the fact that he lit them with an ordinary sulphur match. When they were in a bright glow, and the crow was neatly spitted in front thereof, Gunga Dass began without a word of preamble:—

'There are only two kinds of men, Sar. The alive and the dead. When you are dead you are dead, but when you are alive you live.' (Here the crow demanded his attention for an instant as it twirled before the fire in danger of being burnt to a cinder.) 'If you die at home and do not die when you come to the ghât to be burnt you come here.'

The nature of the reeking village was made plain now, and all that I had known or read of the grotesque and the horrible paled before the fact just communicated by the ex-Brahmin. Sixteen years ago, when I first landed in Bombay, I had been told by a wandering Armenian of the existence, somewhere in India, of a place to which such Hindus as had the misfortune to recover from trance or catalepsy were conveyed and kept, and I recollect laughing heartily at what I was then pleased to consider a traveller's tale. Sitting at the bottom of the sand-trap, the memory of Watson's Hotel, with its swinging punkahs, white-robed servants and the sallow-faced Armenian, rose up in my mind as vividly as a photograph, and I burst into a loud fit of laughter. The contrast was too absurd!

Gunga Dass, as he bent over the unclean bird, watched me curiously. Hindus seldom laugh, and his surroundings were not such as to move him that way. He removed the crow solemnly from the wooden spit and as solemnly devoured it. Then he continued his story, which I give in his own words:—

'In epidemics of the cholera you are carried to be burnt almost before you are dead. When you come to the riverside the cold air, perhaps, makes you alive, and then, if you are only little alive, mud is put on your nose and mouth and you die conclusively. If you are rather more alive, more mud is put; but if you are too lively they let you go and take you away. I was too lively, and made protestation with anger against the indignities that they endeavoured to press upon me. In those days I was Brahmin and proud man. Now I am dead man and eat'—here he eyed the well-gnawed breast bone with the first sign of emotion that I had seen in him since we met—'crows, and—other things. They took me from my sheets when they saw that I was too lively and gave me medicines for one week, and I survived successfully. Then they sent me by rail from my place to Okara Station, with a man to take care of me; and at Okara Station we met two other men, and they conducted us three on camels, in the night, from Okara Station to this place, and they propelled me from the top to the bottom, and the other two succeeded, and I have been here ever since two and a half years. Once I was Brahmin and proud man, and now I eat crows.'

'There is no way of getting out?'

'None of what kind at all. When I first came I made experiments frequently and all the others also, but we have always succumbed to the sand which is precipitated upon our heads.'

'But surely,' I broke in at this point, 'the river-front is open, and it is worth while dodging the bullets; while at night——'

I had already matured a rough plan of escape which a natural instinct of selfishness forbade me sharing with Gunga Dass. He, however, divined my unspoken thought almost as soon as it was formed; and, to my intense astonishment, gave vent to a long low chuckle of derision—the laughter, be it understood, of a superior or at least of an equal.

'You will not'—he had dropped the Sir after his first sentence—'make any escape that way. But you can try. I have tried. Once only.'

The sensation of nameless terror which I had in vain attempted to strive against, overmastered me completely. My long fast—it was now close upon ten o'clock, and I had eaten nothing since tiffin on the previous day—combined with the violent agitation of the ride had exhausted me, and I verily believe that, for a few minutes, I acted as one mad. I hurled myself against the sand-slope. I ran round the base of the crater, blaspheming and praying by turns. I crawled out among the sedges of the river-front, only to be driven back each time in an agony of nervous dread by the rifle-bullets which cut up the sand round me—for I dared not face the death of a mad dog among that hideous crowd—and so fell, spent and raving, at the curb of the well. No one had taken the slightest notice of an exhibition which makes me blush hotly even when I think of it now.

Two or three men trod on my panting body as they drew water, but they were evidently used to this sort of thing, and had no time to waste upon me. Gunga Dass, indeed, when he had banked the embers of his fire with sand, was at some pains to throw half a cupful of fetid water over my head, an attention for which I could have fallen on my knees and thanked him, but he was laughing all the while in the same mirthless, wheezy key that greeted me on my first attempt to force the shoals. And so, in a half-fainting state, I lay till noon. Then, being only a man after all, I felt hungry, and said as much to Gunga Dass, whom I had begun to regard as my natural protector. Following the impulse of the outer world when dealing with natives, I put my hand into my pocket and drew out four annas. The absurdity of the gift struck me at once, and I was about to replace the money.

Gunga Dass, however, cried: 'Give me the money, all you have, or I will get help, and we will kill you!'

A Briton's first impulse, I believe, is to guard the contents of his pockets; but a moment's thought showed me of the folly of differing with the one man who had it in his power to make me comfortable; and with whose help it was possible that I might eventually escape from the crater. I gave him all the money in my possession, Rs. 9-8-5—nine rupees, eight annas, and five pie—for I always keep small change as *bakshish* when I am in camp. Gunga Dass clutched the coins, and hid them at once in his ragged loin-cloth, looking round to assure himself that no one had observed us.

'Now I will give you something to eat,' said he.

What pleasure my money could have given him I am unable to say;

but inasmuch as it did please him I was not sorry that I had parted with it so readily, for I had no doubt that he would have had me killed if I had refused. One does not protest against the doings of a den of wild beasts; and my companions were lower than any beasts. While I eat what Gunga Dass had provided, a coarse *chapatti* and a cupful of the foul well-water, the people showed not the faintest sign of curiosity—that curiosity which is so rampant, as a rule, in an Indian village.

I could even fancy that they despised me. At all events they treated me with the most chilling indifference, and Gunga Dass was nearly as bad. I plied him with questions about the terrible village, and received extremely unsatisfactory answers. So far as I could gather, it had been in existence from time immemorial—whence I concluded that it was at least a century old—and during that time no one had ever been known to escape from it. [I had to control myself here with both hands, lest the blind terror should lay hold of me a second time and drive me raving round the crater.] Gunga Dass took a malicious pleasure in emphasising this point and in watching me wince. Nothing that I could do would induce him to tell me who the mysterious 'They' were.

'It is so ordered,' he would reply, 'and I do not yet know any one who has disobeyed the orders.'

'Only wait till my servant finds that I am missing,' I retorted, 'and I promise you that this place shall be cleared off the face of the earth, and I'll give you a lesson in civility, too, my friend.'

'Your servants would be torn in pieces before they came near this place; and, besides, you are dead, my dear friend. It is not your fault, of course, but none the less you are dead *and* buried.'

At irregular intervals supplies of food, I was told, were dropped down from the land side into the amphitheatre, and the inhabitants fought for them like wild beasts. When a man felt his death coming on he retreated to his lair and died there. The body was sometimes dragged out of the hole and thrown on to the sand, or allowed to rot where it lay.

The phrase 'thrown on to the sand' caught my attention, and I asked Gunga Dass whether this sort of thing was not likely to breed a pestilence.

'That,' said he, with another of his wheezy chuckles, 'you may see for yourself subsequently. You will have much time to make observations.'

Whereat, to his great delight, I winced once more and hastily continued the conversation: 'And how do you live here from day to day? What do you do?' The question elicited exactly the same answer as before—coupled with the information that 'this place is like your European heaven; there is neither marrying nor giving in marriage.'

Gunga Dass had been educated at a Mission School, and, as he himself admitted, had he only changed his religion 'like a wise man,' might have avoided the living grave which was now his portion. But as long as I was with him I fancy he was happy.

Here was a Sahib, a representative of the dominant race, helpless as a child and completely at the mercy of his native neighbours. In a deliberate lazy way he set himself to torture me as a schoolboy would devote a rapturous half-hour to watching the agonies of an impaled beetle, or as a ferret in a blind burrow might glue himself comfortably to the neck of a rabbit. The burden of his conversation was that there was no escape 'of no kind whatever,' and that I should stay here till I died and was 'thrown on to the sand.' If it were possible to forejudge the conversation of the Damned on the advent of a new soul in their abode, I should say that they would speak as Gunga Dass did to me throughout that long afternoon. I was powerless to protest or answer; all my energies being devoted to a struggle against the inexplicable terror that threatened to overwhelm me again and again. I can compare the feeling to nothing except the struggle of a man against the overpowering nausea of the Channel passage—only my agony was of the spirit and infinitely more terrible.

As the day wore on, the inhabitants began to appear in full strength to catch the rays of the afternoon sun, which were now sloping in at the mouth of the crater. They assembled by little knots, and talked among themselves without even throwing a glance in my direction. About four o'clock, so far as I could judge, Gunga Dass rose and dived into his lair for a moment, emerging with a live crow in his hands. The wretched bird was in a most draggled and deplorable condition, but seemed to be in no way afraid of its master. Advancing cautiously to the river-front, Gunga Dass stepped from tussock to tussock until he had reached a smooth patch of sand directly in the line of the boat's fire. The occupants of the boat took no notice. Here he stopped, and, with a couple of dexterous turns of the wrist, pegged the bird on its back with outstretched wings. As was only natural, the crow began to shriek at once and beat the air with its claws. In a few seconds the clamour had attracted the attention of a bevy of wild crows on a shoal a few hundred yards away, where they were discussing something that looked like a corpse. Half a dozen crows flew over at once to see what was going on, and also, as it proved, to attack the pinioned bird. Gunga Dass, who had lain down on a tussock, motioned to me to be quiet, though I fancy this was a needless precaution. In a moment, and before I could see how it happened, a wild crow, who had grappled with the shrieking and helpless bird, was entangled in the latter's claws, swiftly disengaged by Gunga Dass, and pegged down beside its companion in adversity. Curiosity, it seemed, overpowered the rest of the flock, and almost before Gunga Dass and I had time to withdraw to the tussock, two more captives were struggling in the upturned claws of the decoys. So the chase—if I can give it so dignified a name—continued until Gunga Dass had captured seven crows. Five of them he throttled at once, reserving two for further operations another day. I was a good deal impressed by this, to me, novel method of securing food, and complimented Gunga Dass on his skill.

'It is nothing to do,' said he. 'To-morrow you must do it for me. You are stronger than I am.'

This calm assumption of superiority upset me not a little, and I answered peremptorily: 'Indeed, you old ruffian? What do you think I have given you money for?'

'Very well,' was the unmoved reply. 'Perhaps not to-morrow, nor the day after, nor subsequently; but in the end, and for many years, you will catch crows and eat crows, and you will thank your European God that you have crows to catch and eat.'

I could have cheerfully strangled him for this; but judged it best under the circumstances to smother my resentment. An hour later I was eating one of the crows; and, as Gunga Dass had said, thanking my God that I had a crow to eat. Never as long as I live shall I forget that evening meal. The whole population were squatting on the hard sand platform opposite their dens, huddled over tiny fires of refuse and dried rushes. Death, having once laid his hand upon these men and forborne to strike, seemed to stand aloof from them now; for most of our company were old men, bent and worn and twisted with years, and women aged to all appearance as the Fates themselves. They sat together in knots and talked—God only knows what they found to discuss—in low equable tones, curiously in contrast to the strident babble with which natives are accustomed to make day hideous. Now and then an access of that sudden fury which had possessed me in the morning would lay hold on a man or woman; and with yells and imprecations the sufferer would attack the steep slope until, baffled and bleeding, he fell back on the platform incapable of moving a limb. The others would never even raise their eyes when this happened, as men too well aware of the futility of their fellows' attempts and wearied with their useless repetition. I saw four such outbursts in the course of that evening.

Gunga Dass took an eminently business-like view of my situation, and while we were dining—I can afford to laugh at the recollection now, but it was painful enough at the time—propounded the terms of which he would consent to 'do' for me. My nine rupees eight annas, he argued, at the rate of three annas a day, would provide me with food for fifty-one days, or about seven weeks; that is to say, he would be willing to cater for me for that length of time. At the end of it I was to look after myself. For a further consideration—*videlicet* my boots—he would be willing to allow me to occupy the den next to his own, and would supply me with as much dried grass for bedding as he could spare.

'Very well, Gunga Dass,' I replied; 'to the first terms I cheerfully agree, but, as there is nothing on earth to prevent my killing you as you sit here and taking everything that you have' (I thought of the two invaluable crows at the time), 'I flatly refuse to give you my boots and shall take whichever den I please.'

The stroke was a bold one, and I was glad when I saw that it had succeeded. Gunga Dass changed his tone immediately, and disavowed all intention of asking for my boots. At the time it did not strike me as at all strange that I, a Civil Engineer, a man of thirteen years' standing in the Service, and, I trust, an average Englishman, should thus calmly threaten murder and violence against the man who had, for a consideration it is true, taken me under his wing. I had left the world, it seemed, for centuries. I was as certain then as I am now of my own existence, that in the accursed settlement there was no law save that of the strongest; that the living dead men had thrown behind them every canon of the world which had cast them out; and that I had to depend for my own life on my strength and vigilance alone. The crew of the ill-fated *Mignonette* are the only men who would understand my frame of mind. 'At present,' I argued to myself, 'I am strong and a match for six of these wretches. It is imperatively necessary that I should, for my own sake, keep both health and strength until the hour of my release comes—if it ever does.'

Fortified with these resolutions, I ate and drank as much as I could, and made Gunga Dass understand that I intended to be his master, and that the least sign of insubordination on his part would be visited with the only punishment I had it in my power to inflict—sudden and violent death. Shortly after this I went to bed. That is to say, Gunga Dass gave me a double armful of dried bents which I thrust down the mouth of the lair to the right of his, and followed myself, feet foremost; the hole running about nine feet into the sand with a slight downward inclination, and being neatly shored with timbers. From my den, which faced the river-front, I was able to watch the waters of the Sutlej flowing past under the light of a young moon and compose myself to sleep as best I might.

The horrors of that night I shall never forget. My den was nearly as narrow as a coffin, and the sides had been worn smooth and greasy by the contact of innumerable naked bodies, added to which it smelt abominably. Sleep was altogether out of the question to one in my excited frame of mind. As the night wore on, it seemed that the entire amphitheatre was filled with legions of unclean devils that, trooping up from the shoals below, mocked the unfortunates in their lairs.

Personally I am not of an imaginative temperament—very few Engineers are—but on that occasion I was as completely prostrated with nervous terror as any woman. After half an hour or so, however, I was able once more to calmly review my chances of escape. Any exit by the steep sand walls was, of course, impracticable. I had been thoroughly convinced of this some time before. It was possible, just possible, that I might, in the uncertain moonlight, safely run the gauntlet of the rifle shots. The place was so full of terror for me that I was prepared to undergo any risk in leaving it. Imagine my delight, then, when after creeping stealthily to the river-front I found that the infernal boat was not there. My freedom lay before me in the next few steps!

By walking out to the first shallow pool that lay at the foot of the projecting left horn of the horseshoe, I could wade across, turn the flank of the crater, and make my way inland. Without a moment's hesitation I marched briskly past the tussocks where Gunga Dass had snared the crows, and out in the direction of the smooth white sand beyond. My first step from the tufts of dried grass showed me how utterly futile was any hope of escape; for, as I put my foot down, I felt an indescribable drawing, sucking motion of the sand below. Another moment and my leg was swallowed up nearly to the knee. In the moonlight the whole surface of the sand seemed to be shaken with devilish delight at my disappointment. I struggled clear, sweating with terror and exertion, back to the tussocks behind me and fell on my face.

My only means of escape from the semicircle was protected with a quicksand!

How long I lay I have not the faintest idea; but I was roused at the last by the malevolent chuckle of Gunga Dass at my ear. 'I would advise you, Protector of the Poor' (the ruffian was speaking English) 'to return to your house. It is unhealthy to lie down here. Moreover, when the boat returns, you will most certainly be rifled at.' He stood over me in the dim light of the dawn, chuckling and laughing to himself. Suppressing my first impulse to catch the man by the neck and throw him on to the quick sand, I rose sullenly and followed him to the platform below the burrows.

Suddenly, and futilely as I thought while I spoke, I asked: 'Gunga Dass, what is the good of the boat if I can't get out *anyhow?*' I recollect that even in my deepest trouble I had been speculating vaguely on the waste of ammunition in guarding an already well protected foreshore.

Gunga Dass laughed again and made answer: 'They have the boat only in daytime. It is for the reason that *there is a way*. I hope we shall have the pleasure of your company for much longer time. It is a pleasant spot when you have been here some years and eaten roast crow long enough.'

I staggered, numbed and helpless, towards the fetid burrow allotted to me, and fell asleep. An hour or so later I was awakened by a piercing scream— the shrill, high-pitched scream of a horse in pain. Those who have once heard that will never forget the sound. I found some little difficulty in scrambling out of the burrow. When I was in the open, I saw Pornic, my poor old Pornic, lying dead on the sandy soil. How they had killed him I cannot guess. Gunga Dass explained that horse was better than crow, and 'greatest good of greatest number is political maxim. We are now Republic, Mister Jukes, and you are entitled to a fair share of the beast. If you like, we will pass a vote of thanks. Shall I propose?'

Yes, we were a Republic indeed! A Republic of wild beasts penned at the bottom of a pit, to eat and fight and sleep till we died. I attempted no protest of any kind, but sat down and stared at the hideous sight in front of me. In less time almost than it takes me to write this, Pornic's body was divided, in some unclean way or other; the men and women had dragged the fragments on to the platform and were preparing their morning meal. Gunga Dass cooked mine. The almost irresistible impulse to fly at the sand walls until I was wearied laid hold of me afresh, and I had to struggle against it with all my might. Gunga Dass was offensively jocular till I told him that if he addressed another remark of any kind whatever to me I should strangle him where he sat. This silenced him till silence became insupportable, and I bade him say something.

'You will live here till you die like the other Feringhi,' he said coolly, watching me over the fragment of gristle that he was gnawing.

'What other Sahib, you swine? Speak at once, and don't stop to tell me a lie.'

'He is over there,' answered Gunga Dass, pointing to a burrow-mouth about four doors to the left of my own. 'You can see for yourself. He died in the burrow as you will die, and I will die, and as all these men and women and the one child will also die.'

'For pity's sake tell me all you know about him. Who was he? When did he come, and when did he die?'

This appeal was a weak step on my part. Gunga Dass only leered and replied: 'I will not—unless you give me something first.'

Then I recollected where I was, and struck the man between the eyes, partially stunning him. He stepped down from the platform at once, and, cringing and fawning and weeping and attempting to embrace my feet, led me round to the burrow which he had indicated.

'I know nothing whatever about the gentleman. Your God be my witness that I do not. He was as anxious to escape as you were, and he was shot from the boat, though we all did all things to prevent him from attempting. He was shot here.' Gunga Dass laid his hand on his lean stomach and bowed to the earth.

'Well, and what then? Go on!'

'And then—and then, Your Honour, we carried him into his house and gave him water, and put wet cloths on the wound, and he laid down in his house and gave up the ghost.'

'In how long? In how long?'

'About half an hour, after he received his wound. I call Vishn to witness,' yelled the wretched man, 'that I did everything for him. Everything which was possible, that I did!'

He threw himself down on the ground and clasped my ankles. But I had my doubts about Gunga Dass's benevolence, and kicked him off as he lay protesting.

'I believe you robbed him of everything he had. But I can find out in a minute or two. How long was the Sahib here?'

'Nearly a year and a half. I think he must have gone mad. But hear me swear, Protector of the Poor! Won't Your Honour hear me swear that I never touched an article that belonged to him? What is Your Worship going to do?'

I had taken Gunga Dass by the waist and had hauled him on to the platform opposite the deserted burrow. As I did so I thought of my wretched fellow-prisoner's unspeakable misery among all these horrors for eighteen months, and the final agony of dying like a rat in a hole, with a bullet wound in the stomach. Gunga Dass fancied I was going to kill him and howled pitifully. The rest of the population, in the plethora that follows a full flesh meal, watched us without stirring.

'Go inside, Gunga Dass,' said I, 'and fetch it out.'

I was feeling sick and faint with horror now. Gunga Dass nearly rolled off the platform and howled aloud.

'But I am Brahmin, Sahib—a high-caste Brahmin. By your soul, by your father's soul, do not make me do this thing!'

'Brahmin or no Brahmin, by my soul and my father's soul, in you go!' I said, and, seizing him by the shoulders, I crammed his head into the mouth of the burrow, kicked the rest of him in, and, sitting down, covered my face with my hands.

At the end of a few minutes I heard a rustle and a creak; then Gunga Dass in a sobbing, choking whisper speaking to himself; then a soft thud—and I uncovered my eyes.

The dry sand had turned the corpse entrusted to its keeping into a yellow-brown mummy. I told Gunga Dass to stand off while I examined it. The body—clad in an olive-green hunting-suit much stained and worn, with leather pads on the shoulders—was that of a man between thirty and forty, above middle height, with light, sandy hair, long moustache, and a rough unkempt beard. The left canine of the upper jaw was missing, and a portion of the lobe of the right ear was gone. On the second finger of the left hand was a ring—a shield-shaped blood-stone set in gold, with a monogram that might have been either 'B. K.' or 'B. L.' On the third finger of the right hand was a silver ring in the shape of a coiled cobra, much worn and tarnished. Gunga Dass deposited a handful of trifles he had picked out of the burrow at my feet, and, covering the face of the body with my handkerchief, I turned to examine these. I give the full list in the hope that it may lead to the identification of the unfortunate man:—

1. Bowl of a briarwood pipe, serrated at the edge; much worn and blackened; bound with string at the screw.

2. Two patent-lever keys; wards of both broken.

3. Tortoise-shell-handled penknife, silver or nickel, name-plate, marked with monogram 'B. K.'

4. Envelope, postmark undecipherable, bearing a Victorian stamp, addressed to 'Miss Mon——' (rest illegible)—'ham'—'nt.'

5. Imitation crocodile-skin notebook with pencil. First forty-five pages blank; four and a half illegible; fifteen others filled with private memoranda relating chiefly to three persons—a Mrs. L. Singleton, abbreviated several times to 'Lot Single,' 'Mrs. S. May,' and 'Garmison,' referred to in places as 'Jerry' or 'Jack.'

6. Handle of small-sized hunting-knife. Blade snapped short. Buck's horn, diamond-cut, with swivel and ring on the butt; fragment of cotton cord attached.

It must not be supposed that I inventoried all these things on the spot as fully as I have here written them down. The notebook first attracted my attention, and I put it in my pocket with a view to studying it later on. The rest of the articles I conveyed to my burrow for safety's sake, and there, being a methodical man, I inventoried them. I then returned to the corpse and ordered Gunga Dass to help me to carry it out to the river-front. While we were engaged in this, the exploded shell of an old brown cartridge dropped out of one of the pockets and rolled at my feet. Gunga Dass had not seen it; and I fell to thinking that a man does not carry exploded cartridge-cases, especially 'browns,' which will not bear loading twice, about with him when shooting. In other words, that cartridge-case had been fired inside the crater. Consequently there must be a gun somewhere. I was on the verge of asking Gunga Dass, but checked myself, knowing that he would lie. We laid the body down on the edge of the quicksand by the tussocks. It was my intention to push it out and let it be swallowed up—the only possible mode of burial that I could think of. I ordered Gunga Dass to go away.

Then I gingerly put the corpse out on the quicksand. In doing so, it was lying face downward, I tore the frail and rotten khaki shooting-coat open, disclosing a hideous cavity in the back. I have already told you that the dry sand had, as it were, mummified the body. A moment's glance showed that the gaping hole had been caused by a gunshot wound; the gun must have been fired with the muzzle almost touching the back. The shooting-coat, being intact, had been drawn over the body after death, which must have been instantaneous. The secret of the poor wretch's death was plain to me in a flash. Some one of the crater, presumably Gunga Dass, must have shot him with his own gun—the gun that fitted the brown cartridges. He had never attempted to escape in the face of the rifle-fire from the boat.

I pushed the corpse out hastily, and saw it sink from sight literally in a few seconds. I shuddered as I watched. In a dazed, half-conscious way I turned to peruse the notebook. A stained and discoloured slip of paper had been inserted between the binding and the back, and dropped out as I opened the pages. This is what it contained: '*Four out from crow-clump; three left; nine out; two right; three back; two left; fourteen out; two left; seven out; one left; nine back; two right; six back; four right; seven back.*' The paper had been burnt and charred at the edges. What it meant I could not understand. I sat down on the dried bents turning it over and over between my fingers, until I was aware of Gunga Dass standing immediately behind me with glowing eyes and outstretched hands.

'Have you got it?' he panted. 'Will you not let me look at it also? I swear that I will return it.'

'Got what? Return what?' I asked.

'That which you have in your hands. It will help us both.' He stretched out his long, bird-like talons, trembling with eagerness.

'I could never find it,' he continued. 'He had secreted it about his person. Therefore I shot him, but nevertheless I was unable to obtain it.'

Gunga Dass had quite forgotten his little fiction about the rifle-bullet.

I heard him calmly. Morality is blunted by consorting with the Dead who are alive.

'What on earth are you raving about? What is it you want me to give you?'

'The piece of paper in the notebook. It will help us both. Oh, you fool! You fool! Can you not see what it will do for us? We shall escape!'

His voice rose almost to a scream, and he danced with excitement before me. I own I was moved at the chance of getting away.

'Do you mean to say that this slip of paper will help us? What does it mean?'

'Read it aloud! Read it aloud! I beg and I pray to you to read it aloud.'

I did so. Gunga Dass listened delightedly, and drew an irregular line in the sand with his fingers.

'See now! It was the length of his gun-barrels without the stock. I have those barrels. Four gun-barrels out from the place where I caught crows. Straight out do you mind me? Then three left. Ah! Now well I remember how that man worked it out night after night. Then nine out, and so on. Out is always straight before you across the quicksand to the North. He told me so before I killed him.'

'But if you knew all this why didn't you get out before?'

'I did *not* know it. He told me that he was working it out a year and a half ago, and how he was working it out night after night when the boat had gone away, and he could get out near the quicksand safely. Then he said that we would get away together. But I was afraid that he would leave me behind one night when he had worked it all out, and so I shot him. Besides, it is not advisable that the men who once get in here should escape. Only I, and *I* am a Brahmin.'

The hope of escape had brought Gunga Dass's caste back to him. He stood up, walked about and gesticulated violently. Eventually I managed to make him talk soberly, and he told me how this Englishman had spent six months night after night in exploring, inch by inch, the passage across the quicksand; how he had declared it to be simplicity itself up to within about twenty yards of the river bank after turning the flank of the left horn of the horseshoe. This much he had evidently not completely when Gunga Dass shot him with his own gun.

In my frenzy of delight at the possibilities of escape I recollect shaking hands wildly with Gunga Dass, after we had decided that we were to make an attempt to get away that very night. It was weary work waiting throughout the afternoon.

About ten o'clock, as far as I could judge, when the Moon had just risen above the lip of the crater, Gunga Dass made a move for his burrow to bring out the gun-barrels whereby to measure our path. All the other wretched inhabitants had retired to their lairs long ago. The guardian boat drifted down-stream some hours before, and we were utterly alone by the crow-clump. Gunga Dass, while carrying the gun-barrels, let slip the piece of paper which was to be our guide. I stooped down hastily to recover it, and, as I did so, I was aware that the creature was aiming a violent blow at the back of my head with the gun-barrels. It was too late to turn round. I must have received the blow somewhere on the nape of my neck, for I fell sense-less at the edge of the quicksand.

When I recovered consciousness, the Moon was going down, and I was sensible of intolerable pain in the back of my head. Gunga Dass had dis-appeared and my mouth was full of blood. I lay down again and prayed that I might die without more ado. Then the unreasoning fury which I have before mentioned laid hold upon me, and I staggered inland towards the walls of the crater. It seemed that some one was calling to me in a whisper— 'Sahib! Sahib! Sahib!' exactly as my bearer used to call me in the mornings. I fancied that I was delirious until a handful of sand fell at my feet. Then I looked up and saw a head peering down into the amphitheatre—the head of Dunnoo, my dog-boy, who attended to my collies. As soon as he had attracted my attention, he held up his hand and showed a rope. I motioned, staggering to and fro the while, that he should throw it down. It was a couple of leather punkah-ropes knotted together, with a loop at one end. I slipped the loop over my head and under my arms; heard Dunnoo urge some-thing forward; was conscious that I was being dragged, face downward, up the steep sand-slope, and the next instant found myself choked and half-fainting on the sand hills overlooking the crater. Dunnoo, with his face ashy gray in the moonlight, implored me not to stay but to get back to my tent at once.

It seems that he had tracked Pornic's footprints fourteen miles across the sands to the crater; had returned and told my servants, who flatly refused to meddle with any one, white or black, once fallen into the hideous Village of the Dead; whereupon Dunnoo had taken one of my ponies and a couple of punkah ropes, returned to the crater, and hauled me out as I have described.

THE MAN WHO WOULD BE KING

Brother to a Prince and fellow to a beggar if he be found worthy.

❧ THE LAW, as quoted, lays down a fair conduct of life, and one not easy to follow. I have been fellow to a beggar again and again under circumstances which prevented either of us finding out whether the other was worthy. I have still to be brother to a Prince, though I once came near to kinship with what might have been a veritable King and was promised the reversion of a Kingdom—army, law-courts, revenue and policy all complete. But, to-day, I greatly fear that my King is dead, and if I want a crown I must go hunt it for myself.

The beginning of everything was in a railway train upon the road to Mhow from Ajmir. There had been a Deficit in the Budget, which necessitated travelling, not Second-class, which is only half as dear as First-class, but by Intermediate, which is very awful indeed. There are no cushions in the Intermediate class, and the population are either Intermediate, which is Eurasian, or native, which for a long night journey is nasty, or Loafer, which is amusing though intoxicated. Intermediates do not buy from refreshment-rooms. They carry their food in bundles and pots, and buy sweets from the native sweetmeat-sellers, and drink the roadside water. That is why in hot weather Intermediates are taken out of the carriages dead, and in all weathers are most properly looked down upon.

My particular Intermediate happened to be empty till I reached Nasira-bad, when a big black-browed gentleman in shirt-sleeves entered, and, following the custom of Intermediates, passed the time of day. He was a wanderer and a vagabond like myself, but with an educated taste for whiskey. He told tales of things he had seen and done, of out-of-the-way corners of the Empire into which he had penetrated, and of adventures in which he risked his life for a few days' food.

'If India was filled with men like you and me, not knowing more than the crows where they'd get their next day's rations, it isn't seventy millions of revenue the land would be paying—it's seven hundred millions,' said he; and as I looked at his mouth and chin I was disposed to agree with him.

We talked politics—the politics of Loaferdom that sees things from the underside where the lath and plaster is not smoothed off—and we talked postal arrangements because my friend wanted to send a telegram back from the next station to Ajmir, the turning-off place from the Bombay to the Mhow line as you travel westward. My friend had no money beyond eight annas which he wanted for dinner, and I had no money at all, owing to the hitch in the Budget before mentioned. Further, I was going into a wilderness where, though I should resume touch with the Treasury, there were no telegraph offices. I was, therefore, unable to help him in any way.

'We might threaten a Station-master, and make him send a wire on tick,' said my friend, 'but that'd mean enquiries for you and for me, and I've got my hands full these days. Did you say you were travelling back along this line within any days?'

'Within ten,' I said.

'Can't you make it eight?' said he. 'Mine is rather urgent business.'

'I can send your telegram within ten days if that will serve you,' I said.

'I couldn't trust the wire to fetch him now I think of it. It's this way. He leaves Delhi on the 23rd for Bombay. That means he'll be running through Ajmir about the night of the 23rd.'

'But I'm going into the Indian Desert,' I explained.

'Well *and* good,' said he. 'You'll be changing at Marwar Junction to get into Jodhpore territory—you must do that—and he'll be coming through Marwar Junction in the early morning of the 24th by the Bombay Mail. Can you be at Marwar Junction on that time? 'Twon't be inconveniencing you because I know that there's precious few pickings to be got out of these Central India States—even though you pretend to be correspondent of the *Backwoodsman*.'

'Have you ever tried that trick?' I asked.

'Again and again, but the Residents find you out, and then you get escorted to the Border before you've time to get your knife into them. But about my friend here. I *must* give him a word o' mouth to tell him what's come to me or else he won't know where to go. I would take it more than kind of you if you was to come out of Central India in time to catch him at Marwar Junction, and say to him: "He has gone South for the week." He'll know what that means. He's a big man with a red beard, and a great swell he is. You'll find him sleeping like a gentleman with all his luggage round him in a Second-class apartment. But don't you be afraid. Slip down the window and say: "He has gone South for the week," and he'll tumble. It's only cutting your time of stay in those parts by two days. I ask you as a stranger—going to the West,' he said with emphasis.

'Where have *you* come from?' said I.

'From the East,' said he, 'and I am hoping that you will give him the message on the Square—for the sake of my Mother as well as your own.'

Englishmen are not usually softened by appeals to the memory of their mothers; but for certain reasons, which will be fully apparent, I saw fit to agree.

'It's more than a little matter,' said he, 'and that's why I asked you to do it—and now I know that I can depend on you doing it. A Second-class carriage at Marwar Junction, and a red-haired man asleep in it. You'll be sure to remember. I get out at the next station, and I must hold on there till he comes or sends me what I want.'

'I'll give the message if I catch him,' I said, 'and for the sake of your

Mother as well as mine I'll give you a word of advice. Don't try to run the Central India States just now as the correspondent of the *Backwoodsman*. There's a real one knocking about here, and it might lead to trouble.'

'Thank you,' said he simply, 'and when will the swine be gone? I can't starve because he's ruining my work. I wanted to get hold of the Degumber Rajah down here about his father's widow, and give him a jump.'

'What did he do to his father's widow, then?'

'Filled her up with red pepper and slippered her to death as she hung from a beam. I found that out myself and I'm the only man that would dare going into the State to get hush-money for it. They'll try to poison me, same as they did in Chortumna when I went on the loot there. But you'll give the man at Marwar Junction my message?'

He got out at a little roadside station, and I reflected. I had heard, more than once, of men personating correspondents of newspapers and bleeding small Native States with threats of exposure, but I had never met any of the caste before. They lead a hard life, and generally die with great suddenness. The Native States have a wholesome horror of English newspapers, which may throw light on their peculiar methods of government, and do their best to choke correspondents with champagne, or drive them out of their mind with four-in-hand barouches. They do not understand that nobody cares a straw for the internal administration of Native States so long as oppression and crime are kept within decent limits, and the ruler is not drugged, drunk, or diseased from one end of the year to the other. They are the dark places of the earth, full of unimaginable cruelty, touching the Railway and the Telegraph on one side, and, on the other, the days of Harun-al-Raschid. When I left the train I did business with divers Kings, and in eight days passed through many changes of life. Sometimes I wore dress-clothes and consorted with Princes and Politicals, drinking from crystal and eating from silver. Sometimes I lay out upon the ground and devoured what I could get, from a plate made of leaves, and drank the running water, and slept under the same rug as my servant. It was all in the day's work.

Then I headed for the Great Indian Desert upon the proper date, as I had promised, and the night Mail set me down at Marwar Junction, where a funny little, happy-go-lucky, native-managed railway runs to Jodhpore. The Bombay Mail from Delhi makes a short halt at Marwar. She arrived as I got in, and I had just time to hurry to her platform and go down the carriages. There was only one Second-class on the train. I slipped the window and looked down upon a flaming red beard, half covered by a railway rug. That was my man, fast asleep, and I dug him gently in the ribs. He woke with a grunt and I saw his face in the light of the lamps. It was a great and shining face.

'Tickets again?' said he.

'No,' said I. 'I am to tell you that he is gone South for the week. He has gone South for the week!'

The train had begun to move out. The red man rubbed his eyes. 'He has gone South for the week,' he repeated. 'Now that's just like his impidence. Did he say that I was to give you anything? 'Cause I won't.'

'He didn't,' I said and dropped away, and watched the red lights die out in the dark. It was horribly cold because the wind was blowing off the sands. I climbed into my own train—not an Intermediate carriage this time— and went to sleep.

If the man with the beard had given me a rupee I should have kept it as a memento of a rather curious affair. But the consciousness of having done my duty was my only reward.

Later on I reflected that two gentlemen like my friends could not do any good if they foregathered and personated correspondents of newspapers, and might, if they black-mailed one of the little rat-trap states of Central India or Southern Rajputana, get themselves into serious difficulties. I therefore took some trouble to describe them as accurately as I could remember to people who would be interested in deporting them: and succeeded, so I was later informed, in having them headed back from the Degumber borders.

Then I became respectable, and returned to an Office where there were no Kings and no incidents outside the daily manufacture of a newspaper. A newspaper office seems to attract every conceivable sort of person, to the prejudice of discipline. Zenana-mission ladies arrive, and beg that the Editor will instantly abandon all his duties to describe a Christian prize-giving in a back-slum of a perfectly inaccessible village; Colonels who have been over-passed for command sit down and sketch the outline of a series of ten, twelve, or twenty-four leading articles on Seniority *versus* Selection; mission-aries wish to know why they have not been permitted to escape from their regular vehicles of abuse and swear at a brother-missionary under special patronage of the editorial We; stranded theatrical companies troop up to explain that they cannot pay for their advertisements, but on their return from New Zealand or Tahiti will do so with interest; inventors of patent punkah-pulling machines, carriage couplings and unbreakable swords and axle-trees call with specifications in their pockets and hours at their disposal; tea-companies enter and elaborate their prospectuses with the office pens; secretaries of ball-committees clamour to have the glories of their last dance more fully described; strange ladies rustle in and say: 'I want a hundred lady's cards printed *at once*, please,' which is manifestly part of an Editor's duty; and every dissolute ruffian that ever tramped the Grand Trunk Road makes it his business to ask for employment as a proof-reader. And, all the time, the telephone-bell is ringing madly, and Kings are being killed on the Continent, and Empires are saying—'You're another,' and Mister Gladstone is calling down brimstone upon the British Dominions, and the little black copy-boys are whining, '*kaa-pi chay-ha-yeh*' (copy wanted) like tired bees, and most of the paper is as blank as Modred's shield.

But that is the amusing part of the year. There are six other months when none ever come to call, and the thermometer walks inch by inch up to the top of the glass, and the office is darkened to just above reading-light, and the press-machines are red-hot of touch, and nobody writes anything but accounts of amusements in the Hill-stations or obituary notices. Then the telephone becomes a tinkling terror, because it tells you of the sudden deaths of men and women that you knew intimately, and the prickly-heat covers you with a garment, and you sit down and write: 'A slight increase of sickness is reported from the Khuda Janta Khan District. The outbreak is purely sporadic in its nature, and, thanks to the energetic efforts of the District authorities, is now almost at an end. It is, however, with deep regret we record the death,' etc.

Then the sickness really breaks out, and the less recording and reporting the better for the peace of the subscribers. But the Empires and the Kings continue to divert themselves as selfishly as before, and the Foreman thinks that a daily paper really ought to come out once in twenty-four hours, and all the people at the Hill-stations in the middle of their amusements say: 'Good gracious! Why can't the paper be sparkling? I'm sure there's plenty going on up here.'

That is the dark half of the moon, and, as the advertisements say, 'must be experienced to be appreciated.'

It was in that season, and a remarkably evil season, that the paper began running the last issue of the week on Saturday night, which is to say Sunday morning, after the custom of a London paper. This was a great convenience, for immediately after the paper was put to bed, the dawn would lower the thermometer from 96° to almost 84° for half an hour, and in that chill— you have no idea how cold is 84° on the grass until you begin to pray for it —a very tired man could get off to sleep ere the heat roused him.

One Saturday night it was my pleasant duty to put the paper to bed alone. A King or courtier or a courtesan or a Community was going to die or get a new Constitution, or do something that was important on the other side of the world, and the paper was to be held open till the latest possible minute in order to catch the telegram.

It was a pitchy black night, as stifling as a June night can be, and the *loo*, the red-hot wind from the westward, was booming among the tinder-dry trees and pretending that the rain was on its heels. Now and again a spot of almost boiling water would fall on the dust with the flop of a frog, but all our weary world knew that was only pretence. It was a shade cooler in the press-room than the office, so I sat there, while the type ticked and clicked, and the night-jars hooted at the windows, and the all but naked compositors wiped the sweat from their foreheads, and called for water. The thing that was keeping us back, whatever it was, would not come off, though the *loo* dropped and the last type was set, and the whole round earth stood still in the choking heat, with its finger on its lip, to wait the event. I drowsed, and wondered whether the telegraph was a blessing, and whether this dying man, or struggling people, might be aware of the inconvenience the delay was causing. There was no special reason beyond the heat and worry to make tension, but, as the clock-hands crept up to three o'clock and the machines spun their fly-wheels two and three times to see that all was in order, before I said the word that would set them off, I could have shrieked aloud.

Then the roar and rattle of the wheels shivered the quiet into little bits. I rose to go away, but two men in white clothes stood in front of me. The first one said: 'It's him!' The second said: 'So it is!' And they both laughed almost as loudly as the machinery roared, and mopped their foreheads. 'We seed there was a light burning across the road and we were sleeping in that ditch there for coolness, and I said to my friend here, The office is open. Let's come along and speak to him as turned us back from the Degumber State,' said the smaller of the two. He was the man I had met in the Mhow train, and his fellow was the red-bearded man of Marwar Junction. There was no mistaking the eyebrows of the one or the beard of the other.

I was not pleased, because I wished to go to sleep, not to squabble with loafers. 'What do you want?' I asked.

'Half an hour's talk with you, cool and comfortable, in the office,' said the red-bearded man. 'We'd *like* some drink—the Contrack doesn't begin yet, Peachey, so you needn't look—but what we really want is advice. We don't want money. We ask you as a favour, because we found out you did us a bad turn about Degumber State.'

I led from the press-room to the stifling office with the maps on the walls, and the red-haired man rubbed his hands. 'That's something like,' said he. 'This was the proper shop to come to. Now, Sir, let me introduce to you Brother Peachey Carnehan, that's him, and Brother Daniel Dravot, that is *me*, and the less said about our professions the better, for we have been most things in our time. Soldier, sailor, compositor, photographer, proof-reader, street-preacher, and correspondents of the *Backwoodsman* when we thought the paper wanted one. Carnehan is sober, and so am I. Look at us first, and see that's sure. It will save you cutting into my talk. We'll take one of your cigars apiece, and you shall see us light up.'

I watched the test. The men were absolutely sober, so I gave them each a tepid whiskey and soda.

'Well *and* good,' said Carnehan of the eyebrows, wiping the froth from his moustache. 'Let me talk now, Dan. We have been all over India, mostly on foot. We have been boiler-fitters, engine-drivers, petty contractors, and all that, and we have decided that India isn't big enough for such as us.'

They certainly were too big for the office. Dravot's beard seemed to fill half the room and Carnehan's shoulders the other half, as they sat on the big table. Carnehan continued: 'The country isn't half worked out because they that governs it won't let you touch it. They spend all their blessed time in governing it, and you can't lift a spade, nor chip a rock, nor look for oil, nor anything like that without all the Government saying—"Leave it alone, and let us govern." Therefore, such *as* it is, we will let it alone, and go away to some other place where a man isn't crowded and can come to his own. We are not little men, and there is nothing we are afraid of except Drink, and we have signed a Contrack on that. *Therefore*, we are going away to be Kings.'

'Kings in our own right,' muttered Dravot.

'Yes, of course,' I said. 'You've been tramping in the sun, and it's a very warm night, and hadn't you better sleep over the notion? Come tomorrow.'

'Neither drunk nor sunstruck,' said Dravot. 'We have slept over the notion half a year, and require to see Books and Atlases, and we have decided that there is only one place now in the world that two strong men can Sar-a-*whack*. They call it Kafiristan. By my reckoning it's the top right-hand corner of Afghanistan, not more than three hundred miles from Peshawar. They have two-and-thirty heathen idols there, and we'll be the thirty-third and fourth. It's a mountaineous country, and the women of those parts are very beautiful.'

'But that is provided against in the Contrack,' said Carnehan. 'Neither Woman nor Liqu-or, Daniel.'

'And that's all we know, except that no one has gone there, and they fight, and in any place where they fight a man who knows how to drill men can always be a King. We shall go to those parts and say to any King we find—"D'you want to vanquish your foes?" and we will show him how to drill men; for that we know better than anything else. Then we will subvert that King and seize his Throne and establish a Dy-nasty.'

'You'll be cut to pieces before you're fifty miles across the Border,' I said. 'You have to travel through Afghanistan to get to that country. It's one mass of mountains and peaks and glaciers, and no Englishman has been through it. The people are utter brutes, and even if you reached them you couldn't do anything.'

'That's more like,' said Carnehan. 'If you could think us a little more mad we would be more pleased. We have come to you to know about this country, to read a book about it, and to be shown maps. We want you to tell us that we are fools and to show us your books.' He turned to the book-cases.

'Are you at all in earnest?' I said.

'A little,' said Dravot sweetly. 'As big a map as you have got, even if it's all blank where Kafiristan is, and any books you've got. We can read, though we aren't very educated.'

I uncased the big thirty-two-miles-to-the-inch map of India, and two smaller Frontier maps, hauled down volume INF-KAN of the *Encyclopædia Britannica*, and the men consulted them.

'See here!' said Dravot, his thumb on the map. 'Up to Jagdallak, Peachey and me know the road. We was there with Roberts' Army. We'll have to turn off to the right at Jagdallak through Laghmann territory. Then we get among the hills—fourteen thousand feet—fifteen thousand—it will be cold work there, but it don't look very far on the map.'

I handed him Wood on the *Sources of the Oxus*. Carnehan was deep in the *Encyclopædia*.

'They're a mixed lot,' said Dravot reflectively; 'and it won't help us to know the names of their tribes. The more tribes the more they'll fight, and the better for us. From Jagdallak to Ashang. H'mm!'

'But all the information about the country is as sketchy and inaccurate as can be,' I protested. 'No one knows anything about it really. Here's the file of the *United Services' Institute*. Read what Bellew says.'

'Blow Bellew!' said Carnehan. 'Dan, they're a stinkin' lot of heathens, but this book here says they think they're related to us English.'

I smoked while the men pored over *Raverty*, *Wood*, the maps, and the *Encyclopædia*.

'There is no use your waiting,' said Dravot politely. 'It's about four o'clock now. We'll go before six o'clock if you want to sleep, and we won't steal any of the papers. Don't you sit up. We're two harmless lunatics, and if you come to-morrow evening down to the Serai we'll say good-bye to you.'

'You *are* two fools,' I answered. 'You'll be turned back at the Frontier or cut up the minute you set foot in Afghanistan. Do you want any money or a recommendation down-country? I can help you to the chance of work next week.'

'Next week we shall be hard at work ourselves, thank you,' said Dravot. 'It isn't so easy being a King as it looks. When we've got our Kingdom in going order we'll let you know, and you can come up and help us to govern it.'

'Would two lunatics make a Contrack like that?' said Carnehan, with subdued pride, showing me a greasy half-sheet of notepaper on which was written the following. I copied it, then and there, as a curiosity—

This Contract between me and you persuing witnesseth in the name of God—Amen and so forth.

> (One) *That me and you will settle this matter together; i.e., to be Kings of Kafiristan.*
>
> (Two) *That you and me will not, while this matter is being settled, look at any Liquor, nor any Woman black, white, or brown, so as to get mixed up with one or the other harmful.*
>
> (Three) *That we conduct ourselves with Dignity and Discretion, and if one of us gets into trouble the other will stay by him.*
>
> *Signed by you and me this day.*
> *Peachey Taliaferro Carnehan.*
> *Daniel Dravot.*
> *Both Gentlemen at Large.*

'There was no need for the last article,' said Carnehan, blushng modestly; 'but it looks regular. Now you know the sort of men that loafers are—we *are* loafers, Dan, until we get out of India—and *do* you think that we would sign a Contrack like that unless we was in earnest? We have kept away from the two things that make life worth having.'

'You won't enjoy your lives much longer if you are going to try this idiotic adventure. Don't set the office on fire,' I said, 'and go away before nine o'clock.'

I left them still poring over the maps and making notes on the back of the 'Contrack.' 'Be sure to come down to the Serai to-morrow,' were their parting words.

The Kumharsen Serai is the great four-square sink of humanity where the strings of camels and horses from the North load and unload. All the nationalities of Central Asia may be found there, and most of the folk of India proper. Balkh and Bokhara there meet Bengal and Bombay, and try to draw eye-teeth. You can buy ponies, turquoises, Persian pussy-cats, saddlebags, fat-tailed sheep and musk in the Kumharsen Serai, and get many strange things for nothing. In the afternoon I went down to see whether my friends intended to keep their word or were lying there drunk.

A priest attired in fragments of ribbons and rags stalked up to me, gravely twisting a child's paper whirligig. Behind him was his servant bending under the load of a crate of mud toys. The two were loading up two camels, and the inhabitants of the Serai watched them with shrieks of laughter.

'The priest is mad,' said a horse-dealer to me. 'He is going up to Kabul to sell toys to the Amir. He will either be raised to honour or have his head cut off. He came in here this morning and has been behaving madly ever since.'

'The witless are under the protection of God,' stammered a flat-cheeked Usbeg in broken Hindi. 'They foretell future events.'

'Would they could have foretold that my caravan would have been cut up by the Shinwaris almost within shadow of the Pass!' grunted the Eusufzai agent of a Rajputana trading-house whose goods had been diverted into the hands of other robbers just across the Border, and whose misfortunes were the laughing-stock of the bazar. 'Ohé, priest, whence come you and whither do you go?'

'From Roum have I come,' shouted the priest, waving his whirligig; 'from Roum, blown by the breath of a hundred devils across the sea! O thieves, robbers, liars, the blessing of Pir Khan on pigs, dogs, and perjurers! Who will take the protected of God to the North to sell charms that are never still to the Amir? The camels shall not gall, the sons shall not fall sick, and the wives shall remain faithful while they are away, of the men who give me place in their caravan. Who will assist me to slipper the King of the Roos with a golden slipper with a silver heel? The protection of Pir Khan be upon his labours!' He spread out the skirts of his gaberdine and pirouetted between the lines of tethered horses.

'There starts a caravan from Peshawar to Kabul in twenty days, *Huzrut*,' said the Eusufzai trader. 'My camels go therewith. Do thou also go and bring us good-luck.'

'I will go even now!' shouted the priest. 'I will depart upon my winged camels, and be at Peshawar in a day! Ho! Hazar Mir Khan,' he yelled to his servant, 'drive out the camels, but let me first mount my own.'

He leaped on the back of his beast as it knelt, and, turning round to me, cried: 'Come thou also, Sahib, a little along the road, and I will sell thee a charm—an amulet that shall make thee King of Kafiristan.'

Then the light broke upon me, and I followed the two camels out of the Serai till we reached open road and the priest halted.

'What d'you think o' that?' said he in English. 'Carnehan can't talk their patter, so I've made him my servant. He makes a handsome servant. 'Tisn't for nothing that I've been knocking about the country for fourteen years. Didn't I do that talk neat? We'll hitch on to a caravan at Peshawar till we get to Jagdallak, and then we'll see if we can get donkeys for our camels, and strike into Kafiristan. Whirligigs for the Amir, O Lor! Put your hand under the camel-bags and tell me what you feel.'

I felt the butt of a Martini, and another and another.

'Twenty of 'em,' said Dravot placidly. 'Twenty of 'em and ammunition to correspond, under the whirligigs and the mud dolls.'

'Heaven help you if you are caught with those things!' I said. 'A Martini is worth her weight in silver among the Pathans.'

'Fifteen hundred rupees of capital—every rupee we could beg, borrow, or steal—are invested on these two camels,' said Dravot. 'We won't get caught. We're going through the Khaiber with a regular caravan. Who'd touch a poor mad priest?'

'Have you got everything you want?' I asked, overcome with astonishment.

'Not yet, but we shall soon. Give us a memento of your kindness, *Brother*. You did me a service, yesterday, and that time in Marwar. Half my Kingdom shall you have, as the saying is.' I slipped a small charm compass from my watch chain and handed it up to the priest.

'Good-bye,' said Dravot, giving me hand cautiously. 'It's the last time we'll shake hands with an Englishman these many days. Shake hands with him, Carnehan,' he cried, as the second camel passed me.

Carnehan leaned down and shook hands. Then the camels passed away along the dusty road, and I was left alone to wonder. My eye could detect no failure in the disguises. The scene in the Serai proved that they were complete to the native mind. There was just the chance, therefore, that Carnehan and Dravot would be able to wander through Afghanistan without detection. But, beyond, they would find death—certain and awful death.

Ten days later a native correspondent giving me the news of the day from Peshawar, wound up his letter with: 'There has been much laughter here on account of a certain mad priest who is going in his estimation to sell petty gauds and insignificant trinkets which he ascribes as great charms to H.H. the Amir of Bokhara. He passed through Peshawar and associated himself to the Second Summer caravan that goes to Kabul. The merchants are pleased because through superstition they imagine that such mad fellows bring good-fortune.'

The two, then, were beyond the Border. I would have prayed for them, but, that night, a real King died in Europe, and demanded an obituary notice.

*   *   *   *   *

The wheel of the world swings through the same phases again and again. Summer passed and winter thereafter, and came and passed again. The daily paper continued and I with it, and upon the third summer there fell a hot night, a night-issue, and a strained waiting for something to be telegraphed from the other side of the world, exactly as had happened before. A few great men had died in the past two years, the machines worked with more clatter, and some of the trees in the Office garden were a few feet taller. But that was all the difference.

I passed over to the press-room, and went through just such a scene as I have already described. The nervous tension was stronger than it had been two years before, and I felt the heat more acutely. At three o'clock I cried, 'Print off,' and turned to go, when there crept to my chair what was left of a man. He was bent into a circle, his head was sunk between his shoulders, and he moved his feet one over the other like a bear. I could hardly see whether he walked or crawled—this rag-wrapped, whining cripple who addressed me by name, crying that he was come back. 'Can you give me a drink?' he whimpered. 'For the Lord's sake, give me a drink!'

I went back to the office, the man following with groans of pain, and I turned up the lamp.

'Don't you know me?' he gasped, dropping into a chair and he turned his drawn face, surmounted by a shock of gray hair, to the light.

I looked at him intently. Once before had I seen eyebrows that met over the nose in an inch-broad black band, but for the life of me I could not tell where.

'I don't know you,' I said, handing him the whiskey. 'What can I do for you?'

He took a gulp of the spirit raw, and shivered in spite of the suffo-cating heat.

'I've come back,' he repeated; 'and I was the King of Kafiristan—me and Dravot—crowned Kings we was! In this office we settled it—you setting there and giving us the books. I am Peachey—Peachey Taliaferro Carnehan, and you've been setting here ever since—O Lord!'

I was more than a little astonished, and expressed my feelings accord-ingly.

'It's true,' said Carnehan, with a dry cackle, nursing his feet, which were wrapped in rags. 'True as gospel. Kings we were, with crowns upon our heads—me and Dravot—poor Dan—oh, poor, poor Dan, that would never take advice, not though I begged of him!'

'Take the whiskey,' I said, 'and take your own time. Tell me all you can recollect of everything from beginning to end. You got across the border on your camels, Dravot dressed as a mad priest and you his servant. Do you remember that?'

'I ain't mad—yet, but I shall be that way soon. Of course I remember. Keep looking at me, or maybe my words will go all to pieces. Keep looking at me in my eyes and don't say anything.'

I leaned forward and looked into his face as steadily as I could. He dropped one hand upon the table and I grasped it by the wrist. It was twisted like a bird's claw, and upon the back was a ragged, red, diamond-shaped scar.

'No, don't look there. Look at *me*,' said Carnehan. 'That comes afterwards, but for the Lord's sake don't distrack me. We left with that caravan, me and Dravot playing all sorts of antics to amuse the people we were with. Dravot used to make us laugh in the evenings when all the people was cooking their dinners—cooking their dinners, and . . . what did they do then? They lit little fires with sparks that went into Dravot's beard, and we all laughed—fit to die. Little red fires they was, going into Dravot's big red beard—so funny.' His eyes left mine and he smiled foolishly.

'You went as far as Jagdallak with that caravan,' I said at a venture, 'after you had lit those fires. To Jagdallak, where you turned off to try to get into Kafiristan.'

'No, we didn't, neither. What are you talking about? We turned off before Jagdallak, because we heard the roads was good. But they wasn't good enough for our two camels—mine and Dravot's. When we left the caravan, Dravot took off all his clothes and mine too, and said we would be heathen, because the Kafirs didn't allow Mohammedans to talk to them. So we dressed betwixt and between, and such a sight as Daniel Dravot I never saw yet nor expect to see again. He burned half his beard, and slung a sheep-skin over his shoulder, and shaved his head into patterns. He shaved mine, too, and made me wear outrageous things to look like a heathen. That was in a most mountaineous country, and our camels couldn't go along any more because of the mountains. They were tall and black, and coming home I saw them fight like wild goats—there are lots of goats in Kafiristan. And these mountains, they never keep still, no more than the goats. Always fighting they are, and don't let you sleep at night.'

'Take some more whiskey,' I said very slowly. 'What did you and Daniel Dravot do when the camels could go no further because of the rough roads that led into Kafiristan?'

'What did which do? There was a party called Peachey Taliaferro Carnehan that was with Dravot. Shall I tell you about him? He died out there in the cold. Slap from the bridge fell old Peachey, turning and twisting in the air like a penny whirligig that you can sell to the Amir.—No; they was two for three ha'pence, those whirligigs, or I am much mistaken and woeful sore. . . . And then these camels were no use, and Peachey said to Dravot—"For the Lord's sake let's get out of this before our heads are chopped off," and with that they killed the camels all among the mountains, not having anything in particular to eat, but first they took off the boxes with the guns and the ammunition, till two men came along driving four mules. Dravot up and dances in front of them, singing—"Sell me four mules." Says the first man—"If you are rich enough to buy, you are rich enough to rob;" but before ever he could put his hand to his knife, Dravot breaks his neck over his knee, and the other party runs away. So Carnehan loaded the mules with the rifles that was taken off the camels, and together we starts forward into those bitter cold mountaineous parts, and never a road broader than the back of your hand.'

He paused for a moment, while I asked him if he could remember the nature of the country through which he had journeyed.

'I am telling you as straight as I can, but my head isn't as good as it might be. They drove nails through it to make me hear better how Dravot died. The country was mountaineous and the mules were most contrary, and the inhabitants was dispersed and solitary. They went up and up, and down and down, and that other party, Carnehan, was imploring of Dravot not to sing and whistle so loud, for fear of bringing down the tremenjus avalanches. But Dravot says that if a King couldn't sing it wasn't worth being King, and whacked the mules over the rump, and never took no heed for ten cold days. We came to a big level valley all among the mountains, and the mules were near dead, so we killed them, not having anything in special for them or us to eat. We sat upon the boxes, and played odd and even with the cartridges that was jolted out.

'Then ten men with bows and arrows ran down that valley, chasing twenty men with bows and arrows, and the row was tremenjus. They was fair men—fairer than you or me—with yellow hair and remarkable well built. Says Dravot, unpacking the guns—"This is the beginning of the business. We'll fight for the ten men," and with that he fires two rifles at the twenty men, and drops one of them at two hundred yards from the rock where he was sitting. The other men began to run, but Carnehan and Dravot sits on the boxes picking them off at all ranges, up and down the valley. Then we goes up to the ten men that had run across the snow too, and they fires a footy little arrow at us. Dravot he shoots above their heads and they all falls down flat. Then he walks over them and kicks them, and then he lifts them up and shakes hands all round to make them friendly like. He calls them and gives them the boxes to carry, and waves his hand for all the world as though he was King already. They takes the boxes and him across the valley and up the hill into a pine wood on the top, where there was half a dozen big stone idols. Dravot he goes to the biggest—a fellow they call Imbra—and lays a rifle and a cartridge at his feet, rubbing his nose respectful with his own nose, patting him on the head, and saluting in front of it. He turns round to the men and nods his head, and says—"That's all right. I'm in the know too, and all these old jim-jams are my friends." Then he opens his mouth and points down it, and when the first man brings him food, he says—"No;" and when the second man brings him food he says—"No;" but when one of the old priests and the boss of the village brings him food, he says—"Yes;" very haughty, and eats it slow. That was how he came to our first village, without any trouble, just as though we had tumbled from the skies. But we tumbled from one of those damned rope-bridges, you see and—you couldn't expect a man to laugh much after that?'

'Take some more whiskey and go on,' I said. 'That was the first village you came into. How did you get to be King?'

'I wasn't King,' said Carnehan. 'Dravot he was the King, and a handsome man he looked with the gold crown on his head and all. Him and the other party stayed in that village, and every morning Dravot sat by the side of old Imbra, and the people came and worshipped. That was Dravot's order. Then a lot of men came into the valley, and Carnehan and Dravot picks them off with the rifles before they knew where they was, and runs down into the valley and up again the other side and finds another village, same as the first one, and the people all falls down flat on their faces, and Dravot says—"Now what is the trouble between you two villages?" and the people points to a woman, as fair as you or me, that was carried off, and Dravot takes her back to the first village and counts up the dead—eight there was. For each dead man Dravot pours a little milk on the ground and waves his arms like a whirligig and "That's all right," says he. Then he and Carnehan takes the big boss of each village by the arm and walks them down into the valley, and shows them how to scratch a line with a spear right down the valley, and gives each a sod of turf from both sides of the line. Then all the people comes down and shouts like the devil and all, and Dravot says—"Go and dig the land, and be fruitful and multiply," which they did, though they didn't understand. Then we asks the names of things in their lingo—bread and water and fire and idols and such, and Dravot leads the priest of each village up to the idol, and says he must sit there and judge the people, and if anything goes wrong he is to be shot.

'Next week they was all turning up the land in the valley as quiet as bees and much prettier, and the priests heard all the complaints and told Dravot in dumb show what it was about. "That's just the beginning," says Dravot. "They think we're Gods." He and Carnehan picks out twenty good men and shows them how to click off a rifle, and form fours, and advance in line, and they was very pleased to do so, and clever to see the hang of it. Then he takes out his pipe and his baccy-pouch and leaves one at one village, and one at the other, and off we two goes to see what was to be done in the next valley. That was all rock, and there was a little village there, and Carnehan says—"Send 'em to the old valley to plant," and takes 'em there and gives 'em some land that wasn't took before. They were a poor lot, and we blooded 'em with a kid before letting 'em into the new Kingdom. That was to impress the people, and then they settled down quiet, and Carnehan went back to Dravot who had got into another valley, all snow and ice and most mountaineous. There was no people there and the Army got afraid, so Dravot shoots one of them, and goes on till he finds some people in a village, and the Army explains that unless the people wants to be killed they had better not shoot their little matchlocks; for they had matchlocks. We makes friends with the priest and I stays there alone with two of the Army, teaching the men how to drill, and a thundering big Chief comes across the snow with kettle-drums and horns twanging, because he heard there was a new God kicking about. Carnehan sights for the brown of the men half a mile across the snow and wings one of them. Then he sends a message to the Chief that, unless he wished to be killed, he must come and shake hands with me and leave his arms behind. The Chief comes alone first, and Carnehan shakes hands with him and whirls his arms about, same as Dravot used, and very much surprised that Chief was, and strokes my eyebrows. Then Carnehan goes alone to the Chief, and asks him in dumb show if he had an enemy he hated. "I have," says the Chief. So Carnehan weeds out the pick of his men, and sets the two of the Army to show them drill and at the end of two weeks the men can manœuvre about as well as Volunteers. So he marches with the Chief to a great big plain on the top of a mountain, and the Chief's men rushes into a village and takes it; we three Martinis firing into the brown of the enemy. So we took that village too, and I gives the Chief a rag from my coat and says, "Occupy till I come;" which was scriptural. By way of a reminder, when me and the Army was eighteen hundred yards away, I drops a bullet near him standing on the snow, and all the people falls flat on their faces. Then I sends a letter to Dravot wherever he be by land or by sea.'

At the risk of throwing the creature out of train I interrupted—'How could you write a letter up yonder?'

'The letter?—Oh!—The letter! Keep looking at me between the eyes, please. It was a string-talk letter, that we'd learned the way of it from a blind beggar in the Punjab.'

I remember that there had once come to the office a blind man with a knotted twig and a piece of string which he wound round the twig according to some cipher of his own. He could, after the lapse of days or hours, repeat the sentence which he had reeled up. He had reduced the alphabet to eleven primitive sounds; and tried to teach me his method, but I could not understand.

'I sent that letter to Dravot,' said Carnehan; 'and told him to come back because this Kingdom was growing too big for me to handle, and then I struck for the first valley, to see how the priests were working. They called the village we took along with the Chief, Bashkai, and the first village we took, Er-Heb. The priests at Er-Heb was doing all right, but they had a lot of pending cases about land to show me, and some men from another village had been firing arrows at night. I went out and looked for that village, and fired four rounds at it from a thousand yards. That used all the cartridges I cared to spend, and I waited for Dravot, who had been away two or three months, and I kept my people quiet.

'One morning I heard the devil's own noise of drums and horns, and Dan Dravot marches down the hill with his Army and a tail of hundreds of men, and, which was the most amazing, a great gold crown on his head. "My Gord, Carnehan," says Daniel, "this is a tremenjus business, and we've got the whole country as far as it's worth having. I am the son of Alexander by Queen Semiramis, and you're my younger brother and a God too! It's the biggest thing we've ever seen. I've been marching and fighting for six weeks with the Army, and every footy little village for fifty miles has come in rejoiceful; and more than that, I've got the key of the whole show, as you'll see, and I've got a crown for you! I told 'em to make two of 'em at a place called Shu, where the gold lies in the rock like suet in mutton. Gold I've seen, and turquoise I've kicked out of the cliffs, and there's garnets in the sands of the river, and here's a chunk of amber that a man brought me. Call up all the priests, and, here, take your crown."

'One of the men opens a black hair bag, and I slips the crown on. It was too small and too heavy, but I wore it for the glory. Hammered gold it was—five pound weight, like a hoop of a barrel.

"Peachey," says Dravot, "we don't want to fight no more. The Craft's the trick so help me!" and he brings forward that same Chief that I left at Bashkai—Billy Fish we called him afterwards, because he was so like Billy Fish that drove the big tank-engine at Mach on the Bolan in the old days. "Shake hands with him," says Dravot, and I shook hands and nearly dropped, for Billy Fish gave me the Grip. I said nothing, but tried him with the Fellow Craft Grip. He answers, all right, and I tried the Master's Grip, but that was a slip. "A Fellow Craft he is!" I says to Dan. "Does he know the word?"—"He does," says Dan, "and all the priests know. It's a miracle! The Chiefs and the priests can work a Fellow Craft Lodge in a way that's very like ours, and they've cut the marks on the rocks, but they don't know the Third Degree, and they've come to find out. It's Gord's Truth. I've known these long years that the Afghans knew up to the Fellow Craft Degree, but this is a miracle. A God and a Grand-Master of the Craft am I, and a Lodge in the Third Degree I will open, and we'll raise the head priests and the Chiefs of the villages."

' "It's against all the law," I says, "holding a Lodge without warrant from any one; and you know we never held office in any Lodge."

' "It's a master-stroke o' policy," says Dravot. "It means running the country as easy as a four-wheeled bogie on a down grade. We can't stop to enquire now, or they'll turn against us. I've forty Chiefs at my heel, and passed and raised according to their merit they shall be. Billet these men on the villages, and see that we run up a Lodge of some kind. The temple of Imbra will do for the Lodge-room. The women must make aprons as you show them. I'll hold a levee of Chief's to-night and Lodge to-morrow."

'I was fair run off my legs, but I wasn't such a fool as not to see what a pull this Craft business gave us. I showed the priests' families how to make aprons of the degrees, but for Dravot's apron the blue border and marks was made of turquoise lumps on white hide, not cloth. We took a great square stone in the temple for the Master's chair, and little stones for the officers' chairs, and painted the black pavement with white squares, and did what we could to make things regular.

'At the levee which was held that night on the hillside with big bon-fires, Dravot gives out that him and me were Gods and sons of Alexander, and Past Grand-Masters in the Craft, and was come to make Kafiristan a country where every man should eat in peace and drink in quiet, and specially obey us. Then the Chiefs come round to shake hands, and they were so hairy and white and fair it was just shaking hands with old friends. We gave them names according as they was like men we had known in India—Billy Fish, Holly Dilworth, Pikky Kergan, that was Bazar-master when I was at Mhow, and so on, and so on.

'The most amazing miracles was at Lodge next night. One of the old priests was watching us continuous, and I felt uneasy, for I knew we'd have to fudge the Ritual, and I didn't know what the men knew. The old priest was a stranger come in from beyond the village of Bashkai. The minute Dravot puts on the Master's apron that the girls had made for him, the priest fetches a whoop and a howl, and tries to overturn the stone that Dravot was sitting on. "It's all up now," I says. "That comes of meddling with the Craft without warrant!" Dravot never winked an eye, not when ten priests took and tilted over the Grand-Master's chair—which was to say the stone of Imbra. The priest begins rubbing the bottom end of it to clear away the black dirt, and presently he shows all the other priests the Master's Mark, same as was on Dravot's apron, cut into the stone. Not even the priests of the temple of Imbra knew it was there. The old chap falls flat on his face at Dravot's feet and kisses 'em. "Luck again," said Dravot, across the Lodge to me, "they say it's the missing Mark that no one could understand the why of. We're more than safe now." Then he bangs the butt of his gun for a gavel and says: "By virtue of the authority vested in me by my own right hand and the help of Peachey, I declare myself Grand-Master of all Freemasonry in Kafiristan in this the Mother Lodge o' the country, and King of Kafiristan equally with Peachey!" At that he puts on his crown and I puts on mine—I was doing Senior Warden—and we opens the Lodge in most ample form. It was a amazing miracle! The priests moved in Lodge through the first two degrees almost without telling, as if the memory was coming back to them. After that, Peachey and Dravot raised such as was worthy—high priests and Chiefs of far-off villages. Billy Fish was the first, and I can tell you we scared the soul out of him. It was not in any way according to Ritual, but it served our turn. We didn't raise more than ten of the biggest men, because we didn't want to make the Degree common. And they was clamouring to be raised.

' "In another six months," said Dravot, "we'll hold another Communication, and see how you are working." Then he asks them about their villages, and learns that they was fighting one against the other, and were sick and tired of it. And when they wasn't doing that they was fighting with the Mohammedans. "You can fight those when they come into our country," says Dravot. "Tell off every tenth man of your tribes for a Frontier guard, and send two hundred at a time to this valley to be drilled. Nobody is going to be shot or speared any more so long as he does well, and I know that you won't cheat me, because you're white people—sons of Alexander—and not like common, black Mohammedans. You are *my* people, and by God," says he, running off into English at the end—"I'll make a damned fine Nation of you, or I'll die in the making!"

'I can't tell all we did for the next six months, because Dravot did a lot I couldn't see the hang of, and he learned their lingo in a way I never could. My work was to help the people plough, and now and again go out with some of the Army and see what the other villages were doing, and make 'em throw rope-bridges across the ravines which cut up the country horrid. Dravot was very kind to me, but when he walked up and down in the pine wood pulling that bloody red beard of his with both fists I knew he was thinking plans I could not advise about, and I just waited for orders.

'But Dravot never showed me disrepect before the people. They were afraid of me and the Army, but they loved Dan. He was the best of friends with the priests and the Chiefs; but any one could come across the hills with a complaint, and Dravot would hear him out fair, and call four priests together and say what was to be done. He used to call in Billy Fish from Bashkai, and Pikky Kergan from Shu, and an old Chief we called Kafuzelum —it was like enough to his real name—and hold councils with 'em when there was any fighting to be done in small villages. That was his Council of War, and the four priests of Bashkai, Shu, Khawak, and Madora was his Privy Council. Between the lot of 'em they sent me, with forty men and twenty rifles, and sixty men carrying turquoises, into the Ghorband country to buy those hand-made Martini rifles, that come out of the Amir's workshops at Kabul, from one of the Amir's Herati regiments that would have sold the very teeth out of their mouths for turquoises.

'I stayed in Ghorband a month, and gave the Governor there the pick of my baskets for hush-money, and bribed the Colonel of the regiment some more, and, between the two and the tribes-people, we got more than a hundred hand-made Martinis, a hundred good Kohat Jezails that'll throw to six hundred yards, and forty man-loads of very bad ammunition for the rifles. I came back with what I had, and distributed 'em among the men that the Chiefs sent into me to drill. Dravot was too busy to attend to those things, but the old Army that we first made helped me, and we turned out five hundred men that could drill, and two hundred that knew how to hold arms pretty straight. Even those cork-screwed, hand-made guns was a miracle to them. Dravot talked big about powder-shops and factories, walking up and down in the pine wood when the winter was coming on.

' "I won't make a Nation," says he. "I'll make an Empire! These men aren't niggers; they're English! Look at their eyes—look at their mouths. Look at the way they stand up. They sit on chairs in their own houses. They're the Lost Tribes, or something like it, and they've grown to be English. I'll take a census in the spring if the priests don't get frightened. There must be a fair two million of 'em in these hills. The villages are full o' little children. Two million people—two hundred and fifty thousand fighting men—and all English! They only want the rifles and a little drilling. Two hundred and fifty thousand men, ready to cut in on Russia's right flank when she tries for India! Peachey, man," he says, chewing his beard in great hunks, "we shall be Emperors—Emperors of the Earth! Rajah Brooke will be a suckling to us. I'll treat with the Viceroy on equal terms. I'll ask him to send me twelve picked English—twelve that I know of—to help us govern a bit. There's Mackray, Sergeant-pensioner at Segowli—many's the good dinner he's given me, and his wife a pair of trousers. There's Donkin, the Warder of Tounghoo Jail; there's hundreds that I could lay my hand on if I was in India. The Viceroy shall do it for me, I'll send a man through in the spring for those men, and I'll write for a dispensation from the Grand Lodge for what I've done as Grand-Master. That—and all the Sniders that'll be thrown out when the native troops in India take up the Martini. They'll be worn smooth, but they'll do for fighting in these hills. Twelve English, a hundred thousands Sniders run through the Amir's country in driblets—I'd be content with twenty thousand in one year—and we'd be an Empire. When everything was shipshape, I'd hand over the crown—this crown I'm wearing now—to Queen Victoria on my knees, and she'd say: 'Rise up, Sir Daniel Dravot.' Oh, it's big! It's big, I tell you! But there's so much to be done in every place—Bashkai, Khawak, Shu, and everywhere else."

' "What is it?" I says. "There are no more men coming in to be drilled this autumn. Look at those, fat, black clouds. They're bringing the snow."

' "It isn't that," says Daniel, putting his hand very hard on my shoulder; "and I don't wish to say anything that's against you, for no other living man would have followed me and made me what I am as you have done. You're a first-class Commander-in-Chief, and the people know you; but—it's a big country, and somehow you can't help me, Peachey, in the way I want to be helped."

' "Go to your blasted priests, then!" I said, and I was sorry when I made that remark, but it did hurt me sore to find Daniel talking so superior when I'd drilled all the men, and done all he told me.

' "Don't let's quarrel, Peachey," says Daniel without cursing. "You're a King too, and the half of this Kingdom is yours; but can't you see, Peachey, we want cleverer men than us now—three or four of 'em, that we can scatter about for our Deputies. It's a hugeous great State, and I can't always tell the right thing to do, and I haven't time for all I want to do, and here's the winter coming on and all." He put half his beard into his mouth, all red like the gold of his crown.

' "I'm sorry, Daniel," says I. "I've done all I could. I've drilled the men and shown the people how to stack their oats better; and I've brought in those tinware rifles from Ghorband—but I know what you're driving at. I take it Kings always feel oppressed that way."

' "There's another thing too," says Dravot, walking up and down. "The winter's coming and these people won't be giving much trouble, and if they do we can't move about. I want a wife."

' "For Gord's sake leave the women alone!" I says. "We've both got all the work we can, though I *am* a fool. Remember the Contrack, and keep clear o' women."

' "The Contrack only lasted till such time as we was Kings; and Kings we have been these months past," says Dravot, weighing his crown in his hand. "You go get a wife too, Peachey—a nice, strappin', plump girl that'll keep you warm in the winter. They're prettier than English girls, and we can take the pick of 'em. Boil 'em once or twice in hot water, and they'll come out like chicken and ham."

' "Don't tempt me!" I says. "I will not have any dealings with a woman not till we are a dam' sight more settled than we are now. I've been doing the work o' two men, and you've been doing the work o' three. Let's lie off a bit, and see if we can get some better tobacco from Afghan country and run in some good liquor; but no women."

' "Who's talking o' *women?*" says Dravot. "I said *wife*—a Queen to breed a King's son for the King. A Queen out of the strongest tribe, that'll make them your blood-brothers, and that'll lie by your side and tell you all the people thinks about you and their own affairs. That's what I want."

' "Do you remember that Bengali woman I kept at Mogul Serai when I was a plate-layer?" says I. "A fat lot o' good she was to me. She taught me the lingo and one or two other things; but what happened? She ran away with the Station Master's servant and half my month's pay. Then she turned up at Dadur Junction in tow of a half-caste, and had the impidence to say I was her husband—all among the drivers in the running-shed too!"

' "We've done with that," says Dravot, "these women are whiter than you or me, and a Queen I will have for the winter months."

' "For the last time o' asking, Dan, do *not*," I says. "It'll only bring us harm. The Bible says that Kings ain't to waste their strength on women, 'specially when they've got a new raw Kingdom to work over."

' "For the last time of answering I will," said Dravot, and he went away through the pine-trees looking like a big red devil, the sun being on his crown and beard and all.

'But getting a wife was not as easy as Dan thought. He put it before the Council, and there was no answer till Billy Fish said that he'd better ask the girls. Dravot damned them all round. "What's wrong with me?" he shouts, standing by the idol Imbra. "Am I a dog or am I not enough of a man for your wenches? Haven't I put the shadow of my hand over this country? Who stopped the last Afghan raid?" It was me really, but Dravot was too angry to remember. "Who bought your guns? Who repaired the bridges? Who's the Grand-Master of the sign cut in the stone?" says he, and he thumped his hand on the block that he used to sit on in Lodge, and at Council, which opened like Lodge always. Billy Fish said nothing and no more did the others. "Keep your hair on, Dan," said I; "and ask the girls. That's how it's done at Home, and these people are quite English."

' "The marriage of the King is a matter of State," says Dan, in a white-hot rage, for he could feel, I hope, that he was going against his better mind. He walked out of the Council-room, and the others sat still, looking at the ground.

' "Billy Fish," says I to the Chief of Bashkai, "what's the difficulty here? A straight answer to a true friend."

' "You know," says Billy Fish. "How should a man tell you who knows everything? How can daughters of men marry Gods or Devils? It's not proper."

'I remembered something like that in the Bible; but if, after seeing us as long as they had, they still believed we were Gods, it wasn't for me to undeceive them.

' "A God can do anything," says I. "If the King is fond of a girl he'll not let her die."—"She'll have to," said Billy Fish. "There are all sorts of Gods and Devils in these mountains, and now and again a girl marries one of them and isn't seen any more. Besides, you two know the Mark cut in the stone. Only the Gods knows that. We thought you were men till you showed the sign of the Master."

'I wished then that we had explained about the loss of the genuine secrets of a Master-Mason at the first go-off; but I said nothing. All that night there was a blowing of horns in a little dark temple half-way down the hill, and I heard a girl crying fit to die. One of the priests told us that she was being prepared to marry the King.

' "I'll have no nonsense of that kind," says Dan. "I don't want to interfere with your customs, but I'll take my own wife."—"The girl's a little bit afraid," says the priest. "She thinks she's going to die, and they are a-heartening of her up down in the temple."

' "Hearten her very tender, then," says Dravot, "or I'll hearten you with the butt of a gun so you'll never want to be heartened again." He licked his lips, did Dan, and stayed up walking about more than half the night, thinking of the wife that he was going to get in the morning. I wasn't any means comfortable, for I knew that dealings with a woman in foreign parts, though you was a crowned King twenty times over, could not but be risky. I got up very early in the morning while Dravot was asleep, and I saw the priests talking together in whispers, and the Chiefs talking together too, and they looked at me out of the corners of their eyes.

' "What is up, Fish?" I say to the Bashkai man, who was wrapped up in his furs and looking splendid to behold.

' "I can't rightly say," says he; "but if you can make the King drop all this nonsense about marriage, you'll be doing him and me and yourself a great service."

' "That I do believe," says I. "But sure, you know, Billy, as well as me, having fought against and for us, that the King and me are nothing more than two of the finest men that God Almighty ever made. Nothing more, I do assure you."

' "That may be," says Billy Fish, "and yet I should be sorry if it was." He sinks his head upon his great fur cloak for a minute and thinks. "King," says he, "be you man or God or Devil, I'll stick by you to-day. I have twenty of my men with me, and they will follow me. We'll go to Bashkai until the storm blows over."

'A little snow had fallen in the night, and everything was white except the greasy fat clouds that blew down and down from the north. Dravot came out with his crown on his head, swinging his arms and stamping his feet, and looking more pleased than Punch.

' "For the last time, drop it, Dan," says I in a whisper, "Billy Fish here says that there will be a row."

' "A row among my people!" says Dravot. "Not much. Peachey, you're a fool not to get a wife too. Where's the girl?" says he with a voice as loud as the braying of a jackass. "Call up all the Chiefs and priests, and let the Emperor see if his wife suits him."

'There was no need to call any one. They were all there leaning on their guns and spears round the clearing in the centre of the pine wood. A lot of priests went down to the little temple to bring up the girl, and the horns blew fit to wake the dead. Billy Fish saunters round and gets as close to Daniel as he could, and behind him stood his twenty men with match-locks. Not a man of them under six feet. I was next to Dravot, and behind me was twenty men of the regular Army. Up comes the girl, and a strapping wench she was, covered with silver and turquoises but white as death, and looking back every minute at the priests.

' "She'll do," said Dan, looking her over. "What's to be afraid of, lass? Come and kiss me." He puts his arm round her. She shuts her eyes, gives a bit of a squeak, and down goes her face in the side of Dan's flaming red beard.

' "The slut's bitten me! says he, clapping his hand to his neck, and, sure enough, his hand was red with blood. Billy Fish and two of his match-lock-men catches hold of Dan by the shoulders and drags him into the Bashkai lot, while the priests howls in their lingo,—"Neither God nor Devil but a man!" I was all taken aback, for a priest cut at me in front, and the Army behind him began firing into the Bashkai men.

' "God A'mighty!" says Dan. "What is the meaning o' this?"

' "Come back! Come away!" says Billy Fish. "Ruin and Mutiny is the matter. We'll break for Bashkai if we can."

'I tried to give some sort of orders to my men—the men o' the regular Army—but it was no use, so I fired into the brown of 'em with an English Martini and drilled three beggars in a line. The valley was full of shouting, howling creatures, and every soul was shrieking, "Not a God nor a Devil but only a man!" The Bashkai troops stuck to Billy Fish all they were worth, but their matchlocks wasn't half as good as the Kabul breech-loaders, and four of them dropped. Dan was bellowing like a bull, for he was very wrathy; and Billy Fish had a hard job to prevent him running out at the crowd.

' "We can't stand," says Billy Fish. "Make a run for it down the valley! The whole place is against us." The matchlock-men ran, and we went down the valley in spite of Dravot. He was swearing horrible and crying out he was a King. The priests rolled great stones on us, and the regular Army fired hard, and there wasn't more than six men, not counting Dan, Billy Fish, and Me, that came down to the bottom of the valley alive.

'Then they stopped firing and the horns in the temple blew again. "Come away—for Gord's sake come away!" says Billy Fish. "They'll send runners out to all the villages before ever we get to Bashkai. I can protect you there, but I can't do anything now."

'My own notion is that Dan began to go mad in his head from that hour. He stared up and down like a stuck pig. Then he was all for walking back alone and killing the priests with his bare hands; which he could have done. "An Emperor am I," says Daniel, "and next year I shall be a Knight of the Queen."

' "All right, Dan," says I; "but come along now while there's time."

' "It's your fault," says he, "for not looking after your Army better. There was mutiny in the midst, and you didn't know—you damned engine-driving, plate-laying, missionary's-pass-hunting hound!" He sat upon a rock and called me every foul name he could lay tongue to. I was too heart-sick to care, though it was all his foolishness that brought the smash.

' "I'm sorry, Dan," says I, "but there's no accounting for natives. This business is our Fifty-Seven. Maybe we'll make something out of it yet, when we've got to Bashkai."

' "Let's get to Bashkai, then," says Dan, "and, by God, when I come back here again I'll sweep the valley so there isn't a bug in a blanket left!"

'We walked all that day, and all that night Dan was stumping up and down on the snow, chewing his beard and muttering to himself.

' "There's no hope o' getting clear," said Billy Fish. "The priests will have sent runners to the villages to say that you are only men. Why didn't you stick on as Gods till things was more settled? I'm a dead man," says Billy Fish, and he throws himself down on the snow and begins to pray to his Gods.

'Next morning we was in a cruel bad country—all up and down, no level ground at all, and no food either. The six Bashkai men looked at Billy Fish hungry-way as if they wanted to ask something, but they said never a word. At noon we came to the top of a flat mountain all covered with snow, and when we climbed up into it, behold, there was an Army in position waiting in the middle!

' "The runners have been very quick," says Billy Fish, with a little bit of a laugh. "They are waiting for us."

'Three or four men began to fire from the enemy's side, and a chance shot took Daniel in the calf of the leg. That brought him to his senses. He looks across the snow at the Army, and sees the rifles that we had brought into the country.

' "We're done for," says he. "They are Englishmen, these people,— and it's my blasted nonsense that has brought you to this. Get back, Billy Fish, and take your men away; you've done what you could, and now cut for it. Carnehan," says he, "shake hands with me and go along with Billy. Maybe they won't kill you. I'll go and meet 'em alone. It's me that did it. Me, the King!"

' "Go! says I. "Go to Hell, Dan. I'm with you here. Billy Fish, you clear out, and we two will meet those folk."

' "I'm a Chief, says Billy Fish, quite quiet. "I stay with you. My men can go."

'The Bashkai fellows didn't wait for a second word but ran off, and Dan and Me and Billy Fish walked across to where the drums were drumming and the horns were horning. It was cold—awful cold. I've got that cold in the back of my head now. There's a lump of it there.'

The punkah-coolies had gone to sleep. Two kerosene lamps were blazing in the office, and the perspiration poured down my face and splashed on the blotter as I leaned forward. Carnehan was shivering, and I feared that his mind might go. I wiped my face, took a fresh grip of the piteously mangled hands, and said: 'What happened after that?'

The momentary shift of my eyes had broken the clear current.

'What was you pleased to say?' whined Carnehan. 'They took them

without any sound. Not a little whisper all along the snow, not though the King knocked down the first man that set hand on him—not though old Peachey fired his last cartridge into the brown of 'em. Not a single solitary sound did those swines make. They just closed up tight, and I tell you their furs stunk. There was a man called Billy Fish, a good friend of us all, and they cut his throat, Sir, then and there, like a pig; and the King kicks up the bloody snow and says: "We've had a dashed fine run for our money. What's coming next?" But Peachey, Peachey Taliaferro, I tell you, Sir, in confidence as betwixt two friends, he lost his head, Sir. No, he didn't neither. The King lost his head, so he did, all along o' one of those cunning rope-bridges. Kindly let me have the paper-cutter, Sir. It tilted this way. They marched him a mile across that snow to a rope-bridge over a ravine with a river at the bottom. You may have seen such. They prodded him behind like an ox. "Damn your eyes!" says the King. "D'you suppose I can't die like a gentleman?" He turns to Peachey—Peachey that was crying like a child. "I've brought you to this, Peachey," says he. "Brought you out of your happy life to be killed in Kafiristan, where you was late Commander-in-Chief of the Emperor's forces. Say you forgive me, Peachey." —"I do," says Peachey. "Fully and freely do I forgive you, Dan."—"Shake hands, Peachey," says he. "I'm going now." Out he goes, looking neither right nor left, and when he was plumb in the middle of those dizzy dancing ropes,—"Cut, you beggars," he shouts; and they cut, and old Dan fell, turning round and round and round, twenty thousand miles, for he took half an hour to fall till he struck the water, and I could see his body caught on a rock with the gold crown close beside.

'But do you know what they did to Peachey between two pine-trees? They crucified him, Sir, as Peachey's hand will show. They used wooden pegs for his hands and his feet; and he didn't die. He hung there and screamed, and they took him down next day, and said it was a miracle that he wasn't dead. They took him down—poor old Peachey that hadn't done them any harm—that hadn't done them any——'

He rocked to and fro and wept bitterly, wiping his eyes with the back of his scarred hands and moaning like a child for some ten minutes.

'They was cruel enough to feed him up in the temple, because they said he was more of a God than old Daniel that was a man. Then they turned him out on the snow, and told him to go home, and Peachey came home in about a year, begging along the roads quite safe; for Daniel Dravot he walked before and said: "Come along, Peachey. It's a big thing we're doing." The mountains they danced at night, and the mountains they tried to fall on Peachey's head, but Dan he held up his hand, and Peachey came along bent double. He never let go of Dan's hand, and he never let go of Dan's head. They gave it to him as a present in the temple, to remind him not to come again, and though the crown was pure gold, and Peachey was starving, never would Peachey sell the same. You knew Dravot, Sir! You knew Right Worshipful Brother Dravot! Look at him now!'

He fumbled in the mass of rags round his bent waist; brought out a black horsehair bag embroidered with silver thread; and shook therefrom on to my table—the dried, withered head of Daniel Dravot! The morning sun that had long been paling the lamps struck the red beard and blind sunken eyes; struck, too, a heavy circlet of gold studded with raw turquoises, that Carnehan placed tenderly on the battered temples.

'You be'old now,' said Carnehan, 'the Emperor in his 'abit as he lived— the King of Kafiristan with his crown upon his head. Poor old Daniel that was a monarch once!'

I shuddered, for, in spite of defacements manifold, I recognised the head of the man of Marwar Junction. Carnehan rose to go. I attempted to stop him. He was not fit to walk abroad. 'Let me take away the whiskey, and give me a little money,' he gasped. 'I was a King once. I'll go to the Deputy Commissioner and ask to set in the Poorhouse till I get my health. No, thank you, I can't wait till you get a carriage for me. I've urgent private affairs—in the south—at Marwar.'

He shambled out of the office and departed in the direction of the Deputy Commissioner's house. That day at noon I had occasion to go down the blinding hot Mall, and I saw a crooked man crawling along the white dust of the roadside, his hat in his hand, quavering dolorously after the fashion of street-singers at Home. There was not a soul in sight, and he was out of all possible earshot of the houses. And he sang through his nose, turning his head from right to left:—

> 'The Son of Man goes forth to war,
>   A golden crown to gain;
> His blood-red banner streams afar—
>   Who follows in his train?'

I waited to hear no more, but put the poor wretch into my carriage and drove him off to the nearest missionary for eventual transfer to the Asylum. He repeated the hymn twice while he was with me whom he did not in the least recognise, and I left him singing it to the missionary.

Two days later I enquired after his welfare of the Superintendent of the Asylum.

'He was admitted suffering from sun-stroke. He died early yesterday morning,' said the Superintendent. 'Is it true that he was half an hour bareheaded in the sun at midday?'

'Yes,' said I, but do you happen to know if he had anything upon him by any chance when he died?'

'Not to my knowledge,' said the Superintendent.

And there the matter rests.

THE WRECK OF THE VISIGOTH

'Eternal Father, strong to save,
Whose arm hath bound the restless wave,
Who bidst the mighty ocean keep
Its own appointed limits deep.'

⋅⋅§ THE lady passengers were trying the wheezy old harmonium in front of the cuddy, because it was Sunday night. In the patch of darkness near the wheel-grating sat the Captain, and the end of his cheroot burned like a head-lamp. There was neither breath nor motion upon the waters through which the screw was thudding. They spread, dull silver, under the haze of the moonlight till they joined the low coast of Malacca away to the eastward. The voices of the singers at the harmonium were held down by the awnings, and came to us with force.

'Oh, hear us when we cry to Thee,
For those in peril on the sea.'

It was as though the little congregation were afraid of the vastness of the sea. But a laugh followed, and some one said, 'Shall we take it through again a little quicker?' Then the Captain told the story of just such a night, lowering his voice for fear of disturbing the music and the minds of the passengers.

'She was the Visigoth,—five hundred tons, or it may have been six,—in the coasting trade; one of the best steamers and best found on the Kutch-Kasauli line. She wasn't six years old when the thing happened: on just such a night as this, with an oily smooth sea, under brilliant starlight, about a hundred miles from land. To this day no one knows really what the matter was. She was so small that she could not have struck even a log in the water without every soul on board feeling the jar; and even if she had struck something, it wouldn't have made her go down as she did. I was fourth officer then; we had about seven saloon passengers, including the Captain's wife and another woman, and perhaps five hundred deck-passengers going up the coast to a shrine, on just such a night as this, when she was ripping through the level sea at a level nine knots an hour. The man on the bridge, whoever it was, saw that she was sinking at the head. Sinking by the head as she went along. That was the only warning we got. She began to sink as she went along. Of course the Captain was told, and he sent me to wake up the saloon passengers and tell them to come on deck. 'Sounds a curious sort of message that to deliver on a dead still night. The people tumbled up in their dressing-gowns and *pyjamas*, and wouldn't believe me. We were just sinking as fast as we could, and I had to tell 'em that. Then the deck-passengers got wind of it, and all Hell woke up along the decks.

'The rule in these little affairs is to get your saloon passengers off first, then to fill the boats with the balance, and afterwards—God help the extras, that's all. I was getting the starboard stern boat—the mail-boat— away. It hung as it might be over yonder, and as I came along from the cuddy, the deck-passengers hung round me, shoving their money-belts into my hand, taking off their nose-rings and earrings, and thrusting 'em upon me to buy just one chance for life. If I hadn't been so desperately busy, I should have thought it horrible. I put biscuits and water into the boat, and got the two ladies in. One of 'em was the Captain's wife. She had to be put in by main force. You've no notion how women can struggle. The other woman was the wife of an officer going to meet her husband; and there were a couple of passengers beside the lascars. The Captain said he was going to stay with the ship. You see the rule in these affairs, I believe, is that the Captain has to bow gracefully from the bridge and go down. I haven't had a ship under my charge wrecked yet. When that comes, I'll have to do like the others. After the boats were away, and I saw that there was nothing to be got by waiting, I jumped overboard exactly as I might have vaulted over into a flat green field, and struck out for the mail-boat. Another officer did the same thing, but he went for a boat full of natives, and they whacked him on the chest with oars, so he had some difficulty in climbing in.

'It was as well that I reached the mail-boat. There was a compass in it, but the idiots had managed to fill the boat half full of water somehow or another, and none of the crew seemed to know what was required of them. Then the Visigoth went down and took every one with her—ships generally do that; the corpses don't cumber the sea for some time.

'What did I do? I kept all the boats together, and headed into the track of the coasting steamers. The aggravating thing was the thought that we were close to land as far as a big steamer was concerned, and in the middle of eternity as far as regarded a little boat. The sea looks hugeous big from a boat at night.'

> 'Oh, Christ, whose voice the waters heard
> And hushed their ravings at Thy word,
> Who walkedst on the foaming deep
> And calm amidst its rage did keep,—
> Oh, hear us when we cry to Thee,
> For those in peril on the sea!'

sang the passengers cheerily.

'That harmonium is disgracefully out of tune,' said the Captain. 'The sea air affects their insides. Well, as I was saying, we settled down in the boat. The Captain's wife was unconscious; she lay in the bottom of the boat and moaned. I was glad she wasn't threshing about the boat: but what I did think was wrong, was the way the two men passengers behaved. They were useless with funk—out and out fear. They lay in the boat and did nothing. Fetched a groan now and again to show they were alive; but that was all. But the other woman was a jewel. Damn it, it was worth being shipwrecked to have that woman in the boat; she was awfully handsome, and as brave as she was lovely. She helped me bail out the boat, and she worked like a man.

'So we kicked about the sea from midnight till seven the next evening, and then we saw a steamer. "I'll—I'll give you anything I'm wearing to hoist as a signal of distress," said the woman; but I had no need to ask her, for the steamer picked us up and took us back to Bombay. I forgot to tell you that, when the day broke, I couldn't recognise the Captain's wife—widow, I mean. She had changed in the night as if fire had gone over her. I met her a long time afterwards, and even then she hadn't forgiven me for putting her into the boat and obeying the Captain's orders. But the husband of the other woman—he's in the Army—wrote me no end of a letter of thanks. I don't suppose he considered that the way his wife behaved was enough to make any decent man do all he could. The other fellows, who lay in the bottom of the boat and groaned, I've never met. Don't want to. Shouldn't be civil to 'em if I did. And that's how the *Visigoth* went down, for no assignable reason, with eighty bags of mail, five hundred souls, and not a single packet insured, on just such a night as this.'

> 'Oh, Trinity of love and power,
> Our brethren shield in that dread hour,
> From rock and tempest, fire and foe,
> Protect them wheresoe'er they go.
> Thus evermore shall rise to Thee
> Glad hymns of praise by land and sea.'

'Strikes me they'll go on singing that hymn all night. Imperfect sort of doctrine in the last lines, don't you think? They might have run in an extra verse specifying sudden collapse—like the *Visigoth's*. I'm going on to the bridge, now. Good-night,' said the Captain.

And I was left alone with the steady thud, thud, of the screw and the gentle creaking of the boats at the davits.

That made me shudder.

WEE WILLIE WINKIE

'An officer and a gentleman.'

HIS full name was Percival William Williams, but he picked up the other name in a nursery-book, and that was the end of the christened titles. His mother's *ayah* called him Willie-*Baba*, but as he never paid the faintest attention to anything that the *ayah* said, her wisdom did not help matters.

His father was the Colonel of the 195th, and as soon as Wee Willie Winkie was old enough to understand what Military Discipline meant, Colonel Williams put him under it. There was no other way of managing the child. When he was good for a week, he drew good-conduct pay; and when he was bad, he was deprived of his good-conduct stripe. Generally he was bad, for India offers many chances of going wrong to little six-year-olds.

Children resent familiarity from strangers, and Wee Willie Winkie was a very particular child. Once he accepted an acquaintance, he was graciously pleased to thaw. He accepted Brandis, a subaltern of the 195th, on sight. Brandis was having tea at the Colonel's, and Wee Willie Winkie entered strong in the possession of a good-conduct badge won for not chasing the hens round the compound. He regarded Brandis with gravity for at least ten minutes, and then delivered himself of his opinion.

'I like you,' said he slowly, getting off his chair and coming over to Brandis. 'I like you. I shall call you Coppy, because of your hair. Do you *mind* being called Coppy? It is because of ve hair, you know.'

Here was one of the most embarrassing of Wee Willie Winkie's peculiarities. He would look at a stranger for some time, and then, without warning or explanation, would give him a name. And the name stuck. No regimental penalties could break Wee Willie Winkie of this habit. He lost his good-conduct badge for christening the Commissioner's wife 'Pobs'; but nothing that the Colonel could do made the Station forego the nickname, and Mrs. Collen remained 'Pobs' till the end of her stay. So Brandis was christened 'Coppy,' and rose, therefore, in the estimation of the regiment.

If Wee Willie Winkie took an interest in any one, the fortunate man was envied alike by the mess and the rank and file. And in their envy lay no suspicion of self-interest. 'The Colonel's son' was idolised on his own merits entirely. Yet Wee Willie Winkie was not lovely. His face was permanently freckled, as his legs were permanently scratched, and in spite of his mother's almost tearful remonstrances he had insisted upon having his long yellow locks cut short in the military fashion. 'I want my hair like Sergeant Tummil's,' said Wee Willie Winkie, and, his father abetting, the sacrifice was accomplished.

Three weeks after the bestowal of his youthful affections on Lieutenant Brandis—henceforward to be called 'Coppy' for the sake of brevity—Wee Willie Winkie was destined to behold strange things and far beyond his comprehension.

Coppy returned his liking with interest. Coppy had let him wear for five rapturous minutes his own big sword—just as tall as Wee Willie Winkie. Coppy had promised him a terrier puppy, and Coppy had permitted him to witness the miraculous operation of shaving. Nay, more—Coppy had said that even he, Wee Willie Winkie, would rise in time to the ownership of a box of shiny knives, a silver soap-box and a silver-handled 'sputter-brush,' as Wee Willie Winkie called it. Decidedly, there was no one except his father, who could give or take away good-conduct badges at pleasure, half so wise, strong, and valiant as Coppy with the Afghan and Egyptian medals on his breast. Why, then, should Coppy be guilty of the unmanly weakness of kissing—vehemently kissing—a 'big girl,' Miss Allardyce to wit? In the course of a morning ride, Wee Willie Winkie had seen Coppy so doing, and, like the gentleman he was, had promptly wheeled round and cantered back to his groom, lest the groom should also see.

Under ordinary circumstances he would have spoken to his father, but he felt instinctively that this was a matter on which Coppy ought first to be consulted.

'Coppy,' shouted Wee Willie Winkie, reining up outside that subaltern's bungalow early one morning—'I want to see you, Coppy!'

'Come in, young 'un,' returned Coppy, who was at early breakfast in the midst of his dogs. 'What mischief have you been getting into now?'

Wee Willie Winkie had done nothing notoriously bad for three days, and so stood on a pinnacle of virtue.

'*I've* been doing nothing bad,' said he, curling himself into a long chair with a studious affectation of the Colonel's languor after a hot parade. He buried his freckled nose in a tea-cup and, with eyes staring roundly over the rim, asked: 'I say, Coppy, is it pwoper to kiss big girls?'

'By Jove! You're beginning early. Who do you want to kiss?'

'No one. My muvver's always kissing me if I don't stop her. If it isn't pwoper, how was you kissing Major Allardyce's big girl last morning, by ve canal?'

Coppy's brow wrinkled. He and Miss Allardyce had with great craft managed to keep their engagement secret for a fortnight. There were urgent and imperative reasons why Major Allardyce should not know how matters stood for at least another month, and this small marplot had discovered a great deal too much.

'I saw you,' said Wee Willie Winkie calmly. 'But ve *sais* didn't see. I said, "Hut jao!"'

'Oh, you had that much sense, you young Rip,' groaned poor Coppy, half amused and half angry. 'And how many people may you have told about it?'

'Only me myself. You didn't tell when I twied to wide ve buffalo ven my pony was lame; and I fought you wouldn't like.'

'Winkie,' said Coppy enthusiastically, shaking the small hand, 'you're the best of good fellows. Look here, you can't understand all these things. One of these days—hang it, how can I make you see it!—I'm going to marry Miss Allardyce, and then she'll be Mrs. Coppy, as you say. If your young mind is so scandalised at the idea of kissing big girls, go and tell your father.'

'What will happen?' said Wee Willie Winkie, who firmly believed that his father was omnipotent.

'I shall get into trouble,' said Coppy, playing his trump card with an appealing look at the holder of the ace.

'Ven I won't,' said Wee Willie Winkie briefly. 'But my faver says it's un-man-ly to be always kissing, and I didn't fink *you'd* do vat, Coppy.'

'I'm not always kissing, old chap. It's only now and then, and when you're bigger you'll do it too. Your father meant it's not good for little boys.'

'Ah!' said Wee Willie Winkie, now fully enlightened. 'It's like ve sputter-brush?'

'Exactly,' said Coppy gravely.

'But I don't fink I'll ever want to kiss big girls, nor no one, 'cept my muvver. And I *must* vat, you know.'

There was a long pause, broken by Wee Willie Winkie.

'Are you fond of vis big girl, Coppy?'

'Awfully!' said Coppy.

'Fonder van you are of Bell or ve Butcha—or me?'

'It's in a different way,' said Coppy. 'You see, one of these days Miss Allardyce will belong to me, but you'll grow up and command the Regiment and—all sorts of things. It's quite different, you see.'

'Very well,' said Wee Willie Winkie, rising. 'If you're fond of ve big girl, I won't tell any one. I must go now.'

Coppy rose and escorted his small guest to the door, adding—'You're the best of little fellows, Winkie. I tell you what. In thirty days from now you can tell if you like—tell any one you like.'

Thus the secret of the Brandis-Allardyce engagement was dependent on a little child's word. Coppy, who knew Wee Willie Winkie's idea of truth, was at ease, for he felt that he would not break promises. Wee Willie Winkie betrayed a special and unusual interest in Miss Allardyce, and, slowly revolving round that embarrassed young lady, was used to regard her gravely with unwinking eye. He was trying to discover why Coppy should have kissed her. She was not half so nice as his own mother. On the other hand, she was Coppy's property, and would in time belong to him. Therefore, it behooved him to treat her with as much respect as Coppy's big sword or shiny pistol.

The idea that he shared a great secret in common with Coppy kept Wee Willie Winkie unusually virtuous for three weeks. Then the Old Adam broke out, and he made what he called a 'camp-fire' at the bottom of the garden. How could he have foreseen that the flying sparks would have lighted the Colonel's little hay-rick and consumed a week's store for the horses? Sudden and swift was the punishment—deprivation of the good-conduct badge and, most sorrowful of all, two days' confinement to barracks—the house and veranda—coupled with the withdrawal of the light of his father's countenance.

He took the sentence like the man he strove to be, drew himself up with a quivering under-lip, saluted, and, once clear of the room, ran to weep bitterly in his nursery—called by him 'my quarters.' Coppy came in the afternoon and attempted to console the culprit.

'I'm under awwest,' said Wee Willie Winkie mournfully, 'and I didn't ought to speak to you.'

Very early the next morning he climbed on to the roof of the house— that was not forbidden—and beheld Miss Allardyce going for a ride.

'Where are you going?' cried Wee Willie Winkie.

'Across the river,' she answered, and trotted forward.

Now the cantonment in which the 195th lay was bounded on the north by a river—dry in the winter. From his earliest years, Wee Willie Winkie had been forbidden to go across the river, and had noted that even Coppy— the almost almighty Coppy—had never set foot beyond it. Wee Willie Winkie had once been read to, out of a big blue book, the history of the Princess and the Goblins—a most wonderful tale of a land where the Goblins were always warring with the children of men until they were defeated by one Curdie. Ever since that date it seemed to him that the bare black and purple hills across the river were inhabited by Goblins, and, in truth, every one had said that there lived the Bad Men. Even in his own house the lower halves of the windows were covered with green paper on account of the Bad Men who might, if allowed clear view, fire into peaceful drawing-rooms and comfortable bedrooms. Certainly, beyond the river, which was the end of all the Earth, lived the Bad Men. And here was Major Allardyce's big girl, Coppy's property, preparing to venture into their borders! What would Coppy say if anything happened to her? If the Goblins ran off with her as they did with Curdie's Princess? She must at all hazards be turned back.

The house was still. Wee Willie Winkie reflected for a moment on the very terrible wrath of his father; and then—broke his arrest! It was a crime unspeakable. The low sun threw his shadow, very large and very black, on the trim garden-paths, as he went down to the stables and ordered his pony. It seemed to him in the hush of the dawn that all the big world had been bidden to stand still and look at Wee Willie Winkie guilty of mutiny. The drowsy *sais* gave him his mount, and, since the one great sin made all others insignificant, Wee Willie Winkie said that he was going to ride over to Coppy Sahib, and went out at a foot-pace, stepping on the soft mould of the flower-borders.

The devastating track of the pony's feet was the last misdeed that cut him off from all sympathy of Humanity. He turned into the road, leaned forward, and rode as fast as the pony could put foot to the ground in the direction of the river.

But the liveliest of twelve-two ponies can do little against the long canter of a Waler. Miss Allardyce was far ahead, had passed through the crops, beyond the Police-posts, when all the guards were asleep, and her mount was scattering the pebbles of the river-bed as Wee Willie Winkie left the cantonment and British India behind him. Bowed forward and still flogging, Wee Willie Winkie shot into Afghan territory, and could just see Miss Allardyce a black speck, flickering across the stony plain. The reason of her wandering was simple enough. Coppy, in a tone of too-hastily-assumed authority, had told her over night that she must not ride out by the river. And she had gone to prove her own spirit and teach Coppy a lesson.

Almost at the foot of the inhospitable hills, Wee Willie Winkie saw the Waler blunder and come down heavily. Miss Allardyce struggled clear, but her ankle had been severely twisted, and she could not stand. Having fully shown her spirit, she wept, and was surprised by the apparition of a white, wide-eyed child in khaki, on a nearly spent pony.

'Are you badly, badly hurted?' shouted Wee Willie Winkie, as soon as he was within range. 'You didn't ought to be here.'

'I don't know,' said Miss Allardyce ruefully, ignoring the reproof. 'Good gracious, child, what are *you* doing here?'

'You said you was going acwoss ve wiver,' panted Wee Willie Winkie, throwing himself off his pony. 'And nobody—not even Coppy—must go acwoss ve wiver, and I came after you ever so hard, but you wouldn't stop, and now you've hurted yourself, and Coppy will be angwy wiv me, and—I've bwoken my awwest! I've bwoken my awwest!'

The future Colonel of the 195th sat down and sobbed. In spite of the pain in her ankle the girl was moved.

'Have you ridden all the way from cantonments, little man? What for?'

'You belonged to Coppy. Coppy told me so!' wailed Wee Willie Winkie disconsolately. 'I saw him kissing you, and he said he was fonder of you van Bell or ve Butcha or me. And so I came. You must get up and come back. You didn't ought to be here. Vis is a bad place, and I've bwoken my awwest.'

'I can't move, Winkie,' said Miss Allardyce, with a groan. 'I've hurt my foot. What shall I do?'

She showed a readiness to weep anew, which steadied Wee Willie Winkie, who had been brought up to believe that tears were the depth of unmanliness. Still, when one is as great a sinner as Wee Willie Winkie, even a man may be permitted to break down.

'Winkie,' said Miss Allardyce, 'when you've rested a little, ride back and tell them to send out something to carry me back in. It hurts fearfully.'

The child sat still for a little time and Miss Allardyce closed her eyes; the pain was nearly making her faint. She was roused by Wee Willie Winkie tying up the reins on his pony's neck and setting it free with a vicious cut of his whip that made it whicker. The little animal headed towards the cantonments.

'Oh, Winkie! What are you doing?'

'Hush!' said Wee Willie Winkie. 'Vere's a man coming—one of ve Bad Men. I must stay wiv you. My faver says a man must *always* look after a girl. Jack will go home, and ven vey'll come and look for us. Vat's why I let him go.'

Not one man but two or three had appeared from behind the rocks of the hills, and the heart of Wee Willie Winkie sank within him, for just in this manner were the Goblins wont to steal out and vex Curdie's soul. Thus had they played in Curdie's garden, he had seen the picture, and thus had they frightened the Princess's nurse. He heard them talking to each other, and recognised with joy the bastard Pushto that he had picked up from one of his father's grooms lately dismissed. People who spoke that tongue could not be the Bad Men. They were only natives after all.

They came up to the bowlders on which Miss Allardyce's horse had blundered.

Then rose from the rock Wee Willie Winkie, child of the Dominant Race, aged six and three-quarters, and said briefly and emphatically '*Jao!*' The pony had crossed the river-bed.

The men laughed, and laughter from natives was the one thing Wee Willie Winkie could not tolerate. He asked them what they wanted and why they did not depart. Other men with most evil faces and crooked-stocked guns crept out of the shadows of the hills, till, soon, Wee Willie Winkie was face to face with an audience some twenty strong. Miss Allardyce screamed.

'Who are you?' said one of the men.

'I am the Colonel Sahib's son, and my order is that you go at once. You black men are frightening the Miss Sahib. One of you must run into cantonments and take the news that the Miss Sahib has hurt herself, and that the Colonel's son is here with her.'

'Put our feet into the trap?' was the laughing reply. 'Hear this boy's speech!'

'Say that I sent you—I, the Colonel's son. They will give you money.'

'What is the use of this talk? Take up the child and the girl, and we can at least ask for the ransom. Ours are the villages on the heights,' said a voice in the background.

These *were* the Bad Men—worse than Goblins—and it needed all Wee Willie Winkie's training to prevent him from bursting into tears. But he felt that to cry before a native, excepting only his mother's *ayah*, would be an infamy greater than any mutiny. Moreover, he, as future Colonel of the 195th, had that grim regiment at his back.

'Are you going to carry us away?' said Wee Willie Winkie, very blanched and uncomfortable.

'Yes, my little *Sahib Bahadur*,' said the tallest of the men, 'and eat you afterwards.'

'That is child's talk,' said Wee Willie Winkie. 'Men do not eat men.'

A yell of laughter interrupted him, but he went on firmly—'And if you do carry us away, I tell you that all my regiment will come up in a day and kill you all without leaving one. Who will take my message to the Colonel Sahib?'

Speech in any vernacular—and Wee Willie Winkie had a colloquial acquaintance with three—was easy to the boy who could not yet manage his 'r's' and 'th's' aright.

Another man joined the conference, crying: 'O foolish men! What this babe says is true. He is the heart's heart of those white troops. For the sake of peace let them go both, for if he be taken, the regiment will break loose and gut the valley. *Our* villages are in the valley, and we shall not escape. That regiment are devils. They broke Khoda Yar's breastbone with kicks when he tried to take the rifles; and if we touch this child they will fire and rape and plunder for a month, till nothing remains. Better to send a man back to take the message and get a reward. I say that this child is their God, and that they will spare none of us, nor our women, if we harm him.'

It was Din Mahommed, the dismissed groom of the Colonel, who made the diversion, and an angry and heated discussion followed. Wee Willie Winkie, standing over Miss Allardyce, waited the upshot. Surely his 'wegiment,' his own 'wegiment,' would not desert him if they knew of his extremity.

*   *   *   *   *

The riderless pony brought the news to the 195th, though there had been consternation in the Colonel's household for an hour before. The little beast came in through the parade-ground in front of the main barracks, where the men were settling down to play Spoil-five till the afternoon. Devlin, the Colour-Sergeant of E Company, glanced at the empty saddle and tumbled through the barrack-rooms, kicking up each Room Corporal as he passed. 'Up, ye beggars! There's something happened to the Colonel's son,' he shouted.

'He couldn't fall off! S'elp me, 'e *couldn't* fall off,' blubbered a drummer-boy. 'Go an' hunt acrost the river. He's over there if he's anywhere, an' maybe those Pathans have got 'im. For the love o' Gawd don't look for 'im in the nullahs! Let's go over the river.'

'There's sense in Mott yet,' said Devlin. 'E Company, double out to the river—sharp!'

So E Company, in its shirt-sleeves mainly, doubled for the dear life, and in the rear toiled the perspiring Sergeant, adjuring it to double yet faster. The cantonment was alive with the men of the 195th hunting for Wee Willie Winkie, and the Colonel finally overtook E Company, far too exhausted to swear, struggling in the pebbles of the river-bed.

Up the hill under which Wee Willie Winkie's Bad Men were discussing the wisdom of carrying off the child and the girl, a look-out fired two shots.

'What have I said?' shouted Din Mahommed. 'There is the warning! The *pulton* are out already and are coming across the plain! Get away! Let us not be seen with the boy!'

The men waited for an instant, and then, as another shot was fired, withdrew into the hills, silently as they had appeared.

'The wegiment is coming,' said Wee Willie Winkie confidently to Miss Allardyce, 'and it's all wight. Don't cwy!'

He needed the advice himself, for ten minutes later, when his father came up, he was weeping bitterly with his head in Miss Allardyce's lap.

And the men of the 195th carried him home with shouts and rejoicings; and Coppy, who had ridden a horse into a lather, met him, and, to his intense disgust, kissed him openly in the presence of the men.

But there was balm for his dignity. His father assured him that not only would the breaking of arrest be condoned, but that the good-conduct badge would be restored as soon as his mother could sew it on his blouse-sleeve. Miss Allardyce had told the Colonel a story that made him proud of his son.

'She belonged to you, Coppy,' said Wee Willie Winkie, indicating Miss Allardyce with a grimy forefinger. 'I *knew* she didn't ought to go acwoss ve wiver, and I knew ve wegiment would come to me if I sent Jack home.'

'You're a hero, Winkie,' said Coppy—'a *pukka* hero!'

'I don't know what vat means,' said Wee Willie Winkie, 'but you mustn't call me Winkie any no more. I'm Percival Will'am Will'ams.'

And in this manner did Wee Willie Winkie enter into his manhood.

"THEY"

ONE view called me to another; one hill top to its fellow, half across the county, and since I could answer at no more trouble than the snapping forward of a lever, I let the country flow under my wheels. The orchid-studded flats of the East gave way to the thyme, ilex, and grey grass of the Downs; these again to the rich cornland and fig-trees of the lower coast, where you carry the beat of the tide on your left hand for fifteen level miles; and when at last I turned inland through a huddle of rounded hills and woods I had run myself clean out of my known marks. Beyond that precise hamlet which stands godmother to the capital of the United States, I found hidden villages where bees, the only things awake, boomed in eighty-foot lindens that overhung grey Norman churches; miraculous brooks diving under stone bridges built for heavier traffic than would ever vex them again; tithe-barns larger than their churches, and an old smithy that cried out aloud how it had once been a hall of the Knights of the Temple. Gipsies I found on a common where the gorse, bracken, and heath fought it out together up a mile of Roman road; and a little farther on I disturbed a red fox rolling dog-fashion in the naked sunlight.

As the wooded hills closed about me I stood up in the car to take the bearings of that great Down whose ringed head is a landmark for fifty miles across the low countries. I judged that the lie of the country would bring me across some westward running road that went to his feet, but I did not allow for the confusing veils of the woods. A quick turn plunged me first into a green cutting brimful of liquid sunshine, next into a gloomy tunnel where last year's dead leaves whispered and scuffled about my tyres. The strong hazel stuff meeting overhead had not been cut for a couple of generations at least, nor had any axe helped the moss-cankered oak and beech to spring above them. Here the road changed frankly into a carpeted ride on whose brown velvet spent primrose-clumps showed like jade, and a few sickly, white-stalked blue-bells nodded together. As the slope favoured I shut off the power and slid over the whirled leaves, expecting every moment to meet a keeper; but I only heard a jay, far off, arguing against the silence under the twilight of the trees.

Still the track descended. I was on the point of reversing and working my way back on the second speed ere I ended in some swamp, when I saw sunshine through the tangle ahead and lifted the brake.

It was down again at once. As the light beat across my face my fore-wheels took the turf of a great still lawn from which sprang horsemen ten feet high with levelled lances, monstrous peacocks, and sleek round-headed maids of honour—blue, black, and glistening—all of clipped yew. Across the lawn

—the marshalled woods besieged it on three sides—stood an ancient house of lichened and weather-worn stone, with mullioned windows and roofs of rose-red tile. It was flanked by semi-circular walls, also rose-red, that closed the lawn on the fourth side, and at their feet a box hedge grew man-high. There were doves on the roof about the slim brick chimneys, and I caught a glimpse of an octagonal dove-house behind the screening wall.

Here, then, I stayed; a horseman's green spear laid at my breast; held by the exceeding beauty of that jewel in that setting.

"If I am not packed off for a trespasser, or if this knight does not ride a wallop at me," thought I, "Shakespeare and Queen Elizabeth at least must come out of that half-open garden door and ask me to tea."

A child appeared at an upper window, and I thought the little thing waved a friendly hand. But it was to call a companion, for presently another bright head showed. Then I heard a laugh among the yew-peacocks, and turning to make sure (till then I had been watching the house only) I saw the silver of a fountain behind a hedge thrown up against the sun. The doves on the roof cooed to the cooing water; but between the two notes I caught the utterly happy chuckle of a child absorbed in some light mischief.

The garden door—heavy oak sunk deep in the thickness of the wall—opened further: a woman in a big garden hat set her foot slowly on the time-hollowed stone step and as slowly walked across the turf. I was forming some apology when she lifted up her head and I saw that she was blind.

"I heard you," she said. "Isn't that a motor car?"

"I'm afraid I've made a mistake in my road. I should have turned off up above—I never dreamed"—I began.

"But I'm very glad. Fancy a motor car coming into the garden! It will be such a treat——" She turned and made as though looking about her. "You—you haven't seen any one have you—perhaps?"

"No one to speak to, but the children seemed interested at a distance."

"Which?"

"I saw a couple up at the window just now, and I think I heard a little chap in the grounds."

"Oh, lucky you!" she cried, and her face brightened. "I hear them, of course, but that's all. You've seen them and heard them?"

"Yes," I answered. "And if I know anything of children one of them's having a beautiful time by the fountain yonder. Escaped, I should imagine."

"You're fond of children?"

I gave her one or two reasons why I did not altogether hate them.

"Of course, of course," she said. "Then you understand. Then you won't think it foolish if I ask you to take your car through the gardens, once or twice—quite slowly. I'm sure they'd like to see it. They see so little, poor things. One tries to make their life pleasant, but——" she threw out her hands towards the woods. "We're so out of the world here."

"That will be splendid," I said. "But I can't cut up your grass."

She faced to the right. "Wait a minute," she said. "We're at the South gate, aren't we? Behind those peacocks there's a flagged path. We call it the Peacock's Walk. You can't see it from here, they tell me, but if you squeeze along by the edge of the wood you can turn at the first peacock and get on to the flags."

It was a sacrilege to wake that dreaming house-front with the clatter of machinery, but I swung the car to clear the turf, brushed along the edge of the wood and turned in on the broad stone path where the fountain-basin lay like one star-sapphire.

"May I come too?" she cried. "No, please don't help me. They'll like it better if they see me."

She felt her way lightly to the front of the car, and with one foot on the step she called: "Children, oh, children! Look and see what's going to happen!"

The voice would have drawn lost souls from the Pit, for the yearning that underlay its sweetness, and I was not surprised to hear an answering shout behind the yews. It must have been the child by the fountain, but he fled at our approach, leaving a little toy boat in the water. I saw the glint of his blue blouse among the still horsemen.

Very disposedly we paraded the length of the walk and at her request backed again. This time the child had got the better of his panic, but stood far off and doubting.

"The little fellow's watching us," I said. "I wonder if he'd like a ride."

"They're very shy still. Very shy. But, oh, lucky you to be able to see them! Let's listen."

I stopped the machine at once, and the humid stillness, heavy with the scent of box, cloaked us deep. Shears I could hear where some gardener was clipping; a mumble of bees and broken voices that might have been the doves.

"Oh, unkind!" she said wearily.

"Perhaps they're only shy of the motor. The little maid at the window looks tremendously interested."

"Yes?" She raised her head. "It was wrong of me to say that. They are really fond of me. It's the only thing that makes life worth living—when they're fond of you, isn't it? I daren't think what the place would be without them. By the way, is it beautiful?"

"I think it is the most beautiful place I have ever seen."

"So they all tell me. I can feel it, of course, but that isn't quite the same thing."

"Then have you never——?" I began, but stopped abashed.

"Not since I can remember. It happened when I was only a few months old, they tell me. And yet I must remember something, else how could I dream about colours. I see light in my dreams, and colours, but I never see *them*. I only hear them just as I do when I'm awake."

"It's difficult to see faces in dreams. Some people can, but most of us haven't the gift," I went on, looking up at the window where the child stood all but hidden.

"I've heard that too," she said. "And they tell me that one never sees a dead person's face in a dream. Is that true?"

"I believe it is—now I come to think of it."

"But how is it with yourself—yourself?" The blind eyes turned towards me.

"I have never seen the faces of my dead in any dream," I answered.

"Then it must be as bad as being blind."

The sun had dipped behind the woods and the long shades were possessing the insolent horsemen one by one. I saw the light die from off the top of a glossy-leaved lance and all the brave hard green turn to soft black. The house, accepting another day at end, as it had accepted an hundred thousand gone, seemed to settle deeper into its rest among the shadows.

"Have you ever wanted to?" she said after the silence.

"Very much sometimes," I replied. The child had left the window as the shadows closed upon it.

"Ah! So've I, but I don't suppose it's allowed. . . . Where d'you live?"

"Quite the other side of the county—sixty miles and more, and I must be going back. I've come without my big lamp."

"But it's not dark yet. I can feel it."

"I'm afraid it will be by the time I get home. Could you lend me someone to set me on my road at first? I've utterly lost myself."

"I'll send Madden with you to the cross-roads. We are so out of the world, I don't wonder you were lost! I'll guide you round to the front of the house; but you will go slowly, won't you, till you're out of the grounds? It isn't foolish, do you think?"

"I promise you I'll go like this," I said, and let the car start herself down the flagged path.

We skirted the left wing of the house, whose elaborately cast lead guttering alone was worth a day's journey; passed under a great rose-grown gate in the red wall, and so round to the high front of the house which in beauty and stateliness as much excelled the back as that all others I had seen.

"Is it so very beautiful?" she said wistfully when she heard my raptures. "And you like the lead-figures too? There's the old azalea garden behind. They say that this place must have been made for children. Will you help me out, please? I should like to come with you as far as the cross-roads, but I mustn't leave them. Is that you, Madden? I want you to show this gentleman the way to the cross-roads. He has lost his way but—he has seen them."

A butler appeared noiselessly at the miracle of old oak that must be called the front door, and slipped aside to put on his hat. She stood looking at me with open blue eyes in which no sight lay, and I saw for the first time that she was beautiful.

"Remember," she said quietly, "if you are fond of them you will come again," and disappeared within the house.

The butler in the car said nothing till we were nearly at the lodge gates, where catching a glimpse of a blue blouse in a shrubbery I swerved amply lest the devil that leads little boys to play should drag me into child-murder.

"Excuse me," he asked of a sudden, "but why did you do that, Sir?"

"The child yonder."

"Our young gentleman in blue?"

"Of course."

"He runs about a good deal. Did you see him by the fountain, Sir?"

"Oh, yes, several times. Do we turn here?"

"Yes, Sir. And did you 'appen to see them upstairs too?"

"At the upper window? Yes."

"Was that before the mistress come out to speak to you, Sir?"

"A little before that. Why d'you want to know?"

He paused a little. "Only to make sure that—that they had seen the car, Sir, because with children running about, though I'm sure you're driving particularly careful, there might be an accident. That was all, Sir. Here are the cross-roads. You can't miss your way from now on. Thank you, Sir, but that isn't *our* custom, not with——"

"I beg your pardon," I said, and thrust away the British silver.

"Oh, it's quite right with the rest of 'em as a rule. Goodbye, Sir."

He retired into the armour-plated conning tower of his caste and walked away. Evidently a butler solicitous for the honour of his house, and interested, probably through a maid, in the nursery.

Once beyond the signposts at the cross-roads I looked back, but the crumpled hills interlaced so jealously that I could not see where the house had lain. When I asked its name at a cottage along the road, the fat woman who sold sweetmeats there gave me to understand that people with motor cars had small right to live—much less to "go about talking like carriage folk." They were not a pleasant-mannered community.

When I retraced my route on the map that evening I was little wiser. Hawkin's Old Farm appeared to be the survey title of the place, and the old County Gazeteer, generally so ample, did not allude to it. The big house of those parts was Hodnington Hall, Georgian with early Victorian embellishments, as an atrocious steel engraving attested. I carried my difficulty to a neighbour—a deep-rooted tree of that soil—and he gave me a name of a family which conveyed no meaning.

A month or so later—I went again, or it may have been that my car took the road of her own volition. She over-ran the fruitless Downs, threaded every turn of the maze of lanes below the hills, drew through the high-walled woods, impenetrable in their full leaf, came out at the cross-roads where the butler had left me, and a little further on developed an internal trouble which forced me to turn her in on a grass way-waste that cut into a summer-silent hazel wood. So far as I could make sure by the sun and a six-inch Ordnance map, this should be the road flank of that wood which I had first explored from the heights above. I made a mighty serious business of my repairs and a glittering shop of my repair kit, spanners, pump, and the like, which I spread out orderly upon a rug. It was a trap to catch all childhood, for on such a day, I argued, the children would not be far off. When I paused in my work I listened, but the wood was so full of the noises of summer (though the birds had mated) that I could not at first distinguish these from the tread of small cautious feet stealing across the dead leaves. I rang my bell in an alluring manner, but the feet fled, and I repented, for to a child a sudden noise is very real terror. I must have been at work half an hour when I heard in the wood the voice of the blind woman crying: "Children, oh children, where are you?" and the stillness made slow to close on the perfection of that cry. She came towards me, half feeling her way between the tree boles, and though a child it seemed clung to her skirt, it swerved into the leafage like a rabbit as she drew nearer.

"Is that you?" she said, "from the other side of the county?"

"Yes, it's me from the other side of the county."

"Then why didn't you come through the upper woods? They were there just now."

"They were here a few minutes ago. I expect they knew my car had broken down, and came to see the fun."

"Nothing serious, I hope? How do cars break down?"

"In fifty different ways. Only mine has chosen the fifty first."

She laughed merrily at the tiny joke, cooed with delicious laughter, and pushed her hat back.

"Let me hear," she said.

"Wait a moment," I cried, "and I'll get you a cushion."

She set her foot on the rug all covered with spare parts, and stooped above it eagerly. "What delightful things!" The hands through which she saw glanced in the chequered sunlight. "A box here—another box! Why you've arranged them like playing shop!"

"I confess now that I put it out to attract them. I don't need half those things really."

"How nice of you! I heard your bell in the upper wood. You say they were here before that?"

"I'm sure of it. Why are they so shy? That little fellow in blue who was with you just now ought to have got over his fright. He's been watching me like a Red Indian."

"It must have been your bell," she said. "I heard one of them go past me in trouble when I was coming down. They're shy—so shy even with me." She turned her face over her shoulder and cried again: "Children! Oh, children! Look and see!"

"They must have gone off together on their own affairs," I suggested, for there was a murmur behind us of lowered voices broken by the sudden squeaking giggles of childhood. I returned to my tinkerings and she leaned forward, her chin on her hand, listening interestedly.

"How many are they?" I said at last. The work was finished, but I saw no reason to go.

Her forehead puckered a little in thought. "I don't quite know," she said simply. "Sometimes more—sometimes less. They come and stay with me because I love them, you see."

"That must be very jolly," I said, replacing a drawer, and as I spoke I heard the inanity of my answer.

"You—you aren't laughing at me," she cried. "I—I haven't any of my own. I never married. People laugh at me sometimes about them because— because——"

"Because they're savages," I returned. "It's nothing to fret for. That sort laugh at everything that isn't in their own fat lives."

"I don't know. How should I? I only don't like being laughed at about *them*. It hurts; and when one can't see. . . . I don't want to seem silly," her chin quivered like a child's as she spoke, "but we blindies have only one skin, I think. Everything outside hits straight at our souls. It's different with you. You've such good defences in your eyes—looking out—before anyone can really pain you in your soul. People forget that with us."

I was silent reviewing that inexhaustible matter—the more than inherited (since it is also carefully taught) brutality of the Christian peoples, beside which the mere heathendom of the West Coast nigger is clean and restrained. It led me a long distance into myself.

"Don't do that!" she said of a sudden, putting her hands before her eyes.

"What?"

She made a gesture with her hand.

"That! It's—it's all purple and black. Don't! That colour hurts."

"But, how in the world do you know about colours?" I exclaimed, for here was a revelation indeed.

"Colours as colours?" she asked.

"No. *Those* Colours which you saw just now."

"You know as well as I do," she laughed, "else you wouldn't have asked that question. They aren't in the world at all. They're in *you*—when you went so angry."

"D'you mean a dull purplish patch, like port-wine mixed with ink?" I said.

"I've never seen ink or port-wine, but the colours aren't mixed. They are separate—all separate."

"Do you mean black streaks and jags across the purple?"

She nodded. "Yes—if they are like this," and zig-zagged her finger again, "but it's more red than purple—that bad colour."

"And what are the colours at the top of the—whatever you see?"

Slowly she leaned forward and traced on the rug the figure of the Egg itself.

"I see them so," she said, pointing with a grass stem, "white, green, yellow, red, purple, and when people are angry or bad, black across the red— as you were just now."

"Who told you anything about it—in the beginning?" I demanded.

"About the colours? No one. I used to ask what colours were when I was little—in table-covers and curtains and carpets, you see—because some colours hurt me and some made me happy. People told me; and when I got older that was how I saw people." Again she traced the outline of the Egg which it is given to very few of us to see.

"All by yourself?" I repeated.

"All by myself. There wasn't anyone else. I only found out afterwards that other people did not see the Colours."

She leaned against the tree-bole plaiting and unplaiting chance-plucked grass stems. The children in the wood had drawn nearer. I could see them with the tail of my eye frolicking like squirrels.

"Now I am sure you will never laugh at me," she went on after a long silence. "Nor at *them*."

"Goodness! No!" I cried, jolted out of my train of thought. "A man who laughs at a child—unless the child is laughing too—is a heathen!"

"I didn't mean that of course. You'd never laugh *at* children, but I thought—I used to think—that perhaps you might laugh about *them*. So now I beg your pardon. . . . What are you going to laugh at?"

I had made no sound, but she knew.

"At the notion of your begging my pardon. If you had done your duty as a pillar of the state and a landed proprietress you ought to have summoned me for trespass when I barged through your woods the other day. It was disgraceful of me—inexcusable."

She looked at me, her head against the tree trunk—long and steadfastly —this woman who could see the naked soul.

"How curious," she half whispered. "How very curious."

"Why, what have I done?"

"You don't understand . . . and yet you understood about the Colours. Don't you understand?"

She spoke with a passion that nothing had justified, and I faced her bewilderedly as she rose. The children had gathered themselves in a roundel behind a bramble bush. One sleek head bent over something smaller, and the set of the little shoulders told me that fingers were on lips. They too, had some child's tremendous secret. I alone was hopelessly astray there in the broad sunlight.

"No," I said, and shook my head as though the dead eyes could note. "Whatever it is, I don't understand yet. Perhaps I shall later—if you'll let me come again."

"You will come again," she answered. "You will surely come again and walk in the wood."

"Perhaps the children will know me well enough by that time to let me play with them—as a favour. You know what children are like."

"It isn't a matter of favour but of right," she replied, and while I wondered what she meant, a dishevelled woman plunged round the bend of the road, loose-haired, purple, almost lowing with agony as she ran. It was my rude, fat friend of the sweetmeat shop. The blind woman heard and stepped forward. "What is it, Mrs. Madehurst?" she asked.

The woman flung her apron over her head and literally grovelled in the dust, crying that her grandchild was sick to death, that the local doctor was away fishing, that Jenny the mother was at her wit's end, and so forth, with repetitions and bellowings.

"Where's the next nearest doctor?" I asked between paroxysms.

"Madden will tell you. Go round to the house and take him with you. I'll attend to this. Be quick!" She half-supported the fat woman into the shade. In two minutes I was blowing all the horns of Jericho under the front of the House Beautiful, and Madden, in the pantry, rose to the crisis like a butler and a man.

A quarter of an hour at illegal speeds caught us a doctor five miles away. Within the half-hour we had decanted him, much interested in motors, at the door of the sweetmeat shop, and drew up the road to await the verdict.

"Useful things cars," said Madden, all man and no butler. "If I'd had one when mine took sick she wouldn't have died."

"How was it?" I asked.

"Croup. Mrs. Madden was away. No one knew what to do. I drove eight miles in a tax cart for the doctor. She was choked when we came back. This car 'd ha' saved her. She'd have been close on ten now."

"I'm sorry," I said. "I thought you were rather fond of children from what you told me going to the cross-roads the other day."

"Have you seen 'em again, Sir—this mornin'?"

"Yes, but they're well broke to cars. I couldn't get any of them within twenty yards of it."

He looked at me carefully as a scout considers a stranger—not as a menial should lift his eyes to his divinely appointed superior.

"I wonder why," he said just above the breath that he drew.

We waited on. A light wind from the sea wandered up and down the long lines of the woods, and the wayside grasses, whitened already with summer dust, rose and bowed in sallow waves.

A woman, wiping the suds off her arms, came out of the cottage next the sweetmeat shop.

"I've be'n listenin' in de back-yard," she said cheerily. "He says Arthur's unaccountable bad. Did ye hear him shruck just now? Unaccountable bad. I reckon t'will come Jenny's turn to walk in de wood nex' week along Mr. Madden."

"Excuse me, Sir, but your lap-robe is slipping," said Madden deferentially. The woman started, dropped a curtsey, and hurried away.

"What does she mean by 'walking in the wood'?" I asked.

"It must be some saying they use hereabouts. I'm from Norfolk myself," said Madden. "They're an independent lot in this county. She took you for a chauffeur, Sir."

I saw the Doctor come out of the cottage followed by a draggle-tailed wench who clung to his arm as though he could make treaty for her with Death. "Dat sort," she wailed—"dey're just as much to us dat has 'em as if dey was lawful born. Just as much—just as much! An' God he'd be just as pleased if you saved 'un, Doctor. Don't take it from me. Miss Florence will tell ye de very same. Don't leave 'im, Doctor!"

"I know. I know," said the man, "but he'll be quiet for a while now. We'll get the nurse and the medicine as fast as we can." He signalled me to come forward with the car, and I strove not to be privy to what followed; but I saw the girl's face, blotched and frozen with grief, and I felt the hand without a ring clutching at my knees when we moved away.

The Doctor was a man of some humour, for I remember he claimed my car under the Oath of Æsculapius, and used it and me without mercy. First we convoyed Mrs. Madehurst and the blind woman to wait by the sick bed till the nurse should come. Next we invaded a neat county town for prescriptions (the Doctor said the trouble was cerebro-spinal meningitis), and when the County Institute, banked and flanked with scared market cattle, reported itself out of nurses for the moment we literally flung ourselves loose upon the county. We conferred with the owners of great houses—magnates at the ends of overarching avenues whose big-boned womenfolk strode away from their tea-tables to listen to the imperious Doctor. At last a whitehaired lady sitting under a cedar of Lebanon and surrounded by a court of magnificent Borzois—all hostile to motors—gave the Doctor, who received them as from a princess, written orders which we bore many miles at top speed, through a park, to a French nunnery, where we took over in exchange a pallid-faced and trembling Sister. She knelt at the bottom of the tonneau telling her beads without pause till, by short cuts of the Doctor's invention, we had her to the sweetmeat shop once more. It was a long afternoon crowded with mad episodes that rose and dissolved like the dust of our wheels; cross-sections of remote and incomprehensible lives through which we raced at right angles; and I went home in the dusk, wearied out, to dream of the clashing horns of cattle; round-eyed nuns walking in a garden of graves; pleasant tea-parties beneath shaded trees; the carbolic-scented, grey-painted corridors of the County Institute; the steps of shy children in the wood, and the hands that clung to my knees as the motor began to move.

*   *   *   *   *

I had intended to return in a day or two, but it pleased Fate to hold me from that side of the county, on many pretexts, till the elder and the wild rose had fruited. There came at last a brilliant day, swept clear from the south-west, that brought the hills within hand's reach—a day of unstable airs and high filmy clouds. Through no merit of my own I was free, and set the car for the third time on that known road. As I reached the crest of the Downs I felt the soft air change, saw it glaze under the sun; and, looking down at the sea, in that instant beheld the blue of the Channel turn through polished silver and dulled steel to dingy pewter. A laden collier hugging the coast steered outward for deeper water and, across copper-coloured haze, I saw sails rise one by one on the anchored fishing-fleet. In a deep dene behind me an eddy of sudden wind drummed through sheltered oaks, and spun aloft the first day sample of autumn leaves. When I reached the beach road the sea-fog fumed over the brickfields, and the side was telling all the groins of the gale beyond Ushant. In less than an hour summer England vanished in chill grey. We were again the shut island of the North, all the ships of the world bellowing at our perilous gates; and between their outcries ran the piping of bewildered gulls. My cap dripped moisture, the folds of the rug held it in pools or sluiced it away in runnels, and the salt-rime stuck to my lips.

Inland the smell of autumn loaded the thickened fog among the trees, and the drip became a continuous shower. Yet the late flowers—mallow of the wayside, scabious of the field, and dahlia of the garden—showed gay in the midst, and beyond the sea's breath there was little sign of decay in the leaf. Yet in the villages the house doors were all open, and bare-legged, bare-headed children sat at ease on the damp doorsteps to shout "pip-pip" at the stranger.

I made bold to call at the sweetmeat shop, where Mrs. Madehurst met me with a fat woman's hospitable tears. Jenny's child, she said, had died two days after the nun had come. It was, she felt, best out of the way, even though insurance offices, for reasons which she did not pretend to follow, would not willingly insure such stray lives. "Not but what Jenny didn't tend to Arthur as though he'd come all proper at de end of de first year—like Jenny herself." Thanks to Miss Florence, the child had been buried with a pomp which, in Mrs. Madehurst's opinion, more than covered the small irregularity of its birth. She described the coffin, within and without, the glass hearse, and the evergreen lining of the grave.

"But how's the mother?" I asked.

"Jenny? Oh, she'll get over it. I've felt dat way with one or two o' my own. She'll get over. She's walkin' in de wood now."

"In this weather?"

Mrs. Madehurst looked at me with narrowed eyes across the counter.

"I dunno but it opens de 'eart like. Yes, it opens de 'eart. Dat's where losin' and bearin' comes so alike in de long run, we do say."

Now the wisdom of the old wives is greater than that of all the Fathers, and this last oracle sent me thinking so extendedly as I went up the road, that I nearly ran over a woman and a child at the wooded corner by the lodge gates of the House Beautiful.

"Awful weather!" I cried, as I slowed dead for the turn.

"Not so bad," she answered placidly out of the fog. "Mine's used to 'un. You'll find yours indoors, I reckon."

Indoors, Madden received me with professional courtesy, and kind inquiries for the health of the motor, which he would put under cover.

I waited in a still, nut-brown hall, pleasant with late flowers and warmed with a delicious wood fire—a place of good influence and great peace. (Men and women may sometimes, after great effort, achieve a creditable lie; but the house, which is their temple, cannot say anything save the truth of those who have lived in it.) A child's cart and a doll lay on the black-and-white floor, where a rug had been kicked back. I felt that the children had only just hurried away—to hide themselves, most like—in the many turns of the great adzed staircase that climbed statelily out of the hall, or to crouch at gaze behind the lions and roses of the carven gallery above. Then I heard her voice above me, singing as the blind sing—from the soul:—

> In the pleasant orchard-closes.

And all my early summer came back at the call.

> In the pleasant orchard-closes,
>   God bless all our gains say we—
> But may God bless all our losses,
>   Better suits with our degree.

She dropped the marring fifth line, and repeated—

> Better suits with our degree!

I saw her lean over the gallery, her linked hands white as pearl against the oak.

'Is that you—from the other side of the county?" she called.

"Yes, me—from the other side of the county," I answered laughing.

"What a long time before you had to come here again." She ran down the stairs, one hand lightly touching the broad rail. "It's two months and four days. Summer's gone!"

"I meant to come before, but Fate prevented."

"I knew it. Please do something to that fire. They won't let me play with it, but I can feel it's behaving badly. Hit it!"

I looked on either side of the deep fireplace, and found but a half-charred hedge-stake with which I punched a black log into flame.

"It never goes out, day or night," she said, as though explaining. "In case any one comes in with cold toes, you see."

"It's even lovelier inside than it was out," I murmured. The red light poured itself along the age-polished dusky panels till the Tudor roses and lions of the gallery took colour and motion. An old eagle-topped convex mirror gathered the picture into its mysterious heart, distorting afresh the distorted shadows, and curving the gallery lines into the curves of a ship. The day was shutting down in half a gale as the fog turned to stringy scud. Through the uncurtained mullions of the broad window I could see valiant horsemen of the lawn rear and recover against the wind that taunted them with legions of dead leaves.

"Yes, it must be beautiful," she said. "Would you like to go over it? There's still light enough upstairs."

I followed her up the unflinching, wagon-wide staircase to the gallery whence opened the thin fluted Elizabethan doors.

"Feel how they put the latch low down for the sake of the children." She swung a light door inward.

"By the way, where are they?" I asked. "I haven't even heard them to-day."

She did not answer at once. Then, "I can only hear them," she replied softly. "This is one of their rooms—everything ready, you see."

She pointed into a heavily-timbered room. There were little low gate tables and children's chairs. A doll's house, its hooked front half open, faced a great dappled rocking-horse, from whose padded saddle it was but a child's scramble to the broad window-seat overlooking the lawn. A toy gun lay in a corner beside a gilt wooden cannon.

"Surely they've only just gone," I whispered. In the failing light a door creaked cautiously. I heard the rustle of a frock and the patter of feet—quick feet through a room beyond.

"I heard that," she cried triumphantly. "Did you? Children, O children, where are you?"

The voice filled the walls that held it lovingly to the last perfect note, but there came no answering shout such as I had heard in the garden. We hurried on from room to oak-floored room; up a step here, down three steps there; among a maze of passages; always mocked by our quarry. One might as well have tried to work an unstopped warren with a single ferret. There were bolt-holes innumerable—recesses in walls, embrasures of deep slitten windows now darkened, whence they could start up behind us; and abandoned fireplaces, six feet deep in the masonry, as well as the tangle of communicating doors. Above all, they had the twilight for their helper in our game. I had caught one or two joyous chuckles of evasion, and once or twice had seen the silhouette of a child's frock against some darkening window at the end of a passage; but we returned empty-handed to the gallery, just as a middle-aged woman was setting a lamp in its niche.

"No, I haven't seen her either this evening, Miss Florence," I heard her say, "but that Turpin he says he wants to see you about his shed."

"Oh, Mr. Turpin must want to see me very badly. Tell him to come to the hall, Mrs. Madden."

I looked down into the hall whose only light was the dulled fire, and deep in the shadow I saw them at last. They must have slipped down while we were in the passages, and now thought themselves perfectly hidden behind an old gilt leather screen. By child's law, my fruitless chase was as good as an introduction, but since I had taken so much trouble I resolved to force them to come forward later by the simple trick, which children detest, of pretending not to notice them. They lay close, in a little huddle, no more than shadows except when a quick flame betrayed an outline.

"And now we'll have some tea," she said. "I believe I ought to have offered it you at first, but one doesn't arrive at manners somehow when one lives alone and is considered—h'm—peculiar." Then with very pretty scorn, "would you like a lamp to see to eat by?"

"The firelight's much pleasanter, I think." We descended into that delicious gloom and Madden brought tea.

I took my chair in the direction of the screen ready to surprise or be surprised as the game should go, and at her permission, since a hearth is always sacred, bent forward to play with the fire.

"Where do you get these beautiful short faggots from?" I asked idly. "Why, they are tallies!"

"Of course," she said. "As I can't read or write I'm driven back on the early English tally for my accounts. Give me one and I'll tell you what it meant."

I passed her an unburned hazel-tally, about a foot long, and she ran her thumb down the nicks.

"This is the milk-record for the home farm for the month of April last year, in gallons," said she. "I don't know what I should have done without tallies. An old forester of mine taught me the system. It's out of date now for every one else; but my tenants respect it. One of them's coming now to see me. Oh, it doesn't matter. He has no business here out of office hours. He's a greedy, ignorant man—very greedy or—he wouldn't come here after dark."

"Have you much land then?"

"Only a couple of hundred acres in hand, thank goodness. The other six hundred are nearly all let to folk who knew my folk before me, but this Turpin is quite a new man—and a highway robber."

"But are you sure I sha'n't be——?"

"Certainly not. You have the right. He hasn't any children."

"Ah, the children!" I said, and slid my low chair back till it nearly touched the screen that hid them. "I wonder whether they'll come out for me."

There was a murmur of voices—Madden's and a deeper note—at the low, dark side door, and a ginger-headed, canvas-gaitered giant of the unmistakable tenant farmer type stumbled or was pushed in.

"Come to the fire, Mr. Turpin," she said.

"If—if you please, Miss, I'll—I'll be quite as well by the door." He clung to the latch as he spoke like a frightened child. Of a sudden I realised that he was in the grip of some almost overpowering fear.

"Well?"

"About that new shed for the young stock—that was all. These first autumn storms settin' in . . . but I'll come again, Miss." His teeth did not chatter much more than the door latch.

"I think not," she answered levelly. "The new shed—m'm. What did my agent write you on the 15th?"

"I—fancied p'raps that if I came to see you—ma—man to man like, Miss. But——"

His eyes rolled into every corner of the room wide with horror. He half opened the door through which he had entered, but I noticed it shut again—from without and firmly.

"He wrote what I told him," she went on. "You are overstocked already.

Dunnett's Farm never carried more than fifty bullocks—even in Mr. Wright's time. And *he* used cake. You've sixty-seven and you don't cake. You've broken the lease in that respect. You're dragging the heart out of the farm."

"I'm—I'm getting some minerals—superphosphates—next week. I've as good as ordered a truck-load already. I'll go down to the station to-morrow about 'em. Then I can come and see you man to man like, Miss, in the daylight. . . . That gentleman's not going away, is he?" He almost shrieked.

I had only slid the chair a little further back, reaching behind me to tap on the leather of the screen, but he jumped like a rat.

"No. Please attend to me, Mr. Turpin." She turned in her chair and faced him with his back to the door. It was an old and sordid little piece of scheming that she forced from him—his plea for the new cowshed at his landlady's expense, that he might with the covered manure pay his next year's rent out of the valuation after, as she made clear, he had bled the enriched pastures to the bone. I could not but admire the intensity of his greed, when I saw him out-facing for its sake whatever terror it was that ran wet on his forehead.

I ceased to tap the leather—was, indeed, calculating the cost of the shed—when I felt my relaxed hand taken and turned softly between the soft hands of a child. So at last I had triumphed. In a moment I would turn and acquaint myself with those quick-footed wanderers. . . .

The little brushing kiss fell in the centre of my palm—as a gift on which the fingers were, once, expected to close: as the all faithful half-reproachful signal of a waiting child not used to neglect even when grown-ups were busiest—a fragment of the mute code devised very long ago.

Then I knew. And it was as though I had known from the first day when I looked across the lawn at the high window.

I heard the door shut. The woman turned to me in silence, and I felt that she knew.

What time passed after this I cannot say. I was roused by the fall of a log, and mechanically rose to put it back. Then I returned to my place in the chair very close to the screen.

"Now you understand," she whispered, across the packed shadows.

"Yes, I understand—now. Thank you."

"I—I only hear them." She bowed her head in her hands. "I have no right, you know—no other right. I have neither borne nor lost—neither borne nor lost!"

"Be very glad then," said I, for my soul was torn open within me.

"Forgive me!"

She was still, and I went back to my sorrow and my joy.

"It was because I loved them so," she said at last, brokenly. "*That* was why it was, even from the first—even before I knew that they—they were all I should ever have. And I loved them so!"

She stretched out her arms to the shadows and the shadows within the shadow.

"They came because I loved them—because I needed them. I—I must have made them come. Was that wrong, think you?"

"No—no."

"I—I grant you that the toys and—and all that sort of thing were nonsense, but—but I used to so hate empty rooms myself when I was little." She pointed to the gallery. "And the passages all empty. . . . And how could I ever bear the garden door shut? Suppose——"

"Don't! For pity's sake, don't!" I cried. The twilight had brought a cold rain with gusty squalls that plucked at the leaded windows.

"And the same thing with keeping the fire in all night. *I* don't think it so foolish—do you?"

I looked at the broad brick hearth, saw, through tears I believe, that there was no unpassable iron on or near it, and bowed my head.

"I did all that and lots of other things—just to make believe. Then they came. I heard them, but I didn't know that they were not mine by right till Mrs. Madden told me——"

"The butler's wife? What?"

"One of them—I heard—she saw. And knew. Hers! *Not* for me. I didn't know at first. Perhaps I was jealous. Afterwards, I began to understand that it was only because I loved them, not because—— . . . Oh, you *must* bear or lose," she said piteously. "There is no other way—and yet they love me. They must! Don't they?"

There was no sound in the room except the lapping voices of the fire, but we two listened intently, and she at least took comfort from what she heard. She recovered herself and half rose. I sat still in my chair by the screen.

"Don't think me a wretch to whine about myself like this, but—but I'm all in the dark, you know, and *you* can see."

In truth I could see, and my vision confirmed me in my resolve, though that was like the very parting of spirit and flesh. Yet a little longer I would stay since it was the last time.

"You think it is wrong, then?" she cried sharply, though I had said nothing.

"Not for you. A thousand times no. For you it is right. . . . I am grateful to you beyond words. For me it would be wrong. For me only. . . ."

"Why?" she said, but passed her hand before her face as she had done at our second meeting in the wood. "Oh, I see," she went on simply as a child. "For you it would be wrong." Then with a little indrawn laugh, "and, d'you remember, I called you lucky—once—at first. You who must never come here again!"

She left me to sit a little longer by the screen, and I heard the sound of her feet die out along the gallery above.

THE BULL THAT THOUGHT

❧ WESTWARD from a town by the mouths of the Rhône, runs a road so mathematically straight, so barometrically level, that it ranks among the world's measured miles and motorists use it for records.

I had attacked the distance several times, but always with a Mistral blowing, or the unchancy cattle of those parts on the move. But once, running from the East, into a high-piled, almost Egyptian, sunset, there came a night which it would have been sin to have wasted. It was warm with the breath of summer in advance; moonlit till the shadow of every rounded pebble and pointed cypress wind-break lay solid on that vast flat-floored waste; and my Mr. Leggatt, who had slipped out to make sure, reported that the road-surface was unblemished.

"Now," he suggested, "we might see what she'll do under strict road-conditions. She's been pullin' like the Blue de Luxe all day. Unless I'm all off, it's her night out."

We arranged the trial for after dinner—thirty kilometres as near as might be; and twenty-two of them without even a level crossing.

There sat beside me at table d'hôte an elderly, bearded Frenchman wearing the rosette of by no means the lowest grade of the Legion of Honour, who had arrived in a talkative Citroën. I gathered that he had spent much of his life in the French Colonial Service in Annam and Tonquin. When the War came, his years barring him from the front line, he had supervised Chinese woodcutters who, with axe and dynamite, deforested the centre of France for trench-props. He said my chauffeur had told him that I contemplated an experiment. He was interested in cars—had admired mine—would, in short, be greatly indebted to me if I permitted him to assist as an observer. One could not well refuse; and, knowing my Mr. Leggatt, it occurred to me there might also be a bet in the background.

While he went to get his coat, I asked the proprietor his name. "Voiron —Monsieur André Voiron," was the reply. "And his business?" "Mon Dieu! He is Voiron! He is all those things, there!" The proprietor waved his hands at brilliant advertisements on the dining-room walls, which declared that Voiron Frères dealt in wines, agricultural implements, chemical manures, provisions and produce throughout that part of the globe.

He said little for the first five minutes of our trip, and nothing at all for the next ten—it being, as Leggatt had guessed, Esmeralda's night out. But, when her indicator climbed to a certain figure and held there for three blinding kilometres, he expressed himself satisfied, and proposed to me that we should celebrate the event at the hotel. "I keep yonder," said he, "a wine on which I should value your opinion."

On our return, he disappeared for a few minutes, and I heard him rumbling in a cellar. The proprietor presently invited me to the dining-room, where, beneath one frugal light, a table had been set with local dishes of renown. There was, too, a bottle beyond most known sizes, marked black on red, with a date. Monsieur Voiron opened it, and we drank to the health of my car. The velvety, perfumed liquor, between fawn and topaz, neither to sweet nor too dry, creamed in its generous glass. But I knew no wine composed of the whispers of angels' wings, the breath of Eden and the foam and pulse of Youth renewed. So I asked what it might be.

"It is champagne," he said gravely.

"Then what have I been drinking all my life?"

"If you were lucky, before the War, and paid thirty shillings a bottle, it is possible you may have drunk one of our better-class *tisanes*."

"And where does one get this?"

"Here, I am happy to say. Elsewhere, perhaps, it is not so easy. We growers exchange these real wines among ourselves."

I bowed my head in admiration, surrender, and joy. There stood the most ample bottle, and it was not yet eleven o'clock. Doors locked and shutters banged throughout the establishment. Some last servant yawned on his way to bed. Monsieur Voiron opened a window and the moonlight flooded in from a small pebbled court outside. One could almost hear the town of Chambres breathing in its first sleep. Presently, there was a thick noise in the air, the passing of feet and hooves, lowings, and a stifled bark or two. Dust rose over the courtyard wall, followed by the strong smell of cattle.

"They are moving some beasts," said Monsieur Voiron, cocking an ear. "Mine, I think. Yes, I hear Christophe. Our beasts do not like auto-mobiles—so we move at night. You do not know our country—the Crau, here, or the Camargue? I was—I am now, again—of it. All France is good; but this is the best." He spoke, as only a Frenchman can, of his own loved part of his own lovely land.

"For myself, if I were not so involved in all these affairs," he pointed to the advertisements—"I would live on our farm with my cattle, and worship them like a Hindu. You know our cattle of the Camargue, Monsieur. No? It is not an acquaintance to rush upon lightly. There are no beasts like them. They have a mentality superior to that of others. They graze and they ruminate, by choice, facing our Mistral, which is more than some automobiles will do. Also they have in them the potentiality of thought— and when cattle think—I have seen what arrives."

"Are they so clever as all that?" I asked idly.

"Monsieur, when your *sportif* chauffeur camouflaged your limousine so that she resembled one of your Army lorries, I would not believe her capacities. I bet him—ah—two to one—she would not touch ninety kilometres. It was proved that she could. I can give you no proof, but will you believe me if I tell you what a beast who thinks can achieve?"

"After the War," said I spaciously, "everything is credible."

"That is true! Everything inconceivable has happened; but still we learn nothing and we believe nothing. When I was a child in my father's house—before I became a Colonial Administrator—my interest and my affection were among our cattle. We of the old rock live here—have you seen?—in big farms like castles. Indeed, some of them may have been Saracenic. The barns group round them—great white-walled barns, and yards solid as our houses. One gate shuts all. It is a world apart; an administration of all that concerns beasts. It was there I learned something about cattle. You see, they are our playthings in the Camargue and the Crau. The boy measures his strength against the calf that butts him in play among the manure-heaps. He moves in and out among the cows, who are—not so amiable. He rides with the herdsmen in the open to shift the herds. Sooner or later, he meets as bulls the little calves that knocked him over. So it was with me—till it became necessary that I should go to our Colonies." He laughed. "Very necessary. That is a good time in youth, Monsieur, when one does these things which shock our parents. Why is it always Papa who is so shocked and has never heard of such things—and Mamma who supplies the excuses? . . . And when my brother—my elder who stayed and created the business—begged me to return and help him, I resigned my Colonial career gladly enough. I returned to our own lands, and my well-loved, wicked white and yellow cattle of the Camargue and the Crau. My Faith, I could talk of them all night, for this stuff unlocks the heart, without making repentance in the morning. . . . Yes! It was after the War that this happened. There was a calf, among Heaven knows how many of ours— a bull-calf—an infant indistinguishable from his companions. He was sick, and he had been taken up with his mother into the big farmyard at home with us. Naturally the children of our herdsmen practised on him from the first. It is in their blood. The Spaniards make a cult of bull-fighting. Our little devils down here bait bulls as automatically as the English child kicks or throws balls. This calf would chase them with his eyes open, like a cow when she hunts a man. They would take refuge behind our tractors and wine-carts in the centre of the yard: he would chase them in and out as a dog hunts rats. More than that, he would study their psychology, his eyes in their eyes. Yes, he watched their faces to divine which way they would run. He himself, also, would pretend sometimes to charge directly at a boy. Then he would wheel right or left—one could never tell—and knock over some child pressed against a wall who thought himself safe. After this, he would stand over him, knowing that his companions must come to his aid; and when they were all together, waving their jackets across his eyes and pulling his tail, he would scatter them—how he would scatter them! He could kick too, sideways like a cow. He knew his ranges as well as our gunners, and he was as quick on his feet as our Carpentier. I observed him often. Christophe—the man who passed just now—our chief herdsman, who had taught me to ride with our beasts when I was ten—Christophe told me that he was descended from a yellow cow of those days that had chased us once into the marshes. 'He kicks just like her,' said Christophe. 'He can side-kick as he jumps. Have you seen, too, that he is not deceived by the jacket when a boy waves it? He uses it to find the boy. They think they are feeling him. He is feeling them always. He thinks, that one.' I had come to the same conclusion. Yes—the creature was a thinker along the lines necessary to his sport; and he was a humorist also, like so many natural murderers. One knows the type among beasts as well as among men. It possesses a curious truculent mirth—almost indecent but infallibly significant——"

Monsieur Voiron replenished our glasses with the great wine that went better at each descent.

"They kept him for some time in the yards to practise upon. Naturally he became a little brutal; so Christophe turned him out to learn manners among his equals in the grazing lands, where the Camargue joins the Crau. How old was he then? About eight or nine months, I think. We met again a few months later—he and I. I was riding one of our little half-wild horses, along a road of the Crau, when I found myself almost unseated. It was he! He had hidden himself behind a wind-break till we passed, and had then charged my horse from behind. Yes, he had deceived even my little horse! But I recognised him. I gave him the whip across the nose, and I said: 'Apis, for this thou goest to Arles! It was unworthy of thee, between us two.' But that creature had no shame. He went away laughing, like an Apache. If he had dismounted me, I do not think it is I who would have laughed—yearling as he was."

"Why did you want to send him to Arles?" I asked.

"For the bull-ring. When your charming tourists leave us, we institute our little amusements there. Not a real bull-fight, you understand, but young bulls with padded horns, and our boys from hereabouts and in the city, go to play with them. Naturally, before we send them we try them in our yards at home. So we brought up Apis from his pastures. He knew at once that he was among the friends of his youth—he almost shook hands with them—and he submitted like an angel to padding his horns. He investigated the carts and tractors in the yards, to choose his lines of defence and attack. And then—he attacked with an *élan*, and he defended with a tenacity and fore-thought that delighted us. In truth, we were so pleased that I fear we tres-passed upon his patience. We desired him to repeat himself, which no true artist will tolerate. But he gave us fair warning. He went out to the centre of the yard, where there was some dry earth; he kneeled down and—you have seen a calf whose horns fret him thrusting and rooting into a bank? He did just that, very deliberately, till he had rubbed the pads off his horns. Then he rose, dancing on those wonderful feet that twinkled, and he said: 'Now, my friends, the buttons are off the foils. Who begins?' We understood. We finished at once. He was turned out again on the pastures till it should be time to amuse them at our little metropolis. But, some time before he went to Arles—yes, I think I have it correctly—Christophe, who had been out on the Crau, informed me that Apis had assassinated a young bull who had given signs of developing into a rival. That happens, of course, and our herdsmen should prevent it. But Apis had killed in his own style—at dusk, from the ambush of a wind-break—by an oblique charge from behind which knocked the other over. He had then disembowelled him. All very possible, *but*—the murder accomplished—Apis went to the bank of a wind-break, knelt, and carefully, as he had in our yard, cleaned his horns in the earth. Christophe, who had never seen such a thing, at once borrowed (do you know, it is most efficacious when taken that way?) some Holy Water from our little chapel in those pastures, sprinkled Apis (whom it did not affect), and rode in to tell me. It was obvious that a thinker of that bull's type would also be meticulous in his toilette; so, when he was sent to Arles, I warned our consignees to exercise caution with him. Happily, the change of scene, the music, the general attention, and the meeting again with old friends— all our bad boys attended—agreeably distracted him. He became for the time a pure *farceur* again; but his wheelings, his rushes, his rat-huntings were more superb than ever. There was in them now, you understand, a breadth of technique that comes of reasoned art, and, above all, the passion that arrives after experience. Oh, he had learned, out there on the Crau! At the end of his little turn, he was, according to local rules, to be handled in all respects except for the sword, which was a stick, as a professional bull who must die. He was manœuvred into, or he posed himself in, the proper attitude; made his rush; received the point on his shoulder and then—turned about and cantered toward the door by which he had entered the arena. He said to the world: 'My friends, the representation is ended. I thank you for your applause. I go to repose myself.' But our Arlesians, who are—not so clever as some, demanded an encore, and Apis was headed back again. We others from his country, we knew what would happen. He went to the centre of the ring, kneeled, and, slowly, with full parade, plunged his horns alternately in the dirt till the pads came off. Christophe shouts: 'Leave him alone, you straight-nosed imbeciles! Leave him before you must.' But they required emotion; for Rome has always debauched her loved Provincia with bread and circuses. It was given. Have you, Monsieur, ever seen a servant, with pan and broom, sweeping round the baseboard of a room? In a half-minute Apis has them all swept out and over the barrier. Then he demands once more that the door shall be opened to him. It is opened and he retires as though— which truly, is the case—loaded with laurels."

Monsieur Voiron refilled the glasses, and allowed himself a cigarette, which he puffed for some time.

"And afterwards?" I said.

"I am arranging it in my mind. It is difficult to do it justice. Afterwards —yes, afterwards—Apis returned to his pastures and his mistresses and I to my business. I am no longer a scandalous old 'sportif' in shirtsleeves howling encouragement to the yellow son of a cow. I revert to Voiron Frères—wines, chemical manures, *et cetera*. And next year, through some chicane which I have not the leisure to unravel, and also, thanks to our patriarchal system of paying our older men out of the increase of the herds, old Christophe possesses himself of Apis. Oh, yes, he proves it through descent from a certain cow that my father had given his father before the Republic. Beware, Monsieur, of the memory of the illiterate man! An ancestor of Christophe had been a soldier under our Soult against your Beresford, near Bayonne. He fell into the hands of Spanish guerrillas. Christophe and his wife used to tell me the details on certain Saints' Days when I was a child. Now, as compared with our recent war, Soult's campaign and retreat across the Bidassoa——"

"But did you allow Christophe just to annex the bull?" I demanded.

"You do not know Christophe. He had sold him to the Spaniards before he informed me. The Spaniards pay in coin—douros of very pure silver. Our peasants mistrust our paper. You know the saying: 'A thousand francs paper; eight hundred metal, and the cow is yours.' Yes, Christophe sold Apis, who was then two and a half years old, and to Christophe's knowledge thrice at least an assassin."

"How was that?" I said.

"Oh, his own kind only; and always, Christophe told me, by the same oblique rush from behind, the same sideways overthrow, and the same swift disembowelment, followed by this levitical cleaning of the horns. In human life he would have kept a manicurist—this Minotaur. And so, Apis disappears from our country. That does not trouble me. I know in due time I shall be advised. Why? Because, in this land, Monsieur, not a hoof moves between Berre and the Saintes Maries without the knowledge of specialists such as Christophe. The beasts are the substance, and the drama of their lives to them. So when Christophe tells me, a little before Easter Sunday, that Apis makes his début in the bull-ring of a small Catalan town on the road to Barcelona, it is only to pack my car and trundle there across the frontier with him. The place lacked importance and manufactures, but it had produced a matador of some reputation, who was condescending to show his art in his native town. They were even running one special train to the place. Now our French railway system is only execrable, but the Spanish——"

"You went down by road, didn't you?" said I.

"Naturally. It was not too good. Villamarti was the matador's name. He proposed to kill two bulls for the honour of his birthplace. Apis, Christophe told me, would be his second. It was an interesting trip, and that little city by the sea was ravishing. Their bull-ring dates from the middle of the seventeenth century. It is full of feeling. The ceremonial too—when the horsemen enter and ask the Mayor in his box to throw down the keys of the bull-ring—that was exquisitely conceived. You know, if the keys are caught in the horseman's hat, it is considered a good omen. They were perfectly caught. Our seats were in the front row beside the gates where the bulls enter, so we saw everything.

"Villamarti's first bull was not too badly killed. The second matador, whose name escapes me, killed his without distinction—a foil to Villamarti.

And the third, Chisto, a laborious, middle-aged professional who had never risen beyond a certain dull competence, was equally of the background. Oh, they are as jealous as the girls of the Comédie Française, these matadors! Villamarti's troupe stood ready for his second bull. The gates opened, and we saw Apis, beautifully balanced on his feet, peer coquettishly round the corner, as though he were at home. A picador—a mounted man with the long lance-goad—stood near the barrier on his right. He had not even troubled to turn his horse, for the capeadors—the men with the cloaks— were advancing to play Apis—to feel his psychology and intentions, according to the rules that are made for bulls who do not think. . . . I did not realise the murder before it was accomplished! The wheel, the rush, the oblique charge from behind, the fall of horse and man were simultaneous. Apis leaped the horse, with whom he had no quarrel, and alighted, all four feet together (it was enough), between the man's shoulders, changed his beautiful feet on the carcass, and was away, pretending to fall nearly on his nose. Do you follow me? In that instant, by that stumble, he produced the impression that his adorable assassination was a mere bestial blunder. Then, Monsieur, I began to comprehend that it was an artist we had to deal with. He did not stand over the body to draw the rest of the troupe. He chose to reserve that trick. He let the attendants bear out the dead, and went on to amuse himself among the capeadors. Now to Apis, trained among our children in the yards, the cloak was simply a guide to the boy behind it. He pursued, you understand, the person, not the propaganda—the proprietor, not the journal. If a third of our electors of France were as wise, my friend! . . . But it was done leisurely, with humour and a touch of truculence. He romped after one man's cloak as a clumsy dog might do, but I observed that he kept the man on his terrible left side. Christophe whispered to me: 'Wait for his mother's kick. When he has made the fellow confident it will arrive.' It arrived in the middle of a gambol. My God! He lashed out in the air as he frisked. The man dropped like a sack, lifted one hand a little towards his head, and—that was all. So you see, a body was again at his disposition; a second time the cloaks ran up to draw him off, but a second time, Apis refused his grand scene. A second time he acted that his murder was accident and—he convinced his audience! It was as though he had knocked over a bridge-gate in the marshes by mistake. Unbelievable? I saw it."

The memory sent Monsieur Voiron again to the champagne, and I accompanied him.

"But Apis was not the sole artist present. They say Villamarti comes of a family of actors. I saw him regard Apis with a new eye. He, to, began to understand. He took his cloak and moved out to play him before they should bring on another picador. He had his reputation. Perhaps Apis knew it. Perhaps Villamarti reminded him of some boy with whom he had practised at home. At any rate Apis permitted it—up to a certain point; but he did not allow Villamarti the stage. He cramped him throughout. He dived and plunged clumsily and slowly, but always with menace and always closing in. We could see that the man was conforming to the bull—not the bull to the man; for Apis was playing him towards the centre of the ring, and, in a little while—I watched his face—Villamarti knew it. But I could not fathom the creature's motive. 'Wait,' said old Christophe. 'He wants that picador on the white horse yonder. When he reaches his proper distance he will get him. Villamarti is his cover. He used me once that way.' And so it was, my friend! With the clang of one of our own Seventy-fives, Apis dismissed Villamarti with his chest—breasted him over—and had arrived at his objective near the barrier. The same oblique charge; the head carried low for the sweep of the horns; the immense sideways fall of the horse, broken-legged and half-paralysed; the senseless man on the ground and—behold Apis between them, backed against the barrier—his right covered by the horse; his left by the body of the man at his feet. The simplicity of it! Lacking the carts and tractors of his early parade-grounds he, being a genius, had extemporised with the materials at hand, and dug himself in. The troupe closed up again, their left wing broken by the kicking horse, their right immobilised by the man's body which Apis bestrode with significance. Villamarti almost threw himself between the horns, but—it was more an appeal than an attack. Apis refused him. He held his base. A picador was sent at him—necessarily from the front, which alone was open. Apis charged—he who, till then, you realise, had not used the horn! The horse went over backwards, the man half beneath him. Apis halted, hooked him under the heart, and threw him to the barrier. He heard his head crack, but he was dead before he hit the wood. There was no demonstration from the audience. They, also, had begun to realise this Foch among bulls! The arena occupied itself again with the dead. Two of the troupe irresolutely tried to play him—God knows in what hope! —but he moved out to the centre of the ring. 'Look!' said Christophe. 'Now he goes to clean himself. That always frightened me.' He knelt down; he began to clean his horns. The earth was hard. He worried at it in an ecstasy of absorption. As he laid his head along and rattled his ears, it was as though he were interrogating the Devils themselves upon their secrets, and always saying impatiently: 'Yes, I know that—and *that*—and *that!* Tell me more— *more!*' In the silence that covered us, a woman cried: 'He digs a grave! Oh, Saints, he digs a grave!' Some others echoed this—not loudly—as a wave echoes in a grotto of the sea.

"And when his horns were cleaned, he rose up and studied poor Villamarti's troupe, eyes in eyes, one by one, with the gravity of an equal in intellect and the remote and merciless resolution of a master in his art. This was more terrifying than his toilette."

"And they—Villamarti's men?" I asked.

"Like the audience, were dominated. They had ceased to posture, or stamp, or address insults to him. They conformed to him. The two other matadors stared. Only Chisto, the oldest, broke silence with some call or other, and Apis turned his head towards him. Otherwise he was isolated, immobile—sombre—meditating on those at his mercy. Ah!

"For some reason the trumpet sounded for the *banderillas*—those gay hooked darts that are planted in the shoulders of bulls who do not think, after their neck-muscles are tired by lifting horses. When such bulls feel the pain, they check for an instant, and, in that instant, the men step gracefully aside. Villamarti's banderillero answered the trumpet mechanically—like one condemned. He stood out, poised the darts and stammered the usual patter of invitation. . . . And after? I do not assert that Apis shrugged his shoulders, but he reduced the episode to its lowest elements, as could only a bull of Gaul. With his truculence was mingled always—owing to the shortness of his tail—a certain Rabelaisian abandon, especially when viewed from the rear. Christophe had often commented upon it. Now, Apis brought that quality into play. He circulated round that boy, forcing him to break up his beautiful poses. He studied him from various angles, like an incompetent photographer. He presented to him every portion his anatomy except his shoulders. At intervals he feigned to run in upon him. My God, he was cruel! But his motive was obvious. He was playing for a laugh from the spectators which should synchronise with the fracture of the human morale. It was achieved. The boy turned and ran towards the barrier. Apis was on him before the laugh ceased; passed him; headed him—what do I say?—herded him off to the left, his horns beside and a little in front of his chest: he did not intend him to escape into a refuge. Some of the troupe would have closed in, but Villamarti cried: 'If he wants him he will take him. Stand!' They stood. Whether the boy slipped or Apis nosed him over I could not see. But he dropped, sobbing. Apis halted like a car with four brakes, struck a pose, smelt him very completely and turned away. It was dismissal more ignominious than degradation at the head of one's battalion. The representation was finished. Remained only for Apis to clear his stage of the subordinate characters.

"Ah! His gesture then! He gave a dramatic start—this Cyrano of the Camargue—as though he was aware of them for the first time. He moved. All their beautiful breeches twinkled for an instant along the top of the barrier. He held the stage alone! But Christophe and I, we trembled! For, observe, he had now involved himself in a stupendous drama of which he only could supply the third act. And, except for an audience on the razor-edge of emotion, he had exhausted his material. Molière himself—we have forgotten, my friend, to drink to the health of that great soul—might have been at a loss. And Tragedy is but a step behind Failure. We could see the four or five Civil Guards, who are sent always to keep order, fingering the breeches of their rifles. They were but waiting a word from the Mayor to fire on him, as they do sometimes at a bull who leaps the barrier among the spectators. They would, of course, have killed or wounded several people—but that would not have saved Apis."

Monsieur Voiron drowned the thought at once, and wiped his beard.

"At that moment Fate—the Genius of France, if you will—sent to assist in the incomparable finale, none other than Chisto, the eldest, and, I should have said (but never again will I judge!) the least inspired of all; mediocrity itself but, at heart—and it is the heart that conquers always, my friend—at heart an artist. He descended stiffly into the arena, alone and assured. Apis regarded him, his eyes in his eyes. The man took stance, with his cloak, and called to the bull as to an equal: 'Now, Señor, we will show these honourable caballeros something together.' He advanced thus against this thinker who at a plunge—a kick—a thrust—could, we all knew, have extinguished him. My dear friend, I wish I could convey to you something of the unaffected bonhomie, the humour, the delicacy, the consideration bordering on respect even, with which Apis, the supreme artist, responded to this invitation. It was the Master, wearied after a strenuous hour in the atelier, unbuttoned and at ease with some not inexpert but limited disciple. The telepathy was instantaneous between them. And for good reason! Christophe said to me: 'All's well. That Chisto began among the bulls. I was sure of it when I heard him call just now. He has been a herdsman. He'll pull it off.' There was a little feeling and adjustment, at first, for mutual distances and allowances.

"Oh, yes! And here occurred a gross impertinence of Villamarti. He had, after an interval, followed Chisto—to retrieve his reputation. My Faith! I can conceive the elder Dumas slamming his door on an intruder precisely as Apis did. He raced Villamarti into the nearest refuge at once. He stamped his feet outside it, and he snorted: 'Go! I am engaged with an artist!' Villamarti went—his reputation left behind for ever.

"Apis returned to Chisto saying: 'Forgive the interruption. I am not always master of my time, but you were about to observe, my dear confrère . . . ?' Then the play began. Out of compliment to Chisto, Apis chose as his objective (every bull varies in this respect) the inner edge of the cloak—that nearest to the man's body. This allows but a few millimetres clearance in charging. But Apis trusted himself as Chisto trusted him, and, this time, he conformed to the man, with inimitable judgment and temper. He allowed himself to be played into the shadow or the sun, as the delighted audience demanded. He raged enormously; he feigned defeat; he despaired in statuesque abandon, and thence flashed into fresh paroxysms of wrath—but always with the detachment of the true artist who knows he is but the vessel of an emotion whence others, not he, must drink. And never once did he forget that honest Chisto's cloak was to him the gauge by which to spare even a hair on the skin. He inspired Chisto too. My God! His youth returned to that meritorious beef-sticker—the desire, the grace, and the beauty of his early dreams. One could almost see that girl of the past for whom he was rising, rising to these present heights of skill and daring. It was his hour too—a miraculous hour of dawn returned to gild the sunset. All he knew was at Apis' disposition. Apis acknowledged it with all that he had learned at home, at Arles and in his lonely murders on our grazing-grounds. He flowed round Chisto like a river of death—round his knees, leaping at his shoulders, kicking just clear of one side or the other of his head; behind his back hissing as he shaved by; and once or twice—inimitable!—he reared wholly up before him while Chisto slipped back from beneath the avalanche of that instructed body. Those two, my dear friend, held five thousand people dumb with no sound but of their breathings—regular as pumps. It was unbearable. Beast and man realised together that we needed a change of note—a *détente*. They relaxed to pure buffoonery. Chisto fell back and talked to him outrageously. Apis pretended he had never heard such language. The audience howled with delight. Chisto slapped him; he took liberties with his short tail, to the end of which he clung while Apis pirouetted; he played about him in all postures; he had become the herdsman again—gross, careless, brutal, but comprehending. Yet Apis was always the more consummate clown. All that time (Christophe and I saw it) Apis drew off towards the gates of the *toril* where so many bulls enter but—have you ever heard of one that returned? We knew that Apis knew that as he had saved Chisto, so Chisto would save him. Life is sweet to us all; to the artist who lives many lives in one, sweetest. Chisto did not fail him. At the last, when none could laugh any longer, the man threw his cape across the bull's back, his arm round his neck. He flung up a hand at the gate, as Villamarti, young and commanding but *not* a herdsman, might have raised it, and he cried: 'Gentlemen, open to me and my honourable little donkey.' They opened—I have misjudged Spaniards in my time!—those gates opened to the man and the bull together, and closed behind them. And then? From the Mayor to the Guarda Civile they went mad for five minutes, till the trumpets blew and the fifth bull rushed out—an unthinking black Andalusian. I suppose some one killed him. My friend, my very dear friend, to whom I have opened my heart, I confess that I did not watch. Christophe and I we were weeping together like children of the same Mother. Shall we drink to Her?"

AN HABITATION ENFORCED

My friend, if cause doth wrest thee,
Ere folly hath much oppressed thee,
Far from acquaintance kest thee
Where country may digest thee . . .
Thank God that so hath blessed thee,
And sit down, Robin, and rest thee.

THOMAS TUSSER

&§ IT CAME without warning, at the very hour his hand was outstretched
to crumple the Holz and Gunsberg Combine. The New York doctors called
it overwork, and he lay in a darkened room, one ankle crossed above the other,
tongue pressed into palate, wondering whether the next brain-surge of prickly
fires would drive his soul from all anchorages. At last they gave judgment.
With care he might in two years return to the arena, but for the present he
must go across the water and do no work whatever. He accepted the terms.
It was capitulation; but the Combine that had shivered beneath his knife
gave him all the honours of war. Gunsberg himself, full of condolences, came
to the steamer and filled the Chapins' suite of cabins with overwhelming
flower-works.

"Smilax," said George Chapin when he saw them. "Fitz is right. I'm
dead; only I don't see why he left out the 'In Memoriam' on the ribbons!"

"Nonsense!" his wife answered, and poured him his tincture. "You'll
be back before you can think."

He looked at himself in the mirror, surprised that his face had not been
branded by the hells of the past three months. The noise of the decks worried
him, and he lay down, his tongue only a little pressed against his palate.

An hour later he said: "Sophie, I feel sorry about taking you away from
everything like this. I—I suppose we're the two loneliest people on God's
earth to-night."

Said Sophie his wife, and kissed him: "Isn't it something to you that
we're going together?"

They drifted about Europe for months—sometimes alone, sometimes
with chance-met gipsies of their own land. From the North Cape to the
Blue Grotto at Capri they wandered, because the next steamer headed that
way, or because some one had set them on the road. The doctors had warned
Sophie that Chapin was not to take interest even in other men's interests;
but a familiar sensation at the back of the neck after one hour's keen talk
with a Nauheimed railway magnate saved her any trouble. He nearly wept.

"And I'm over thirty," he cried. "With all I meant to do!"

"Let's call it a honeymoon," said Sophie. "D'you know, in all the six years we've been married, you've never told me what you meant to do with your life?"

"With my life? What's the use? It's finished now." Sophie looked up quickly from the Bay of Naples. "As far as my business goes, I shall have to live on my rents like that architect at San Moritz."

"You'll get better if you don't worry; and even if it takes time, there are worse things than—— How much have you?"

"Between four and five million. But it isn't the money. You know it isn't. It's the principle. How could you respect me? You never did, the first year after we married, till I went to work like the others. Our tradition and upbringing are against it. We can't accept *those* ideals."

"Well, I suppose I married you for some sort of ideal," she answered, and they returned to their forty-third hotel.

In England they missed the alien tongues of Continental streets that reminded them of their own polyglot cities. In England all men spoke one tongue, speciously like American to the ear, but on cross-examination unintelligible.

"Ah, but you have not seen England," said a lady with iron-grey hair. They had met her in Vienna, Bayreuth, and Florence, and were grateful to find her again at Claridge's, for she commanded situations, and knew where prescriptions are most carefully made up. "You ought to take an interest in the home of our ancestors—as I do."

"I've tried for a week, Mrs. Shonts," said Sophie, "but I never get any further than tipping German waiters."

"These men are not the true type," Mrs. Shonts went on. "I know where you should go."

Chapin pricked up his ears, anxious to run anywhere from the streets on which quick men, something of his kidney, did the business denied to him.

"We hear and we obey, Mrs. Shonts," said Sophie, feeling his unrest as he drank the loathed British tea.

Mrs. Shonts smiled, and took them in hand. She wrote widely and telegraphed far on their behalf till, armed with her letter of introduction, she drove them into that wilderness which is reached from an ash-barrel of a station called Charing Cross. They were to go to Rocketts—the farm of one Cloke, in the southern counties—where, she assured them, they would meet the genuine England of folklore and song.

Rocketts they found after some hours, four miles from a station, and, so far as they could judge in the bumpy darkness, twice as many from a road. Trees, kine, and the outlines of barns showed shadowy about them when they alighted, and Mr. and Mrs. Cloke, at the open door of a deep stone-floored kitchen, made them shyly welcome. They lay in an attic beneath a wavy whitewashed ceiling, and because it rained, a wood fire was made in an iron basket on a brick hearth, and they fell asleep to the chirping of mice and the whimper of flames.

When they woke it was a fair day, full of the noises of birds, the smell of box lavender, and fried bacon, mixed with an elemental smell they had never met before.

"This," said Sophie, nearly pushing out the thin casement in an attempt to see round the corner, "is—what did the hack—cabman say to the railway porter about my trunk—'quite on the top?'"

"No; 'a little bit of all right.' I feel farther away from anywhere than I've ever felt in my life. We must find out where the telegraph office is."

"Who cares?" said Sophie, wandering about, hairbrush in hand, to admire the illustrated weekly pictures pasted on door and cupboard.

But there was no rest for the alien soul till he had made sure of the telegraph office. He asked the Clokes's daughter, laying breakfast, while Sophie plunged her face in the lavender bush outside the low window.

"Go to the stile a-top o' the Barn field," said Mary, "and look across Pardons to the next spire. It's directly under. You can't miss it—not if you keep to the footpath. My sister's the telegraphist there. But you're in the three-mile radius, sir. The boy delivers telegrams directly to this door from Pardons village."

"One has to take a good deal on trust in this country," he murmured.

Sophie looked at the close turf, scarred only with last night's wheels, at two ruts which wound round a rickyard, and at the circle of still orchard about the half-timbered house.

"What's the matter with it?" she said. "Telegrams delivered to the Vale of Avalon, of course," and she beckoned in an earnest-eyed hound of engaging manners and no engagements, who answered, at times, to the name of Rambler. He led them, after breakfast, to the rise behind the house where the stile stood against the skyline, and, "I wonder what we shall find now," said Sophie, frankly prancing with joy on the grass.

It was a slope of gap-hedged fields possessed to their centres by clumps of brambles. Gates were not, and the rabbit-mined, cattle-rubbed posts leaned out and in. A narrow path doubled among the bushes, scores of white tails twinkled before the racing hound, and a hawk rose, whistling shrilly.

"No roads, no nothing!" said Sophie, her short skirt hooked by briers. "I thought all England was a garden. There's your spire, George, across the valley. How curious!"

They walked toward it through an all-abandoned land. Here they found the ghost of a patch of lucerne that had refused to die: there a harsh fallow surrendered to yard-high thistles; and here a breadth of rampant kelk feigning to be lawful crop. In the ungrazed pastures swaths of dead stuff caught their feet, and the ground beneath glistened with sweat. At the bottom of the valley a little brook had undermined its footbridge, and frothed in the wreckage. But there stood great woods on the slopes beyond—old, tall, and brilliant, like unfaded tapestries against the walls of a ruined house.

"All this within a hundred miles of London," he said. "'Looks as if it had had nervous prostration, too." The footpath turned the shoulder of a slope, through a thicket of rank rhododendrons, and crossed what had once been a carriage drive, which ended in the shadow of two gigantic holm-oaks.

"A house!" said Sophie, in a whisper. "A Colonial house!"

Behind the blue-green of the twin trees rose a dark-bluish brick Georgian pile, with a shell-shaped fan-light over its pillared door. The hound had gone off on his own foolish quests. Except for some stir in the branches and the flight of four startled magpies, there was neither life nor sound about the square house, but it looked out of its long windows most friendlily.

"Cha-armed to meet you, I'm sure," said Sophie, and curtsied to the ground. "George, this is history I can understand. We began here." She curtsied again.

The June sunshine twinkled on all the lights. It was as though an old lady, wise in three generations' experience, but for the present sitting out, bent to listen to her flushed and eager grandchild.

"I *must* look!" Sophie tiptoed to a window, and shaded her eyes with her hand. "Oh, this room's half-full of cotton-bales—wool, I suppose! But I can see a bit of the mantelpiece. George, do come! Isn't that some one?"

She fell back behind her husband. The front door opened slowly, to show the hound, his nose white with milk, in charge of an ancient of days clad in a blue linen ephod curiously gathered on breast and shoulders.

"Certainly," said George, half aloud. "Father Time himself. This is where he lives, Sophie."

"We came," said Sophie weakly. "Can we see the house? I'm afraid that's our dog."

"No, 'tis Rambler," said the old man. "He's been at my swill-pail again. Staying at Rocketts, be ye? Come in. Ah! you runagate!"

The hound broke from him, and he tottered after him down the drive. They entered the hall—just such a high light hall as such a house should own. A slim-balustered staircase, wide and shallow and once creamy-white, climbed out of it under a long oval window. On either side delicately moulded doors gave on to wool-lumbered rooms, whose sea-green mantelpieces were adorned with nymphs, scrolls, and Cupids in low relief.

"What's the firm that makes these things?" cried Sophie, enraptured. "Oh, I forgot! These must be the originals. Adams, is it? I never dreamed of anything like that steel-cut fender. Does he mean us to go everywhere?"

"He's catching the dog," said George, looking out. "We don't count."

They explored the first or ground floor, delighted as children playing burglars.

"This is like all England," she said at last. "Wonderful, but no explanation. You're expected to know it beforehand. Now, let's try upstairs."

The stairs never creaked beneath their feet. From the broad landing they entered a long, green-panelled room lighted by three full-length windows, which overlooked the forlorn wreck of a terraced garden, and wooded slopes beyond.

"The drawing-room, of course." Sophie swam up and down it. "That mantelpiece—Orpheus and Eurydice—is the best of them all. Isn't it marvellous? Why, the room seems furnished with nothing in it! How's that, George?"

"It's the proportions. I've noticed it."

"I saw a Heppelwhite couch once"—Sophie laid her finger to her flushed cheek and considered. "With two of them—one on each side—you wouldn't need anything else. Except—there must be one perfect mirror over that mantelpiece."

"Look at that view. It's a framed Constable," her husband cried.

"No; it's a Morland—a parody of a Morland. But about that couch, George. Don't you think Empire might be better than Heppelwhite? Dull gold against that pale green? It's a pity they don't make spinets nowadays."

"I believe you can get them. Look at that oak wood behind the pines."

" 'While you sat and played toccatas stately at the clavichord,' " Sophie hummed, and, head on one side, nodded to where the perfect mirror should hang.

Then they found bedrooms with dressing-rooms and powdering-closets, and steps leading up and down—boxes of rooms, round, square, and octagonal, with enriched ceilings and chased door-locks.

"Now about servants. Oh!" She had darted up the last stairs to the chequered darkness of the top floor, where loose tiles lay among broken laths, and the walls were scrawled with names, sentiments, and hop records. "They've been keeping pigeons here," she cried.

"And you could drive a buggy through the roof anywhere," said George.

"That's what I say," the old man cried below them on the stairs. "Not a dry place for my pigeons at all."

"But why was it allowed to get like this?" said Sophie.

" 'Tis with housen as teeth," he replied. "Let 'em go too far, and there's nothing to be done. Time was they was minded to sell her, but none would buy. She was too far away along from any place. Time was they'd ha' lived here theyselves, but they took and died."

"Here?" Sophie moved beneath the light of a hole in the roof.

"Nah—none dies here excep' falling off ricks and such. In London they died." He plucked a lock of wool from his blue smock. "They was no staple—neither the Elphicks nor the Moones. Shart and brittle all of 'em. Dead they be seventeen year, for I've been here caretakin' twenty-five."

"Who does all the wool belong to downstairs?" George asked.

"To the estate. I'll show you the back parts if ye like. You're from America, ain't ye? I've had a son there once myself." They followed him down the main stairway. He paused at the turn and swept one hand toward the wall. "Plenty room here for your coffin to come down. Seven foot and three men at each end wouldn't brist the paint. If I die in my bed they'll 'ave to up-end me like a milk-can. 'Tis all luck, d'ye see?"

He led them on and on, through a maze of back-kitchens, dairies, larders, and sculleries, that melted along covered ways into a farm-house, visibly older than the main building, which again rambled out among barns, byres, pig-pens, stalls and stables to the dead fields behind.

"Somehow," said Sophie, sitting exhausted on an ancient well-curb— "somehow one wouldn't insult these lovely old things by filling them with hay."

George looked at long stone walls upholding reaches of silvery-oak weather-boarding; buttresses of mixed flint and bricks; outside stairs, stone upon arched stone; curves of thatch where grass sprouted; roundels of house-leeked tiles, and a huge paved yard populated by two cows and the repentant Rambler. He had not thought of himself or of the telegraph office for two and a half hours.

"But why," said Sophie, as they went back through the crater of stricken fields,—"why is one expected to know everything in England? Why do they never tell?"

"You mean about the Elphicks and the Moones?" he answered.

"Yes—and the lawyers and the estate. Who are they? I wonder whether those painted floors in the green room were real oak. Don't you like us exploring things together—better than Pompeii?"

George turned once more to look at the view. "Eight hundred acres go with the house—the old man told me. Five farms altogether. Rocketts is one of 'em."

"I like Mrs. Cloke. But what is the old house called?"

George laughed. "That's one of the things you're expected to know. He never told me."

The Clokes were more communicative. That evening and thereafter for a week they gave the Chapins the official history, as one gives it to lodgers, of Friars Pardon—the house and its five farms. But Sophie asked so many questions, and George was so humanly interested, that, as confidence in the strangers grew, they launched, with observed and acquired detail, into the lives and deaths and doings of the Elphicks and the Moones and their collaterals, the Haylings and the Torrells. It was a tale told serially by Cloke in the barn, or his wife in the dairy, the last chapters reserved for the kitchen o' nights by the big fire, when the two had been half the day exploring about the house, where old Iggulden, of the blue smock, cackled and chuckled to see them. The motives that swayed the characters were beyond their comprehension; the fates that shifted them were gods they had never met; the sidelights Mrs. Cloke threw on act and incident were more amazing than anything in the record. Therefore the Chapins listened delightedly, and blessed Mrs. Shonts.

"But why—why—why—did So-and-so do so-and-so?" Sophie would demand from her seat by the pothook; and Mrs. Cloke would answer, smoothing her knees, "For the sake of the place."

"I give it up," said George one night in their own room. "People don't seem to matter in this country compared to the places they live in. The way *she* tells it, Friars Pardon was a sort of Moloch."

"Poor old thing!" They had been walking round the farms as usual before tea. "No wonder they loved it. Think of the sacrifices they made for it. Jane Elphick married the younger Torrell to keep it in the family. The octagonal room with the moulded ceiling next to the big bedroom was hers. Now what did *he* tell you while he was feeding the pigs?" said Sophie.

"About the Torrell cousins and the uncle who died in Java. They lived at Burnt House—behind High Pardons, where that brook is all blocked up."

"No; Burnt House is under High Pardons Wood, *before* you come to Gale Anstey," Sophie corrected.

"Well, old man Cloke said——"

Sophie threw open the door and called down into the kitchen, where the Clokes were covering the fire: "Mrs. Cloke, isn't Burnt House under High Pardons?"

"Yes, my dear, of course," the soft voice answered absently. A cough. "I beg your pardon, Madam. What was it you said?"

"Never mind. I prefer it the other way," Sophie laughed, and George re-told the missing chapter as she sat on the bed.

"Here to-day an' gone to-morrow," said Cloke warningly. "They've paid their first month, but we've only that Mrs. Shonts's letter for guarantee."

"None she sent never cheated us yet. It slipped out before I thought. She's a most humane young lady. They'll be going away in a little. An' you've talked a lot too, Alfred."

"Yes, but the Elphicks are all dead. No one can bring my loose talking home to me. But why do they stay on and stay on so?"

In due time George and Sophie asked each other that question, and put it aside. They argued that the climate—a pearly blend, unlike the hot and cold ferocities of their native land—suited them, as the thick stillness of the nights certainly suited George. He was saved even the sight of a metalled road, which, as presumably leading to business, wakes desire in a man; and the telegraph office at the village of Friars Pardon, where they sold picture post-cards and peg-tops, was two walking miles across the fields and woods. For all that touched his past among his fellows, or their remembrance of him, he might have been in another planet; and Sophie, whose life had been very largely spent among husbandless wives of lofty ideals, had no wish to leave this present of God. The unhurried meals, the foreknowledge of deliciously empty hours to follow, the breadths of soft sky under which they walked together and reckoned time only by their hunger or thirst; the good grass beneath their feet that cheated the miles; their discoveries, always together, amid the farms—Griffons, Rocketts, Burnt House, Gale Anstey, and the Home Farm, where Iggulden of the blue smock-frock would waylay them, and they would ransack the old house once more; the long wet afternoons when they tucked up their feet on the bedroom's deep window-sill over against the apple-trees, and talked together as never till then had they found time to talk—these things contented her soul, and her body throve.

"Have you realized," she asked one morning, "that we've been here absolutely alone for the last thirty-four days?"

"Have you counted them?" he asked.

"Did you like them?" she replied.

"I must have. I didn't think about them. Yes, I have. Six months ago I should have fretted myself sick. Remember at Cairo? I've only had two or three bad times. Am I getting better, or is it senile decay?"

"Climate, all climate." Sophie swung her new-bought English boots, as she sat on the stile overlooking Friars Pardon, behind the Cloke's barn.

"One must take hold of things though," he said, "if it's only to keep one's hand in." His eyes did not flicker now as they swept the empty fields. "Mustn't one?"

"Lay out a Morristown links over Gale Anstey. I dare say you could hire it."

"No, I'm not as English as that—nor as Morristown. Cloke says all the farms here could be made to pay."

"Well, I'm Anastasia in the 'Treasure of Franchard.' I'm content to be alive and purr. There's no hurry."

"No." He smiled. "All the same, I'm going to see after my mail."

"You promised you wouldn't have any."

"There's some business coming through that's amusing me. Honest. It doesn't get on my nerves at all."

"Want a secretary?"

"No, thanks, old thing! Isn't that quite English?"

"Too English! Go away." But none the less in broad daylight she returned the kiss. "I'm off to Pardons. I haven't been to the house for nearly a week."

"How've you decided to furnish Jane Elphick's bedroom?" he laughed, for it had come to be a permanent Castle in Spain between them.

"Black Chinese furniture and yellow silk brocade," she answered, and ran downhill. She scattered a few cows at a gap with a flourish of a ground-ash that Iggulden had cut for her a week ago, and singing as she passed under the holm-oaks, sought the farm-house at the back of Friars Pardon. The old man was not to be found, and she knocked at his half-opened door, for she needed him to fill her idle forenoon. A blue-eyed sheep-dog, a new friend, and Rambler's old enemy, crawled out and besought her to enter.

Iggulden sat in his chair by the fire, a thistle-spud between his knees, his head drooped. Though she had never seen death before, her heart, that missed a beat, told her that he was dead. She did not speak or cry, but stood outside the door, and the dog licked her hand. When he threw up his nose, she heard herself saying: "Don't howl! Please don't begin to howl, Scottie, or I shall run away!"

She held her ground while the shadows in the rickyard moved toward noon; sat after a while on the steps by the door, her arms round the dog's neck, waiting till some one should come. She watched the smokeless chimneys of Friars Pardon slash its roofs with shadow, and the smoke of Iggulden's last lighted fire gradually thin and cease. Against her will she fell to wondering how many Moones, Elphicks, and Torrells had been swung round the turn of the broad hall stairs. Then she remembered the old man's talk of being "up-ended like a milk-can," and buried her face on Scottie's neck. At last a horse's feet clinked upon flags, rustled in the old grey straw of the rickyard, and she found herself facing the vicar—a figure she had seen at church declaiming impossibilities (Sophie was a Unitarian) in an unnatural voice.

"He's dead," she said, without preface.

"Old Iggulden? I was coming for a talk with him." The vicar passed in uncovered. "Ah!" she heard him say. "Heart-failure! How long have you been here?"

"Since a quarter to eleven." She looked at her watch earnestly and saw that her hand did not shake.

"I'll sit with him now till the doctor comes. D'you think you could tell him, and—yes, Mrs. Betts in the cottage with the wistaria next the blacksmith's? I'm afraid this has been rather a shock to you."

Sophie nodded, and fled toward the village. Her body failed her for a moment; she dropped beneath a hedge, and looked back at the great house. In some fashion its silence and stolidity steadied her for her errand.

Mrs. Betts, small, black-eyed, and dark, was almost as unconcerned as Friars Pardon.

"Yiss, yiss, of course. Dear me! Well, Iggulden he had had his day in my father's time. Muriel, get me my little blue bag, please. Yiss, ma'am. They come down like ellum-branches in still weather. No warnin' at all. Muriel, my bicycle's be'ind the fowl-house. I'll tell Dr. Dallis, ma'am."

She trundled off on her wheel like a brown bee, while Sophie—heaven above and earth beneath changed—walked stiffly home, to fall over George at his letters, in a muddle of laughter and tears.

"It's all quite natural for *them*," she gasped. " 'They come down like ellum-branches in still weather. Yiss, ma'am.' No, there wasn't anything in the least horrible, only—only—Oh, George, that poor shiny stick of his between his poor, thin knees! I couldn't have borne it if Scottie had howled. I didn't know the vicar was so—so sensitive. He said he was afraid it was ra-rather a shock. Mrs. Betts told me to go home, and I wanted to collapse on her floor. But I didn't disgrace myself. I—I couldn't have left him—could I?"

"You're sure you've took no 'arm?" cried Mrs. Cloke, who had heard the news by farm-telegraphy, which is older but swifter than Marconi's.

"No. I'm perfectly well," Sophie protested.

"You lay down till tea-time." Mrs. Cloke patted her shoulder. "*They*'ll be very pleased, though she 'as 'ad no proper understandin' for twenty years."

"They" came before twilight—a black-bearded man in moleskins, and a little palsied old woman, who chirruped like a wren.

"I'm his son," said the man to Sophie, among the lavender bushes.

"We 'ad a difference—twenty year back, and didn't speak since. But I'm his son all the same, and we thank you for the watching."

"I'm only glad I happened to be there," she answered, and from the bottom of her heart she meant it.

"We heard he spoke a lot o' you—one time an' another since you came. We thank you kindly," the man added.

"Are you the son that was in America?" she asked.

"Yes, ma'am. On my uncle's farm, in Connecticut. He was what they call road-master there."

"Whereabouts in Connecticut?" asked George over her shoulder.

"Veering Holler was the name. I was there six year with my uncle."

"How small the world is!" Sophie cried. "Why, all my mother's people come from Veering Hollow. There must be some there still—the Lashmars. Did you ever hear of them?"

"I remember hearing that name, seems to me," he answered, but his face was blank as the back of a spade.

A little before dusk a woman in grey, striding like a foot-soldier, and bearing on her arm a long pole, crashed through the orchard calling for food. George, upon whom the unannounced English worked mysteriously, fled to the parlour; but Mrs. Cloke came forward beaming. Sophie could not escape.

"We've only just heard of it," said the stranger, turning on her. "I've been out with the otter-hounds all day. It was a splendidly sportin' thing——"

"Did you—er—kill?" said Sophie. She knew from books she could not go far wrong here.

"Yes, a dry bitch—seventeen pounds," was the answer. "A splendidly sportin' thing of you to do. Poor old Iggulden——"

"Oh—that!" said Sophie, enlightened.

"If there had been any people at Pardons it would never have happened. He'd have been looked after. But what can you expect from a parcel of London solicitors?"

Mrs. Cloke murmured something.

"No. I'm soaked from the knees down. If I hang about I shall get chilled. A cup of tea, Mrs. Cloke, and I can eat one of your sandwiches as I go." She wiped her weather-worn face with a green and yellow silk handkerchief.

"Yes, my lady!" Mrs. Cloke ran and returned swiftly.

"Our land marches with Pardons for a mile on the south," she explained, waving the full cup, "but one has quite enough to do with one's own people without poachin'. Still, if I'd known, I'd have sent Dora, of course. Have you seen her this afternoon, Mrs. Cloke? No? I wonder whether that girl did sprain her ankle. Thank you." It was a formidable hunk of bread and bacon that Mrs. Cloke presented. "As I was sayin', Pardons is a scandal! Lettin' people die like dogs. There ought to be people there who do their duty. You've done yours, though there wasn't the faintest call upon you. Good night. Tell Dora, if she comes, I've gone on."

She strode away, munching her crust, and Sophie reeled breathless into the parlour, to shake the shaking George.

"Why did you keep catching my eye behind the blind? Why didn't you come out and do your duty?"

"Because I should have burst. Did you see the mud on its cheek?" he said.

"Once. I daren't look again. Who is she?"

"God—a local deity then. Anyway, she's another of the things you're expected to know by instinct."

Mrs. Cloke, shocked at their levity, told them that it was Lady Conant, wife of Sir Walter Conant, Baronet, a large landholder in the neighbourhood, and if not God, at least His visible Providence.

George made her talk of that family for an hour.

"Laughter," said Sophie afterward in their own room, "is the mark of the savage. Why couldn't you control your emotions? It's all real to *her*."

"It's all real to me. That's my trouble," he answered in an altered tone. "Anyway, it's real enough to mark time with. Don't you think so?"

"What d'you mean?" she asked quickly, though she knew his voice.

"That I'm better. I'm well enough to kick."

"What at?"

"This!" He waved his hand round the one room. "I must have something to play with till I'm fit for work again."

"Ah!" She sat on the bed and leaned forward, her hands clasped. "I wonder if it's good for you."

"We've been better here than anywhere," he went on slowly. "One could always sell it again."

She nodded gravely, but her eyes sparkled.

"The only thing that worries me is what happened this morning. I want to know how you feel about it. If it's on your nerves in the least we can have the old farm at the back of the house pulled down, or perhaps it has spoiled the notion for you?"

"Pull it down?" she cried. "You've no business faculty. Why, that's where we could live while we're putting the big house in order. It's almost under the same roof. No! What happened this morning seemed to be more of a—of a leading than anything else. There *ought* to be people at Pardons. Lady Conant's quite right."

"I was thinking more of the woods and the roads. I could double the value of the place in six months."

"What do they want for it?" She shook her head, and her loosened hair fell glowingly about her cheeks.

"Seventy-five thousand dollars. They'll take sixty-eight."

"Less than half what we paid for our old yacht when we married. And we didn't have a good time in her. You were——"

"Well, I discovered I was too much of an American to be content to be a rich man's son. You aren't blaming me for that?"

"Oh, no. Only it was a very businesslike honeymoon. How far are you along with the deal, George?"

"I can mail the deposit on the purchase money to-morrow morning, and we can have the thing completed in a fortnight or three weeks—if you say so."

"Friars Pardon—Friars Pardon!" Sophie chanted rapturously, her dark gray eyes big with delight. "All the farms? Gale Anstey, Burnt House, Rocketts, the Home Farm, and Griffons? Sure you've got 'em all?"

"Sure." He smiled.

"And the woods? High Pardons Wood, Lower Pardons, Suttons, Dutton's Shaw, Reuben's Ghyll, Maxey's Ghyll, and both the Oak Hangers? Sure you've got 'em all?"

"Every last stick. Why, you know them as well as I do." He laughed. "They say there's five thousand—a thousand pounds' worth of lumber—timber they call it—in the Hangers alone."

"Mrs. Cloke's oven must be mended first thing, *and* the kitchen roof. I think I'll have all this white-washed," Sophie broke in, pointing to the ceiling. "The whole place is a scandal. Lady Conant is quite right. George, when did you begin to fall in love with the house? In the green room—that first day? I did."

"I'm not in love with it. One must do something to mark time till one's fit for work."

"Or when we stood under the oaks, and the door opened? Oh! Ought I to go to poor Iggulden's funeral?" She sighed with utter happiness.

"Wouldn't they call it a liberty—*now*?" said he.

"But I liked him."

"But you didn't own him at the date of his death."

"That wouldn't keep me away. Only, they made such a fuss about the watching"—she caught her breath—"it might be ostentatious from that point of view, too. Oh, George"—she reached for his hand—"we're two little orphans moving in worlds not realized, and we shall make some bad breaks. But we're going to have the time of our lives."

"We'll run up to London to-morrow, and see if we can hurry those English law—solicitors. I want to get to work."

They went. They suffered many things ere they returned across the fields in a fly one Saturday night, nursing a two by two-and-a-half box of deeds and maps—lawful owners of Friars Pardon and the five decayed farms therewith.

"I do most sincerely 'ope and trust you'll be 'appy, Madam," Mrs. Cloke gasped, when she was told the news by the kitchen fire.

"Goodness! It isn't a marriage!" Sophie exclaimed, a little awed; for to them the joke, which to an American means work, was only just beginning.

"If it's took in a proper spirit"—Mrs. Cloke's eye turned toward her oven.

"Send and have that mended to-morrow," Sophie whispered.

"We couldn't 'elp noticing," said Cloke slowly, "from the times you walked there, that you an' your lady was drawn to it, but—but I don't know as we ever precisely thought——" His wife's glance checked him.

"That we were that sort of people," said George. "We aren't sure of it ourselves yet."

"Perhaps," said Cloke, rubbing his knees, "just for the sake of saying something, perhaps you'll park it?"

"What's that?" said George.

"Turn it all into a fine park like Violet Hill"—he jerked a thumb to westward—"that Mr. Sangres bought. It was four farms, and Mr. Sangres made a fine park of them, with a herd of faller deer."

"Then it wouldn't be Friars Pardon," said Sophie. "Would it?"

"I don't know as I've ever heard Pardons was ever anything but wheat an' wool. Only some gentlemen say that parks are less trouble than tenants." He laughed nervously. "But the gentry, o' course, they keep on pretty much as they was used to."

"I see," said Sophie. "How did Mr. Sangres make his money?"

"I never rightly heard. It was pepper an' spices, or it may ha' been gloves. No. Gloves was Sir Reginald Liss at Marley End. Spices was Mr. Sangres. He's a Brazilian gentleman—very sunburnt like."

"Be sure o' one thing. You won't 'ave any trouble," said Mrs. Cloke, just before they went to bed.

Now the news of the purchase was told to Mr. and Mrs. Cloke alone at 8 P. M. of a Saturday. None left the farm till they set out for church next morning. Yet when they reached the church and were about to slip aside into their usual seats, a little beyond the font, where they could see the red-furred tails of the bell-ropes waggle and twist at ringing time, they were swept forward irresistibly, a Cloke on either flank (and yet they had not walked with the Clokes), upon the ever-retiring bosom of a black-gowned verger, who ushered them into a room of a pew at the head of the left aisle, under the pulpit.

"This," he sighed reproachfully, "is the Pardons' Pew," and shut them in.

They could see little more than the choir boys in the chancel, but to the roots of the hair of their necks they felt the congregation behind mercilessly devouring them by look.

"*When the wicked man turneth away*." The strong, alien voice of the priest vibrated under the hammer-beam roof, and a loneliness unfelt before swamped their hearts, as they searched for places in the unfamiliar Church of England service. The Lord's Prayer—"Our Father, *which* art"—set the seal on that desolation. Sophie found herself thinking how in other lands their purchase would long ere this have been discussed from every point of view in a dozen prints, forgetting that George for months had not been allowed to glance at those black and bellowing head-lines. Here was nothing but silence—not even hostility! The game was up to them; the other players hid their cards and waited. Suspense, she felt, was in the air, and when her sight cleared, saw, indeed, a mural tablet of a footless bird brooding upon the carven motto, "Wayte awhyle—wayte awhyle."

At the Litany George had trouble with an unstable hassock, and drew the slip of carpet under the pew-seat. Sophie pushed her end back also, and shut her eyes against a burning that felt like tears. When she opened them she was looking at her mother's maiden name, fairly carved on a blue flagstone on the pew floor:

Ellen Lashmar. ob. 1796. ætat. 27.

She nudged George and pointed. Sheltered, as they kneeled, they looked for more knowledge, but the rest of the slab was blank.

" 'Ever hear of her?" he whispered.

"Never knew any of us came from here."

"Coincidence?"

"Perhaps. But it makes me feel better," and she smiled and winked away a tear on her lashes, and took his hand while they prayed for "all women labouring of child"—not "in the perils of child-birth"; and the sparrows who had found their way through the guards behind the glass windows chirped above the faded gilt and alabaster family tree of the Conants.

The baronet's pew was on the right of the aisle. After service its inhabitants moved forth without haste, but so as to block effectively a dusky person with a large family who champed in their rear.

"Spices, I think," said Sophie, deeply delighted as the Sangres closed up after the Conants. "Let 'em get away, George."

But when they came out many folk whose eyes were one still lingered by the lych-gate.

"I want to see if any more Lashmars are buried here," said Sophie.

"Not now. This seems to be show day. Come home quickly," he replied.

A group of families, the Clokes a little apart, opened to let them through. The men saluted with jerky nods, the women with remnants of a curtsey. Only Iggulden's son, his mother on his arm, lifted his hat as Sophie passed.

"Your people," said the clear voice of Lady Conant in her ear.

"I suppose so," said Sophie, blushing, for they were within two yards of her; but it was not a question.

"Then that child looks as if it were coming down with mumps. You ought to tell the mother she shouldn't have brought it to church."

"I can't leave 'er be'ind, my lady," the woman said. "She'd set the 'ouse afire in a minute, she's that forward with the matches. Ain't you, Maudie dear?"

"Has Dr. Dallas seen her?"

"Not yet, my lady."

"He must. You can't get away, of course. M—m! My idiotic maid is coming in for her teeth to-morrow at twelve. She shall pick her up—at Gale Anstey, isn't it?—at eleven."

"Yes. Thank you very much, my lady."

"I oughtn't to have done it," said Lady Conant apologetically, "but there has been no one at Pardons for so long that you'll forgive my poaching. Now, can't you lunch with us? The vicar usually comes too. I don't use the horses on a Sunday"—she glanced at the Brazilian's silver-plated chariot. "It's only a mile across the fields."

"You—you're very kind," said Sophie, hating herself because her lip trembled.

"My dear," the compelling tone dropped to a soothing gurgle, "d'you suppose I don't know how it feels to come to a strange county—country I should say—away from one's own people? When I first left the Shires—I'm Shropshire, you know—I cried for a day and a night. But fretting doesn't make loneliness any better. Oh, here's Dora. She *did* sprain her leg that day."

"I'm as lame as a tree still," said the tall maiden frankly. "You ought to go out with the otter-hounds, Mrs. Chapin. I believe they're drawing your water next week."

Sir Walter had already led off George, and the vicar came up on the other side of Sophie. There was no escaping the swift procession or the leisurely lunch, where talk came and went in low-voiced eddies that had the village for their centre. Sophie heard the vicar and Sir Walter address her husband lightly as Chapin! (She also remembered many women known in a previous life who habitually addressed their husbands as Mr. Such-an-one.) After lunch Lady Conant talked to her explicitly of maternity as that is achieved in cottages and farm-houses remote from aid, and of the duty thereto of the mistress of Pardons.

A gate in a beech hedge, reached across triple lawns, let them out before tea-time into the unkempt south side of their land.

"I want your hand, please," said Sophie as soon as they were safe among the beech boles and the lawless hollies. "D'you remember the old maid in 'Providence and the Guitar' who heard the Commissary swear, and hardly reckoned herself a maiden lady afterward? Because I'm a relative of hers. Lady Conant is——"

"Did you find out anything about the Lashmars?" he interrupted.

"I didn't ask. I'm going to write to Aunt Sydney about it first. Oh, Lady Conant said something at lunch about their having bought some land from some Lashmars a few years ago. I found it was at the beginning of last century."

"What did you say?"

"I said, 'Really, how interesting!' Like that. I'm not going to push myself forward. I've been hearing about Mr. Sangres's efforts in that direction. And you? I couldn't see you behind the flowers. Was it very deep water, dear?"

George mopped a brow already browned by outdoor exposures.

"Oh no—dead easy," he answered. "I've bought Friars Pardon to prevent Sir Walter's birds straying."

A cock pheasant scuttered through the dry leaves and exploded almost under their feet. Sophie jumped.

"That's one of 'em," said George calmly.

"Well, your nerves are better, at any rate," said she. "Did you tell 'em you'd bought the thing to play with?"

"No. That was where my nerve broke down. I only made one bad break —I think. I said I couldn't see why hiring land to men to farm wasn't as much a business proposition as anything else."

"And what did they say?"

"They smiled. I shall know what that smile means some day. They don't waste their smiles. D'you see that track by Gale Anstey?"

They looked down from the edge of the hanger over a cup-like hollow. People by two and threes in their Sunday best filed slowly along the paths that connected farm to farm.

"I've never seen so many on our land before," said Sophie. "Why is it?"

"To show us we mustn't shut up their rights of way."

"Those cow-tracks we're been using cross lots?" said Sophie forcibly.

"Yes. Any one of 'em would cost us two thousand pounds each in legal expenses to close."

"But we don't want to," she said.

"The whole community would fight if we did."

"But it's our land. We can do what we like."

"It's *not* our land. We've only paid for it. We belong to it, and it belongs to the people—our people they call 'em. I've been to lunch with the English too."

They passed slowly from one bracken-dotted field to the next—flushed with pride of ownership, plotting alterations and restorations at each turn; halting in their tracks to argue, spreading apart to embrace two views at once, or closing in to consider one. Couples moved out of their way, but smiling covertly.

"We shall make some bad breaks," he said at last.

"Together, though. You won't let any one else in, will you?"

"Except the contractors. This syndicate handles this proposition by its little lone."

"But you might feel the want of some one," she insisted.

"I shall—but it will be you. It's business, Sophie, but it's going to be good fun."

"Please God," she answered flushing, and cried to herself as they went back to tea. "It's worth it. Oh, it's worth it."

The repairing and moving into Friars Pardon was business of the most varied and searching, but all done English fashion, without friction. Time and money alone were asked. The rest lay in the hands of beneficent advisers from London, or spirits, male and female, called up by Mr. and Mrs. Cloke from the wastes of the farms. In the centre stood George and Sophie, a little aghast, their interests reaching out on every side.

"I ain't sayin' anything against Londoners," said Cloke, self-appointed clerk of the outer works, consulting engineer, head of the immigration bureau, and superintendent of woods and forests; "but your own people won't go about to make more than a fair profit out of you."

"How is one to know?" said George.

"Five years from now, or so on, maybe, you'll be lookin' over your first year's accounts, and, knowin' what you'll know then, you'll say: 'Well, Billy Beartup'—or Old Cloke as it might be—'did me proper when I was new.' No man likes to have that sort of thing laid up against him."

"I think I see," said George. "But five years is a long time to look ahead."

"I doubt if that oak Billy Beartup throwed in Reuben's Ghyll will be fit for her drawin'-room floor in less than seven," Cloke drawled.

"Yes, that's my work," said Sophie. (Billy Beartup of Griffons, a woodman by training and birth, a tenant farmer by misfortune of marriage, had laid his broad axe at her feet a month before.) "Sorry if I've committed you to another eternity."

"And we shan't even know where we've gone wrong with *your* new carriage drive before that time either," said Cloke, ever anxious to keep the balance true—with an ounce or two in Sophie's favour. The past four months had taught George better than to reply. The carriage road winding up the hill was his present keen interest. They set off to look at it, and the imported American scraper which had blighted the none too sunny soul of "Skim" Winsh, the carter. But young Iggulden was in charge now, and under his guidance, Buller and Roberts, the great horses, moved mountains.

"You lif' her like that, an' you tip her like that," he explained to the gang. "My uncle he was road-master in Connecticut."

"Are they roads yonder?" said Skim, sitting under the laurels.

"No better than accommodation roads. Dirt, they call 'em. They'd suit you, Skim."

"Why?" said the incautious Skim.

" 'Cause you'd take no hurt when you fall out of your cart drunk on a Saturday," was the answer.

"I didn't last time neither," Skim roared.

After the lough laugh, old Whybarne of Gale Anstey piped feebly, "Well, dirt or no dirt, there's no denyin' Chapin knows a good job when he sees it. 'E don't build one day and dee-stroy the next, like that nigger Sangres."

"*She's* the one that knows her own mind," said Pinky, brother to Skim Winsh, and a Napoleon among carters who had helped to bring the grand piano across the fields in the autumn rains.

"She had ought to," said Iggulden. "Whoa, Buller! She's a Lashmar. They never was double-thinking."

"Oh, you found that? Has the answer come from your uncle?" said Skim, doubtful whether so remote a land as America had posts.

The others looked at him scornfully. Skim was always a day behind the fair.

Iggulden rested from his labours. "She's a Lashmar right enough. I started up to write to my uncle at once—the month after she said her folks came from Veering Holler."

"Where there ain't any roads?" Skim interrupted, but none laughed.

"My uncle he married an American woman for his second, and she took it up like a—like the coroner. She's a Lashmar out of the old Lashmar place, 'fore they sold to Conants. She ain't no Toot Hill Lashmar, nor any o' the Crayford lot. Her folk come out of the ground here, neither chalk nor forest, but wildishers. They sailed over to America—I've got it all writ down by my uncle's woman—in eighteen hundred an' nothing. My uncle says they're all slow begetters like."

"Would they be gentry yonder now?" Skim asked.

"Nah—there's no gentry in America, no matter how long you're there. It's against their law. There's only rich and poor allowed. They've been lawyers and such like over yonder for a hundred years—but she's a Lashmar for all that."

"Lord! What's a hundred years?" said Whybarne, who had seen seventy-eight of them.

"An' they write too, from yonder—my uncle's woman writes—that you can still tell 'em by headmark. Their hair's foxy-red still—an' they throw out when they walk. *He's* in-toed—treads like a gipsy; but you watch, an' you'll see 'er throw out—like a colt."

"Your trace wants taking up." Pinky's large ears had caught the sound of voices, and as the two broke through the laurels the men were hard at work, their eyes on Sophie's feet.

She had been less fortunate in her inquiries than Iggulden, for her Aunt Sydney of Meriden (a badged and certificated Daughter of the Revolution to boot) answered her inquiries with a two-paged discourse on patriotism, the leaflets of a Village Improvement Society, of which she was president, and a demand for an overdue subscription to a Factory Girls' Reading Circle. Sophie burned it all in the Orpheus and Eurydice grate, and kept her own counsel.

"What I want to know," said George, when Spring was coming, and the gardens needed thought, "is who will ever pay me for my labour? I've put in at least half a million dollars' worth already."

"Sure you're not taking too much out of yourself?" his wife asked.

"Oh, no; I haven't been conscious of myself all winter." He looked at his brown English gaiters and smiled. "It's all behind me now. I believe I could sit down and think of all that—those months before we sailed."

"Don't—ah, don't!" she cried.

"But I must go back one day. You don't want to keep me out of business always—or do you?" He ended with a nervous laugh.

Sophie sighed as she drew her own ground-ash (of old Iggulden's cutting) from the hall rack.

"Aren't you overdoing it too? You look a little tired," he said.

"You make me tired. I'm going to Rocketts to see Mrs. Cloke about Mary." (This was the sister of the telegraphist, promoted to be sewing-maid at Pardons.) "Coming?"

"I'm due at Burnt House to see about the new well. By the way, there's a sore throat at Gale Anstey——"

"That's my province. Don't interfere. The Whybarne children always have sore throats. They do it for jujubes."

"Keep away from Gale Anstey till I make sure, honey. Cloke ought to have told me."

"These people don't tell. Haven't you learnt that yet? But I'll obey, me lord. See you later!"

She set off afoot, for within the three main roads that bounded the blunt triangle of the estate (even by night one could scarcely hear the carts on them), wheels were not used except for farm work. The footpaths served all other purposes. And though at first they had planned improvements, they had soon fallen in with the customs of their hidden kingdom, and moved about the soft-footed ways by woodland, hedgerow, and shaw as freely as the rabbits. Indeed, for the most part Sophie walked bareheaded beneath her helmet of chestnut hair; but she had been plagued of late by vague aches, which she explained to Mrs. Cloke, who asked some questions. How it came about Sophie never knew, but after a while behold Mrs. Cloke's arm was about her waist, and her head was on that deep bosom behind the shut kitchen door.

"My dear! My dear!" the elder woman almost sobbed. "An' d'you mean to tell me you never suspicioned? Why—why—where *was* you ever taught anything at all? Of *course* it is. It's what we've been only waitin' for, all of us. Time and again I've said to Lady——" she checked herself. "An' now we shall be as we should be."

"But—but—but——" Sophie whimpered.

"An' to see you buildin' your nest so busy—pianos and books—an' never thinkin' of a nursery!"

"No more I did." Sophie sat bolt upright, and began to laugh.

"Time enough yet." The fingers tapped thoughtfully on the broad knee. "But—they must be strange-minded folk over yonder with you! Have you thought to send for your mother? She dead? My dear, my dear! Never mind! She'll be happy where she knows. 'Tis God's work. An' we was only waitin' for it, for you've never failed in your duty yet. It ain't your way. *What* did you say about my Mary's doings?" Mrs. Cloke's face hardened as she pressed her chin on Sophie's forehead. "If any of your girls thinks to be'ave arbitrary now, I'll—— But they won't my dear. I'll see they do their duty too. Be sure you'll 'ave no trouble."

When Sophie walked back across the fields heaven and earth changed about her as on the day of old Iggulden's death. For an instant she thought of the wide turn of the staircase, and the new ivory-white paint that no coffin corner could scar, but presently the shadow passed in a pure wonder and bewilderment that made her reel. She leaned against one of their new gates and looked over their lands for some other stay.

"Well," she said resignedly, half aloud, "we must try to make him feel that he isn't a third in our party," and turned the corner that looked over Friars Pardon, giddy, sick, and faint.

Of a sudden the house they had bought for a whim stood up as she had never seen it before, low-fronted, broad-winged, ample, prepared by course of generations for all such things. As it had steadied her when it lay desolate, so now that it had meaning from their few months of life within, it soothed and promised good. She went alone and quickly into the hall, and kissed either door-post, whispering: "Be good to me. You know! You've never failed in your duty yet."

When the matter was explained to George, he would have sailed at once to their own land, but this Sophie forbade.

"I don't want science," she said. "I just want to be loved, and there isn't time for that at home. Besides," she added, looking out of the window, "it would be desertion."

George was forced to soothe himself with linking Friars Pardon to the telegraph system of Great Britain by telephone—three-quarters of a mile of poles, put in by Whybarne and a few friends. One of these was a foreigner from the next parish. Said he when the line was being run: "There's an old ellum right in our road. Shall us throw her?"

"Toot Hill parish folk, neither grace nor good luck, God help 'em." Old Whybarne shouted the local proverb from three poles down the line. "We ain't goin' to lay any axe-iron to coffin-wood here—not till we know where we are yet awhile. Swing round 'er, swing round!"

To this day, then, that sudden kink in the straight line across the upper pasture remains a mystery to Sophie and George. Nor can they tell why Skim Winsh, who came to his cottage under Dutton Shaw most musically drunk at 10.45 P. M. of every Saturday night, as his father had done before him, sang no more at the bottom of the garden steps, where Sophie always feared he would break his neck. The path was undoubtedly an ancient right of way, and at 10.45 P. M. on Saturdays Skim remembered it was his duty to posterity to keep it open—till Mrs. Cloke spoke to him—once. She spoke likewise to her daughter Mary, sewing-maid at Pardons, and to Mary's best new friend, the five-foot-seven imported London house-maid, who taught Mary to trim hats, and found the country dullish.

But there was no noise—at no time was there any noise—and when Sophie walked abroad she met no one in her path unless she had signified a wish that way. Then they appeared to protest that all was well with them and their children, their chickens, their roofs, their water-supply, and their sons in the police or the railway service.

"But don't you find it dull, dear?" said George, loyally doing his best not to worry as the months went by.

"I've been so busy putting my house in order I haven't had time to think," said she. "Do you?"

"No—no. If I could only be sure of you."

She turned on the green drawing-room's couch (it was Empire, not Heppelwhite after all), and laid aside a list of linen and blankets.

"It has changed everything, hasn't it?" she whispered.

"Oh, Lord, yes. But I still think if we went back to Baltimore——"

"And missed our first real summer together. No thank you, me lord."

"But we're absolutely alone."

"Isn't that what I'm doing my best to remedy? Don't you worry. I like it—like it to the marrow of my little bones. You don't realize what her house means to a woman. We thought we were living in it last year, but we hadn't begun to. Don't you rejoice in your study, George?"

"I prefer being here with you." He sat down on the floor by the couch and took her hand.

"Seven," she said, as the French clock struck. "Year before last you'd just be coming back from business."

He winced at the recollection, then laughed. "Business! I've been at work ten solid hours to-day."

"Where did you lunch? With the Conants?"

"No; at Dutton Shaw, sitting on a log, with my feet in a swamp. But we've found out where the old spring is, and we're going to pipe it down to Gale Anstey next year."

"I'll come and see to-morrow. Oh, please open the door, dear. I want to look down the passage. Isn't that corner by the stair-head lovely where the sun strikes in?" She looked through half-closed eyes at the vista of ivory-white and pale green all steeped in liquid gold.

"There's a step out of Jane Elphick's bedroom," she went on—"and *his* first step in the world ought to be up. I shouldn't wonder if those people hadn't put it there on purpose. George, will it make any odds to you if he's a girl?"

He answered, as he had many times before, that his interest was his wife, not the child.

"Then you're the only person who thinks so." She laughed. "Don't be silly, dear. It's expected. *I* know. It's my duty. I shan't be able to look our people in the face if I fail."

"What concern is it of theirs, confound 'em!"

"You'll see. Luckily the tradition of the house is boys, Mrs. Cloke says, so I'm provided for. Shall you ever begin to understand these people? I shan't."

"And we bought it for fun—for fun!" he groaned. "And here we are held up for goodness knows how long!"

"Why? Were you thinking of selling it?" He did not answer. "Do you remember the second Mrs. Chapin?" she demanded.

This was a bold, brazen little black-browed woman—a widow for choice

—who on Sophie's death was guilefully to marry George for his wealth and ruin him in a year. George being busy, Sophie had invented her some two years after her marriage, and conceived she was alone among wives in so doing.

"You aren't going to bring *her* up again?" he asked anxiously.

"I only want to say that I should hate any one who bought Pardons ten times worse than I used to hate the second Mrs. Chapin. Think what we've put into it of our two selves."

"At least a couple of million dollars. I know I could have made——" He broke off.

"The beasts!" she went on. "They'd be sure to build a red-brick lodge at the gates, and cut the lawn up for bedding out. You must leave instructions in your will that *he's* never to do that, George, won't you?"

He laughed and took her hand again but said nothing till it was time to dress. Then he muttered: "What the devil use is a man's country to him when he can't do business in it?"

Friars Pardon stood faithful to its tradition. At the appointed time was born, not that third in their party to whom Sophie meant to be so kind, but a godling; in beauty, it was manifest, excelling Eros, as in wisdom Confucius; an enhancer of delights, a renewer of companionships and an interpreter of Destiny. This last George did not realise till he met Lady Conant striding through Dutton Shaw a few days after the event.

"My dear fellow," she cried, and slapped him heartily on the back, "I can't tell you how glad we all are.—Oh, *she*'ll be all right. (There's never been any trouble over the birth of an heir at Pardons.) Now where the dooce is it?" She felt largely in her leather-bound skirt and drew out a small silver mug. "I sent a note to your wife about it, but my silly ass of a groom forgot to take this. You can save me a tramp. Give her my love." She marched off amid her guard of grave Airedales.

The mug was worn and dented: above the twined initials, G. L., was the crest of a footless bird and the motto: "Wayte awhyle—wayte awhyle."

"That's the other end of the riddle," Sophie whispered, when he saw her that evening. "Read her note. The English write beautiful notes."

The warmest of welcomes to your little man. I hope he will appreciate his native land now he has come to it. Though you have said nothing we cannot, of course, look on him as a little stranger, and so I am sending him the old Lashmar christening mug. It has been with us since Gregory Lashmar, your great-grandmother's brother—

George stared at his wife.

"Go on," she twinkled, from the pillows.

—mother's brother, sold his place to Walter's family. We seem to have acquired some of your household gods at that time, but nothing survives except the mug and the old cradle, which I found in the potting-shed and am having put in order for you. I hope little George—Lashmar, he will be too, won't he?—will live to see his grandchildren cut their teeth on his mug.

Affectionately yours,

ALICE CONANT

P. S.—How quiet you've kept about it all!

"Well, I'm——"

"Don't swear," said Sophie. "Bad for the infant mind."

"But how in the world did she get at it? Have you ever said a word about the Lashmars?"

"You know the only time—to young Iggulden at Rocketts—when Iggulden died."

"Your great-grandmother's brother! She's traced the whole connection —more than your Aunt Sydney could do. What does she mean about our keeping quiet?"

Sophie's eyes sparkled. "I've thought that out too. We've got back at the English at last. Can't you see that *she* thought that we thought my mother's being a Lashmar was one of those things we'd expect the English to find out for themselves, and that's impressed her?" She turned the mug in her white hands, and sighed happily. " 'Wayte awhyle—wayte awhyle.' That's not a bad motto, George. It's been worth it."

"But still I don't quite see——"

"I shouldn't wonder if they don't think our coming here was part of a deep-laid scheme to be near our ancestors. *They'd* understand that. And look how they've accepted us, all of them."

"Are we so undesirable in ourselves?" George grunted.

"Be just, me lord. That wretched Sangres man has twice our money. Can you see Marm Conant slapping him between the shoulders? Not by a jugful! The poor beast doesn't exist!"

"Do you think it's that then?" He looked toward the cot by the fire where the godling snorted.

"The minute I get well I shall find out from Mrs. Cloke what every Lashmar gives in doles (that's nicer than tips) every time a Lashmite is born. I've done my duty thus far, but there's much expected of me."

Entered here Mrs. Cloke, and hung worshipping over the cot. They showed her the mug and her face shone. "Oh, now Lady Conant's sent it, it'll be all proper, ma'am, won't it? 'George' of course he'd have to be, but seein' what he is we was hopin'—all your people was hopin'—it 'ud be 'Lashmar' too, and that 'ud just round it out. A very 'andsome mug—quite unique, I should imagine. 'Wayte awhyle—wayte awhyle.' That's true with the Lashmars, I've heard. Very slow to fill their houses, they are. Most like Master George won't open 'is nursery till he's thirty."

"Poor lamb!" cried Sophie. "But how did you know my folk were Lashmars?"

Mrs. Cloke thought deeply. "I'm sure I can't quite say, ma'am, but I've a belief likely that it was something you may have let drop to young Iggulden when you was at Rocketts. That *may* have been what give us an inkling. An' so it came out, one thing in the way o' talk leading to another, and those American people at Veering Holler was very obligin' with news, I'm told, ma'am."

"Great Scott!" said George, under his breath. "And this is the simple peasant!"

"Yiss," Mrs. Cloke went on. "An' Cloke was only wonderin' this afternoon—your pillow's slipped my dear, you mustn't lie that a-way—just for the sake o' sayin' something, whether you wouldn't think well now of getting the Lashmar farms back, sir. They don't rightly round off Sir Walter's estate. They come caterin' across us more. Cloke, 'e 'ud be glad to show you over any day."

"But Sir Walter doesn't want to sell, does he?"

"We can find out from his bailiff, sir, but"—with cold contempt—"I think that trained nurse is just comin' up from her dinner, so I'm afraid we'll 'ave to ask you, sir . . . Now, Master George—Ai-ie! Wake a litty minute, lammie!"

A few months later the three of them were down at the brook in the Gale Anstey woods to consider the rebuilding of a footbridge carried away by spring floods. George Lashmar Chapin wanted all the bluebells on God's earth that day to eat, and Sophie adored him in a voice like to the cooing of a dove; so business was delayed.

"Here's the place," said his father at last among the water forget-me-nots. "But where the deuce are the larch-poles, Cloke? I told you to have them down here ready."

"We'll get 'em down if you say so," Cloke answered, with a thrust of the underlip they both knew.

"But I did say so. What on earth have you brought that timber-tug here for? We aren't building a railway bridge. Why, in America, half-a-dozen two-by-four bits would be ample."

"I don't know nothin' about that," said Cloke. "An' I've nothin' to say against larch—if you want to make a temp'ry job of it. I ain't 'ere to tell you what isn't so, sir; an' you can't say I ever come creepin' up on you, or tryin' to lead you further in than you set out——"

A year ago George would have danced with impatience. Now he scraped a little mud off his old gaiters with his spud, and waited.

"All I say is that you can put up larch and make a temp'ry job of it; and by the time the young master's married it'll have to be done again. Now, I've brought down a couple of as sweet six-by-eight oak timbers as we've ever drawed. You put 'em in an' it's off your mind for good an' all. T'other way—I don't say it ain't right, I'm only just sayin' what I think—but t'other way, he'll no sooner be married than we'll 'ave it *all* to do again. You've no call to regard my words, but you can't get out of *that*."

"No," said George after a pause; "I've been realising that for some time. Make it oak then; we can't get out of it."

THE HOUSE SURGEON

ON AN evening after Easter Day, I sat at a table in a homeward bound steamer's smoking-room, where half a dozen of us told ghost stories. As our party broke up a man, playing Patience in the next alcove, said to me: "I didn't quite catch the end of that last story about the Curse on the family's first-born."

"It turned out to be drains," I explained. "As soon as new ones were put into the house the Curse was lifted, I believe. I never knew the people myself."

"Ah! I've had *my* drains up twice; I'm on gravel too."

"You don't mean to say you've a ghost in your house? Why didn't you join our party?"

"Any more orders, gentlemen, before the bar closes?" the steward interrupted.

"Sit down again, and have one with me," said the Patience player. "No, it isn't a ghost. Our trouble is more depression than anything else."

"How interesting! Then it's nothing any one can see?"

"It's—it's nothing worse than a little depression. And the odd part is that there hasn't been a death in the house since it was built—in 1863. The lawyer said so. That decided me—my good lady, rather—and he made me pay an extra thousand for it."

"How curious. Unusual, too!" I said.

"Yes; ain't it? It was built for three sisters—Moultrie was the name—three old maids. They all lived together; the eldest owned it. I bought it from her lawyer a few years ago, and if I've spent a pound on the place first and last, I must have spent five thousand. Electric light, new servants' wing, garden—all that sort of thing. A man and his family ought to be happy after so much expense, ain't it?" He looked at me through the bottom of his glass.

"Does it affect your family much?"

"My good lady—she's a Greek, by the way—and myself are middle-aged. We can bear up against depression; but it's hard on my little girl. I say little; but she's twenty. We send her visiting to escape it. She almost lived at hotels and hydros last year, but that isn't pleasant for her. She used to be a canary—a perfect canary—always singing. You ought to hear her. She doesn't sing now. That sort of thing's unwholesome for the young, ain't it?"

"Can't you get rid of the place?" I suggested.

"Not except at a sacrifice, and we are fond of it. Just suits us three. We'd love it if we were allowed."

"What do you mean by not being allowed?"

"I mean because of the depression. It spoils everything."

"What's it like exactly?"

"I couldn't very well explain. It must be seen to be appreciated, as the auctioneers say. Now, I was much impressed by the story you were telling just now."

"It wasn't true," I said.

"My tale is true. If you would do me the pleasure to come down and spend a night at my little place, you'd learn more than you would if I talked till morning. Very likely 'twouldn't touch your good self at all. You might be—immune, ain't it? On the other hand, if this influenza—influence *does* happen to affect you, why, I think it will be an experience."

While he talked he gave me his card, and I read his name was L. Maxwell M'Leod, Esq., of Holmescroft. A City address was tucked away in a corner.

"My business," he added, "used to be furs. If you are interested in furs —I've given thirty years of my life to 'em."

"You're very kind," I murmured.

"Far from it, I assure you. I can meet you next Saturday afternoon anywhere in London you choose to name, and I'll be only too happy to motor you down. It ought to be a delightful run at this time of year—the rhododendrons will be out. I mean it. You don't know how truly I mean it. Very probably—it won't affect you at all. And—I think I may say I have the finest collection of narwhal tusks in the world. All the best skins and horns have to go through London, and L. Maxwell M'Leod, he knows where they come from, and where they go to. That's his business."

For the rest of the voyage up-channel Mr. M'Leod talked to me of the assembling, preparation, and sale of the rare furs; and told me things about the manufacture of fur-lined coats which quite shocked me. Somehow or other, when we landed on Wednesday, I found myself pledged to spend that week-end with him at Holmescroft.

On Saturday he met me with a well-groomed motor, and ran me out, in an hour and a half, to an exclusive residential district of dustless roads and elegantly designed country villas, each standing in from three to five acres of perfectly appointed land. He told me land was selling at eight hundred pounds the acre, and the new golf links, whose Queen Anne pavilion we passed, had cost nearly twenty-four thousand pounds to create.

Holmescroft was a large, two-storied, low, creeper-covered residence. A verandah at the south side gave on to a garden and two tennis courts, separated by a tasteful iron fence from a most park-like meadow of five or six acres, where two Jersey cows grazed. Tea was ready in the shade of a promising copper beech, and I could see groups on the lawn of young men and maidens appropriately clothed, playing lawn tennis in the sunshine.

"A pretty scene, ain't it?" said Mr. M'Leod. "My good lady's sitting under the tree, and that's my little girl in pink on the far court. But I'll take you to your room, and you can see 'em all later."

He led me through a wide parquet-floored hall furnished in pale lemon, with huge Cloisonnée vases, an ebonized and gold grand piano, and banks of pot flowers in Benares brass bowls, up a pale oak staircase to a spacious landing, where there was a green velvet settee trimmed with silver. The blinds were down, and the light lay in parallel lines on the floors.

He showed me my room, saying cheerfully: "You may be a little tired. One often is without knowing it after a run through traffic. Don't come down till you feel quite restored. We shall all be in the garden."

My room was rather warm, and smelt of perfumed soap. I threw up the window at once, but it opened so close to the floor and worked so clumsily that I came within an ace of pitching out, where I should certainly have ruined a rather lop-sided laburnum below. As I set about washing off the journey's dust, I began to feel a little tired. But, I reflected, I had not come down here in this weather and among these new surroundings to be depressed; so I began to whistle.

And it was just then that I was aware of a little grey shadow, as it might have been a snowflake seen against the light, floating at an immense distance in the background of my brain. It annoyed me, and I shook my head to get rid of it. Then my brain telegraphed that it was the forerunner of a swift-striding gloom which there was yet time to escape if I would force my thoughts away from it, as a man leaping for life forces his body forward and away from the fall of a wall. But the gloom overtook me before I could take in the meaning of the message. I moved toward the bed, every nerve already aching with the foreknowledge of the pain that was to be dealt it, and sat down, while my amazed and angry soul dropped, gulf by gulf, into that horror of great darkness which is spoken of in the Bible, and which, as auctioneers say, must be experienced to be appreciated.

Despair upon despair, misery upon misery, fear after fear, each causing their distinct and separate woe, packed in upon me for an unrecorded length of time, until at last they blurred together, and I heard a click in my brain like the click in the ear when one descends in a diving bell, and I knew that the pressures were equalised within and without, and that, for the moment, the worst was at an end. But I knew also that at any moment the darkness might come down anew; and while I dwelt on this speculation precisely as a man torments a raging tooth with his tongue, it ebbed away into the little grey shadow on the brain of its first coming, and once more I heard my brain, which knew what would recur, telegraph to every quarter for help, release or diversion.

The door opened, and M'Leod reappeared. I thanked him politely, saying I was charmed with my room, anxious to meet Mrs. M'Leod, much refreshed with my wash, and so on and so forth. Beyond a little stickiness at the corners of my mouth, it seemed to me that I was managing my words admirably, the while that I myself cowered at the bottom of unclimbable pits. M'Leod laid his hand on my shoulder, and said: "You've got it now already, ain't it?"

"Yes," I answered. "It's making me sick!"

"It will pass off when you come outside. I give you my word it will then pass off. Come!"

I shambled out behind him, and wiped my forehead in the hall.

"You mustn't mind," he said. "I expect the run tired you. My good lady is sitting there under the copper beech."

She was a fat woman in an apricot-coloured gown, with a heavily powdered face, against which her black long-lashed eyes showed like currants in dough. I was introduced to many fine ladies and gentlemen of those parts. Magnificently appointed landaus and covered motors swept in and out of the drive, and the air was gay with the merry outcries of the tennis players.

As twilight drew on they all went away, and I was left alone with Mr. and Mrs. M'Leod, while tall menservants and maidservants took away the tennis and tea things. Miss M'Leod had walked a little down the drive with a light-haired young man, who apparently knew everything about every South American railway stock. He had told me at tea that these were the days of financial specialisation.

"I think it went off beautifully, my dear," said Mr. M'Leod to his wife; and to me: "You feel all right now, ain't it? Of course you do."

Mrs. M'Leod surged across the gravel. Her husband skipped nimbly before her into the south verandah, turned a switch, and all Holmescroft was flooded with light.

"You can do that from your room also," he said as they went in. "There is something in money, ain't it?"

Miss M'Leod came up behind me in the dusk. "We have not yet been introduced," she said, "but I suppose you are staying the night?"

"Your father was kind enough to ask me," I replied.

She nodded. "Yes, I know; and you know to, don't you. I saw your face when you came to shake hands with mamma. You felt the depression very soon. It is simply frightful in that bedroom sometimes. What do you think it is—bewitchment? In Greece, where I was a little girl, it might have been; but not in England, do you think? Or *do* you?"

"I don't know what to think," I replied. "I never felt anything like it. Does it happen often?"

"Yes, sometimes. It comes and goes."

"Pleasant!" I said, as we walked up and down the gravel at the lawn edge. "What has been your experience of it?"

"That is difficult to say, but—sometimes that—that depression is like as it were"—she gesticulated in most un-English fashion—"a light. Yes, like a light turned into a room—only a light of blackness, do you understand?—into a happy room. For sometimes we are so happy, all we three—so very happy. Then this blackness, it is turned on us just like—ah, I know what I mean now—like the head-lamp of a motor, and we are eclipsed. And there is another thing——"

The dressing-gong roared, and we entered the over-lighted hall. My dressing was a brisk athletic performance, varied with outbursts of song—careful attention paid to articulation and expression. But nothing happened. As I hurried downstairs, I thanked Heaven that nothing had happened.

Dinner was served breakfast fashion; the dishes were placed on the sideboard over heaters, and we helped ourselves.

"We always do this when we are alone, so we talk better," said Mr. M'Leod.

"And we are always alone," said the daughter.

"Cheer up, Thea. It will all come right," he insisted.

"No, papa." She shook her dark head. "Nothing is right while *it* comes."

"It is nothing that we ourselves have ever done in our lives—that I will swear to you," said Mrs. M'Leod suddenly. "And we have changed our servants several times. So we know it is not *them*."

"Never mind. Let us enjoy ourselves while we can," said Mr. M'Leod, opening the champagne.

But we did not enjoy ourselves. The talk failed. There were long silences.

"I beg your pardon," I said, for I thought some one at my elbow was about to speak.

"Ah! That is the other thing!" said Miss M'Leod. Her mother groaned.

We were silent again, and, in a few seconds it must have been, a live grief beyond words—not ghostly dread or horror, but aching, helpless grief—overwhelmed us, each, I felt, according to his or her nature, and held steady like the beam of a burning-glass. Behind that pain I was conscious there was a desire on somebody's part to explain something on which some tremendously important issue hung.

Meantime I rolled bread pills and remembered my sins; M'Leod considered his own reflection in a spoon; his wife seemed to be praying, and the girl fidgeted desperately with hands and feet, till the darkness passed on—as though the malignant rays of a burning-glass had been shifted from us.

"There," said Miss M'Leod, half rising. "Now you see what makes a happy home. Oh, sell it—sell it, father mine, and let us go away!"

"But I've spent thousands on it. You shall go to Harrogate next week, Thea dear."

"I'm only just back from hotels. I am *so* tired of packing."

"Cheer up, Thea. It is over. You know it does not often come here twice in the same night. I think we shall dare now to be comfortable."

He lifted a dish-cover, and helped his wife and daughter. His face was lined and fallen like an old man's after debauch, but his hand did not shake, and his voice was clear. As he worked to restore us by speech and action, he reminded me of a grey-muzzled collie herding demoralised sheep.

After dinner we sat round the dining-room fire—the drawing-room might have been under the Shadow for aught we knew—talking with the intimacy of gipsies by the wayside, or of wounded comparing notes after a skirmish. By eleven o'clock the three between them had given me every name and detail they could recall that in any way bore on the house, and what they knew of its history.

We went to bed in a fortifying blaze of electric light. My one fear was that the blasting gust of depression would return—the surest way, of course, to bring it. I lay awake till dawn, breathing quickly and sweating lightly, beneath what De Quincey inadequately describes as "the oppression of inexpiable guilt." Now as soon as the lovely day was broken, I fell into the most terrible of all dreams—that joyous one in which all past evil has not only been wiped out of our lives, but has never been committed; and in the very bliss of our assured innocence, before our loves shriek and change countenance, we wake to the day we have earned.

It was a coolish morning, but we preferred to breakfast in the south verandah. The forenoon we spent in the garden, pretending to play games that come out of boxes, such as croquet and clock golf. But most of the time we drew together and talked. The young man who knew all about South American railways took Miss M'Leod for a walk in the afternoon, and at five M'Leod thoughtfully whirled us all up to dine in town.

"Now, don't say you will tell the Psychological Society, and that you will come again," said Miss M'Leod, as we parted. "Because I know you will not."

"You should not say that," said her mother. "You should say, 'Goodbye, Mr. Perseus. Come again.'"

"Not him!" the girl cried. "He has seen the Medusa's head!"

Looking at myself in the restaurant's mirrors, it seemed to me that I had not much benefited by my week-end. Next morning I wrote out all my Holmescroft notes at fullest length, in the hope that by so doing I could put it all behind me. But the experience worked on my mind, as they say certain imperfectly understood rays work on the body.

I am less calculated to make a Sherlock Holmes than any man I know, for I lack both method and patience, yet the idea of following up the trouble to its source fascinated me. I had no theory to go on, except a vague idea that I had come between two poles of a discharge, and had taken a shock meant for some one else. This was followed by a feeling of intense irritation. I waited cautiously on myself, expecting to be overtaken by horror of the supernatural, but my self persisted in being humanly indignant, exactly as though it had been the victim of a practical joke. It was in great pains and upheavals—that I felt in every fibre—but its dominant idea, to put it coarsely, was to get back a bit of its own. By this I knew that I might go forward if I could find the way.

After a few days it occurred to me to go to the office of Mr. J. M. M. Baxter—the solicitor who had sold Holmescroft to M'Leod. I explained I had some notion of buying the place. Would he act for me in the matter?

Mr. Baxter, a large, greyish, throaty-voiced man, showed no enthusiasm. "I sold it to Mr. M'Leod," he said. "It 'ud scarcely do for me to start on the running-down tack now. But I can recommend——"

"I know he's asking an awful price," I interrupted, "and atop of it he wants an extra thousand for what he calls your clean bill of health."

Mr. Baxter sat up in his chair. I had all his attention.

"Your guarantee with the house. Don't you remember it?"

"Yes, yes. That no death had taken place in the house since it was built. I remember perfectly."

He did not gulp as untrained men do when they lie, but his jaws moved stickily, and his eyes, turning towards the deed boxes on the wall, dulled. I counted seconds, one, two, three—one, two, three—up to ten. A man, I knew, can live through ages of mental depression in that time.

"I remember perfectly." His mouth opened a little as though it had tasted old bitterness.

"Of course *that* sort of thing doesn't appeal to me." I went on. "I don't expect to buy a house free from death."

"Certainly not. No one does. But it was Mr. M'Leod's fancy—his wife's rather, I believe; and since we could meet it—it was my duty to my clients—at whatever cost to my own feelings—to make him pay."

"That's really why I came to you. I understood from him you knew the place well."

"Oh, yes. Always did. It originally belonged to some connections of mine."

"The Misses Moultrie, I suppose. How interesting! They must have loved the place before the country round about was built up."

"They were very fond of it indeed."

"I don't wonder. So restful and sunny. I don't see how they could have brought themselves to part with it."

Now it is one of the most constant peculiarities of the English that in polite conversation—and I had striven to be polite—no one ever does or sells anything for mere money's sake.

"Miss Agnes—the youngest—fell ill" (he spaced his words a little), "and, as they were very much attached to each other, that broke up the home."

"Naturally. I fancied it must have been something of that kind. One doesn't associate the Staffordshire Moultries" (my Demon of Irresponsibility at that instant created 'em), "with—with being hard up."

"I don't know whether we're related to them," he answered importantly. "We may be, for our branch of the family comes from the Midlands."

I give this talk at length, because I am so proud of my first attempt at detective work. When I left him, twenty minutes later, with instructions to move against the owner of Holmescroft, with a view to purchase, I was more bewildered than any Doctor Watson at the opening of a story.

Why should a middle-aged solicitor turn plovers' egg colour and drop his jaw when reminded of so innocent and festal a matter as that no death had ever occurred in a house that he had sold? If I knew my English vocabulary at all, the tone in which he said the youngest sister "fell ill" meant that she had gone out of her mind. That might explain his change of countenance, and it was just possible that her demented influence still hung about Holmescroft; but the rest was beyond me.

I was relieved when I reached M'Leod's City office, and could tell him what I had done—not what I thought.

M'Leod was quite willing to enter into the game of the pretended purchase, but did not see how it would help if I knew Baxter.

"He's the only living soul I can get at who was connected with Holmescroft," I said.

"Ah! Living soul is good," said M'Leod. "At any rate our little girl will be pleased that you are still interested in us. Won't you come down some day this week?"

"How is it there now?" I asked.

He screwed up his face. "Simply frightful!" he said. "Thea is at Droitwich."

"I should like it immensely, but I must cultivate Baxter for the present. You'll be sure and keep him busy your end, won't you?"

He looked at me with quiet contempt. "Do not be afraid. I shall be a good Jew. I shall be my own solicitor."

Before a fortnight was over, Baxter admitted ruefully that M'Leod was better than most firms in the business. We buyers were coy, argumentative, shocked at the price of Holmescroft, inquisitive, and cold by turns, but Mr. M'Leod the seller easily met and surpassed us; and Mr. Baxter entered every letter, telegram, and consultation at the proper rates in a cinematograph-film of a bill. At the end of a month he said it looked as though M'Leod, thanks to him, were really going to listen to reason. I was many pounds out of pocket, but I had learned something of Mr. Baxter on the human side. I deserved it. Never in my life have I worked to conciliate, amuse, and flatter a human being as I worked over my solicitor.

It appeared that he golfed. Therefore, I was an enthusiastic beginner, anxious to learn. Twice I invaded his office with a bag (M'Leod lent it) full of the spelicans needed in this detestable game, and a vocabulary to match. The third time the ice broke, and Mr. Baxter took me to his links, quite ten miles off, where in a maze of tramway lines, railroads, and nursery-maids, we skelped our divotted way round nine holes like barges plunging through head seas. He played vilely and had never expected to meet any one worse; but as he realised my form, I think he began to like me, for he took me in hand by the two hours together. After a fortnight he could give me no more than a stroke a hole, and when, with this allowance, I once managed to beat him by one, he was honestly glad, and assured me that I should be a golfer if I stuck to it. I was sticking to it for my own ends, but now and again my conscience pricked me; for the man was a nice man. Between games he supplied me with odd pieces of evidence, such as that he had known the Moultries all his life, being their cousin, and that Miss Mary, the eldest, was an unforgiving woman who would never let bygones be. I naturally wondered what she might have against him; and somehow connected him unfavourably with mad Agnes.

"People ought to forgive and forget," he volunteered one day between rounds. "Specially where, in the nature of things, they can't be sure of their deductions. Don't you think so?"

"It all depends on the nature of the evidence on which one forms one's judgment," I answered.

"Nonsense!" he cried. "I'm lawyer enough to know that there's nothing in the world so misleading as circumstantial evidence. Never was."

"Why? Have you ever seen men hanged on it?"

"Hanged? People have been supposed to be eternally lost on it," his face turned grey again. "I don't know how it is with you, but my consolation is that God must know. He *must!* Things that seem on the face of 'em like murder, or say suicide, may appear different to God. Heh?"

"That's what the murderer and the suicide can always hope—I suppose."

"I have expressed myself clumsily as usual. The facts as God knows 'em —may *be* different—even after the most clinching evidence. I've always said that—both as a lawyer and a man, but some people won't—I don't want to judge 'em—we'll say they can't—believe it; whereas *I* say there's always a working chance—a certainty—that the worst hasn't happened." He stopped and cleared his throat. "Now, let's come on! This time next week I shall be taking my holiday."

"What links?" I asked carelessly, while twins in a perambulator got out of our line of fire.

"A potty little nine-hole affair at a hydro in the Midlands. My cousins stay there. Always will. Not but what the fourth and the seventh holes take some doing. You could manage it, though," he said encouragingly. "You're doing much better. It's only your approach shots that are weak."

"You're right. I can't approach for nuts! I shall go to pieces while you're away—with no one to coach me," I said mournfully.

"I haven't taught you anything," he said, delighted with the compliment.

"I owe all I've learned to you, anyhow. When will you come back?"

"Look here," he began. "I don't know your engagements, but I've no one to play with at Burry Mills. Never have. Why couldn't you take a few days off and join me there? I warn you it will be rather dull. It's a throat and gout place—baths, massage, electricity, and so forth. But the fourth and the seventh holes really take some doing."

"I'm for the game," I answered valiantly; Heaven well knowing that I hated every stroke and word of it.

"That's the proper spirit. As their lawyer I must ask you not to say anything to my cousins about Holmescroft. It upsets 'em. Always did. But speaking as man to man, it would be very pleasant for me if you could see your way to——"

I saw it as soon as decency permitted, and thanked him sincerely. According to my now well-developed theory he had certainly misappropriated his aged cousins' monies under power of attorney, and had probably driven poor Agnes Moultrie out of her wits, but I wished that he was not so gentle, and good-tempered, and innocent-eyed.

Before I joined him at Burry Mills Hydro, I spent a night at Holmescroft. Miss M'Leod had returned from her Hydro, and first we made very merry on the open lawn in the sunshine over the manners and customs of the English resorting to such places. She knew dozens of hydros, and warned me how to behave in them, while Mr. and Mrs. M'Leod stood aside and adored her.

"Ah! That's the way she always comes back to us," he said. "Pity it wears off so soon, ain't it? You ought to hear her sing 'With mirth thou pretty bird.'"

We had the house to face through the evening, and there we neither laughed nor sung. The gloom fell on us as we entered, and did not shift till ten o'clock, when we crawled out, as it were, from beneath it.

"It has been bad this summer," said Mrs. M'Leod in a whisper after we realised that we were freed. "Sometimes I think the house will get up and cry out—it is so bad."

"How?"

"Have you forgotten what comes after the depression?"

So then we waited about the small fire, and the dead air in the room presently filled and pressed down upon us with the sensation (but words are useless here) as though some dumb and bound power were striving against gag and bond to deliver its soul of an articulate word. It passed in a few minutes, and I fell to thinking about Mr. Baxter's conscience and Agnes Moultrie, gone mad in the well-lit bedroom that waited me. These reflections secured me a night during which I rediscovered how, from purely mental causes, a man can be physically sick; but the sickness was bliss compared to my dreams when the birds waked. On my departure, M'Leod gave me a beautiful narwhal's horn, much as a nurse gives a child sweets for being brave at a dentist's.

"There's no duplicate of it in the world," he said, "else it would have come to old Max M'Leod," and he tucked it into the motor. Miss M'Leod on the far side of the car whispered, "Have you found out anything, Mr. Perseus?"

I shook my head.

"Then I shall be chained to my rock all my life," she went on. "Only don't tell papa."

I supposed she was thinking of the young gentleman who specialised in South American rails, for I noticed a ring on the third finger of her left hand.

I went straight from that house to Burry Mills Hydro, keen for the first time in my life on playing golf, which is guaranteed to occupy the mind. Baxter had taken me a room communicating with his own, and after lunch introduced me to a tall, horse-headed elderly lady of decided manners, whom a white-haired maid pushed along in a bath-chair through the park-like grounds of the Hydro. She was Miss Mary Moultrie, and she coughed and cleared her throat just like Baxter. She suffered—she told me it was a Moultrie caste-mark—from some obscure form of chronic bronchitis, complicated with spasm of the glottis; and, in a dead, flat voice, with a sunken eye that looked and saw not, told me what washes, gargles, pastilles, and inhalations she had proved most beneficial. From her I was passed on to her younger sister, Miss Elizabeth, a small and withered thing with twitching lips, victim, she told me, to very much the same sort of throat, but secretly devoted to another set of medicines. When she went away with Baxter and the bath-chair, I fell across a major of the Indian army with gout in his glassy eyes, and a stomach which he had taken all round the Continent. He laid everything before me; and him I escaped only to be confided in by a matron with a tendency to follicular tonsilitis and eczema. Baxter waited hand and foot on his cousins till five o'clock, trying, as I saw, to atone for his treatment of the dead sister. Miss Mary ordered him about like a dog.

"I warned you it would be dull," he said when we met in the smoking-room.

"It's tremendously interesting," I said. "But how about a look round the links?"

"Unluckily damp always affects my eldest cousin. I've got to buy her a new bronchitis-kettle. Arthurs broke her old one yesterday."

We slipped out to the chemist's shop in the town, and he bought a large glittering tin thing whose workings he explained.

"I'm used to this sort of work. I come up here pretty often," he said. "I've the family throat too."

"You're a good man," I said. "A very good man."

He turned towards me in the evening light among the beeches, and his face was changed to what it might have been a generation before.

"You see," he said huskily, "there was the youngest—Agnes. Before she fell ill, you know. But she didn't like leaving her sisters. Never would." He hurried on with his odd-shaped load and left me among the ruins of my black theories. The man with that face had done Agnes Moultrie no wrong.

*   *   *   *   *

We never played our game. I was waked between two and three in the morning from my hygienic bed by Baxter in an ulster over orange and white pyjamas, which I should never have suspected from his character.

"My cousin has had some sort of a seizure," he said. "Will you come? I don't want to wake the doctor. Don't want to make a scandal. Quick!"

So I came quickly, and led by the white-haired Arthurs in a jacket and petticoat, entered a double-bedded room reeking with steam and Friar's Balsam. The electrics were all on. Miss Mary—I knew her by her height—was at the open window, wrestling with Miss Elizabeth, who gripped her round the knees. Miss Mary's hand was at her own throat, which was streaked with blood.

"She's done it. She's done it too!" Miss Elizabeth panted. "Hold her! Help me!"

"Oh, I say! Women don't cut their throats," Baxter whispered.

"My God! Has she cut her throat?" the maid cried out, and with no warning rolled over in a faint. Baxter pushed her under the wash-basins, and leaped to hold the gaunt woman who crowed and whistled as she struggled toward the window. He took her by the shoulder, and she struck out wildly.

"All right! She's only cut her hand," he said. "Wet towel—quick!"

While I got that he pushed her backward. Her strength seemed almost as great as his. I swabbed at her throat when I could, and found no mark; then helped him to control her a little. Miss Elizabeth leaped back to bed, wailing like a child.

"Tie up her hand somehow," said Baxter. "Don't let it drip about the place. She"—he stepped on broken glass in his slippers, "she must have smashed a pane."

Miss Mary lurched towards the open window again, dropped on her knees, her head on the sill, and lay quiet, surrendering the cut hand to me.

"What did she do?" Baxter turned towards Miss Elizabeth in the far bed.

"She was going to throw herself out of the window," was the answer. "I stopped her, and sent Arthurs for you. Oh, we can never hold up our heads again!"

Miss Mary writhed and fought for breath. Baxter found a shawl which he threw over her shoulders.

"Nonsense!" said he. "That isn't like Mary;" but his face worked when he said it.

"You wouldn't believe about Aggie, John. Perhaps you will now!" said Miss Elizabeth. "I saw her do it, and she's cut her throat too!"

"She hasn't," I said. "It's only her hand."

Miss Mary suddenly broke from us with an indescribable grunt, flew, rather than ran, to her sister's bed, and there shook her as one furious schoolgirl would shake another.

"No such thing," she croaked. "How dare you think so, you wicked little fool?"

"Get into bed, Mary," said Baxter. "You'll catch a chill."

She obeyed, but sat up with the grey shawl round her lean shoulders, glaring at her sister. "I'm better now," she panted. "Arthurs let me sit out too long. Where's Arthurs? The kettle."

"Never mind Arthurs," said Baxter. "You get the kettle." I hastened to bring it from the side table. "Now, Mary, as God sees you, tell me what you've done."

His lips were dry, and he could not moisten them with his tongue.

Miss Mary applied herself to the mouth of the kettle, and between indraws of steam said: "The spasm came on just now, while I was asleep. I was nearly choking to death. So I went to the window. I've done it often before, without waking any one. Bessie's such an old maid about draughts. I tell you I was choking to death. I couldn't manage the catch, and I nearly fell out. That window opens too low. I cut my hand trying to save myself. Who has tied it up in this filthy handkerchief? I wish you had had my throat, Bessie. I never was nearer dying!" She scowled on us all impartially, while her sister sobbed.

From the bottom of the bed we heard a quivering voice: "Is she dead? Have they took her away? Oh, I never could bear the sight o' blood!"

"Arthurs," said Miss Mary, "you are an hireling. Go away!"

It is my belief that Arthurs crawled out on all fours, but I was busy picking up broken glass from the carpet.

Then Baxter, seated by the side of the bed, began to cross-examine in a voice I scarcely recognised. No one could for an instant have doubted the genuine rage of Miss Mary against her sister, her cousin, or her maid; and that a doctor should have been called in—for she did me the honour of calling me doctor—was the last drop. She was choking with her throat; had rushed to the window for air; had near pitched out, and in catching at the window bars had cut her hand. Over and over she made this clear to the intent Baxter. Then she turned on her sister and tongue-lashed her savagely.

"You mustn't blame me," Miss Bessie faltered at last. "You know what we think of night and day."

"I'm coming to that," said Baxter. "Listen to me. What you did, Mary, misled four people into thinking you—you meant to do away with yourself."

"Isn't one suicide in the family enough? Oh God, help and pity us! You *couldn't* have believed that!" she cried.

"The evidence was complete. Now, don't you think," Baxter's finger wagged under her nose—"*can't* you think that poor Aggie did the same thing at Holmescroft when she fell out of the window?"

"She had the same throat," said Miss Elizabeth. "Exactly the same symptoms. Don't you remember, Mary?"

"Which was her bedroom?" I asked of Baxter in an undertone.

"Over the south verandah, looking on to the tennis lawn."

"I nearly fell out of that very window when I was at Holmescroft— opening it to get some air. The sill doesn't come much above your knees," I said.

"You hear that, Mary? Mary, do you hear what this gentleman says? Won't you believe that what nearly happened to you must have happened to poor Aggie that night? For God's sake—for her sake—Mary, *won't* you believe?"

There was a long silence while the steam kettle puffed.

"If I could have proof—if I could have proof," said she, and broke into most horrible tears.

Baxter motioned to me, and I crept away to my room, and lay awake till morning, thinking more specially of the dumb Thing at Holmescroft which wished to explain itself. I hated Miss Mary as perfectly as though I had known her for twenty years, but I felt that, alive or dead, I should not like her to condemn me.

Yet at mid-day, when I saw Miss Mary in her bath-chair, Arthurs behind and Baxter and Miss Elizabeth on either side, in the park-like grounds of the Hydro, I found it difficult to arrange my words.

"Now that you know all about it," said Baxter aside, after the first strangeness of our meeting was over, "it's only fair to tell you that my poor cousin did not die in Holmescroft at all. She was dead when they found her under the window in the morning. Just dead."

"Under that laburnum outside the window?" I asked, for I suddenly remembered the crooked evil thing.

"Exactly. She broke the tree in falling. But no death has ever taken place in the house, so far as we were concerned. You can make yourself quite easy on that point. Mr. M'Leod's extra thousand for what you call the 'clean bill of health' was something toward my cousin's estate when we sold. It was my duty as their lawyer to get it for them—at any cost to my own feelings."

I know better than to argue when the English talk about their duty. So I agreed with my solicitor.

"Their sister's death must have been a great blow to your cousins," I went on. The bath-chair was behind me.

"Unspeakable," Baxter whispered. "They brooded on it day and night. No wonder. If their theory of poor Aggie making away with herself was correct, she was eternally lost!"

"Do you believe that she made away with herself?"

"No, thank God! Never have! And after what happened to Mary last night, I see perfectly what happened to poor Aggie. She had the family throat too. By the way, Mary thinks you are a doctor. Otherwise she wouldn't like your having been in her room."

"Very good. Is she convinced now about her sister's death?"

"She'd give anything to be able to believe it, but she's a hard woman, and brooding along certain lines makes one groovy. I have sometimes been afraid of her reason—on the religious side, don't you know. Elizabeth doesn't matter. Brain of a hen. Always had."

Here Arthurs summoned me to the bath-chair, and the ravaged face, beneath its knitted Shetland wool hood, of Miss Mary Moultrie.

"I need not remind you, I hope, of the seal of secrecy—absolute secrecy —in your profession," she began. "Thanks to my cousin's and my sister's stupidity, you have found out——" she blew her nose.

"Please don't excite her, sir," said Arthurs at the back.

"But, my dear Miss Moultrie, I only know what I've seen, of course, but it seems to me that what you thought was a tragedy in your sister's case, turns out, on your own evidence, so to speak, to have been an accident—a dreadfully sad one—but absolutely an accident."

"Do you believe that too?" she cried. "Or are you only saying it to comfort me?"

"I believe it from the bottom of my heart. Come down to Holmescroft for an hour—for half an hour—and satisfy yourself."

"Of what? You don't understand. I see the house every day—every night. I am always there in spirit—waking or sleeping. I couldn't face it in reality."

"But you must," I said. "If you go there in the spirit the greater need for you to go there in the flesh. Go to your sister's room once more, and see the window—I nearly fell out of it myself. It's—it's awfully low and danger-ous. That would convince you," I pleaded.

"Yet Aggie had slept in that room for years," she interrupted.

"You've slept in your room here for a long time, haven't you? But you nearly fell out of the window when you were choking."

"That is true. That is one thing true," she nodded. "And I might have been killed as—perhaps—Aggie was killed."

"In that case your own sister and cousin and maid would have said you had committed suicide, Miss Moultrie. Come down to Holmescroft, and go over the place just once."

"You are lying," she said quite quietly. "You don't want me to come down to see a window. It is something else. I warn you we are Evangelicals. We don't believe in prayers for the dead. 'As the tree falls——' "

"Yes. I daresay. But you persist in thinking that your sister committed suicide——"

"No! No! I have always prayed that I might have misjudged her."

Arthurs at the bath-chair spoke up: "Oh, Miss Mary! you *would* 'ave it from the first that poor Miss Aggie 'ad made away with herself; an', of course, Miss Bessie took the notion from you. Only Master—Mister John stood out, and—and I'd 'ave taken my Bible oath you was making away with yourself last night."

Miss Mary leaned towards me, one finger on my sleeve.

"If going to Holmescroft kills me," she said, "you will have the murder of a fellow-creature on your conscience for all eternity."

"I'll risk it," I answered. Remembering what torment the mere reflection of her torments had cast on Holmescroft, and remembering, above all, the dumb Thing that filled the house with its desire to speak, I felt that there might be worse things.

Baxter was amazed at the proposed visit, but at a nod from that terrible woman went off to make arrangements. Then I sent a telegram to M'Leod bidding him and his vacate Holmescroft for that afternoon. Miss Mary should be alone with her dead, as I had been alone.

I expected untold trouble in transporting her, but to do her justice, the promise given for the journey, she underwent it without murmur, spasm, or unnecessary word. Miss Bessie, pressed in a corner by the window, wept behind her veil, and from time to time tried to take hold of her sister's hand. Baxter wrapped himself in his newly found happiness as selfishly as a bridegroom, for he sat still and smiled.

"So long as I know that Aggie didn't make away with herself," he explained, "I tell you frankly I don't care what happened. She's as hard as a rock—Mary. Always was. She won't die."

We led her out on to the platform like a blind woman, and so got her into the fly. The half-hour crawl to Holmescroft was the most racking experience of the day. M'Leod had obeyed my instructions. There was no one visible in the house or the gardens; and the front door stood open.

Miss Mary rose from beside her sister, stepped forth first, and entered the hall.

"Come, Bessie," she cried.

"I daren't. Oh, I daren't."

"Come!" Her voice had altered. I felt Baxter start. "There's nothing to be afraid of."

"Good heavens!" said Baxter. "She's running up the stairs. We'd better follow."

"Let's wait below. She's going to the room."

We heard the door of the bedroom I knew open and shut, and we waited in the lemon-coloured hall, heavy with the scent of flowers.

"I've never been into it since it was sold," Baxter sighed. "What a lovely, restful place it is! Poor Aggie used to arrange the flowers."

"Restful?" I began, but stopped of a sudden, for I felt all over my bruised soul that Baxter was speaking truth. It was a light, spacious, airy house, full of the sense of well-being and peace—above all things, of peace. I ventured into the dining-room where the thoughtful M'Leod's had left a small fire. There was no terror there, present or lurking, and in the drawing-room, which for good reasons we had never cared to enter, the sun and the peace and the scent of the flowers worked together as is fit in an inhabited house. When I returned to the hall, Baxter was sweetly asleep on a couch, looking most unlike a middle-aged solicitor who had spent a broken night with an exacting cousin.

There was ample time for me to review it all—to felicitate myself upon my magnificent acumen (barring some errors about Baxter as a thief and possibly a murderer), before the door above opened, and Baxter, evidently a light sleeper, sprang awake.

"I've had a heavenly little nap," he said, rubbing his eyes with the backs of his hands like a child. "Good Lord! That's not their step!"

But it was. I had never before been privileged to see the Shadow turned backward on the dial—the years ripped bodily off poor human shoulders—old sunken eyes filled and alight—harsh lips moistened and human.

"John," Miss Mary called, "I know now. Aggie didn't do it!" and "She didn't do it!" echoed Miss Bessie, and giggled.

"I did not think it wrong to say a prayer," Miss Mary continued. "Not for her soul, but for our peace. Then I was convinced."

"Then we got conviction," the younger sister piped.

"We've misjudged poor Aggie, John. But I feel she knows now. Wherever she is, she knows that we know she is guiltless."

"Yes, she knows. I felt it too," said Miss Elizabeth.

"I never doubted," said John Baxter, whose face was beautiful at that hour. "Not from the first. Never have!"

"You never offered me proof, John. Now, thank God, it will not be the same any more. I can think henceforward of Aggie without sorrow." She tripped, absolutely tripped, across the hall. "What ideas these Jews have of arranging furniture!" She spied me behind a big Cloisonnée vase.

"I've seen the window," she said remotely. "You took a great risk in advising me to undertake such a journey. However, as it turns out . . . I forgive you, and I pray you may never know what mental anguish means! Bessie! Look at this peculiar piano! Do you suppose, Doctor, these people would offer one tea? I miss mine."

"I will go and see," I said, and explored M'Leod's new-built servants' wing. It was in the servants' hall that I unearthed the M'Leod family, bursting with anxiety.

"Tea for three, quick," I said. "If you ask me any questions now, I shall have a fit!" So Mrs. M'Leod got it, and I was butler, amid murmured apologies from Baxter, still smiling and self-absorbed, and the cold disapproval of Miss Mary, who thought the pattern of the china vulgar. However, she ate well, and even asked me whether I would not like a cup of tea for myself.

They went away in the twilight—the twilight that I had once feared. They were going to an hotel in London to rest after the fatigues of the day, and as their fly turned down the drive, I capered on the door step, with the all-darkened house behind me.

Then I heard the uncertain feet of the M'Leods and bade them not to turn on the lights, but to feel—to feel what I had done; for the Shadow was gone, with the dumb desire in the air. They drew short, but afterwards deeper, breaths, like bathers entering chill water, separated one from the other, moved about the hall, tiptoed upstairs, raced down, and then Miss M'Leod, and I believe her mother, though she denies this, embraced me. I know M'Leod did.

It was a disgraceful evening. To say we rioted through the house is to put it mildly. We played a sort of Blind Man's Buff along the darkest passages, in the unlighted drawing-room, and little dining-room, calling cheerily to each other after each exploration that here, and here, and here, the trouble had removed itself. We came up to the bedroom—mine for the night again—and sat, the women on the bed, and we men on chairs, drinking in blessed draughts of peace and comfort and cleanliness of soul, while I told them my tale in full, and received fresh praise, thanks, and blessings.

When the servants, returned from their day's outing, gave us a supper of cold fried fish, M'Leod had sense enough to open no wine. We had been practically drunk since nightfall, and grew incoherent on water and milk.

"I like that Baxter," said M'Leod. "He's a sharp man. The death wasn't in the house, but he ran it pretty close, ain't it?"

"And the joke of it is that he supposes I want to buy the place from you," I said. "Are you selling?"

"Not for twice what I paid for it—now," said M'Leod. "I'll keep you in furs all your life, but not our Holmescroft."

"No—never our Holmescroft," said Miss M'Leod. "We'll ask him here on Tuesday, mamma." They squeezed each other's hands.

"Now tell me," said Mrs. M'Leod—"that tall one I saw out of the scullery window—did she tell you she was always here in the spirit? I hate her. She made all this trouble. It was not her house after she had sold it. What do you think?"

"I suppose," I answered, "she brooded over what she believed was her sister's suicide night and day—she confessed she did—and her thoughts being concentrated on this place, they felt like a—like a burning glass."

"Burning glass is good," said M'Leod.

"I said it was like a light of blackness turned on us," cried the girl, twiddling her ring. "That must have been when the tall one thought worst about her sister and the house."

"Ah, the poor Aggie!" said Mrs. M'Leod. "The poor Aggie, trying to tell every one it was not so! No wonder we felt Something wished to say Something. Thea, Max, do you remember that night——"

"We need not remember any more," M'Leod interrupted. "It is not our trouble. They have told each other now."

"Do you think, then," said Miss M'Leod, "that those two, the living ones, were actually told something—upstairs—in your—in the room?"

"I can't say. At any rate they were made happy, and they ate a big tea afterwards. As your father says, it is not our trouble any longer—thank God!"

"Amen!" said M'Leod. "Now, Thea, let us have some music after all these months. 'With mirth, thou pretty bird,' ain't it? You ought to hear that."

And in the half-lighted hall, Thea sang an old English song that I had never heard before.

> With mirth, thou pretty bird, rejoice
> Thy Maker's praise enhanced;
> Lift up thy shrill and pleasant voice,
> Thy God is high advanced!
> Thy food before He did provide,

And gives it in a fitting side,
   Wherewith be thou sufficed!
Why shouldst thou now unpleasant be,
   Thy wrath against God venting,
That He a little bird made thee,
   Thy silly head tormenting,
Because He made thee not a man?
Oh, Peace! He hath well thought thereon,
   Therewith be thou sufficed!

WITHOUT BENEFIT OF CLERGY

Before my Spring I garnered Autumn's gain,
Out of her time my field was white with grain,
   The year gave up her secrets to my woe.
Forced and deflowered each sick season lay,
In mystery of increase and decay;
I saw the sunset ere men saw the day,
   Who am too wise in that I should not know.
                           BITTER WATERS

I

'BUT if it be a girl?'

'Lord of my life, it cannot be. I have prayed for so many nights, and sent gifts to Sheikh Badl's shrine so often, that I know God will give us a son—a man-child that shall grow into a man. Think of this and be glad. My mother shall be his mother till I can take him again, and the mullah of the Pattan mosque shall cast his nativity—God send he be born in an auspicious hour!—and then, and then thou wilt never weary of me, thy slave.'

'Since when hast thou been a slave, my queen?'

'Since the beginning—till this mercy came to me. How could I be sure of thy love when I knew that I had been bought with silver?'

'Nay, that was the dowry. I paid it to thy mother.'

'And she has buried it, and sits upon it all day long like a hen. What talk is yours of dower! I was bought as though I had been a Lucknow dancing-girl instead of a child.'

'Art thou sorry for the sale?'

'I have sorrowed; but to-day I am glad. Thou wilt never cease to love me now?—answer, my king.'

'Never—never. No.'

'Not even though the *mem-log*—the white women of thy own blood—love thee? And remember, I have watched them driving in the evening; they are very fair.'

'I have seen fire-balloons by the hundred. I have seen the moon, and—then I saw no more fire-balloons.'

Ameera clapped her hands and laughed. 'Very good talk,' she said. Then with an assumption of great stateliness, 'It is enough. Thou hast my permission to depart,—if thou wilt.'

The man did not move. He was sitting on a low red-lacquered couch in a room furnished only with blue and white floor-cloth, some rugs, and a very complete collection of native cushions. At his feet sat a woman of sixteen, and she was all but all the world in his eyes. By every rule and law she should have been otherwise, for he was an Englishman, and she a Mussulman's daughter bought two years before from her mother, who, being left without money, would have sold Ameera shrieking to the Prince of Darkness if the price had been sufficient.

It was a contract entered into with a light heart; but even before the girl had reached her bloom she came to fill the greater portion of John Holden's life. For her, and the withered hag her mother, he had taken a little house overlooking the great red-walled city, and found,—when the marigolds had sprung up by the well in the courtyard and Ameera had established herself according to her own ideas of comfort, and her mother had ceased grumbling at the inadequacy of the cooking-places, the distance from the daily market, and at matters of house-keeping in general,—that the house was to him his home. Any one could enter his bachelor's bunga-low by day or night, and the life that he led there was an unlovely one. In the house in the city his feet only could pass beyond the outer courtyard to the women's rooms; and when the big wooden gate was bolted behind him he was king in his own territory, with Ameera for queen. And there was going to be added to this kingdom a third person whose arrival Holden felt inclined to resent. It interfered with his perfect happiness. It disar-ranged the orderly peace of the house that was his own. But Ameera was wild with delight at the thought of it, and her mother not less so. The love of a man, and particularly a white man, was at the best an inconstant affair, but it might, both women argued, be held fast by a baby's hands. 'And then,' Ameera would always say, 'then he will never care for the white *mem-log*. I hate them all—I hate them all.'

'He will go back to his own people in time,' said the mother; 'but by the blessing of God that time is yet afar off.'

Holden sat silent on the couch thinking of the future, and his thoughts were not pleasant. The drawbacks of a double life are manifold. The Government, with singular care, had ordered him out of the station for a fortnight on special duty in the place of a man who was watching by the bedside of a sick wife. The verbal notification of the transfer had been edged by a cheerful remark that Holden ought to think himself lucky in being a bachelor and a free man. He came to break the news to Ameera.

'It is not good,' she said slowly, 'but it is not all bad. There is my mother here, and no harm will come to me—unless indeed I die of pure joy. Go thou to thy work and think no troublesome thoughts. When the days are done I believe . . . nay, I am sure. And—and then I shall lay *him* in thy arms, and thou wilt love me for ever. The train goes to-night, at midnight is it not? Go now, and do not let thy heart be heavy by cause of me. But thou wilt not delay in returning? Thou wilt not stay on the road to talk to the bold white *mem-log*. Come back to me swiftly, my life.'

As he left the courtyard to reach his horse that was tethered to the gate-post, Holden spoke to the white-haired old watchman who guarded

the house, and bade him under certain contingencies despatch the filled-up telegraph-form that Holden gave him. It was all that could be done, and with the sensations of a man who has attended his own funeral Holden went away by the night mail to his exile. Every hour of the day he dreaded the arrival of the telegram, and every hour of the night he pictured to himself the death of Ameera. In consequence his work for the State was not of first-rate quality, nor was his temper towards his colleagues of the most amiable. The fortnight ended without a sign from his home, and, torn to pieces by his anxieties, Holden returned to be swallowed up for two precious hours by a dinner at the club, wherein he heard, as a man hears in a swoon, voices telling him how execrably he had performed the other man's duties, and how he had endeared himself to all his associates. Then he fled on horseback through the night with his heart in his mouth. There was no answer at first to his blows on the gate, and he had just wheeled his horse round to kick it in when Pir Khan appeared with a lantern and held his stirrup.

'Has aught occurred?' said Holden.

'The news does not come from my mouth, Protector of the Poor, but——' He held out his shaking hand as befitted the bearer of good news who is entitled to a reward.

Holden hurried through the courtyard. A light burned in the upper room. His horse neighed in the gateway, and he heard a shrill little wail that sent all the blood into the apple of his throat. It was a new voice, but it did not prove that Ameera was alive.

'Who is there?' he called up the narrow brick staircase.

There was a cry of delight from Ameera, and then the voice of the mother, tremulous with old age and pride—'We be two women and—the—man—thy—son.'

On the threshold of the room Holden stepped on a naked dagger, that was laid there to avert ill-luck, and it broke at the hilt under his impatient heel.

'God is great!' cooed Ameera in the half-light. 'Thou hast taken his misfortunes on thy head.'

'Ay, but how is it with thee, life of my life? Old woman, how is it with her?'

'She has forgotten her sufferings for joy that the child is born. There is no harm; but speak softly,' said the mother.

'It only needed thy presence to make me all well.' said Ameera. 'My king, thou hast been very long away. What gifts hast thou for me? Ah, ah! It is I that bring gifts this time. Look, my life, look. Was there ever such a babe? Nay, I am too weak even to clear my arm from him.'

'Rest then, and do not talk. I am here, *bachari* [little woman].'

'Well said, for there is a bond and a heel-rope [*peecharee*] between us now that nothing can break. Look—canst thou see in this light? He is without spot or blemish. Never was such a man-child. *Ya illah!* he shall be a pundit—no, a trooper of the Queen. And, my life, dost thou love me as well as ever, though I am faint and sick and worn? Answer truly.'

'Yea. I love as I have loved, with all my soul. Lie still, pearl, and rest.'

'Then do not go. Sit by my side here—so. Mother, the lord of this house needs a cushion. Bring it.' There was an almost imperceptible movement on the part of the new life that lay in the hollow of Ameera's arm. 'Aho!' she said, her voice breaking with love. 'The babe is a champion from his birth. He is kicking me in the side with mighty kicks. Was there ever such a babe! And he is ours to us—thine and mine. Put thy hand on his head, but carefully, for he is very young, and men are unskilled in such matters.'

Very cautiously Holden touched with the tips of his fingers the downy head.

'He is of the faith,' said Ameera; 'for lying here in the night-watches I whispered the call to prayer and the profession of faith into his ears. And it is most marvellous that he was born upon a Friday, as I was born. Be careful of him, my life; but he can almost grip with his hands.'

Holden found one helpless little hand that closed feebly on his finger. And the clutch ran through his body till it settled about his heart. Till then his sole thought had been for Ameera. He began to realise that there was some one else in the world, but he could not feel that it was a veritable son with a soul. He sat down to think, and Ameera dozed lightly.

'Get hence, *sahib*,' said her mother under her breath. 'It is not good that she should find you here on waking. She must be still.'

'I go,' said Holden submissively. 'Here be rupees. See that my *baba* gets fat and finds all that he needs.'

The chink of the silver roused Ameera. 'I am his mother, and no hireling,' she said weakly. 'Shall I look to him more or less for the sake of money? Mother, give it back. I have born my lord a son.'

The deep sleep of weakness came upon her almost before the sentence was completed. Holden went down to the courtyard very softly with his heart at ease. Pir Khan, the old watchman, was chuckling with delight. 'This house is now complete,' he said, and without further comment thrust into Holden's hands the hilt of a sabre worn many years ago when he, Pir Khan, served the Queen in the police. The bleat of a tethered goat came from the well-kerb.

'There be two,' said Pir Khan, 'two goats of the best. I bought them, and they cost much money; and since there is no birth-party assembled their flesh will be all mine. Strike craftily, *sahib!* 'Tis an ill-balanced sabre at the best. Wait till they raise their heads from cropping the marigolds.'

'And why?' said Holden, bewildered.

'For the birth-sacrifice. What else? Otherwise the child being unguarded from fate may die. The Protector of the Poor knows the fitting words to be said.'

Holden had learned them once with little thought that he would ever speak them in earnest. The touch of the cold sabre-hilt in his palm turned suddenly to the clinging grip of the child upstairs—the child that was his own son—and a dread of loss filled him.

'Strike!' said Pir Khan. 'Never life came into the world but life was paid for it. See, the goats have raised their heads. Now! With a drawing cut!'

Hardly knowing what he did Holden cut twice as he muttered the Mahomedan prayer that runs: 'Almighty! In place of this my son I offer life for life, blood for blood, head for head, bone for bone, hair for hair, skin for skin.' The waiting horse snorted and bounded in his pickets at the smell of the raw blood that spirted over Holden's riding-boots.

'Well smitten!' said Pir Khan, wiping the sabre. 'A swordsman was lost in thee. Go with a light heart, Heaven-born. I am thy servant, and the servant of thy son. May the Presence live a thousand years and . . . the flesh of the goats is all mine?' Pir Khan drew back richer by a month's pay. Holden swung himself into the saddle and rode off through the low-hanging wood-smoke of the evening. He was full of riotous exultation, alternating with a vast vague tenderness directed towards no particular object, that made him choke as he bent over the neck of his uneasy horse. 'I never felt like this in my life,' he thought. 'I'll go to the club and pull myself together.'

A game of pool was beginning, and the room was full of men. Holden entered, eager to get to the light and the company of his fellows, singing at the top of his voice—

In Baltimore a-walking, a lady I did meet!

'Did you?' said the club-secretary from his corner. 'Did she happen to tell you that your boots were wringing wet? Great goodness, man, it's blood!'

'Bosh!' said Holden, picking his cue from the rack. May I cut in? It's dew. I've been riding through high crops. My faith! my boots are in a mess though!

'And if it be a girl she shall wear a wedding-ring,
And if it be a boy he shall fight for his king,
With his dirk, and his cap, and his little jacket blue,
He shall walk the quarter-deck—'

'Yellow on blue—green next player,' said the marker monotonously.

He shall walk the quarter-deck,—Am I green, marker? *He shall walk the quarter-deck,*—eh! that's a bad shot,—*As his daddy used to do!*'

'I don't see that you have anything to crow about,' said a zealous junior civilian acidly. 'The Government is not exactly pleased with your work when you relieved Sanders.'

'Does that mean a wigging from headquarters?' said Holden with an abstracted smile. 'I think I can stand it.'

The talk beat up round the ever-fresh subject of each man's work, and steadied Holden till it was time to go to his dark empty bungalow, where his butler received him as one who knew all his affairs. Holden remained awake for the greater part of the night, and his dreams were pleasant ones.

II

'How old is he now?'

'*Ya illah!* What a man's question! He is all but six weeks old; and on this night I go up to the housetop with thee, my life, to count the stars. For that is auspicious. And he was born on a Friday under the sign of the Sun, and it has been told to me that he will outlive us both and get wealth. Can we wish for aught better, beloved?'

'There is nothing better. Let us go up to the roof, and thou shalt count the stars—but a few only, for the sky is heavy with cloud.'

'The winter rains are late, and maybe they come out of season. Come, before all the stars are hid. I have put on my richest jewels.'

'Thou hast forgotten the best of all.'

'*Ai!* Ours. He comes also. He has never yet seen the skies.'

Ameera climbed the narrow staircase that led to the flat roof. The child, placid and unwinking, lay in the hollow of her right arm, gorgeous in silver-fringed muslin with a small skull-cap on his head. Ameera wore all that she valued most. The diamond nose-stud that takes the place of the Western patch in drawing attention to the curve of the nostril, the gold ornament in the centre of the forehead studded with tallow-drop emeralds and flawed rubies, the heavy circlet of beaten gold that was fastened around her neck by the softness of the pure metal, and the chinking curb-patterned silver anklets hanging low over the rosy ankle-bone. She was dressed in jade-green muslin as befitted a daughter of the Faith, and from shoulder to elbow and elbow to wrist ran bracelets of silver tied with floss silk, frail glass bangles slipped over the wrist in proof of the slenderness of the hand, and certain heavy gold bracelets that had no part in her country's ornaments but, since they were Holden's gift and fastened with a cunning European snap, delighted her immensely.

They sat down by the low white parapet of the roof, overlooking the city and its lights.

'They are happy down there,' said Ameera. 'But I do not think that they are as happy as we. Nor do I think the white *mem-log* are as happy. And thou?'

'I know they are not.'

'How dost thou know?'

'They give their children over to the nurses.'

'I have never seen that,' said Ameera with a sigh, 'nor do I wish to see. Ahi!'—she dropped her head on Holden's shoulder,—'I have counted forty stars, and I am tired. Look at the child, love of my life, he is counting too.'

The baby was staring with round eyes at the dark of the heavens. Ameera placed him in Holden's arms, and he lay there without a cry.

'What shall we call him among ourselves?' she said. 'Look! Art thou ever tired of looking? He carries thy very eyes. But the mouth——'

'Is thine, most dear. Who should know better than I?'

' 'Tis such a feeble mouth. Oh, so small! And yet it holds my heart between its lips. Give him to me now. He has been too long away.'

'Nay, let him lie; he has not yet begun to cry.'

'When he cries thou wilt give him back—eh? What a man of mankind thou art! If he cried he were only the dearer to me. But, my life, what little name shall we give him?'

The small body lay close to Holden's heart. It was utterly helpless and very soft. He scarcely dared to breathe for fear of crushing it. The caged green parrot that is regarded as a sort of guardian-spirit in most native households moved on its perch and fluttered a drowsy wing.

'There is the answer,' said Holden. 'Mian Mittu has spoken. He shall be the parrot. When he is ready he will talk mightily and run about. Mian Mittu is the parrot in thy—in the Mussulman tongue, is it not?'

'Why put me so far off?' said Ameera fretfully. 'Let it be like unto some English name—but not wholly. For he is mine.'

'Then call him Tota, for that is likest English.'

'Ay, Tota, and that is still the parrot. Forgive me, my lord, for a minute ago, but in truth he is too little to wear all the weight of Mian Mittu for name. He shall be Tota—our Tota to us. Hearest thou, O small one? Littlest, thou art Tota.' She touched the child's cheek, and he waking wailed, and it was necessary to return him to his mother, who soothed him with the wonderful rhyme of *Aré koko, Jaré koko!* which says:

Oh crow! Go crow! Baby's sleeping sound,
And the wild plums grow in the jungle, only a penny a pound.
Only a penny a pound, *baba*, only a penny a pound.

Reassured many times as to the price of those plums, Tota cuddled himself down to sleep. The two sleek, white well-bullocks in the courtyard were steadily chewing the cud of their evening meal; old Pir Khan squatted at the head of Holden's horse, his police sabre across his knees, pulling drowsily at a big water-pipe that croaked like a bull-frog in a pond. Ameera's mother sat spinning in the lower verandah, and the wooden gate was shut and barred. The music of a marriage-procession came to the roof above the gentle hum of the city, and a string of flying-foxes crossed the face of the low moon.

'I have prayed,' said Ameera after a long pause, 'I have prayed for two things. First, that I may die in thy stead if thy death is demanded, and in the second that I may die in the place of the child. I have prayed to the Prophet and to Beebee Miriam [the Virgin Mary]. Thinkest thou either will hear?'

'From thy lips who would not hear the lightest word?'

'I asked for straight talk, and thou hast given me sweet talk. Will my prayers be heard?'

'How can I say? God is very good.'

'Of that I am not sure. Listen now. When I die, or the child dies, what is thy fate? Living, thou wilt return to the bold white *mem-log*, for kind calls to kind.'

'Not always.'

'With a woman, no; with a man it is otherwise. Thou wilt in this life, later on, go back to thine own folk. That I could almost endure, for I should be dead. But in thy very death thou wilt be taken away to a strange place and a paradise that I do not know.'

'Will it be paradise?'

'Surely, for who would harm thee? But we two—I and the child—shall be elsewhere, and we cannot come to thee, nor canst thou come to us. In the old days, before the child was born, I did not think of these things; but now I think of them always. It is very hard talk.'

'It will fall as it will fall. To-morrow we do not know, but to-day and love we know well. Surely we are happy now.'

'So happy that it were well to make our happiness assured. And thy

Beebee Miriam should listen to me; for she is also a woman. But then she would envy me! It is not seemly for men to worship a woman.'

Holden laughed aloud at Ameera's little spasm of jealousy.

'Is it not seemly? Why didst thou not turn me from worship of thee, then?'

'Thou a worshipper! And of me? My king, for all thy sweet words, well I know that I am thy servant and thy slave, and the dust under thy feet. And I would not have it otherwise. See!'

Before Holden could prevent her she stooped forward and touched his feet; recovering herself with a little laugh she hugged Tota closer to her bosom. Then, almost savagely—

'Is it true that the bold white *mem-log* live for three times the length of my life? Is it true that they make their marriages not before they are old women?'

'They marry as do others—when they are women.'

'That I know, but they wed when they are twenty-five. Is that true?'

'That is true.'

'*Ya illah!* At twenty-five! Who would of his own will take a wife even of eighteen? She is a woman—aging every hour. Twenty-five! I shall be an old woman at that age, and—— Those *mem-log* remain young for ever. How I hate them!'

'What have they to do with us?'

'I cannot tell. I know only that there may now be alive on this earth a woman ten years older than I who may come to thee and take thy love ten years after I am an old woman, gray-headed, and the nurse of Tota's son. That is unjust and evil. They should die too.'

'Now, for all thy years thou art a child, and shalt be picked up and carried down the staircase.'

'Tota! Have a care for Tota, my lord! Thou at least art as foolish as any babe!' Ameera tucked Tota out of harm's way in the hollow of her neck, and was carried downstairs laughing in Holden's arms, while Tota opened his eyes and smiled after the manner of the lesser angels.

He was a silent infant, and, almost before Holden could realise that he was in the world, developed into a small gold-coloured little god and unquestioned despot of the house overlooking the city. Those were months of absolute happiness to Holden and Ameera—happiness withdrawn from the world, shut in behind the wooden gate that Pir Khan guarded. By day Holden did his work with an immense pity for such as were not so fortunate as himself, and a sympathy for small children that amazed and amused many mothers at the little station-gatherings. At nightfall he returned to Ameera,—Ameera, full of the wondrous doings of Tota; how he had been seen to clap his hands together and move his fingers with intention and purpose—which was manifestly a miracle—how later, he had of his own initiative crawled out of his low bedstead on to the floor and swayed on both feet for the space of three breaths.

'And they were long breaths, for my heart stood still with delight,' said Ameera.

Then Tota took the beasts into his councils—the well-bullocks, the little gray squirrels, the mongoose that lived in a hole near the well, and especially Mian Mittu, the parrot, whose tail he grievously pulled, and Mian Mittu screamed till Ameera and Holden arrived.

'O villain! Child of strength! This to thy brother on the house-top! Tobah, tobah! Fie! Fie! But I know a charm to make him wise as Suleiman and Aflatoun [Solomon and Plato]. Now look,' said Ameera. She drew from an embroidered bag a handful of almonds. 'See! we count seven. In the name of God!'

She placed Mian Mittu, very angry and rumpled, on the top of his cage, and seating herself between the babe and the bird she cracked and peeled an almond less white than her teeth. 'This is a true charm, my life, and do not laugh. See! I give the parrot one half and Tota the other.' Mian Mittu with careful beak took his share from between Ameera's lips, and she kissed the other half into the mouth of the child, who ate it slowly with wondering eyes. 'This I will do each day of seven, and without doubt he who is ours will be a bold speaker and wise. Eh, Tota, what wilt thou be when thou art a man and I am gray-headed? Tota tucked his fat legs into adorable creases. He could crawl, but he was not going to waste the spring of his youth in idle speech. He wanted Mian Mittu's tail to tweak.

When he was advanced to the dignity of a silver belt—which, with a magic square engraved on silver and hung round his neck, made up the greater part of his clothing—he staggered on a perilous journey down the garden to Pir Khan and proffered him all his jewels in exchange for one little ride on Holden's horse, having seen his mother's mother chaffering with pedlars in the verandah. Pir Khan wept and set the untried feet on his own gray head in sign of fealty, and brought the bold adventurer to his mother's arms, vowing that Tota would be a leader of men ere his beard was grown.

One hot evening, while he sat on the roof between his father and mother watching the never-ending warfare of the kites that the city boys flew, he demanded a kite of his own with Pir Khan to fly it, because he had a fear of dealing with anything larger than himself, and when Holden called him a 'spark,' he rose to his feet and answered slowly in defence of his new-found individuality, 'Hum'park nahin hai. Hum admi hai [I am no spark, but a man].'

The protest made Holden choke and devote himself very seriously to a consideration of Tota's future. He need hardly have taken the trouble. The delight of that life was too perfect to endure. Therefore it was taken away as many things are taken away in India—suddenly and without warning. The little lord of the house, as Pir Khan called him, grew sorrowful and complained of pains who had never known the meaning of pain. Ameera, wild with terror, watched him through the night, and in the dawning of the second day the life was shaken out of him by fever—the seasonal autumn fever. It seemed altogether impossible that he could die, and neither Ameera nor Holden at first believed the evidence of the little body on the bedstead. Then Ameera beat her head against the wall and would have flung herself down the well in the garden had Holden not restrained her by main force.

One mercy only was granted to Holden. He rode to his office in broad daylight and found waiting him an unusually heavy mail that demanded concentrated attention and hard work. He was not, however, alive to this kindness of the gods.

III

The first shock of a bullet is no more than a brisk pinch. The wrecked body does not send in its protest to the soul till ten or fifteen seconds later. Holden realised his pain slowly, exactly as he had realised his happiness, and with the same imperious necessity for hiding all trace of it. In the beginning he only felt that there had been a loss, and that Ameera needed comforting, where she sat with her head on her knees shivering as Mian Mittu from the house-top called, Tota! Tota! Tota! Later all his world and the daily life of it rose up to hurt him. It was an outrage that any one of the children at the band-stand in the evening should be alive and clamorous, when his own child lay dead. It was more than mere pain when one of them touched him, and stories told by over-fond fathers of their children's latest performances cut him to the quick. He could not declare his pain. He had neither help, comfort, nor sympathy; and Ameera at the end of each weary day would lead him through the hell of self-questioning reproach which is reserved for those who have lost a child, and believe that with a little—just a little—more care it might have been saved.

'Perhaps,' Ameera would say, 'I did not take sufficient heed. Did I, or did I not? The sun on the roof that day when he played so long alone and I was—ahi! braiding my hair—it may be that the sun then bred the fever. If I had warned him from the sun he might have lived. But, oh my life, say that I am guiltless! Thou knowest that I loved him as I love thee. Say that there is no blame on me, or I shall die—I shall die!'

'There is no blame,—before God, none. It was written and how could we do aught to save? What has been, has been. Let it go, beloved.'

'He was all my heart to me. How can I let the thought go when my arm tells me every night that he is not here? Ahi! Ahi! O Tota, come back to me—come back again, and let us be all together as it was before!'

'Peace, peace! For thine own sake, and for mine also, if thou lovest me—rest.'

'By this I know thou dost not care; and how shouldst thou? The white men have hearts of stone and souls of iron. Oh, that I had married a man of mine own people—though he beat me—and had never eaten the bread of an alien!'

'Am I an alien—mother of my son?'

'What else—*Sahib?* . . . Oh, forgive me—forgive! The death has driven me mad. Thou art the life of my heart, and the light of my eyes, and the breath of my life, and—and I have put thee from me, though it was but for a moment. If thou goest away, to whom shall I look for help? Do not be angry. Indeed, it was the pain that spoke and not thy slave.'

'I know, I know. We be two who were three. The greater need therefore that we should be one.'

They were sitting on the roof as of custom. The night was a warm one in early spring, and sheet-lightning was dancing on the horizon to a broken tune played by far-off thunder. Ameera settled herself in Holden's arms.

'The dry earth is lowing like a cow for the rain, and I—I am afraid. It was not like this when we counted the stars. But thou lovest me as much as before, though a bond is taken away? Answer!'

'I love more because a new bond has come out of the sorrow that we have eaten together, and that thou knowest.'

'Yea, I knew,' said Ameera in a very small whisper. 'But it is good to hear thee say so, my life, who art so strong to help. I will be a child no more, but a woman and an aid to thee. Listen! Give me my *sitar* and I will sing bravely.'

She took the light silver-studded *sitar* and began a song of the great hero Rajah Rasalu. The hand failed on the strings, the tune halted, checked, and at a low note turned off to the poor little nursery-rhyme about the wicked crow—

And the wild plums grow in the jungle, only a penny a pound.
Only a penny a pound, *baba*—only . . .

Then came the tears, and the piteous rebellion against fate till she slept, moaning a little in her sleep, with the right arm thrown clear of the body as though it protected something that was not there. It was after this night that life became a little easier for Holden. The ever-present pain of loss drove him into his work, and the work repaid him by filling up his mind for nine or ten hours a day. Ameera sat alone in the house and brooded, but grew happier when she understood that Holden was more at ease, according to the custom of women. They touched happiness again, but this time with caution.

'It was because we loved Tota that he died. The jealousy of God was upon us,' said Ameera. 'I have hung up a large black jar before our window to turn the evil eye from us, and we must make no protestations of delight, but go softly underneath the stars, lest God find us out. Is that not good talk, worthless one?'

She had shifted the accent on the word that means 'beloved,' in proof of the sincerity of her purpose. But the kiss that followed the new christening was a thing that any deity might have envied. They went about henceforward saying, 'It is naught, it is naught; and hoping that all the Powers heard.

The Powers were busy on other things. They had allowed thirty million people four years of plenty wherein men fed well and the crops were certain, and the birthrate rose year by year; the districts reported a purely agricultural population varying from nine hundred to two thousand to the square mile of the overburdened earth; and the Member for Lower Tooting, wandering about India in pot-hat and frock-coat, talked largely of the benefits of British rule and suggested as the one thing needful the establishment of a duly qualified electoral system and a general bestowal of the franchise. His long-suffering hosts smiled and made him welcome, and when he paused to admire, with pretty picked words, the blossom of the blood-red *dhak*-tree that had flowered untimely for a sign of what was coming, they smiled more than ever.

It was the Deputy Commissioner of Kot-Kumharsen, staying at the club for a day, who lightly told a tale that made Holden's blood run cold as he overheard the end.

'He won't bother any one any more. Never saw a man so astonished in my life. By Jove, I thought he meant to ask a question in the House about it. Fellow-passenger in his ship—dined next him—bowled over by cholera and died in eighteen hours. You needn't laugh, you fellows. The Member for Lower Tooting is awfully angry about it; but he's more scared. I think he's going to take his enlightened self out of India.'

'I'd give a good deal if he were knocked over. It might keep a few vestrymen of his kidney to their own parish. But what's this about cholera? It's full early for anything of that kind,' said the warden of an unprofitable salt-lick.

'Don't know,' said the Deputy Commissioner reflectively. 'We've got locusts with us. There's sporadic cholera all along the north—at least we're calling it sporadic for decency's sake. The spring crops are short in five districts, and nobody seems to know where the rains are. It's nearly March now. I don't want to scare anybody, but it seems to me that Nature's going to audit her accounts with a big red pencil this summer.'

'Just when I wanted to leave, too!' said a voice across the room.

'There won't be much leave this year, but there ought to be a great deal of promotion. I've come in to persuade the Government to put my pet canal on the list of famine-relief works. It's an ill-wind that blows no good. I shall get that canal finished at last.'

'Is it the old programme then,' said Holden; 'famine, fever, and cholera?'

'Oh no. Only local scarcity and an unusual prevalence of seasonal sickness. You'll find it all in the reports if you live till next year. You're a lucky chap. *You* haven't got a wife to send out of harm's way. The hill-stations ought to be full of women this year.'

'I think you're inclined to exaggerate the talk in the *bazars*,' said a young civilian in the Secretariat. 'Now I have observed——'

'I daresay you have,' said the Deputy Commissioner, 'but you've a great deal more to observe, my son. In the meantime, I wish to observe to you——' and he drew him aside to discuss the construction of the canal that was so dear to his heart. Holden went to his bungalow and began to understand that he was not alone in the world, and also that he was afraid for the sake of another,—which is the most soul-satisfying fear known to man.

Two months later, as the Deputy had foretold, Nature began to audit her accounts with a red pencil. On the heels of the spring-reapings came a cry for bread, and the Government, which had decreed that no man should die of want, sent wheat. Then came the cholera from all four quarters of the compass. It struck a pilgrim-gathering of half a million at a sacred shrine. Many died at the feet of their god; the others broke down and ran over the face of the land carrying the pestilence with them. It smote a walled city and killed two hundred a day. The people crowded the trains, hanging on to the footboards and squatting on the roofs of the carriages, and the cholera followed them, for at each station they dragged out the dead and the dying. They died by the roadside, and the horses of the Englishmen shied at the corpses in the grass. The rains did not come, and the earth turned to iron lest man should escape death by hiding in her. The English sent their wives away to the hills and went about their work, coming forward as they were bidden to fill the gaps in the fighting-line. Holden, sick with fear of losing his chiefest treasure on earth, had done his best to persuade Ameera to go away with her mother to the Himalayas.

'Why should I go' she said one evening on the roof.

'There is sickness, and people are dying, and all the white *mem-log* have gone.'

'All of them?'

'All—unless perhaps there remain some old scald-head who vexes her husband's heart by running risk of death.'

'Nay; who stays is my sister, and thou must not abuse her, for I will be a scald-head too. I am glad all the bold *mem-log* are gone.'

'Do I speak to a woman or a babe? Go to the hills and I will see to it that thou goest like a queen's daughter. Think, child. In a red-lacquered bullock-cart, veiled and curtained, with brass peacocks upon the pole and red cloth hangings. I will send two orderlies for guard, and——'

'Peace! Thou art the babe in speaking thus. What use are those toys to me? *He* would have patted the bullocks and played with the housings. For his sake, perhaps,—thou hast made me very English—I might have gone. Now I will not. Let the *mem-log* run.'

'Their husbands are sending them, beloved.'

'Very good talk. Since when hast thou been my husband to tell me what to do? I have but borne thee a son. Thou art only all the desire of my soul to me. How shall I depart when I know that if evil befall thee by the breadth of so much as my littlest finger-nail—is that not small?—I should be aware of it though I were in paradise. And here, this summer thou mayest die—*ai, janee, die!* and in dying they might call to tend thee a white woman, and she would rob me in the last of thy love!'

'But love is not born in a moment or on a death-bed!'

'What dost thou know of love, stoneheart? She would take thy thanks at least and, by God and the Prophet and Beebee Miriam the mother of thy Prophet, that I will never endure. My lord and my love, let there be no more foolish talk of going away. Where thou art, I am. It is enough.' She put an arm round his neck and a hand on his mouth.

There are not many happinesses so complete as those that are snatched under the shadow of the sword. They sat together and laughed, calling each other openly by every pet name that could move the wrath of the gods. The city below them was locked up in its own torments. Sulphur fires blazed in the streets; the conches in the Hindu temples screamed and bellowed, for the gods were inattentive in those days. There was a service in the great Mahomedan shrine, and the call to prayer from the minarets was almost unceasing. They heard the wailing in the houses of the dead, and once the shriek of a mother who had lost a child and was calling for its return. In the gray dawn they saw the dead borne out through the city gates, each litter with its own little knot of mourners. Wherefore they kissed each other and shivered.

It was a red and heavy audit, for the land was very sick and needed a little breathing-space ere the torrent of cheap life should flood it anew. The children of immature fathers and undeveloped mothers made no resistance. They were cowed and sat still, waiting till the sword should be sheathed in November if it were so willed. There were gaps among the English, but the gaps were filled. The work of superintending famine-relief, cholera-sheds, medicine-distribution, and what little sanitation was possible, went forward because it was so ordered.

Holden had been told to keep himself in readiness to move to replace the next man who should fall. There were twelve hours in each day when he could not see Ameera, and she might die in three. He was considering what his pain would be if he could not see her for three months, or if she died out of his sight. He was absolutely certain that her death would be demanded—so certain that when he looked up from the telegram and saw Pir Khan breathless in the doorway, he laughed aloud. 'And?' said he,——

'When there is a cry in the night and the spirit flutters into the throat, who has a charm that will restore? Come swiftly, Heaven-born! It is the black cholera.'

Holden galloped to his home. The sky was heavy with clouds, for the long-deferred rains were near and the heat was stifling. Ameera's mother met him in the courtyard, whimpering, 'She is dying. She is nursing herself into death. She is all but dead. What shall I do, *sahib*?'

Ameera was lying in the room in which Tota had been born. She made no sign when Holden entered, because the human soul is a very lonely thing and, when it is getting ready to go away, hides itself in a misty borderland where the living may not follow. The black cholera does its work quietly and without explanation. Ameera was being thrust out of life as though the Angel of Death had himself put his hand upon her. The quick breathing seemed to show that she was either afraid or in pain, but neither eyes nor mouth gave any answer to Holden's kisses. There was nothing to be said or done. Holden could only wait and suffer. The first drops of the rain began to fall on the roof, and he could hear shouts of joy in the parched city.

The soul came back a little and the lips moved. Holden bent down to listen. 'Keep nothing of mine,' said Ameera. 'Take no hair from my head. *She* would make thee burn it later on. That flame I should feel. Lower! Stoop lower! Remember only that I was thine and bore thee a son. Though thou wed a white woman to-morrow, the pleasure of receiving in thy arms thy first son is taken from thee for ever. Remember me when thy son is born—the one that shall carry thy name before all men. His misfortunes be on my head. I bear witness—I bear witness'—the lips were forming the words on his ear—'that there is no God but—thee, beloved!'

Then she died. Holden sat still, and all thought was taken from him,—till he heard Ameera's mother lift the curtain.

'Is she dead, *sahib?*'

'She is dead.'

'Then I will mourn, and afterwards take an inventory of the furniture in this house. For that will be mine. The *sahib* does not mean to resume it? It is so little, so very little, *sahib*, and I am an old woman. I would like to lie softly.'

'For the mercy of God be silent a while. Go out and mourn where I cannot hear.'

'*Sahib*, she will be buried in four hours.'

'I know the custom. I shall go ere she is taken away. That matter is in thy hands. Look to it, that the bed on which—on which she lies——'

'Aha! That beautiful red-lacquered bed. I have long desired——'

'That the bed is left here untouched for my disposal. All else in the house is thine. Hire a cart, take everything, go hence, and before sunrise let there be nothing in this house but that which I have ordered thee to respect.'

'I am an old woman. I would stay at least for the days of mourning, and the rains have just broken. Whither shall I go?'

'What is that to me? My order is that there is a going. The house-gear is worth a thousand rupees and my orderly shall bring thee a hundred rupees to-night.'

'That is very little. Think of the cart-hire.'

'It shall be nothing unless thou goest, and with speed. O woman, get hence and leave me with my dead!'

The mother shuffled down the staircase, and in her anxiety to take stock of the house-fittings forgot to mourn. Holden stayed by Ameera's side and the rain roared on the roof. He could not think connectedly by reason of the noise, though he made many attempts to do so. Then four sheeted ghosts glided dripping into the room and stared at him through their veils. They were the washers of the dead. Holden left the room and went out to his horse. He had come in a dead, stifling calm through ankle-deep dust. He found the courtyard a rain-lashed pond alive with frogs; a torrent of yellow water ran under the gate, and a roaring wind drove the bolts of the rain like buckshot against the mud-walls. Pir Khan was shivering in his little hut by the gate, and the horse was stamping uneasily in the water.

'I have been told the *sahib's* order,' said Pir Khan. 'It is well. This house is now desolate. I go also, for my monkey-face would be a reminder of that which has been. Concerning the bed, I will bring that to thy house yonder in the morning; but remember, *sahib*, it will be to thee a knife turning in a green wound. I go upon a pilgrimage, and I will take no money. I have grown fat in the protection of the Presence whose sorrow is my sorrow. For the last time I hold his stirrup.'

He touched Holden's foot with both hands and the horse sprang out into the road, where the creaking bamboos were whipping the sky and all the frogs were chuckling. Holden could not see for the rain in his face. He put his hands before his eyes and muttered—

'Oh you brute! You utter brute!'

The news of his trouble was already in his bungalow. He read the knowledge in his butler's eyes when Ahmed Khan brought in food, and for the first and last time in his life laid a hand upon his master's shoulder, saying, 'Eat, *sahib*, eat. Meat is good against sorrow. I also have known. Moreover the shadows come and go, *sahib*; the shadows come and go. These be curried eggs.'

Holden could neither eat nor sleep. The heavens sent down eight inches of rain in that night and washed the earth clean. The waters tore down walls, broke roads, and scoured open the shallow graves on the Mahomedan burying-ground. All next day it rained, and Holden sat still in his house considering his sorrow. On the morning of the third day he received a telegram which said only, 'Ricketts, Myndonie. Dying. Holden relieve. Immediate.' Then he thought that before he departed he would look at the house wherein he had been master and lord. There was a break in the weather, and the rank earth steamed with vapour.

He found that the rains had torn down the mud pillars of the gateway, and the heavy wooden gate that had guarded his life hung lazily from one hinge. There was grass three inches high in the courtyard; Pir Khan's lodge was empty, and the sodden thatch sagged between the beams. A gray squirrel was in possession of the verandah, as if the house had been unten-anted for thirty years instead of three days. Ameera's mother had removed everything except some mildewed matting. The *tick-tick* of the little scorpions as they hurried across the floor was the only sound in the house. Ameera's room and the other one where Tota had lived were heavy with mildew; and the narrow staircase leading to the roof was streaked and stained with rain-borne mud. Holden saw all these things, and came out again to meet in the road Durga Dass, his landlord,—portly, affable, clothed in white muslin, and driving a Cee-spring buggy. He was overlooking his property to see how the roofs stood the stress of the first rains.

'I have heard,' said he, 'you will not take this place any more, *sahib*?'

'What are you going to do with it?'

'Perhaps I shall let it again.'

'Then I will keep it on while I am away.'

Durga Dass was silent for some time. 'You shall not take it on, *sahib*,' he said. 'When I was a young man I also——, but to-day I am a member of the Municipality. Ho! Ho! No. When the birds have gone what need to keep the nest? I will have it pulled down—the timber will sell for something always. It shall be pulled down, and the Municipality shall make a road across, as they desire, from the burning-ghat to the city wall, so that no man may say where this house stood.'

THE MARK OF THE BEAST

Your Gods and my Gods—do you or I know which are the stronger?

NATIVE PROVERB

◆§ EAST of Suez, some hold, the direct control of Providence ceases; Man being there handed over to the power of the Gods and Devils of Asia, and the Church of England Providence only exercising an occasional and modified supervision in the case of Englishmen.

This theory accounts for some of the more unnecessary honors of life in India: it may be stretched to explain my story.

My friend Strickland of the Police, who knows as much of the natives as is good for any man, can bear witness to the facts of the case. Dumoise, our doctor, also saw what Strickland and I saw. The inference which he drew from the evidence was entirely incorrect. He is dead now; he died, in a rather curious manner, which has been elsewhere described.

When Fleete came to India he owned a little money and some land in the Himalayas, near a place called Dharmsala. Both properties had been left him by an uncle, and he came out to finance them. He was a big, heavy, genial, and inoffensive man. His knowledge of natives was, of course, limited, and he complained of the difficulties of the language.

He rode in from his place in the hills to spend New Year in the station, and he stayed with Strickland. On New Year's Eve there was a big dinner at the club, and the night was excusably wet. When men foregather from the uttermost ends of the Empire, they have a right to be riotous. The Frontier had sent down a contingent o' Catch-'em-Alive-O's who had not seen twenty white faces a year, and were used to ride fifteen miles to dinner at the next Fort at the risk of a Khyberee bullet where there drinks should lie. They profited by their new security, for they tried to play pool with a curled-up hedgehog found in the garden, and one of them carried the marker round the room in his teeth. Half a dozen planters had come in from the south and were talking 'horse' to the Biggest Liar in Asia, who was try to cap all their stories at once. Everybody was there, and there was a general closing up of ranks and taking stock of our losses in dead or disabled that had fallen during the past year. It was a very wet night, and I remember that we sang 'Auld Lang Syne' with our feet in the Polo Championship Cup, and our heads among the stars, and swore that we were all dear friends. Then some of us went away and annexed Burma, and some tried to open up the Soudan and were opened up by Fuzzies in that cruel scrub outside Suakim, and some found stars and medals, and some were married, which was bad, and some did other things which were worse, and the others of us stayed in our chains and strove to make money on insufficient experiences.

Fleete began the night with sherry and bitters, drank champagne steadily up to the dessert, then raw, rasping Capri with all the strength of whisky, took Benedictine with his coffee, four or five whiskies and sodas to improve his pool strokes, beer and bones at half-past two, winding up with old brandy. Consequently, when he came out, at half-past three in the morning, into fourteen degrees of frost, he was very angry with his horse for coughing, and tried to leapfrog into the saddle. The horse broke away and went to his stables; so Strickland and I formed a Guard of Dishonour to take Fleete home.

Our road lay through the bazaar, close to a little temple of Hanuman, the Monkey-god, who is a leading divinity worthy of respect. All gods have good points, just as have all priests. Personally, I attach much importance to Hanuman, and am kind to his people—the great gray apes of the hills. One never knows when one may want a friend.

There was a light in the temple, and as we passed, we could hear voices of men chanting hymns. In a native temple, the priests rise at all hours of the night to do honour to their god. Before we could stop him, Fleete dashed up the steps, patted two priests on the back, and was gravely grinding the ashes of his cigar-butt into the forehead of the red stone image of Hanuman. Strickland tried to drag him out, but he sat down and said solemnly:

'Shee that? Mark of the B—beasht! *I* made it. Ishn't it fine?'

In half a minute the temple was alive and noisy, and Strickland, who knew what came of polluting gods, said that things might occur. He, by virtue of his official position, long residence in the country, and weakness for going among the natives, was known to the priests and he felt unhappy. Fleete sat on the ground and refused to move. He said that 'good old Hanuman' made a very soft pillow.

Then, without any warning, a Silver Man came out of a recess behind the image of the god. He was perfectly naked in that bitter, bitter cold, and his body shone like frosted silver, for he was what the Bible calls 'a leper as white as snow.' Also he had no face, because he was a leper of some years' standing and his disease was heavy upon him. We two stooped to haul Fleete up, and the temple was filling and filling with folk who seemed to spring from the earth, when the Silver Man ran in under our arms, making a noise exactly like the mewing of an otter, caught Fleete round the body and dropped his head on Fleete's breast before we could wrench him away. Then he retired to a corner and sat mewing while the crowd blocked all the doors.

The priests were very angry until the Silver Man touched Fleete. That nuzzling seemed to sober them.

At the end of a few minutes' silence one of the priests came to Strickland and said, in perfect English, 'Take your friend away. He has done with Hanuman, but Hanuman has not done with him.' The crowd gave room and we carried Fleete into the road.

Strickland was very angry. He said that we might all three have been knifed, and that Fleete should thank his stars that he had escaped without injury.

Fleete thanked no one. He said that he wanted to go to bed. He was gorgeously drunk.

We moved on, Strickland silent and wrathful, until Fleete was taken with violent shivering fits and sweating. He said that the smells of the bazaar were overpowering, and he wondered what slaughter-houses were permitted so near English residences. 'Can't you smell the blood?' said Fleete.

We put him to bed at last, just as the dawn was breaking, and Strickland invited me to have another whisky and soda. While we were drinking he talked of the trouble in the temple, and admitted that it baffled him completely. Strickland hates being mystified by natives, because his business in life is to overmatch them with their own weapons. He has not yet succeeded in doing this, but in fifteen or twenty years he will have made some small progress.

'They should have mauled us,' he said, 'instead of mewing at us. I wonder what they meant. I don't like it one little bit.'

I said that the Managing Committee of the temple would in all probability bring a criminal action against us for insulting their religion. There was a section of the Indian Penal Code which exactly met Fleete's offence. Strickland said he only hoped and prayed that they would do this. Before I left I looked into Fleete's room, and saw him lying on his right side, scratching his left breast. Then I went to bed cold, depressed, and unhappy, at seven o'clock in the morning.

At one o'clock I rode over to Strickland's house to inquire after Fleete's head. I imagined that it would be a sore one. Fleete was breakfasting and seemed unwell. His temper was gone, for he was abusing the cook for not supplying him with an underdone chop. A man who can eat raw meat after a wet night is a curiosity. I told Fleete this and he laughed.

'You breed queer mosquitoes in these parts,' he said. 'I've been bitten to pieces, but only in one place.'

'Let's have a look at the bite,' said Strickland. 'It may have gone down since this morning.'

While the chops were being cooked, Fleete opened his shirt and showed us, just over his left breast, a mark, the perfect double of the black rosettes—the five or six irregular blotches arranged in a circle—on a leopard's hide. Strickland looked and said, 'It was only pink this morning. It's grown black now.'

Fleete ran to a glass.

'By jove!' he said, this is nasty. What is it?

We could not answer. Here the chops came in, all red and juicy, and

Fleete bolted three in a most offensive manner. He ate on his right grinders only, and threw his head over his right shoulder as he snapped the meat. When he had finished, it struck him that he had been behaving strangely, for he said apologetically, 'I don't think I ever felt so hungry in my life. I've bolted like an ostrich.'

After breakfast Strickland said to me, 'Don't go. Stay here, and stay for the night.'

Seeing that my house was not three miles from Strickland's, this request was absurd. But Strickland insisted, and was going to say something when Fleete interrupted by declaring in a shamefaced way that he felt hungry again. Strickland sent a man to my house to fetch over my bedding and a horse, and we three went down to Strickland's stables to pass the hours until it was time to go out for a ride. The man who has a weakness for horses never wearies of inspecting them; and when two men are killing time in this way they gather knowledge and lies the one from the other.

There were five horses in the stables, and I shall never forget the scene as we tried to look them over. They seemed to have gone mad. They reared and screamed and nearly tore up their pickets; they sweated and shivered and lathered and were distraught with fear. Strickland's horses used to know him as well as his dogs; which made the matter more curious. We left the stable for fear of the brutes throwing themselves in their panic. Then Strickland turned back and called me. The horses were still frightened, but they let us 'gentle' and make much of them, and put their heads in our bosoms.

'They aren't afraid of us,' said Strickland. 'D'you know, I'd give three months' pay if *Outrage* here could talk.'

But *Outrage* was dumb and could only cuddle up to his master and blow out his nostrils, as is the custom of horses when they wish to explain things but can't. Fleete came up when we were in the stalls, and as soon as the horses saw him, their fright broke out afresh. It was all that we could do to escape from the place unkicked. Strickland said, 'They don't seem to love you, Fleete.'

'Nonsense,' said Fleete; 'my mare will follow me like a dog.' He went to her; she was in a loose-box; but as he slipped the bars she plunged, knocked him down, and broke away into the garden. I laughed, but Strickland was not amused. He took his moustache in both fists and pulled at it till it nearly came out. Fleete, instead of going off to chase his property, yawned, saying that he felt sleepy. He went to house to lie down, which was a foolish way of spending New Year's Day.

Strickland sat with me in the stables and asked if I had noticed anything peculiar in Fleete's manner. I said that he ate his food like a beast; but that this might have been the result of living alone in the hills out of the reach of society as refined and elevating as ours for instance. Strickland was not amused. I do not think that he listened to me, for his next sentence referred to the mark on Fleete's breast, and I said that it might have been caused by blister-flies, or that it was possibly a birth-mark newly born and now visible for the first time. We both agreed that it was unpleasant to look at, and Strickland found occasion to say that I was a fool.

'I can't tell you what I think now,' said he, 'because you would call me a madman; but you must stay with me for the next few days, if you can. I want you to watch Fleete, but don't tell me what you think till I have made up my mind.'

'But I am dining out to-night,' I said.

'So am I,' said Strickland, 'and so is Fleete. At least if he doesn't change his mind.'

We walked about the garden smoking, but saying nothing—because we were friends, and talking spoils good tobacco—till our pipes were out. Then we went to wake up Fleete. He was wide awake and fidgeting about his room.

'I say, I want some more chops,' he said. 'Can I get them?'

We laughed and said, 'Go and change. The ponies will be round in a minute.'

'All right,' said Fleete. 'I'll go when I get the chops—underdone ones, mind.'

He seemed to be quite in earnest. It was four o'clock, and we had had breakfast at one; still, for a long time, he demanded those underdone chops. Then he changed into riding clothes and went out into the verandah. His pony—the mare had not been caught—would not let him come near. All three horses were unmanageable—mad with fear—and finally Fleete said that he would stay at home and get something to eat. Strickland and I rode out wondering. As we passed the temple of Hanuman, the Silver Man came out and mewed at us.

'He is not one of the regular priests of the temple,' said Strickland. 'I think I should peculiarly like to lay my hands on him.'

There was no spring in our gallop on the racecourse that evening. The horses were stale, and moved as though they had been ridden out.

'The fright after breakfast has been too much for them,' said Strickland.

That was the only remark he made through the remainder of the ride. Once or twice I think he swore to himself; but that did not count.

We came back in the dark at seven o'clock, and saw that there were no lights in the bungalow. 'Careless ruffians my servants are!' said Strickland.

My horse reared at something on the carriage drive, and Fleete stood up under its nose.

'What are you doing, grovelling about the garden?' said Strickland.

But both horses bolted and nearly threw us. We dismounted by the stables and returned to Fleete, who was on his hands and knees under the orange-bushes.

'What the devil's wrong with you?' said Strickland.

'Nothing, nothing in the world,' said Fleete, speaking very quickly and thickly. 'I've been gardening—botanising you know. The smell of the earth is delightful. I think I'm going for a walk—a long walk—all night.'

Then I saw that there was something excessively out of order some-where, and I said to Strickland, 'I am not dining out.'

'Bless you!' said Strickland. 'Here, Fleete, get up. You'll catch fever there. Come in to dinner and let's have the lamps lit. We'll all dine at home.'

Fleete stood up unwillingly, and said, 'No lamps—no lamps. It's much nicer here. Let's dine outside and have some more chops—lots of 'em and underdone—bloody ones with gristle.'

Now a December evening in Northern India is bitterly cold, and Fleete's suggestion was that of a maniac.

'Come in,' said Strickland sternly. 'Come in at once.'

Fleete came, and when the lamps were brought, we saw that he was literally plastered with dirt from head to foot. He must have been rolling in the garden. He shrank from the light and went to his room. His eyes were horrible to look at. There was a green light behind them, not in them, if you understand, and the man's lower lip hung down.

Strickland said, 'There is going to be trouble—big trouble—to-night. Don't you change your riding-things.'

We waited and waited for Fleete's reappearance, and ordered dinner in the meantime. We could hear him moving about his own room, but there was no light there. Presently from the room came the long-drawn howl of a wolf.

People write and talk lightly of blood running cold and hair standing up and things of that kind. Both sensations are too horrible to be trifled with. My heart stopped as though a knife had been driven through it, and Strickland turned as white as the tablecloth.

The howl was repeated, and was answered by another howl far across the fields.

That set the gilded roof on the horror. Strickland dashed into Fleete's room. I followed, and we saw Fleete getting out of the window. He made beast-noises in the back of his throat. He could not answer us when we shouted at him. He spat.

I don't quite remember what followed, but I think that Strickland must have stunned him with the long boot-jack or else I should never have been able to sit on his chest. Fleete could not speak, he could only snarl, and his snarls were those of a wolf, not of a man. The human spirit must have been giving way all day and have died out with the twilight. We were dealing with a beast that had once been Fleete.

The affair was beyond any human and rational experience. I tried to say 'Hydrophobia,' but the word wouldn't come, because I knew that I was lying.

We bound this beast with leather thongs of the punkah-rope, and tied its thumbs and big toes together, and gagged it with a shoe-horn, which makes a very efficient gag if you know how to arrange it. Then we carried it into the dining-room, and sent a man to Dumoise, the doctor, telling him to come over at once. After we had despatched the messenger and were drawing breath, Strickland said, 'It's no good. This isn't any doctor's work. I, also, knew that he spoke the truth.

The beast's head was free, and it threw it about from side to side. Any one entering the room would have believed that we were curing a wolf's pelt. That was the most loathsome accessory of all.

Strickland sat with his chin in the heel of his fist, watching the beast as it wriggled on the ground, but saying nothing. The shirt had been torn open in the scuffle and showed the black rosette mark on the left breast. It stood out like a blister.

In the silence of the watching we heard something without mewing like a she-otter. We both rose to our feet, and, I answer for myself, not Strickland, felt sick—actually and physically sick. We told each other, as did the men in *Pinafore*, that it was the cat.

Dumoise arrived, and I never saw a little man so unprofessionally shocked. He said that it was a heart-rending case of hydrophobia, and that nothing could be done. At least any palliative measures would only prolong the agony. The beast was foaming at the mouth. Fleete, as we told Dumoise, had been bitten by dogs once or twice. Any man who keeps half a dozen terriers must expect a nip now and again. Dumoise could offer no help. He could only certify that Fleete was dying of hydrophobia. The beast was then howling, for it had managed to spit out the shoe-horn. Dumoise said that he would be ready to certify to the cause of death, and that the end was certain. He was a good little man, and he offered to remain with us; but Strickland refused the kindness. He did not wish to poison Dumoise's New Year. He would only ask him not to give the real cause of Fleete's death to the public.

So Dumoise left, deeply agitated; and as soon as the noise of the cart-wheels had died away, Strickland told me, in a whisper, his suspicions. They were so wildly improbable that he dared not say them out aloud; and I, who entertained all Strickland's beliefs, was so ashamed of owning to them that I pretended to disbelieve.

'Even if the Silver Man had bewitched Fleete for polluting the image of Hanuman, the punishment could not have fallen so quickly.'

As I was whispering this the cry outside the house rose again, and the beast fell into a fresh paroxysm of struggling till we were afraid that the thongs that held it would give way.

'Watch!' said Strickland. 'If this happens six times I shall take the law into my own hands. I order you to help me.'

He went into his room and came out in a few minutes with the barrels of an old shot-gun, a piece of fishing-line, some thick cord, and his heavy wooden bedstead. I reported that the convulsions had followed the cry by two seconds in each case, and the beast seemed perceptibly weaker.

Strickland muttered, 'But he can't take away the life! He can't take away the life!'

I said, though I knew that I was arguing against myself, 'It may be a cat.

It must be a cat. If the Silver Man is responsible, why does he dare to come here?'

Strickland arranged the wood on the hearth, put the gun-barrels into the glow of the fire, spread the twine on the table and broke a walking stick in two. There was one yard of fishing line, gut, lapped with wire, such as is used for *mahseer*-fishing, and he tied the two ends together in a loop.

Then he said, 'How can we catch him? He must be taken alive and unhurt.'

I said that we must trust in Providence, and go out softly with polo-sticks into the shrubbery at the front of the house. The man or animal that made the cry was evidently moving round the house as regularly as a night-watchman. We could wait in the bushes till he came by and knock him over.

Strickland accepted this suggestion, and we slipped out from a bath-room window into the front verandah and then across the carriage drive into the bushes.

In the moonlight we could see the leper coming round the corner of the house. He was perfectly naked, and from time to time he mewed and stopped to dance with his shadow. It was an unattractive sight, and thinking of poor Fleete, brought to such degradation by so foul a creature, I put away all my doubts and resolved to help Strickland from the heated gun-barrels to the loop of twine—from the loins to the head and back again—with all tortures that might be needful.

The leper halted in the front porch for a moment and we jumped out on him with the sticks. He was wonderfully strong, and we were afraid that he might escape or be fatally injured before we caught him. We had an idea that lepers were frail creatures, but this proved to be incorrect. Strickland knocked his legs from under him and I put my foot on his neck. He mewed hideously, and even through my riding-boots I could feel that his flesh was not the flesh of a clean man.

He struck at us with his hand and feet-stumps. We looped the lash of a dog-whip round him, under the armpits, and dragged him backwards into the hall and so into the dining-room where the beast lay. There we tied him with trunk-straps. He made no attempt to escape, but mewed.

When we confronted him with the beast the scene was beyond description. The beast doubled backwards into a bow as though he had been poisoned with strychnine, and moaned in the most pitiable fashion. Several other things happened also, but they cannot be put down here.

'I think I was right,' said Strickland. 'Now we will ask him to cure this case.'

But the leper only mewed. Strickland wrapped a towel round his hand and took the gun-barrels out of the fire. I put the half of the broken walking stick through the loop of fishing-line and buckled the leper comfortably to Strickland's bedstead. I understood then how men and women and little children can endure to see a witch burnt alive; for the beast was moaning on the floor, and though the Silver Man had no face, you could see horrible feelings passing through the slab that took its place, exactly as waves of heat play across red-hot iron—gun-barrels for instance.

Strickland shaded his eyes with his hands for a moment and we got to work. This part is not to be printed.

* * * * *

The dawn was beginning to break when the leper spoke. His mewings had not been satisfactory up to that point. The beast had fainted from exhaustion and the house was very still. We unstrapped the leper and told him to take away the evil spirit. He crawled to the beast and laid his hand upon the left breast. That was all. Then he fell face down and whined, drawing in his breath as he did so.

We watched the face of the beast, and saw the soul of Fleete coming back into the eyes. Then a sweat broke out on the forehead and the eyes— they were human eyes—closed. We waited for an hour but Fleete still slept. We carried him to his room and bade the leper go, giving him the bedstead, and the sheet on the bedstead to cover his nakedness, the gloves and the towels with which we had touched him, and the whip that had been hooked round his body. He put the sheet about him and went out into the early morning without speaking or mewing.

Strickland wiped his face and sat down. A night-gong, far away in the city, made seven o'clock.

'Exactly four-and-twenty hours!' said Strickland. 'And I've done enough to ensure my dismissal from the service, besides permanent quarters in a lunatic asylum. Do you believe that we are awake?'

The red-hot gun-barrel had fallen on the floor and was singeing the carpet. The smell was entirely real.

That morning at eleven we two together went to wake up Fleete. We looked and saw that the black leopard-rosette on his chest had disappeared. He was very drowsy and tired, but as soon as he saw us, he said, 'Oh! Confound you fellows. Happy New Year to you. Never mix your liquors. I'm nearly dead.'

'Thanks for your kindness, but you're over time,' said Strickland. 'To-day is the morning of the second. You've slept the clock round with a vengeance.'

The door opened, and little Dumoise put his head in. He had come on foot, and fancied that we were laying out Fleete.

'I've brought a nurse,' said Dumoise. 'I suppose that she can come in for . . . what is necessary.'

'By all means,' said Fleete cheerily, sitting up in bed. 'Bring on your nurses.'

Dumoise was dumb. Strickland led him out and explained that there must have been a mistake in the diagnosis. Dumoise remained dumb and left the house hastily. He considered that his professional reputation had been injured, and was inclined to make a personal matter of the recovery.

Strickland went out too. When he came back, he said that he had been to call on the Temple of Hanuman to offer redress for the pollution of the god, and had been solemnly assured that no white man had ever touched the idol and that he was an incarnation of all the virtues labouring under a delusion. 'What do you think?' said Strickland.

I said, ' "There are more things . . ." '

But Strickland hates that quotation. He says that I have worn it threadbare.

One other curious thing happened which frightened me as much as anything in all the night's work. When Fleete was dressed he came into the dining-room and sniffed. He had a quaint trick of moving his nose when he sniffed. 'Horrid doggy smell, here,' said he. 'You should really keep those terriers of yours in better order. Try sulphur, Strick.'

But Strickland did not answer. He caught hold of the back of a chair, and, without warning, went into an amazing fit of hysterics. It is terrible to see a strong man overtaken with hysteria. Then it struck me that we had fought for Fleete's soul with the Silver Man in that room, and had disgraced ourselves as Englishmen for ever, and I laughed and gasped and gurgled just as shamefully as Strickland, while Fleete thought that we had both gone mad. We never told him what we had done.

Some years later, when Strickland had married and was a church-going member of society for his wife's sake, we reviewed the incident dispassionately, and Strickland suggested that I should put it before the public.

I cannot myself see that this step is likely to clear up the mystery; because, in the first place, no one will believe a rather unpleasant story, and, in the second, it is well known to every right-minded man that the gods of the heathen are stone and brass, and any attempt to deal with them otherwise is justly condemned.

THE RETURN OF IMRAY

The doors were wide, the story saith,
Out of the night came the patient wraith,
He might not speak, and he could not stir
A hair of the Baron's minniver—
Speechless and strengthless, a shadow thin,
He roved the castle to seek his kin.
And oh, 'twas a piteous thing to see
The dumb ghost follow his enemy!

THE BARON

IMRAY achieved the impossible. Without warning, for no conceivable motive, in his youth, at the threshold of his career he chose to disappear from the world—which is to say, the little Indian station where he lived.

Upon a day he was alive, well, happy, and in great evidence among the billiard-tables at his Club. Upon a morning, he was not, and no manner of search could make sure where he might be. He had stepped out of his place; he had not appeared at his office at the proper time, and his dogcart was not upon the public roads. For these reasons, and because he was hampering, in a microscopical degree, the administration of the Indian Empire, that Empire paused for one microscopical moment to make inquiry into the fate of Imray. Ponds were dragged, wells were plumbed, telegrams were despatched down the lines of railways and to the nearest seaport town—twelve hundred miles away; but Imray was not at the end of the drag-ropes nor the telegraph wires. He was gone, and his place knew him no more. Then the work of the great Indian Empire swept forward, because it could not be delayed, and Imray from being a man became a mystery—such a thing as men talk over at their tables in the Club for a month, and then forget utterly. His guns, horses, and carts were sold to the highest bidder. His superior officer wrote an altogether absurd letter to his mother, saying that Imray had unaccountably disappeared, and his bungalow stood empty.

After three or four months of the scorching hot weather had gone by, my friend Strickland, of the Police, saw fit to rent the bungalow from the native landlord. This was before he was engaged to Miss Youghal—an affair which has been described in another place—and while he was pursuing his investigations into native life. His own life was sufficiently peculiar, and men complained of his manners and customs. There was always food in his house, but there were no regular times for meals. He ate, standing up and walking about, whatever he might find at the sideboard, and this is not good for human beings. His domestic equipment was limited to six rifles, three shot-guns, five saddles, and a collection of stiff-jointed mahseer-rods, bigger and

stronger than the largest salmon-rods. These occupied one-half of his bungalow, and the other half was given up to Strickland and his dog Tietjens—an
enormous Rampur slut who devoured daily the rations of two men. She
spoke to Strickland in a language of her own; and whenever, walking abroad,
she saw things calculated to destroy the peace of Her Majesty the Queen-
Empress, she returned to her master and laid information. Strickland would
take steps at once, and the end of his labours was trouble and fine and im-
prisonment for other people. The natives believed that Tietjens was a
familiar spirit, and treated her with the great reverence that is born of hate
and fear. One room in the bungalow was set apart for her special use. She
owned a bedstead, a blanket, and a drinking-trough, and if any one came
into Strickland's room at night her custom was to knock down the invader
and give tongue till some one came with a light. Strickland owed his life to
her, when he was on the Frontier, in search of a local murderer, who came
in the gray dawn to send Strickland much farther than the Andaman Islands.
Tietjens caught the man as he was crawling into Strickland's tent with a
dagger between his teeth; and after his record of iniquity was established in
the eyes of the law he was hanged. From that date Tietjens wore a collar of
rough silver, and employed a monogram on her night-blanket; and the blanket
was of double woven Kashmir cloth, for she was a delicate dog.

Under no circumstances would she be separated from Strickland; and
once, when he was ill with fever, made great trouble for the doctors, because
she did not know how to help her master and would not allow another
creature to attempt aid. Macarnaght, of the Indian Medical Service, beat her
over her head with a gun-butt before she could understand that she must
give room for those who could give quinine.

A short time after Strickland had taken Imray's bungalow, my business
took me through that Station, and naturally, the Club quarters being full, I
quartered myself upon Strickland. It was a desirable bungalow, eight-roomed
and heavily thatched against any chance of leakage from rain. Under the
pitch of the roof ran a ceiling-cloth which looked just as neat as a white-
washed ceiling. The landlord had repainted it when Strickland took the
bungalow. Unless you knew how Indian bungalows were built you would
never have suspected that above the cloth lay the dark three-cornered cavern
of the roof, where the beams and the underside of the thatch harboured all
manner of rats, bats, ants, and foul things.

Tietjens met me in the verandah with a bay like the boom of the bell
of St. Paul's, putting her paws on my shoulder to show she was glad to see
me. Strickland had contrived to claw together a sort of meal which he called
lunch, and immediately after it was finished went out about his business. I
was left alone with Tietjens and my own affairs. The heat of the summer had
broken up and turned to the warm damp of the rains. There was no motion
in the heated air, but the rain fell like ramrods on the earth, and flung up a
blue mist when it splashed back. The bamboos, and the custard-apples, the
poinsettias, and the mango-trees in the garden stood still while the warm

water lashed through them, and the frogs began to sing among the aloe hedges. A little before the light failed, and when the rain was at its worst, I sat in the back verandah and heard the water roar from the eaves, and scratched myself because I was covered with the thing called prickly-heat. Tietjens came out with me and put her head in my lap and was very sorrowful; so I gave her biscuits when tea was ready, and I took tea in the back verandah on account of the little coolness found there. The rooms of the house were dark behind me. I could smell Strickland's saddlery and the oil on his guns, and I had no desire to sit among these things. My own servant came to me in the twilight, the muslin of his clothes clinging tightly to his drenched body, and told me that a gentleman had called and wished to see some one. Very much against my will, but only because of the darkness of the rooms, I went into the naked drawing-room, telling my man to bring the lights. There might or might not have been a caller waiting—it seemed to me that I saw a figure by one of the windows—but when the lights came there was nothing save the spikes of the rain without, and the smell of the drinking earth in my nostrils. I explained to my servant that he was no wiser than he ought to be, and went back to the verandah to talk to Tietjens. She had gone out into the wet, and I could hardly coax her back to me; even with biscuits with sugar tops. Strickland came home, dripping wet, just before dinner, and the first thing he said was.

'Has any one called?'

I explained, with apologies, that my servant had summoned me into the drawing-room on a false alarm; or that some loafer had tried to call on Strickland, and thinking better of it had fled after giving his name. Strickland ordered dinner, without comment, and since it was a real dinner with a white tablecloth attached, we sat down.

At nine o'clock Strickland wanted to go to bed, and I was tired too. Tietjens, who had been lying underneath the table, rose up, and swung into the least exposed verandah as soon as her master moved to his own room, which was next to the stately chamber set apart for Tietjens. If a mere wife had wished to sleep out of doors in that pelting rain it would not have mattered; but Tietjens was a dog, and therefore the better animal. I looked at Strickland, expecting to see him flay her with a whip. He smiled queerly, as a man would smile after telling some unpleasant domestic tragedy. 'She has done this ever since I moved in here,' said he. 'Let her go.'

The dog was Strickland's dog, so I said nothing, but I felt all that Strickland felt in being thus made light of. Tietjens encamped outside my bedroom window, and storm after storm came up, thundered on the thatch, and died away. The lightning spattered the sky as a thrown egg spatters a barn-door, but the light was pale blue, not yellow; and, looking through my split bamboo blinds, I could see the great dog standing, not sleeping, in the verandah, the hackles alift on her back and her feet anchored as tensely as the drawn wire-rope of a suspension bridge. In the very short pauses of the thunder I tried to sleep, but it seemed that some one wanted me very urgently.

He, whoever he was, was trying to call me by name, but his voice was no more than a husky whisper. The thunder ceased, and Tietjens went into the garden and howled at the low moon. Somebody tried to open my door, walked about and about through the house and stood breathing heavily in the verandahs, and just when I was falling asleep I fancied that I heard a wild hammering and clamouring above my head or on the door.

I ran into Strickland's room and asked him whether he was ill, and had been calling for me. He was lying on his bed half dressed, a pipe in his mouth. 'I thought you'd come,' he said. 'Have I been walking round the house recently?'

I explained that he had been tramping in the dining-room and the smoking-room and two or three other places, and he laughed and told me to go back to bed. I went back to bed and slept till the morning, but through all my mixed dreams I was sure I was doing some one an injustice in not attending to his wants. What those wants were I could not tell; but a fluttering, whispering, bolt-fumbling, lurking, loitering Someone was reproaching me for my slackness, and, half awake, I heard the howling of Tietjens in the garden and the threshing of the rain.

I lived in that house for two days. Strickland went to his office daily, leaving me alone for eight or ten hours with Tietjens for my only companion. As long as the full light lasted I was comfortable, and so was Tietjens; but in the twilight she and I moved into the back verandah and cuddled each other for company. We were alone in the house, but none the less it was much too fully occupied by a tenant with whom I did not wish to interfere. I never saw him, but I could see the curtains between the rooms quivering where he had just passed through; I could hear the chairs creaking as the bamboos sprung under a weight that had just quitted them; and I coud feel when I went to get a book from the dining-room that somebody was waiting in the shadows of the front verandah till I should have gone away. Tietjens made the twilight more interesting by glaring into the darkened rooms with every hair erect, and following the motions of something that I could not see. She never entered the rooms, but her eyes moved interestedly: that was quite sufficient. Only when my servant came to trim the lamps and make all light and habitable she would come in with me and spend her time sitting on her haunches, watching an invisible extra man as he moved about behind my shoulder. Dogs are cheerful companions.

I explained to Strickland, gently as might be, that I would go over to the Club and find for myself quarters there. I admired his hospitality, was pleased with his guns and rods, but I did not much care for his house and its atmosphere. He heard me out to the end, and then smiled very wearily, but without contempt, for he is a man who understands things. 'Stay on,' he said, 'and see what this thing means. All you have talked about I have known since I took the bungalow. Stay on and wait. Tietjens has left me. Are you going too?'

I had seen him through one little affair, connected with a heathen idol, that had brought me to the doors of a lunatic asylum, and I had no desire to help him through further experiences. He was a man to whom unpleasant-nesses arrived as do dinners to ordinary people.

Therefore I explained more clearly than ever that I liked him im-mensely, and would be happy to see him in the daytime; but that I did not care to sleep under his roof. This was after dinner, when Tietjens had gone out to lie in the verandah.

' 'Pon my soul, I don't wonder,' said Strickland, with his eyes on the ceiling-cloth. 'Look at that!'

The tails of two brown snakes were hanging between the cloth and the cornice of the wall. They threw long shadows in the lamplight.

'If you are afraid of snakes of course——' said Strickland.

I hate and fear snakes, because if you look into the eyes of any snake you will see that it knows all and more of the mystery of man's fall, and that it feels all the contempt that the Devil felt when Adam was evicted from Eden. Besides which its bite is generally fatal, and it twists up trouser legs.

'You ought to get your thatch overhauled,' I said. 'Give me a mahseer-rod, and we'll poke 'em down.'

'They'll hide among the roof-beams,' said Strickland. 'I can't stand snakes overhead. I'm going up into the roof. If I shake 'em down, stand by with a cleaning-rod and break their backs.'

I was not anxious to assist Strickland in his work, but I took the cleaning-rod and waited in the dining-room while Strickland brought a gardener's ladder from the verandah, and set it against the side of the room. The snake-tails drew themselves up and disappeared. We could hear the dry rushing scuttle of long bodies running over the baggy ceiling-cloth. Strickland took a lamp with him, while I tried to make clear to him the danger of hunting roof-snakes between a ceiling-cloth and a thatch, apart from the deterioration of property caused by ripping out ceiling-cloths.

'Nonsense!' said Strickland. 'They're sure to hide near the walls by the cloth. The bricks are too cold for 'em, and the heat of the room is just what they like.' He put his hand to the corner of the stuff and ripped it from the cornice. It gave with a great sound of tearing, and Strickland put his head through the opening into the dark of the angle of the roof-beams. I set my teeth and lifted the rod, for I had not the least knowledge of what might descend.

'H'm!' said Strickland, and his voice rolled and rumbled in the roof. 'There's room for another set of rooms up here, and, by Jove, some one is occupying 'em!'

'Snakes?' I said from below.

'No. It's a buffalo. Hand me up the two last joints of a mahseer-rod, and I'll prod it. It's lying on the main roof-beam.'

I handed up the rod.

'What a nest for owls and serpents! No wonder the snakes live here,' said Strickland, climbing farther into the roof. I could see his elbow thrusting with the rod. 'Come out of that, whoever you are! Heads below there! It's falling.'

I saw the ceiling-cloth nearly in the centre of the room bag with a shape that was pressing it downwards and downwards towards the lighted lamp on the table. I snatched the lamp out of danger and stood back. Then the cloth ripped out from the walls, tore, split, swayed, and shot down upon the table something that I dared not look at, till Strickland had slid down the ladder and was standing by my side.

He did not say much, being a man of few words; but he picked up the loose end of the tablecloth and threw it over the remnants on the table.

'It strikes me,' said he, putting down the lamp, 'our friend Imray has come back. Oh! you would, would you?'

There was a movement under the cloth, and a little snake wriggled out, to be back-broken by the butt of the mahseer-rod. I was sufficiently sick to make no remarks worth recording.

Strickland meditated, and helped himself to drinks. The arrangement under the cloth made no more signs of life.

'Is it Imray?' I said.

Strickland turned back the cloth for a moment, and looked.

'It is Imray,' he said; 'and his throat is cut from ear to ear.'

Then we spoke, both together and to ourselves: 'That's why he whispered about the house.'

Tietjens, in the garden, began to bay furiously. A little later her great nose heaved open the dining-room door.

She sniffed and was still. The tattered ceiling-cloth hung down almost to the level of the table, and there was hardly room to move away from the discovery.

Tietjens came in and sat down; her teeth bared under her lip and her forepaws planted. She looked at Strickland.

'It's a bad business, old lady,' said he. 'Men don't climb up into the roofs of their bungalows to die, and they don't fasten up the ceiling cloth behind 'em. Let's think it out.'

'Let's think it out somewhere else,' I said.

'Excellent idea! Turn the lamps out. We'll get into my room.'

I did not turn the lamps out. I went into Strickland's room first, and allowed him to make the darkness. Then he followed me, and we lit tobacco and thought. Strickland thought. I smoked furiously, because I was afraid.

'Imray is back,' said Strickland. 'The question is—who killed Imray? Don't talk, I've a notion of my own. When I took this bungalow I took over most of Imray's servants. Imray was guileless and inoffensive, wasn't he?'

I agreed; though the heap under the cloth had looked neither one thing nor the other.

'If I call in all the servants they will stand fast in a crowd and lie like Aryans. What do you suggest?'

'Call 'em in one by one,' I said.

'They'll run away and give the news to all their fellows,' said Strickland. 'We must segregate 'em. Do you suppose your servant knows anything about it?'

'He may, for aught I know; but I don't think it's likely. He has only been here two or three days,' I answered. 'What's your notion?'

'I can't quite tell. How the dickens did the man get the wrong side of the ceiling-cloth?'

There was a heavy coughing outside Strickland's bedroom door. This showed that Bahadur Khan, his body-servant, had waked from sleep and wished to put Strickland to bed.

'Come in,' said Strickland. 'It's a very warm night, isn't it?'

Bahadur Khan, a great, green-turbaned, six-foot Mahomedan, said that it was a very warm night; but that there was more rain pending, which, by his Honour's favour, would bring relief to the country.

'It will be so, if God pleases,' said Strickland, tugging off his boots. 'It is in my mind, Bahadur Khan, that I have worked thee remorselessly for many days—ever since that time when thou first camest into my service. What time was that?'

'Has the Heaven-born forgotten? It was when Imray Sahib went secretly to Europe without warning given; and I—even I—came into the honoured service of the protector of the poor.'

'And Imray Sahib went to Europe?'

'It is so said among those who were his servants.'

'And thou wilt take service with him when he returns?'

'Assuredly, Sahib. He was a good master, and cherished his dependants.'

'That is true. I am very tired, but I go buck-shooting to-morrow. Give me the little sharp rifle that I use for black-buck; it is in the case yonder.'

The man stooped over the case; handed barrels, stock, and fore-end to Strickland, who fitted all together, yawning dolefully. Then he reached down to the gun-case, took a solid-drawn cartridge, and slipped it into the breech of the .360 Express.

'And Imray Sahib has gone to Europe secretly! That is very strange, Bahadur Khan, is it not?'

'What do I know of the ways of the white man, Heaven-born?'

'Very little, truly. But thou shalt know more anon. It has reached me that Imray Sahib has returned from his so long journeys, and that even now he lies in the next room, waiting his servant.'

'Sahib!'

The lamplight slid along the barrels of the rifle as they levelled themselves at Bahadur Khan's broad breast.

'Go and look!' said Strickland. 'Take a lamp. Thy master is tired, and he waits thee. Go!'

The man picked up a lamp, and went into the dining-room, Strickland following, and almost pushing him with the muzzle of the rifle. He looked for a moment at the black depths behind the ceiling-cloth; at the writhing snake under foot; and last, a gray glaze settling on his face, at the thing under the tablecloth.

'Hast thou seen?' said Strickland after a pause.

'I have seen. I am clay in the white man's hands. What does the Presence do?'

'Hang thee within the month. What else?'

'For killing him? Nay, Sahib, consider. Walking among us, his servants, he cast his eyes upon my child, who was four years old. Him he bewitched, and in ten days he died of the fever—my child!'

'What said Imray Sahib?'

'He said he was a handsome child, and patted him on the head; wherefore my child died. Wherefore I killed Imray Sahib in the twilight, when he had come back from office, and was sleeping. Wherefore I dragged him up into the roof-beams and made all fast behind him. The Heaven-born knows all things. I am the servant of the Heaven-born.'

Strickland looked at me above the rifle, and said, in the vernacular, 'Thou art witness to this saying? He has killed.'

Bahadur Khan stood ashen gray in the light of the one lamp. The need for justification came upon him very swiftly. 'I am trapped,' he said, 'but the offence was that man's. He cast an evil eye upon my child, and I killed and hid him. Only such as are served by devils,' he glared at Tietjens, couched stolidly before him, 'only such could know what I did.'

'It was clever. But thou shouldst have lashed him to the beam with a rope. Now, thou thyself wilt hang by a rope. Orderly!'

A drowsy policeman answered Strickland's call. He was followed by another, and Tietjens sat wondrous still.

'Take him to the police-station,' said Strickland. 'There is a case toward.'

'Do I hang, then?' said Bahadur Khan, making no attempt to escape, and keeping his eyes on the ground.

'If the sun shines or the water runs—yes!' said Strickland.

Bahadur Khan stepped back one long pace, quivered, and stood still. The two policemen waited further orders.

'Go!' said Strickland.

'Nay; but I go very swiftly,' said Bahadur Khan. 'Look! I am even now a dead man.'

He lifted his foot, and to the little toe there clung the head of the half-killed snake, firm fixed in the agony of death.

'I come of land-holding stock,' said Bahadur Khan, rocking where he stood. 'It were a disgrace to me to go to the public scaffold: therefore I take this way. Be it remembered that the Sahib's shirts are correctly enumerated, and that there is an extra piece of soap in his washbasin. My child was bewitched, and I slew the wizard. Why should you seek to slay me with the rope? My honour is saved, and—and—I die.'

At the end of an hour he died, as they die who are bitten by the little brown *karait*, and the policemen bore him and the thing under the tablecloth to their appointed places. All were needed to make clear the disappearance of Imray.

'This,' said Strickland, very calmly, as he climbed into bed, 'is called the nineteenth century. Did you hear what that man said?'

'I heard,' I answered. 'Imray made a mistake.'

'Simply and solely through not knowing the nature of the Oriental, and the coincidence of a little seasonal fever. Bahadur Khan had been with him for four years.'

I shuddered. My own servant had been with me for exactly that length of time. When I went over to my own room I found my man waiting, impassive as the copper head on a penny, to pull off my boots.

'What has befallen Bahadur Khan?' said I.

'He was bitten by a snake and died. The rest the Sahib knows,' was the answer.

'And how much of this matter hast thou known?'

'As much as might be gathered from One coming in in the twilight to seek satisfaction. Gently, Sahib. Let me pull off those boots.'

I had just settled to the sleep of exhaustion when I heard Strickland shouting from his side of the house—

'Tietjens has come back to her place!'

And so she had. The great deerhound was couched statelily on her own bedstead on her own blanket, while, in the next room, the idle, empty, ceiling-cloth waggled as it trailed on the table.

NAMGAY DOOLA

There came to the beach a poor exile of Erin,
The dew on his wet robe hung heavy and chill;
Ere the steamer that brought him had passed out of hearin',
He was Alderman Mike inthrojuicin' a bill!

AMERICAN SONG

ONCE upon a time there was a King who lived on the road to Thibet, very many miles in the Himalayas. His Kingdom was eleven thousand feet above the sea and exactly four miles square; but most of the miles stood on end owing to the nature of the country. His revenues were rather less than four hundred pounds yearly, and they were expended in the maintenance of one elephant and a standing army of five men. He was tributary to the Indian Government, who allowed him certain sums for keeping a section of the Himalaya-Thibet road in repair. He further increased his revenues by selling timber to the railway-companies; for he would cut the great deodar trees in his one forest, and they fell thundering into the Sutlej river and were swept down to the plains three hundred miles away and became railway-ties. Now and again this King, whose name does not matter, would mount a ringstraked horse and ride scores of miles to Simla-town to confer with the Lieutenant-Governor on matters of state, or to assure the Viceroy that his sword was at the service of the Queen-Empress. Then the Viceroy would cause a ruffle of drums to be sounded, and the ringstraked horse and the cavalry of the State —two men in tatters—and the herald who bore the silver stick before the King would trot back to their own place, which lay between the tail of a heaven-climbing glacier and a dark birch-forest.

Now, from such a King, always remembering that he possessed one veritable elephant, and could count his descent for twelve hundred years, I expected, when it was my fate to wander through his dominions, no more than mere license to live.

The night had closed in rain, and rolling clouds blotted out the lights of the villages in the valley. Forty miles away, untouched by cloud or storm, the white shoulder of Donga Pa—the Mountain of the Council of the Gods —upheld the Evening Star. The monkeys sang sorrowfully to each other as they hunted for dry roosts in the fern-wreathed trees, and the last puff of the day-wind brought from the unseen villages the scent of damp wood-smoke, hot cakes, dripping undergrowth, and rotting pine-cones. That is the true smell of the Himalayas, and if once it creeps into the blood of a man, that man will at the last, forgetting all else, return to the hills to die. The clouds closed and the smell went away, and there remained nothing in all the world except chilling white mist and the boom of the Sutlej river racing through the valley below. A fat-tailed sheep, who did not want to die, bleated piteously at my tent door. He was scuffling with the Prime Minister and the Director-General of Public Education, and he was a royal gift to me and my camp servants. I expressed my thanks suitably, and asked if I might have audience of the King. The Prime Minister readjusted his turban, which had fallen off in the struggle, and assured me that the King would be very pleased to see me. Therefore I despatched two bottles as a foretaste, and when the sheep had entered upon another incarnation went to the King's Palace through the wet. He had sent his army to escort me, but the army stayed to talk with my cook. Soldiers are very much alike all the world over.

The Palace was a four-roomed and whitewashed mud and timber house, the finest in all the hills for a day's journey. The King was dressed in a purple velvet jacket, white muslin trousers, and a saffron-yellow turban of price. He gave me audience in a little carpeted room opening off the palace courtyard which was occupied by the Elephant of State. The great beast was sheeted and anchored from trunk to tail, and the curve of his back stood out grandly against the mist.

The Prime Minister and the Director-General of Public Education were present to introduce me, but all the court had been dismissed, lest the two bottles aforesaid should corrupt their morals. The King cast a wreath of heavy-scented flowers round my neck as I bowed, and inquired how my honoured presence had the felicity to be. I said that through seeing his auspicious countenance the mists of the night had turned into sunshine, and that by reason of his beneficent sheep his good deeds would be remembered by the Gods. He said that since I had set my magnificent foot in his Kingdom the crops would probably yield seventy per cent more than the average. I said that the fame of the King had reached to the four corners of the earth, and that the nations gnashed their teeth when they heard daily of the glories of his realm and the wisdom of his moon-like Prime Minister and lotus-like Director-General of Public Education.

Then we sat down on clean white cushions, and I was at the King's right hand. Three minutes later he was telling me that the state of the maize crop was something disgraceful, and that the railway-companies would not pay him enough for his timber. The talk shifted to and fro with the bottles, and we discussed very many stately things, and the King became confidential on the subject of Government generally. Most of all he dwelt on the short-comings of one of his subjects, who, from all I could gather, had been paralyzing the executive.

'In the old days,' said the King, 'I could have ordered the Elephant yonder to trample him to death. Now I must e'en send him seventy miles across the hills to be tried, and his keep would be upon the State. The Elephant eats everything.'

'What be the man's crimes, Rajah Sahib?' said I.

'Firstly, he is an outlander and no man of mine own people. Secondly, since of my favour I gave him land upon his first coming, he refuses to pay revenue. Am I not the lord of the earth, above and below, entitled by right and custom to one-eighth of the crop? Yet this devil, establishing himself, refuses to pay a single tax; and he brings a poisonous spawn of babes.'

'Cast him into jail,' I said.

'Sahib,' the King answered, shifting a little on the cushions, 'once and only once in these forty years sickness came upon me so that I was not able to go abroad. In that hour I made a vow to my God that I would never again cut man or woman from the light of the sun and the air of God; for I perceived the nature of the punishment. How can I break my vow? Were it only the lopping of a hand or a foot I should not delay. But even that is impossible now that the English have rule. One or another of my people'—he looked obliquely at the Director-General of Public Education—'would at once write a letter to the Viceroy, and perhaps I should be deprived of my ruffle of drums.'

He unscrewed the mouthpiece of his silver water-pipe, fitted a plain amber mouthpiece, and passed his pipe to me. 'Not content with refusing revenue,' he continued, 'this outlander refuses also the *begar*' (this was the corvée or forced labour on the roads) 'and stirs my people up to the like treason. Yet he is, when he wills, an expert log-snatcher. There is none better or bolder among my people to clear a block of the river when the logs stick fast.'

'But he worships strange Gods,' said the Prime Minister deferentially.

'For that I have no concern,' said the King, who was as tolerant as Akbar in matters of belief. 'To each man his own God and the fire or Mother Earth for us all at last. It is the rebellion that offends me.'

'The King has an army,' I suggested. 'Has not the King burned the man's house and left him naked to the night dews?'

'Nay, a hut is a hut, and it holds the life of a man. But once, I sent my army against him when his excuses became wearisome: of their heads he brake three across the top with a stick. The other two men ran away. Also the guns would not shoot.'

I had seen the equipment of the infantry. One-third of it was an old muzzle-loading fowling-piece, with a ragged rust-hole where the nipples should have been, one-third a wire-bound matchlock with a worm-eaten stock, and one-third a four-bore flint duck-gun without a flint.

'But it is to be remembered,' said the King, reaching out for the bottle, 'that he is a very expert log-snatcher and a man of a merry face. What shall I do to him, Sahib?'

This was interesting. The timid hill-folk would as soon have refused taxes to their king as revenues to their Gods.

'If it be the King's permission,' I said, 'I will not strike my tents till the third day and I will see this man. The mercy of the King is God-like, and rebellion is like unto the sin of witchcraft. Moreover, both the bottles and another be empty.'

'You have my leave to go,' said the King.

Next morning a crier went through the state proclaiming that there was a log-jam on the river and that it behoved all loyal subjects to remove it. The people poured down from their villages to the moist warm valley of poppy-fields; and the King and I went with them. Hundreds of dressed deodar-logs had caught on a snag of rock, and the river was bringing down more logs every minute to complete the blockade. The water snarled and wrenched and worried at the timber, and the population of the state began prodding the nearest logs with a pole in the hope of starting a general movement. Then there went up a shout of 'Namgay Doola! Namgay Doola!' and a large red-haired villager hurried up, stripping off his clothes as he ran.

'That is he. That is the rebel,' said the King. 'Now will the dam be cleared.'

'But why has he red hair?' I asked, since red hair among hill-folks is as common as blue or green.

'He is an outlander,' said the King. 'Well done! Oh well done!'

Namgay Doola had scrambled out on the jam and was clawing out the butt of a log with a rude sort of boat-hook. It slid forward slowly as an alligator moves, three or four others followed it, and the green water spouted through the gaps they had made. Then the villagers howled and shouted and scrambled across the logs, pulling and pushing the obstinate timber, and the red head of Namgay Doola was chief among them all. The logs swayed and chafed and groaned as fresh consignments from upstream battered the now weakening dam. All gave way at last in a smother of foam, racing logs, bobbing black heads and confusion indescribable. The river tossed everything before it. I saw the red head go down with the last remnants of the jam and disappear between the great grinding tree-trunks. It rose close to the bank and blowing like a grampus. Namgay Doola wrung the water out of his eyes and made obeisance to the King. I had time to observe him closely. The virulent redness of his shock head and beard was most startling; and in the thicket of hair wrinkled above high cheek bones shone two very merry blue eyes. He was indeed an outlander, but yet a Thibetan in language, habit, and attire. He spoke the Lepcha dialect with an indescribable softening of the gutturals. It was not so much a lisp as an accent.

'Whence comest thou?' I asked.

'From Thibet.' He pointed across the hills and grinned. That grin went straight to my heart. Mechanically I held out my hand and Namgay Doola shook it. No pure Thibetan would have understood the meaning of the gesture. He went away to look for his clothes, and as he climbed back to his village, I heard a joyous yell that seemed unaccountably familiar. It was the whooping of Namgay Doola.

'You see now,' said the King, 'why I would not kill him. He is a bold man among my logs, but,' and he shook his head like a schoolmaster, 'I know that before long there will be complaints of him in the court. Let us return to the Palace and do justice.' It was that King's custom to judge his subjects every day between eleven and three o'clock. I saw him decide equitably in weighty matter of trespass, slander, and a little wife-stealing. Then his brow clouded and he summoned me.

'Again it is Namgay Doola,' he said, despairingly. 'Not content with refusing revenue on his own part, he has bound half his village by an oath to the like treason. Never before has such a thing befallen me! Nor are my taxes heavy.'

A rabbit-faced villager, with a blush-rose stuck behind his ear, advanced trembling. He had been in the conspiracy, but had told everything and hoped for the King's favour.

'O King,' said I, 'if it be the King's will let this matter stand over till the morning. Only the Gods can do right swiftly, and it may be that yonder villager has lied.'

'Nay, for I know the nature of Namgay Doola; but since a guest asks let the matter remain. Wilt thou speak harshly to this red-headed outlander? He may listen to thee.'

I made an attempt that very evening, but for the life of me I could not keep my countenance. Namgay Doola grinned persuasively, and began to tell me about a big brown bear in a poppy-field by the river. Would I care to shoot it? I spoke austerely on the sin of conspiracy, and the certainty of punishment. Namgay Doola's face clouded for a moment. Shortly afterwards he withdrew from my tent, and I heard him singing to himself softly among the pines. The words were unintelligible to me, but the tune, like his liquid insinuating speech, seemed the ghost of something strangely familiar.

> 'Dir hané mard-i-yemen dir
> To weeree ala gee.'

sang Namgay Doola again and again, and I racked my brain for that lost tune. It was not till after dinner that I discovered some one had cut a square foot of velvet from the centre of my best camera-cloth. This made me so angry that I wandered down the valley in the hope of meeting the big brown bear. I could hear him grunting like a discontented pig in the poppy-field, and I waited shoulder deep in the dew-dripping Indian corn to catch him after his meal. The moon was at full and drew out the rich scent of the tasselled crop. Then I heard the anguished bellow of a Himalayan cow, one of the little black crummies no bigger than Newfoundland dogs. Two shadows that looked like a bear and her cub hurried past me. I was in act to fire when I saw that they had each a brilliant red head. The lesser animal was trailing some rope behind it that left a dark track on the path. They passed within six feet of me, and the shadow of the moonlight lay velvet-black on their faces. Velvet-black was exactly the word, for by all the powers of moonlight they were masked in the velvet of my camera-cloth! I marvelled and went to bed.

Next morning the Kingdom was in uproar. Namgay Doola, men said, had gone forth in the night and with a sharp knife had cut off the tail of a cow belonging to the rabbit-faced villager who had betrayed him. It was sacrilege unspeakable against the Holy Cow. The State desired his blood, but he had retreated into his hut, barricaded the doors and windows with big stones, and defied the world.

The King and I and the populace approached the hut cautiously. There was no hope of capturing the man without loss of life, for from a hole in the wall projected the muzzle of an extremely well-cared-for gun—the only gun in the State that could shoot. Namgay Doola had narrowly missed a villager just before we came up. The Standing Army stood. It could do no more, for when it advanced pieces of sharp shale flew from the windows. To these were added from time to time showers of scalding water. We saw red heads bobbing up and down in the hut. The family of Namgay Doola were aiding their sire, and blood-curdling yells of defiance were the only answers to our prayers.

'Never,' said the King, puffing, 'has such a thing befallen my State. Next year I will certainly buy a little cannon.' He looked at me imploringly.

'Is there any priest in the Kingdom to whom he will listen?' said I, for a light was beginning to break upon me.

'He worships his own God,' said the Prime Minister. 'We can starve him out.'

'Let the white man approach,' said Namgay Doola from within. 'All others I will kill. Send me the white man.'

The door was thrown open and I entered the smoky interior of a Thibetan hut crammed with children. And every child had flaming red hair. A raw cow's-tail lay on the floor, and by its side two pieces of black velvet— my black velvet—rudely hacked into the semblance of masks.

'And what is this shame, Namgay Doola?' said I.

He grinned more winningly than ever. 'There is no shame,' said he. 'I did but cut off the tail of that man's cow. He betrayed me. I was minded to shoot him, Sahib. But not to death. Indeed not to death. Only in the legs.'

'And why at all, since it is the custom to pay revenue to the King? Why at all?'

'By the God of my father I cannot tell,' said Namgay Doola.

'And who was thy father?'

'The same that had this gun.' He showed me his weapon—a Tower musket bearing date 1832 and the stamp of the Honourable East India Company.

'And thy father's name?' said I.

'Timlay Doola,' said he. 'At the first, I being then a little child, it is in my mind that he wore a red coat.'

'Of that I have no doubt. But repeat the name of thy father thrice or four times.'

He obeyed, and I understood whence the puzzling accent in his speech came. 'Thimla Dhula,' said he excitedly. 'To this hour I worship his God.'

'May I see that God?'

'In a little while—at twilight time.'

'Rememberest thou aught of thy father's speech?'

'It is long ago. But there is one word which he said often. Thus "*Shun.*" Then I and my brethren stood upon our feet, our hands to our sides. Thus.'

'Even so. And what was thy mother?'

'A woman of the hills. We be Lepchas of Darjeeling, but me they call an outlander because my hair is as thou seest.'

The Thibetan woman, his wife, touched him on the arm gently. The long parley outside the fort had lasted far into the day. It was now close upon twilight—the hour of the Angelus. Very solemnly, the red-headed brats rose from the floor and formed a semicircle. Namgay Doola laid his gun against the wall, lighted a little oil lamp, and set it before a recess in the wall. Pulling aside a curtain of dirty cloth, he revealed a worn brass crucifix leaning against the helmet-badge of a long forgotten East India regiment. 'Thus did my father,' he said, crossing himself clumsily. The wife and children followed suit. Then all together they struck up the wailing chant that I heard on the hillside—

> Dir hané mard-i-yemen dir
> To weeree ala gee.

I was puzzled no longer. Again and again they crooned, as if their hearts would break, their version of the chorus of the *Wearing of the Green*—

> They're hanging men and women too,
> For the wearing of the green.

A diabolical inspiration came to me. One of the brats, a boy about eight years old, was watching me as he sang. I pulled out a rupee, held the coin between finger and thumb and looked—only looked—at the gun against the wall. A grin of brilliant and perfect comprehension overspread the face of the child. Never for an instant stopping the song, he held out his hand for the money, and then slid the gun to my hand. I might have shot Namgay Doola as he chanted. But I was satisfied. The blood-instinct of the race held true. Namgay Doola drew the curtain across the recess. Angelus was over.

'Thus my father sang. There was much more, but I have forgotten, and I do not know the purport of these words, but it may be that the God will understand. I am not of this people, and I will not pay revenue.'

'And why?'

Again that soul-compelling grin. 'What occupation would be to me between crop and crop? It is better than scaring bears. But these people do not understand.' He picked the masks from the floor, and looked in my face as simply as a child.

'By what road didst thou attain knowledge to make these devilries?' I said, pointing.

'I cannot tell. I am but a Lepcha of Darjeeling, and yet the stuff——'

'Which thou hast stolen.'

'Nay, surely. Did I steal? I desired it so. The stuff—the stuff—what else should I have done with the stuff?' He twisted the velvet between his fingers.

'But the sin of maiming the cow—consider that.'

'That is true; but oh, Sahib, that man betrayed me and I had no thought—but the heifer's tail waved in the moonlight and I had my knife. What else should I have done? The tail came off ere I was aware. Sahib, thou knowest more than I.'

'That is true,' said I. 'Stay within the door. I go to speak to the King.'

The population of the State were ranged on the hillsides. I went forth and spoke to the King.

'O King,' said I. 'Touching this man there be two courses open to thy wisdom. Thou canst either hang him from a tree, he and his brood, till there remains no hair that is red within the land.'

'Nay,' said the King. 'Why should I hurt the little children?'

They had poured out of the hut door and were making plump obeisance to everybody. Namgay Doola waited with his gun across his arm.

'Or thou canst, discarding the impiety of the cow-maiming, raise him to honour in thy Army. He comes of a race that will not pay revenue. A red flame is in his blood which comes out of the top of his head in that glowing hair. Make him chief of the Army. Give him honour as may befall, and full allowance of work, but look to it, O King, that neither he nor his hold a foot of earth from thee henceforward. Feed him with words and favour, and also liquor from certain bottles that thou knowest of, and he will be a bulwark of defence. But deny him even a tuft of grass for his own. This is the nature that God has given him. Moreover he has brethren——'

The State groaned unanimously.

'But if his brethren come, they will surely fight with each other till they die; or else the one will always give information concerning the other. Shall he be of thy Army, O King? Choose.'

The King bowed his head, and I said, 'Come forth, Namgay Doola, and command the King's Army. Thy name shall no more be Namgay in the mouths of men, but Patsay Doola, for as thou hast said, I know.'

Then Namgay Doola, new christened Patsay Doola, son of Timlay Doola, which is Tim Doolan gone very wrong indeed, clasped the King's feet, cuffed the Standing Army, and hurried in an agony of contrition from temple to temple, making offerings for the sin of cattle-maiming.

And the King was so pleased with my perspicacity, that he offered to sell me a village for twenty pounds sterling. But I buy no villages in the Himalayas so long as one red head flares between the tail of the heaven-climbing glacier and the dark birch-forest.

I know that breed.

MOTI GUJ—MUTINEER

ONCE upon a time there was a coffee-planter in India who wished to clear some forest land for coffee-planting. When he had cut down all the trees and burned the under-wood the stumps still remained. Dynamite is expensive and slow-fire slow. The happy medium for stump-clearing is the lord of all beasts, who is the elephant. He will either push the stump out of the ground with his tusks, if he has any, or drag it out with ropes. The planter, therefore, hired elephants by ones and twos and threes, and fell to work. The very best of all the elephants belonged to the very worst of all the drivers or mahouts; and the superior beast's name was Moti Guj. He was the absolute property of his mahout, which would never have been the case under native rule, for Moti Guj was a creature to be desired by kings; and his name, being translated, meant the Pearl Elephant. Because the British Government was in the land, Deesa, the mahout, enjoyed his property undisturbed. He was dissipated. When he had made much money through the strength of his elephant, he would get extremely drunk and give Moti Guj a beating with a tent-peg over the tender nails of the forefeet. Moti Guj never trampled the life out of Deesa on these occasions, for he knew that after the beating was over Deesa would embrace his trunk and weep and call him his love and his life and the liver of his soul, and give him some liquor. Moti Guj was very fond of liquor—arrack for choice, though he would drink palm-tree toddy if nothing better offered. Then Deesa would go to sleep between Moti Guj's forefeet, and as Deesa generally chose the middle of the public road, and as Moti Guj mounted guard over him and would not permit horse, foot, or cart to pass by, traffic was congested till Deesa saw fit to wake up.

There was no sleeping in the daytime on the planter's clearing: the wages were too high to risk. Deesa sat on Moti Guj's neck and gave him orders, while Moti Guj rooted up the stumps—for he owned a magnificent pair of tusks; or pulled at the end of a rope—for he had a magnificent pair of shoulders, while Deesa kicked him behind the ears and said he was the king of elephants. At evening time Moti Guj would wash down his three hundred pounds' weight of green food with a quart of arrack, and Deesa would take a share and sing songs between Moti Guj's legs till it was time to go to bed. Once a week Deesa led Moti Guj down to the river, and Moti Guj lay on his side luxuriously in the shallows, while Deesa went over him with a coir-swab and a brick. Moti Guj never mistook the pounding blow of the latter for the smack of the former that warned him to get up and turn over on the other side. Then Deesa would look at his feet, and examine his eyes, and turn up the fringes of his mighty ears in case of sores or budding ophthalmia. After inspection. the two would 'come up with a song from the sea,' Moti Guj all black and shining, waving a torn tree branch twelve feet long in his trunk, and Deesa knotting up his own long wet hair.

It was a peaceful, well-paid life till Deesa felt the return of the desire to drink deep. He wished for an orgie. The little draughts that led nowhere were taking the manhood out of him.

He went to the planter, and 'My mother's dead,' said he, weeping.

'She died on the last plantation two months ago; and she died once before that when you were working for me last year,' said the planter, who knew something of the ways of nativedom.

'Then it's my aunt, and she was just the same as a mother to me,' said Deesa, weeping more than ever. 'She has left eighteen small children entirely without bread, and it is I who must fill their little stomachs,' said Deesa, beating his head on the floor.

'Who brought you the news?' said the planter.

'The post,' said Deesa.

'There hasn't been a post here for the past week. Get back to your lines!'

'A devastating sickness has fallen on my village, and all my wives are dying,' yelled Deesa, really in tears this time.

'Call Chihun, who comes from Deesa's village,' said the planter. 'Chihun, has this man a wife?'

'He!' said Chihun. 'No. Not a woman of our village would look at him. They'd sooner marry the elephant.' Chihun snorted. Deesa wept and bellowed.

'You will get into a difficulty in a minute,' said the planter. 'Go back to your work!'

'Now I will speak Heaven's truth,' gulped Deesa, with an inspiration. 'I haven't been drunk for two months. I desire to depart in order to get properly drunk afar off and distant from this heavenly plantation. Thus I shall cause no trouble.'

A flickering smile crossed the planter's face. 'Deesa,' said he, 'you've spoken the truth, and I'd give you leave on the spot if anything could be done with Moti Guj while you're away. You know that he will only obey your orders.'

'May the Light of the Heavens live forty thousand years. I shall be absent but ten little days. After that, upon my faith and honour and soul, I return. As to the inconsiderable interval, have I the gracious permission of the Heaven-born to call up Moti Guj?'

Permission was granted, and, in answer to Deesa's shrill yell, the lordly tusker swung out of the shade of a clump of trees where he had been squirting dust over himself till his master should return.

'Light of my heart, Protector of the Drunken, Mountain of Might, give ear,' said Deesa, standing in front of him.

Moti Guj gave ear, and saluted with his trunk. 'I am going away,' said Deesa.

Moti Guj's eyes twinkled. He liked jaunts as well as his master One could snatch all manner of nice things from the roadside then.

'But you, you fubsy old pig, must stay behind and work.'

The twinkle died out as Moti Guj tried to look delighted. He hated stump-hauling on the plantation. It hurt his teeth.

'I shall be gone for ten days, O Delectable One. Hold up your near forefoot and I'll impress the fact upon it, warty toad of a dried mud-puddle.' Deesa took a tent-peg and banged Moti Guj ten times on the nails. Moti Guj grunted and shuffled from foot to foot.

'Ten days,' said Deesa, 'you must work and haul and root trees as Chihun here shall order you. Take up Chihun and set him on your neck!' Moti Guj curled the tip of his trunk, Chihun put his foot there and was swung on to the neck. Deesa handed Chihun the heavy *ankus*, the iron elephant-goad.

Chihun thumped Moti Guj's bald head as a paviour thumps a kerbstone. Moti Guj trumpeted.

'Be still, hog of the backwoods. Chihun's your mahout for ten days. And now bid me good-bye, beast after mine own heart. Oh, my lord, my king! Jewel of all created elephants, lily of the herd, preserve your honoured health; be virtuous. Adieu!'

Moti Guj lapped his trunk round Deesa and swung him into the air twice. That was his way of bidding the man good-bye.

'He'll work now,' said Deesa to the planter. 'Have I leave to go?'

The planter nodded, and Deesa dived into the woods. Moti Guj went back to haul stumps.

Chihun was very kind to him, but he felt unhappy and forlorn notwithstanding. Chihun gave him balls of spices, and tickled him under the chin, and Chihun's little baby cooed to him after work was over, and Chihun's wife called him a darling; but Moti Guj was a bachelor by instinct, as Deesa was. He did not understand the domestic emotions. He wanted the light of his universe back again—the drink and the drunken slumber, the savage beatings and the savage caresses.

None the less he worked well, and the planter wondered. Deesa had vagabonded along the roads till he met a marriage procession of his own caste and, drinking, dancing, and tippling, had drifted past all knowledge of the lapse of time.

The morning of the eleventh day dawned, and there returned no Deesa. Moti Guj was loosed from his ropes for the daily stint. He swung clear, looked round, shrugged his shoulders, and began to walk away, as one having business elsewhere.

'Hi! ho! Come back, you,' shouted Chihun. 'Come back, and put me on your neck, Misborn Mountain. Return, Splendour of the Hillsides. Adornment of all India, heave to, or I'll bang every toe off your fat forefoot!'

Moti Guj gurgled gently, but did not obey. Chihun ran after him with a rope and caught him up. Moti Guj put his ears forward, and Chihun knew what that meant, though he tried to carry it off with high words.

'None of your nonsense with me,' said he. 'To your pickets, Devil-son.'

'Hrrump!' said Moti Guj, and that was all—that and the forebent ears.

Moti Guj put his hands in his pockets, chewed a branch for a toothpick, and strolled about the clearing, making jest of the other elephants, who had just set to work.

Chihun reported the state of affairs to the planter, who came out with a dog-whip and cracked it furiously. Moti Guj paid the white man the compliment of charging him nearly a quarter of a mile across the clearing and 'Hrrumping' him into the verandah. Then he stood outside the house chuckling to himself, and shaking all over with the fun of it, as an elephant will.

'We'll thrash him,' said the planter. 'He shall have the finest thrashing that ever elephant received. Give Kala Nag and Nazim twelve foot of chain apiece, and tell them to lay on twenty blows.'

Kala Nag—which means Black Snake—and Nazim were two of the biggest elephants in the lines, and one of their duties was to administer the graver punishments, since no man can beat an elephant properly.

They took the whipping-chains and rattled them in their trunks as they sidled up to Moti Guj, meaning to hustle him between them. Moti Guj had never, in all his life of thirty-nine years, been whipped, and he did not intend to open new experiences. So he waited, weaving his head from right to left, and measuring the precise spot in Kala Nag's fat side where a blunt tusk would sink deepest. Kala Nag had no tusks; the chain was his badge of authority; but he judged it good to swing wide of Moti Guj at the last minute, and seem to appear as if he had brought out the chain for amusement. Nazim turned round and went home early. He did not feel fighting-fit that morning, and so Moti Guj was left standing alone with his ears cocked.

That decided the planter to argue no more, and Moti Guj rolled back to his inspection of the clearing. An elephant who will not work, and is not tied up, is not quite so manageable as an eighty-one ton gun loose in a heavy sea-way. He slapped old friends on the back and asked them if the stumps were coming away easily; he talked nonsense concerning labour and the inalienable rights of elephants to a long 'nooning'; and, wandering to and fro, thoroughly demoralized the garden till sundown, when he returned to his pickets for food.

'If you won't work you shan't eat,' said Chihun angrily. 'You're a wild elephant, and no educated animal at all. Go back to your jungle.'

Chihun's little brown baby, rolling on the floor of the hut, stretched its fat arms to the huge shadow in the doorway. Moti Guj knew well that it was the dearest thing on earth to Chihun. He swung out his trunk with a fascinating crook at the end, and the brown baby threw itself shouting upon it. Moti Guj made fast and pulled up till the brown baby was crowing in the air twelve feet above his father's head.

'Great Chief!' said Chihun. 'Flour cakes of the best, twelve in number, two feet across, and soaked in rum shall be yours on the instant, and two hundred pounds' weight of fresh-cut young sugar-cane therewith. Deign only to put down safely that insignificant brat who is my heart and my life to me.'

Moti Guj tucked the brown baby comfortably between his forefeet, that could have knocked into toothpicks all Chihun's hut, and waited for his food. He ate it, and the brown baby crawled away. Moti Guj dozed, and thought of Deesa. One of the many mysteries connected with the elephant is that his huge body needs less sleep than anything else that lives. Four or five hours in the night suffice—two just before midnight, lying down on one side; two just after one o'clock, lying down on the other. The rest of the silent hours are filled with eating and fidgeting and long grumbling soliloquies.

At midnight, therefore, Moti Guj strode out of his pickets, for a thought had come to him that Deesa might be lying drunk somewhere in the dark forest with none to look after him. So all that night he chased through the undergrowth, blowing and trumpeting and shaking his ears. He went down to the river and blared across the shallows where Deesa used to wash him, but there was no answer. He could not find Deesa, but he disturbed all the elephants in the lines, and nearly frightened to death some gypsies in the woods.

At dawn Deesa returned to the plantation. He had been very drunk indeed, and he expected to fall into trouble for outstaying his leave. He drew a long breath when he saw that the bungalow and the plantation were still uninjured; for he knew something of Moti Guj's temper; and reported himself with many lies and salaams. Moti Guj had gone to his pickets for breakfast. His night exercise had made him hungry.

'Call up your beast,' said the planter, and Deesa shouted in the mysterious elephant-language, that some mahouts believe came from China at the birth of the world, when elephants and not men were masters. Moti Guj heard and came. Elephants do not gallop. They move from spots at varying rates of speed. If an elephant wished to catch an express train he could not gallop, but he could catch the train. Thus Moti Guj was at the planter's door almost before Chihun noticed that he had left his pickets. He fell into Deesa's arms trumpeting with joy, and the man and beast wept and slobbered over each other, and handled each other from head to heel to see that no harm had befallen.

'Now we will get to work,' said Deesa. 'Lift me up, my son and my joy.'

Moti Guj swung him up and the two went to the coffee-clearing to look for irksome stumps.

The planter was too astonished to be very angry.

THE MIRACLE OF PURUN BHAGAT

The night we felt the Earth would move
　　We stole and plucked him by the hand,
Because we loved him with the love
　　That knows but cannot understand.

And when the roaring hillside broke
　　And all our world fell down in rain,
We saved him, we the Little Folk;
　　But lo! he will not come again!

Mourn now, we saved him for the sake
　　Of such poor love as wild ones may.
Mourn ye! Our brother does not wake
　　And his own kind drive us away!

DIRGE OF THE LANGURS

ॐ THERE was once a man in India who was Prime Minister of one of the semi-independent native States in the north-western part of the country. He was a Brahmin, so high-caste that caste ceased to have any particular meaning for him; and his father had been an important official in the gay-coloured tag-rag and bob-tail of an old-fashioned Hindu Court. But as Purun Dass grew up he realised that the ancient order of things was changing, and that if any one wished to get on he must stand well with the English, and imitate all the English believed to be good. At the same time a native official must keep his own master's favour. This was a difficult game, but the quiet, close-mouthed young Brahmin, helped by a good English education at a Bombay University, played it coolly, and rose, step by step, to be Prime Minister of the kingdom. That is to say, he held more real power than his master, the Maharajah.

When the old king—who was suspicious of the English, their railways and telegraphs—died, Purun Dass stood high with his young successor, who had been tutored by an Englishman; and between them, though he always took care that his master should have the credit, they established schools for little girls, made roads, and started State dispensaries and shows of agricultural implements, and published a yearly blue-book on the 'Moral and Material Progress of the State,' and the Foreign Office and the Government of India were delighted. Very few native States take up English progress without reservations, for they will not believe, as Purun Dass showed he did, that what is good for the Englishman must be twice as good for the Asiatic. The Prime Minister became the honoured friend of Viceroys and

Governors, and Lieutenant-Governors, and medical missionaries, and common missionaries, and hard-riding English officers who came to shoot in the State preserves, as well as of whole hosts of tourists who travelled up and down India in the cold weather, showing how things ought to be managed. In his spare time he would endow scholarships for the study of medicine and manufactures on strictly English lines, and write letters to the *Pioneer*, the greatest Indian daily paper, explaining his master's aims and objects.

At last he went to England on a visit, and had to pay enormous sums to the priests when he came back; for even so high-caste a Brahmin as Purun Dass lost caste by crossing the black sea. In London he met and talked with every one worth knowing—men whose names go all over the world—and saw a great deal more than he said. He was given honorary degrees by learned universities, and he made speeches and talked of Hindu social reform to English ladies in evening dress, till all London cried, 'This is the most fascinating man we have ever met at dinner since cloths were first laid!'

When he returned to India there was a blaze of glory, for the Viceroy himself made a special visit to confer upon the Maharajah the Grand Cross of the Star of India—all diamonds and ribbons and enamel; and at the same ceremony, while the cannon boomed, Purun Dass was made a Knight Commander of the Order of the Indian Empire; so that his named stood Sir Purun Dass, K.C.I.E.

That evening at dinner in the big Viceregal tent he stood up with the badge and the collar of the Order on his breast, and replying to the toast of his master's health, made a speech that few Englishmen could have surpassed.

Next month, when the city had returned to its sun-baked quiet, he did a thing no Englishman would have dreamed of doing, for, so far as the world's affairs went, he died. The jeweled order of his knighthood returned to the Indian Government, and a new Prime Minister was appointed to the charge of affairs, and a great game of General Post began in all the subordinate appointments. The priests knew what had happened and the people guessed; but India is the one place in the world where a man can do as he pleases and nobody asks why; and the fact that Dewan Sir Purun Dass, K.C.I.E., had resigned position, palace, and power, and taken up the begging-bowl and ochre-coloured dress of a Sunnyasi or holy man, was considered nothing extraordinary. He had been, as the Old Law recommends, twenty years a youth, twenty years a fighter—though he had never carried a weapon in his life—and twenty years head of a household. He had used his wealth and his power for what he knew both to be worth; he had taken honour when it came his way; he had seen men and cities far and near, and men and cities had stood up and honoured him. Now he would let these things go, as a man drops the cloak he needs no longer.

Behind him, as he walked through the city gates, an antelope skin and brass-handled crutch under his arm, and a begging-bowl of polished brown *coco-de-mer* in his hand, barefoot, alone, with eyes cast on the ground —behind him they were firing salutes from the bastions in honour of his happy successor. Purun Dass nodded. All that life was ended; and he bore it no more ill-will or good-will than a man bears to a colourless dream of the night. He was a Sunnyasi—a houseless, wandering mendicant, depending on his neighbours for his daily bread; and so long as there is a morsel to divide in India neither priest nor beggar starves. He had never in his life tasted meat, and very seldom eaten even fish. A five-pound note would have covered his personal expenses for food through any one of the many years in which he had been absolute master of millions of money. Even when he was being lionised in London he had held before him his dream of peace and quiet—the long, white, dusty Indian road, printed all over with bare feet, the incessant, slow-moving traffic, and the sharp-smelling wood-smoke curling up under the fig-trees in the twilight, where the way-farers sat at their evening meal.

When the time came to make that dream true the Prime Minister took the proper steps, and in three days you might more easily have found a bubble in the trough of the long Atlantic seas than Purun Dass among the roving, gathering, separating millions of India.

At night his antelope skin was spread where the darkness overtook him —sometimes in a Sunnyasi monastery by the roadside; sometimes by a mud pillar shrine of Kala Pir, where the Jogis, who are another misty division of holy men, would receive him as they do those who know what castes and divisions are worth; sometimes on the outskirts of a little Hindu village, where the children would steal up with the food their parents had prepared; and sometimes on the pitch of the bare grazing-grounds where the flame of his stick fire waked the drowsy camels. It was all one to Purun Dass—or Purun Bhagat, as he called himself now. Earth, people, and food were all one. But, unconsciously, his feet drew him northward and eastward; from the south to Rohtak; from Rohtak to Kurnool; from Kurnool to ruined Samanah, and then up-stream along the dried bed of the Gugger river that fills only when the rain falls in the hills, till, one day, he saw the far line of the great Himalayas.

Then Purun Bhagat smiled, for he remembered that his mother was of Rajput Brahmin birth, from Kulu way—a Hill-woman, always homesick for the snows—and that the least touch of Hill blood draws a man in the end back to where he belongs.

'Yonder,' said Purun Bhagat, breasting the lower slopes of the Sewaliks, where the cacti stand up like seven-branched candlesticks, 'yonder I shall sit down and get knowledge;' and the cool wind of the Himalayas whistled about his ears as he trod the road that led to Simla.

The last time he had come that way it had been in state, with a clattering cavalry escort, to visit the gentlest and most affable of Viceroys; and the two had talked for an hour together about mutual friends in London, and what the Indian common folk really thought of things. This time Purun Bhagat paid no calls, but leaned on the rail of the Mall, watching the glorious view of the Plains spread out forty miles below, till a native

Mohammedan policeman told him he was obstructing traffic; and Purun Bhagat salaamed reverently to the Law, because he knew the value of it, and was seeking for a Law of his own. Then he moved on, and slept that night in an empty hut at Chota Simla, which looks like the very last end of the earth, but it was only the beginning of his journey. He followed the Himalaya-Thibet road, the little ten-foot track that is blasted out of solid rock, or strutted out on timbers over gulfs a thousand feet deep; that dips into warm, wet, shut-in valleys, and climbs across bare, grassy hill-shoulders where the sun strikes like a burning-glass; or turns through dripping, dark forests where the tree-ferns dress the trunks from head to heel, and the pheasant calls to his mate. And he met Thibetan herdsmen with their dogs and flocks of sheep, each sheep with a little bag of borax on his back, and wandering wood-cutters, and cloaked and blanketed Lamas from Thibet, coming into India on pilgrimage, and envoys of little solitary Hill-states, posting furiously on ring-streaked and piebald ponies, or the cavalcade of a Rajah paying a visit, or else for a long, clear day he would see nothing more than a black bear grunting and rooting down below in the valley. When he first started, the roar of the world he had left still rang in his ears, as the roar of a tunnel rings a little after the train has passed through; but when he had put the Mutteeanee Pass behind him that was all done, and Purun Bhagat was alone with himself, walking, wondering, and thinking, his eyes on the ground, and his thoughts with the clouds.

One evening he crossed the highest pass he had met till then— it had been a two days' climb—and came out on a line of snow-peaks that belted all the horizon—mountains from fifteen to twenty thousand feet high, looking almost near enough to hit with a stone, though they were fifty or sixty miles away. The pass was crowned with dense, dark forest— deodar, walnut, wild cherry, wild olive, and wild pear but mostly deodar, which is the Himalayan cedar; and under the shadow of the deodars stood a deserted shrine to Kali—who is Durga, who is Sitala, who is sometimes worshipped against the smallpox.

Purun Dass swept the stone floor clean, smiled at the grinning statue, made himself a little mud fireplace at the back of the shrine, spread his antelope skin on a bed of fresh pine needles, tucked his *bairagi*—his brass-handled crutch—under his armpit, and sat down to rest.

Immediately below him the hillside fell away, clean and cleared for fifteen hundred feet, to where a little village of stone-walled houses, with roofs of beaten earth, clung to the steep tilt. All round it tiny terraced fields lay out like aprons of patchwork on the knees of the mountain, and cows no bigger than beetles grazed between the smooth stone circles of the threshing-floors. Looking across the valley the eye was deceived by the size of things, and could not at first realise that what seemed to be low scrub, on the opposite mountain-flank, was in truth a forest of hundred-foot pines. Purun Bhagat saw an eagle swoop across the enormous hollow, but the great bird dwindled to a dot ere it was half-way over. A few bands of scattered clouds strung up and down the valley, catching on a shoulder of the hills, or rising up and dying out when they were level with the head of the pass. And 'Here shall I find peace,' said Purun Bhagat.

Now, a Hill-man makes nothing of a few hundred feet up or down, and as soon as the villagers saw the smoke in the deserted shrine, the village priest climbed up the terraced hillside to welcome the stranger.

When he met Purun Bhagat's eyes—the eyes of a man used to control thousands—he bowed to the earth, took the begging-bowl without a word, and returned to the village, saying, 'We have at last a holy man. Never have I seen such a man. He is of the plains—but pale coloured—a Brahmin of the Brahmins.' Then all the housewives of the village said, 'Think you he will stay with us?' and each did her best to cook the most savoury meal for the Bhagat. Hill-food is very simple, but with buckwheat and Indian corn, and rice and red pepper, and little fish out of the stream in the little valley, and honey from the flue-like hives built in the stone walls, and dried apricots, and turmeric, and wild ginger, and bannocks of flour, a devout woman can make good things; and it was a full bowl that the priest carried to the Bhagat. Was he going to stay? asked the priest. Would he need a *chela*—a disciple—to beg for him? Had he a blanket against the cold weather? Was the food good?

Purun Bhagat ate, and thanked the giver. It was in his mind to stay. That was sufficient, said the priest. Let the begging-bowl be placed outside the shrine, in the hollow made by those two twisted roots, and daily should the Bhagat be fed; for the village felt honoured that such a man—he looked timidly into the Bhagat's face—should tarry among them.

That day saw the end of Purun Bhagat's wanderings. He had come to the place appointed for him—the silence and the space. After this, time stopped, and he, sitting at the mouth of the shrine, could not tell whether he were alive or dead; a man with control of his limbs, or a part of the hills, and the clouds, and the shifting rain, and sunlight. He would repeat a Name softly to himself a hundred hundred times, till, at each repetition, he seemed to move more and more out his body, sweeping up to the doors of some tremendous discovery; but, just as the door was opening, his body would drag him back, and, with grief, he felt he was locked up again in the flesh and bones of Purun Bhagat.

Every morning the filled begging-bowl was laid silently in the crotch of the roots outside the shrine. Sometimes the priest brought it; sometimes a Ladakhi trader, lodging in the village, and anxious to get merit, trudged up the path; but, more often, it was the woman who had cooked the meal overnight; and she would murmur, hardly above her breath: 'Speak for me before the gods, Bhagat. Speak for such an one, the wife of so-and-so!' Now and then some bold child would be allowed the honour, and Purun Bhagat would hear him drop the bowl and run as fast as his little legs could carry him, but the Bhagat never came down to the village. It was laid out like a map at his feet. He could see the evening gatherings held on the circle of the threshing-floors, because that was the only level ground; could see the wonderful unnamed green of the young rice, the indigo blues of the Indian corn; the dock-like patches of buckwheat, and, in its season, the red bloom of the amaranth, whose tiny seeds, being neither grain nor pulse, make a food that can be lawfully eaten by Hindus in time of fasts.

When the year turned, the roofs of the huts were all little squares of purest gold, for it was on the roofs that they laid out their cobs of the corn to dry. Hiving and harvest, rice-sowing and husking, passed before his eyes, all embroidered down there on the many-sided fields, and he thought of them all, and wondered what they all led to at the long last.

Even in populated India a man cannot a day sit still before the wild things run over him as though he were a rock; and in that wilderness very soon the wild things, who knew Kali's Shrine well, came back to look at the intruder. The *langurs*, the big gray-whiskered monkeys of the Himalayas, were, naturally, the first, for they are alive with curiosity; and when they had upset the begging-bowl, and rolled it round the floor, and tried their teeth on the brass-handled crutch, and made faces at the antelope skin, they decided that the human being who sat so still was harmless. At evening, they would leap down from the pines, and beg with their hands for things to eat, and then swing off in graceful curves. They liked the warmth of the fire, too, and huddled round it till Purun Bhagat had to push them aside to throw on more fuel; and in the morning, as often as not, he would find a furry ape sharing his blanket. All day long, one or other of the tribe would sit by his side, staring out at the snows, crooning and looking unspeakably wise and sorrowful.

After the monkeys came the *barasingh*, that big deer which is like our red deer, but stronger. He wished to rub off the velvet of his horns against the cold stones of Kali's statue, and stamped his feet when he saw the man at the shrine. But Purun Bhagat never moved, and, little by little, the royal stag edged up and nuzzled his shoulder. Purun Bhagat slid one cool hand along the hot antlers, and the touch soothed the fretted beast, who bowed his head, and Purun Bhagat very softly rubbed and ravelled off the velvet. Afterwards, the *barasingh* brought his doe and fawn—gentle things that mumbled on the holy man's blanket—or would come alone at night, his eyes green in the fire-flicker, to take his share of fresh walnuts. At last, the musk-deer, the shyest and almost the smallest of the deerlets, came, too, her big, rabbity ears erect; even brindled, silent *mushick-nabha* must needs find out what the light in the shrine meant, and drop her moose-like nose into Purun Bhagat's lap, coming and going with the shadows of the fire. Purun Bhagat called them all 'my brothers,' and his low call of 'Bhai! Bhai!' would draw them from the forest at noon if they were within earshot. The Himalayan black bear, moody and suspicious—Sona, who has the V-shaped white mark under his chin—passed that way more than once; and since the Bhagat showed no fear, Sona showed no anger, but watched him, and came closer, and begged a share of the caresses, and a dole of bread or wild berries. Often, in the still dawns, when the Bhagat would climb to the very crest of the notched pass to watch the red day walking along the peaks of the snows, he would find Sona shuffling and grunting at his heels, thrusting a curious forepaw under fallen trunks, and bringing it away with a *whoof* of impatience; or his early steps would wake Sona where he lay curled up, and the great brute, rising erect, would think to fight, till he heard the Bhagat's voice and knew his best friend.

Nearly all hermits and holy men who live apart from the big cities have the reputation of being able to work miracles with the wild things, but all the miracle lies in keeping still, in never making a hasty movement, and, for a long time, at least, in never looking directly at a visitor. The villagers saw the outlines of the *barasingh* stalking like a shadow through the dark forest behind the shrine; saw the *minaul*, the Himalayan pheasant, blazing in her best colours before Kali's statue; and the *langurs* on their haunches, inside, playing with the walnut shells. Some of the children, too, had heard Sona singing to himself, bear-fashion, behind the fallen rocks, and the Bhagat's reputation as miracle-worker stood firm.

Yet nothing was further from his mind than miracles. He believed that all things were one big Miracle, and when a man knows that much he knows something to go upon. He knew for a certainty that there was nothing great and nothing little in this world; and day and night he strove to think out his way into the heart of things, back to the place whence his soul had come.

So thinking, his untrimmed hair fell down about his shoulders, the stone slab at the side of the antelope-skin was dented into a little hole by the foot of his brass-handled crutch, and the place between the tree-trunks, where the begging-bowl rested day after day, sunk and wore into a hollow almost as smooth as the brown shell itself; and each beast knew his exact place at the fire. The fields changed their colours with the seasons; the threshing-floors filled and emptied, and filled again and again; and again and again, when winter came, the *langurs* frisked among the branches feathered with light snow, till the mother-monkeys brought their sad-eyed little babies up from the warmer valleys with the spring. There were few changes in the village. The priest was older, and many of the little children who used to come with the begging-dish sent their own children now; and when you asked of the villagers how long their holy man had lived in Kali's Shrine at the head of the pass, they answered, 'Always.'

Then came such summer rains as had not been known in the Hills for many seasons. Through three good months the valley was wrapped in cloud and soaking mist—steady, unrelenting downfall, breaking off into thunder-shower after thunder-shower. Kali's Shrine stood above the clouds, for the most part, and there was a whole month in which the Bhagat never caught a glimpse of his village. It was packed away under a white floor of cloud that swayed and shifted and rolled on itself and bulged upward, but never broke from its piers—the streaming flanks of the valley.

All that time he heard nothing but the sound of a million little waters, overhead from the trees, and underfoot along the ground, soaking through the pine-needles, dripping from the tongues of draggled fern, and spouting in newly-torn muddy channels down the slopes. Then the sun came out, and drew forth the good incense of the deodars and the rhododendrons, and that far-off, clean smell the Hill People call 'the smell of the snows.' The hot sunshine lasted for a week, and then the rains gathered together for their last downpour, and the water fell in sheets that flayed off the skin of the ground and leaped back in mud. Purun Bhagat heaped his fire high that night, for he was sure his brothers would need warmth; but never a beast came to the shrine, though he called and called till he dropped asleep, wondering what had happened in the woods.

It was in the black heart of the night, the rain drumming like a thousand drums, that he was roused by a plucking at his blanket, and, stretching out, felt the little hand of a *langur*. 'It is better here than in the trees,' he said sleepily, loosening a fold of blanket; 'take it and be warm.' The monkey caught his hand and pulled hard. 'Is it food, then?' said Purun Bhagat. 'Wait awhile, and I will prepare some.' As he kneeled to throw fuel on the fire the *langur* ran to the door of the shrine, crooned, and ran back again, plucking at the man's knee.

'What is it? What is thy trouble, Brother?' said Purun Bhagat, for the *langur's* eyes were full of things that he could not tell. 'Unless one of thy caste be in a trap—and none set traps here—I will not go into that weather. Look, Brother, even the *barasingh* comes for shelter.'

The deer's antlers clashed as he strode into the shrine, clashed against the grinning statue of Kali. He lowered them in Purun Bhagat's direction and stamped uneasily, hissing through his half-shut nostrils.

'Hai! Hai! Hai!' said the Bhagat, snapping his fingers. 'Is *this* payment for a night's lodging?' But the deer pushed him towards the door, and as he did so Purun Bhagat heard the sound of something opening with a sigh, and saw two slabs of the floor draw away from each other, while the sticky earth below smacked its lips.

'Now I see,' said Purun Bhagat. 'No blame to my brothers that they did not sit by the fire to-night. The mountain is falling. And yet—why should I go?' His eye fell on the empty begging-bowl, and his face changed. 'They have given me good food daily since—since I came, and, if I am not swift, tomorrow there will not be one mouth in the valley. Indeed, I must go and warn them below. Back there, Brother! Let me get to the fire.'

The *barasingh* backed unwillingly as Purun Bhagat drove a torch deep into the flame, twirling it till it was well lit. 'Ah! ye came to warn me,' he said, rising. 'Better than that we shall do, better than that. Out, now, and lend me thy neck, Brother, for I have but two feet.'

He clutched the bristling withers of the *barasingh* with his right hand, held the torch away with his left, and stepped out of the shrine into the desperate night. There was no breath of wind, but the rain nearly drowned the torch as the great deer hurried down the slope, sliding on his haunches. As soon as they were clear of the forest more of the Bhagat's brothers joined them. He heard, though he could not see, the *langurs* pressing about him, and behind them the *uhh! uhh!* of Sona. The rain matted his long white hair into ropes; the water splashed beneath his bare feet, and his yellow robe clung to his frail old body, but he stepped down steadily, leaning against the *barasingh*. He was no longer a holy man, but Sir Purun Dass, K.C.I.E., Prime Minister of no small State, a man accustomed to command, going out to save life. Down the steep plashy path they poured all together, the Bhagat and his brothers, down and down till the deer clicked and stumbled on the wall of a threshing-floor, and snorted because he smelt Man. Now they were at the head of the one crooked village street, and the Bhagat beat with his crutch at the barred windows of the blacksmith's house as his torch blazed up in the shelter of the eaves. 'Up and out!' cried Purun Bhagat; and he did not know his own voice, for it was years since he had spoken aloud to a man. 'The hill falls! The hill is falling! Up and out, oh, you within!'

'It is our Bhagat,' said the blacksmith's wife. 'He stands among his beasts. Gather the little ones and give the call.'

It ran from house to house, while the beasts, cramped in the narrow way, surged and huddled round the Bhagat, and Sona puffed impatiently.

The people hurried into the street—they were no more than seventy souls all told—and in the glare of their torches they saw their Bhagat holding back the terrified *barasingh*, while the monkeys plucked piteously at his skirts, and Sona sat on his haunches and roared.

'Across the valley and up the next hill!' shouted Purun Bhagat. 'Leave none behind! We follow!'

Then the people ran as only Hill-folk can run, for they knew that in a landslip you must climb for the highest ground across the valley. They fled, splashing through the little river at the bottom, and panted up the terraced fields on the far side, while the Bhagat and his brethren followed. Up and up the opposite mountain they climbed, calling to each other by name— the roll-call of the village—and at their heels toiled the big *barasingh*, weighted by the failing strength of Purun Bhagat. At last the deer stopped in the shadow of a deep pine-wood, five hundred feet up the hillside. His instinct, that had warned him of the coming slide, told him he would be safe here.

Purun Bhagat dropped fainting by his side, for the chill of the rain and that fierce climb was killing him; but first he called to the scattered torches ahead, 'Stay and count your numbers;' then, whispering to the deer as he saw the lights gather in a cluster: 'Stay with me, Brother. Stay—till—I—go!'

There was a sigh in the air that grew to a mutter, and a mutter that grew to a roar, and a roar that passed all sense of hearing, and the hillside on which the villagers stood was hit in the darkness, and rocked to the blow.

Then a note as steady, deep, and true as the deep C of the organ drowned everything for perhaps five minutes, while the very roots of the pines quivered to it. It died away, and the sound of the rain falling on miles of hard ground and grass changed to the muffled drums of water on soft earth. That told its own tale.

Never a villager—not even the priest—was bold enough to speak to the Bhagat who had saved their lives. They crouched under the pines and waited till the day. When it came they looked across the valley, and saw that what had been forest, and terraced field, and track-threaded grazing-ground was one raw, red, fan-shaped smear, with a few trees flung head-down on the scarp. That red ran high up the hill of their refuge, damming back the little river, which had begun to spread into a brick-coloured lake. Of the village, of the road to the shrine, of the shrine itself, and the forest behind, there was no trace. For one mile in width and two thousand feet in sheer depth the mountain-side had come away bodily, planed clean from head to heel.

And the villagers, one by one, crept through the wood to pray before their Bhagat. They saw the *barasingh* standing over him, who fled when they came near, and they heard the *langurs* wailing in the branches, and Sona moaning up the hill; but their Bhagat was dead, sitting cross-legged, his back against a tree, his crutch under his armpit, and his face turned to the north-east.

The priest said: 'Behold a miracle after a miracle, for in this very attitude must all Sunnyasis be buried! Therefore, where he now is we will build the temple to our holy man.'

They built the temple before a year was ended, a little stone and earth shrine, and they called the hill the Bhagat's Hill, and they worship there with lights and flowers and offerings to this day. But they do not know that the saint of their worship is the late Sir Purun Dass, K.C.I.E., D.C.L., Ph.D., etc., once Prime Minister of the progressive and enlightened state of Mohiniwala, and honorary or corresponding member of more learned and scientific societies than will ever do any good in this world or the next.

THE INCARNATION OF KRISHNA MULVANEY

Wohl auf, my bully cavaliers,
   We ride to church to-day,
The man that hasn't got a horse
   Must steal one straight away.

.   .   .   .   .   .

Be reverent, men, remember
   This is a Gottes haus.
Du, Conrad, cut along der aisle
   And schenck der whiskey aus.
HANS BREITMANN'S RIDE TO CHURCH

ONCE upon a time, very far from England, there lived three men who loved each other so greatly that neither man nor woman could come between them. They were in no sense refined, nor to be admitted to the outerdoor mats of decent folk, because they happened to be private soldiers in Her Majesty's Army; and private soldiers of our service have small time for self-culture. Their duty is to keep themselves and their accoutrements specklessly clean, to refrain from getting drunk more often than is necessary, to obey their superiors, and to pray for a war. All these things my friends accomplished; and of their own motion threw in some fighting-work for which the Army Regulations did not call. Their fate sent them to serve in India, which is not a golden country, though poets have sung otherwise. There men die with great swiftness, and those who live suffer many and curious things. I do not think that my friends concerned themselves much with the social or political aspects of the East. They attended a not unimportant war on the northern frontier, another one on our western boundary, and a third in Upper Burma. Then their regiment sat still to recruit, and the boundless monotony of cantonment life was their portion. They were drilled morning and evening on the same dusty parade-ground. They wandered up and down the same stretch of dusty white road, attended the same church and the same grog-shop, and slept in the same lime-washed barn of a barrack for two long years. There was Mulvaney, the father in the craft, who had served with various regiments from Bermuda to Halifax, old in war, scarred, reckless, resourceful, and in his pious hours an unequalled soldier. To him turned for help and comfort six and a half feet of slow-moving, heavy-footed Yorkshireman, born on the wolds, bred in the dales, and educated chiefly among the carriers' carts at the back of York railway-station. His name was Learoyd, and his chief virtue an unmitigated patience which helped him to win fights. How Ortheris, a fox-terrier of a Cockney, ever came to be one of the trio, is a mystery which even to-day I cannot explain. 'There was always three av us,' Mulvaney used to say. 'An' by the grace av God, so long as our service lasts, three av us they'll always be. 'Tis betther so.'

They desired no companionship beyond their own, and it was evil for any man of the regiment who attempted to dispute with them. Physical argument was out of the question as regarded Mulvaney and the Yorkshire-man; and assault on Ortheris meant a combined attack from these twain—a business which no five men were anxious to have on their hands. There-fore they flourished, sharing their drinks, their tobacco, and their money; good luck and evil; battle and the chances of death; life and the chances of happiness from Calicut in southern, to Peshawur in northern India.

Through no merit of my own it was my good fortune to be in a measure admitted to their friendship—frankly by Mulvaney from the beginning, sullenly and with reluctance by Learoyd, and suspiciously by Ortheris, who held to it that no man not in the Army could fraternise with a red-coat. 'Like to like,' said he. 'I'm a bloomin' sodger—he's a bloomin' civilian. 'Tain't natural—that's all.'

But that was not all. They thawed progressively, and in the thawing told me more of their lives and adventures than I am ever likely to write.

Omitting all else, this tale begins with the Lamentable Thirst that was at the beginning of First Causes. Never was such a thirst—Mulvaney told me so. They kicked against their compulsory virtue, but the attempt was only successful in the case of Ortheris. He, whose talents were many, went forth into the highways and stole a dog from a 'civilian'—*videlicet*, some one, he knew not who, not in the Army. Now that civilian was but newly connected by marriage with the colonel of the regiment, and outcry was made from quarters least anticipated by Ortheris, and, in the end, he was forced, lest a worse thing should happen, to dispose at ridiculously unremunerative rates of as promising a small terrier as ever graced one end of a leading string. The purchase-money was barely sufficient for one small outbreak which led him to the guard-room. He escaped, however, with nothing worse than a severe reprimand, and a few hours of punishment drill. Not for nothing had he acquired the reputation of being 'the best soldier of his inches' in the regi-ment. Mulvaney had taught personal cleanliness and efficiency as the first articles of his companions' creed. 'A dhirty man,' he was used to say, in the speech of his kind, 'goes to Clink for a weakness in the knees, an' is coort-martialled for a pair av socks missin'; but a clane man, such as is an ornament to his service—a man whose buttons are gold, whose coat is wax upon him, an' whose 'coutrements are widout a speck—*that* man may, spakin' in reason, do fwhat he likes an' dhrink from day to divil. That's the pride av bein' dacint.'

We sat together, upon a day, in the shade of a ravine far from the barracks, where a watercourse used to run in rainy weather. Behind us was the scrub jungle, in which jackals, peacocks, the gray wolves of the North-

Western Provinces, and occasionally a tiger estrayed from Central India, were supposed to dwell. In front lay the cantonment, glaring white under a glaring sun; and on either side ran the broad road that led to Delhi.

It was the scrub that suggested to my mind the wisdom of Mulvaney taking a day's leave and going upon a shooting-tour. The peacock is a holy bird throughout India, and he who slays one is in danger of being mobbed by the nearest villagers; but on the last occasion that Mulvaney had gone forth, he had contrived, without in the least offending local religious susceptibilities, to return with six beautiful peacock skins which he sold to profit. It seemed just possible then——

'But fwhat manner av use is ut to me goin' out widout a dhrink? The ground's powdher-dhry underfoot, an' ut gets unto the throat fit to kill,' wailed Mulvaney, looking at me reproachfully. 'An' a peacock is not a bird you can catch the tail av onless ye run. Can a man run on wather—an' jungle-wather too?'

Ortheris had considered the question in all its bearings. He spoke, chewing his pipe-stem meditatively the while:

> 'Go forth, return in glory,
> To Clusium's royal 'ome:
> An' round these bloomin' temples 'ang
> The bloomin' shields o' Rome.

You better go. You ain't like to shoot yourself—not while there's a chanst of liquor. Me an' Learoyd 'll stay at 'ome an' keep shop—'case o' anythin' turnin' up. But you go out with a gas-pipe gun an' ketch the little peacockses or somethin'. You kin get one day's leave easy as winkin'. Go along an' get it, an' get peacockses or somethin'.'

'Jock,' said Mulvaney, turning to Learoyd, who was half asleep under the shadow of the bank. He roused slowly.

'Sitha, Mulvaaney, go,' said he.

And Mulvaney went; cursing his allies with Irish fluency and barrack-room point.

'Take note,' said he, when he had won his holiday, and appeared dressed in his roughest clothes with the only other regimental fowling-piece in his hand. 'Take note, Jock, an' you Orth'ris, I am goin' in the face av my own will—all for to please you. I misdoubt anythin' will come av permiscuous huntin' afther peacockses in a desolit lan'; an' I know that I will lie down an' die wid thirrrst. Me catch peacockses for you, ye lazy scutts—an' be sacrificed by the peasanthry—Ugh!'

He waved a huge paw and went away.

At twilight, long before the appointed hour, he returned empty-handed, much begrimed with dirt.

'Peacockses?' queried Ortheris from the safe rest of a barrack-room table whereon he was smoking cross-legged, Learoyd fast asleep on a bench.

'Jock,' said Mulvaney without answering, as he stirred up the sleeper. 'Jock, can ye fight? Will ye fight?'

Very slowly the meaning of the words communicated itself to the half-roused man. He understood—and again—what might these things mean? Mulvaney was shaking him savagely. Meantime the men in the room howled with delight. There was war in the confederacy at last—war and the breaking of bonds.

Barrack-room etiquette is stringent. On the direct challenge must follow the direct reply. This is more binding than the ties of tried friendship. Once again Mulvaney repeated the question. Learoyd answered by the only means in his power, and so swiftly that the Irishman had barely time to avoid the blow. The laughter around increased. Learoyd looked bewilderedly at his friend—himself as greatly bewildered. Ortheris dropped from the table because his world was falling.

'Come outside,' said Mulvaney, and as the occupants of the barrack-room prepared joyously to follow, he turned and said furiously, 'There will be no fight this night—onless any wan av you is wishful to assist. The man that does, follows on.'

No man moved. The three passed out into the moonlight, Learoyd fumbling with the buttons of his coat. The parade-ground was deserted except for the scurrying jackals. Mulvaney's impetuous rush carried his companions far into the open ere Learoyd attempted to turn round and continue the discussion.

'Be still now. 'Twas my fault for beginnin' things in the middle av an end, Jock. I should ha' comminst wid an explanation; but Jock, dear, on your sowl are ye fit, think you, for the finest fight that iver was—betther than fightin' me? Considher before ye answer.'

More than ever puzzled, Learoyd turned round two or three times, felt an arm, kicked tentatively, and answered, 'Ah'm fit.' He was accustomed to fight blindly at the bidding of the superior mind.

They sat them down, the men looking on from afar, and Mulvaney untangled himself in mighty words.

'Followin' your fools' scheme I wint out into the thrackless desert beyond the barricks. An' there I met a pious Hindu dhriving a bullock-kyart. I tuk ut for granted he wud be delighted for to convoy me a piece, an' I jumped in——'

'You long, lazy, black-haired swine,' drawled Ortheris, who would have done the same thing under similar circumstances.

' 'Twas the height av policy. That naygur-man dhruv miles an' miles—as far as the new railway line they're buildin' now back av the Tavi river. " 'Tis a kyart for dhirt only," says he now an' again timoreously, to get me out av ut. "Dhirt I am," sez I, "an' the dhryest that you iver kyarted. Dhrive on, me son, an glory be wid you." At that I wint to slape, an' took no heed till he pulled up on the embankmint av the line where the coolies were pilin' mud. There was a matther av two thousand coolies on that line—you remimber that. Prisintly a bell rang, an' they throops off to a big pay-shed. "Where's the white man in charge?" sez I to my kyart-dhriver. "In the shed," sez he, "engaged on a riffle."—"A fwhat?" sez I. "Riffle," sez he. "You take ticket. He take money. You get nothin'."—"Oho!" sez I, "that's fwhat the shuperior an' cultivated man calls a raffle, me misbeguided child av darkness an' sin. Lead on to that raffle, though fwhat the mischief 'tis doin' so far away from uts home—which is the charity-bazaar at Christmas, an' the colonel's wife grinnin' behind the tea-table—is more than I know." Wid that I wint to the shed an' found 'twas pay-day among the coolies. Their wages was on a table forninst a big, fine, red buck av a man—sivun fut high, four fut wide, an' three fut thick, wid a fist on him like a corn-sack. He was payin' the coolies fair an' easy, but he wud ask each man if he wud raffle that month, an' each man sez, "Yes," av course. Thin he wud deduct from their wages accordin'. Whin all was paid, he filled an ould cigar-box full av gun-wads an' scatthered ut among the coolies. They did not take much joy av that performince, an' small wondher. A man close to me picks up a black gun-wad an' sings out, "I have ut."—"Good may ut do you," sez I. The coolie wint forward to this big, fine, red man, who threw a cloth off av the most sumpshus, jooled, enamelled an' variously bedivilled sedan-chair I iver saw.'

'Sedan-chair! Put your 'ead in a bag. That was a palanquin. Don't yer know a palanquin when you see it?' said Ortheris with great scorn.

'I chuse to call ut sedan-chair, an' chair ut shall be, little man,' continued the Irishman. ' 'Twas a most amazin' chair—all lined wid pink silk an' fitted wid red silk curtains. "Here ut is," sez the red man. "Here ut is," sez the coolie, and he grinned weakly-ways. "Is ut any use to you?" sez the red man. "No," sez the coolie; "I'd like to make a presint av ut to you."—"I am graciously pleased to accept that same," sez the red man; an' at that all the coolies cried aloud in fwhat was mint for cheerful notes, an' wint back to their diggin', lavin' me alone in the shed. The red man saw me, an' his face grew blue on his big, fat neck. "Fwhat d'you want here?" sez he. "Standin'-room an' no more," sez I, "onless it may be fwhat ye niver had, an' that's manners, ye rafflin' ruffian," for I was not goin' to have the Service throd upon. "Out of this," sez he. "I'm in charge av this section av construction."—"I'm in charge av mesilf," sez I, "an' it's like I will stay a while. D'ye raffle much in these parts?"—"Fwhat's that to you?" sez he. "Nothin'," sez I, "but a great dale to you, for begad I'm thinkin' you get the full half av your revenue from that sedan-chair. Is ut always raffled so?" I sez, an' wid that I wint to a coolie to ask questions. Bhoys, that man's name is Dearsley, an' he's been rafflin' that ould sedan-chair monthly this matther av nine months. Ivry coolie on the section takes a ticket—or he gives 'em the go—wanst a month on pay-day. Ivry coolie that wins ut gives ut back to him, for 'tis too big to carry away, an' he'd sack the man that thried to sell ut. That Dearsley has been makin' the rowlin' wealth av Roshus by nefarious rafflin'. Think av the burnin' shame to the sufferin' coolie-man that the army in Injia are bound to protect an' nourish in their bosoms! Two thousand coolies defrauded wanst a month!'

'Dom t' coolies. Has't gotten t' cheer, man?' said Learoyd.

'Hould on. Havin' onearthed this amazin' an' stupenjus fraud committed by the man Dearsley, I hild a council av war; he thryin' all the time to sejuce me into a fight with opprobrious language. That sedan-chair niver belonged by right to any foreman av coolies. 'Tis a king's chair or a quane's. There's gold on ut an' silk an' all manner av trapesemints. Bhoys, 'tis not for me to countenance any sort av wrong-doin'—me bein' the ould man—but——anyway he has had ut nine months, an' he dare not make throuble av ut was taken from him. Five miles away, or ut may be six——'

There was a long pause, and the jackals howled merrily. Learoyd bared one arm, and contemplated it in the moonlight. Then he nodded partly to himself and partly to his friends. Ortheris wriggled with suppressed emotion.

'I thought ye wud see the reasonableness av ut,' said Mulvaney. 'I made bould to say as much to the man before. He was for a direct front attack—fut, horse, an' guns——an' all for nothin', seein' that I had no thransport to convey the machine away. "I will not argue wid you," sez I, "this day, but subsequintly, Mister Dearsley, me rafflin' jool, we talk ut out lengthways. 'Tis no good policy to swindle the naygur av his hard-earned emolumints, an' by presint informashin' "'—'twas the kyart man that tould me—'ye've been perpethrating that same for nine months. But I'm a just man," sez I, "an' overlookin' the presumpshin that yondher settee wid the gilt top was not come by honust"—at that he turned sky-green, so I knew things was more thrue than tellable—"not come by honust, I'm willin' to compound the felony for this month's winnin's." '

'Ah! Ho!" from Learoyd and Ortheris.

'That man Dearsley's rushin' on his fate,' continued Mulvaney, solemnly wagging his head. 'All Hell had no name bad enough for me that tide. Faith, he called me a robber! Me! that was savin' him from continuin' in his evil ways widout a remonstrince—an' to a man av conscience a remonstrince may change the chune av his life. " 'Tis not for me to argue," sez I, "fwhatever ye are, Mister Dearsley, but, by my hand, I'll take away the temptation for you that lies in that sedan-chair."—"You will have to fight me for ut," sez he, "for well I know you will never dare make report to any one."—"Fight I will," sez I, "but not this day, for I'm rejuced for want av nourishment."—"Ye're an ould bould hand," sez he, sizin' me up an' down; "an' a jool av a fight we will have. Eat now an' dhrink, an' go your way." Wid that he gave me some hump an' whisky—good whisky—an' we talked av this an' that the while. "It goes hard on me now," sez I, wipin' my mouth, "to confiscate that piece av furniture, but justice is justice."—"Ye've not got ut yet," sez he; "there's the fight between."—"There is," sez I, "an' a good fight. Ye shall have the pick av the best quality in my rigimint for the dinner you have given this day." Thin I came hot-foot to you two. Hould your tongue, the both. 'Tis this way. To-morrow we three will go there an' he shall have his pick betune me an' Jock. Jock's a deceivin' fighter, for he is all fat to the eye, an' he moves slow. Now, I'm all beef to the look, an' I move quick. By my reckonin' the Dearsley man won't take me; so me an' Orth'ris 'll see fair play. Jock, I tell you, 'twill be big fightin'—whipped, wid the cream above the jam. Afther the business 'twill take a good three av us—Jock 'll be very hurt—to haul away that sedan-chair.'

'Palanquin.' This from Ortheris.

'Fwhatever ut is, we must have ut. 'Tis the only sellin' piece av property widin reach that we can get so cheap. An' fwhat's a fight afther all? He has robbed the naygur-man, dishonust. We rob him honust for the sake av the whisky he gave me.'

'But wot'll we do with the bloomin' article when we've got it? Them palanquins are as big as 'ouses, an' uncommon 'ard to sell, as McCleary said when ye stole the sentry-box from the Curragh.'

'Who's goin' to do t' fightin'?' said Learoyd, and Ortheris subsided. The three returned to barracks without a word. Mulvaney's last argument clinched the matter. This palanquin was property, vendible, and to be attained in the simplest and least embarrassing fashion. It would eventually become beer. Great was Mulvaney.

Next afternoon a procession of three formed itself and disappeared into the scrub in the direction of the new railway line. Learoyd alone was without care, for Mulvaney dived darkly into the future, and little Ortheris feared the unknown. What befell at that interview in the lonely pay-shed by the side of the half-built embankment, only a few hundred coolies know, and their tale is a confusing one, running thus—

'We were at work. Three men in red coats came. They saw the Sahib—Dearsley Sahib. They made oration; and noticeably the small man among the red-coats. Dearsley Sahib also made oration, and used many very strong words. Upon this talk they departed together to an open space, and there the fat man in the red coat fought with Dearsley Sahib after the custom of white men—with his hands, making no noise, and never at all pulling Dearsley Sahib's hair. Such of us as were not afraid beheld these things for just so long a time as a man needs to cook the mid-day meal. The small man in the red coat had possessed himself of Dearsley Sahib's watch. No, he did not steal that watch. He held it in his hand, and at certain seasons made outcry, and the twain ceased their combat, which was like the combat of young bulls in spring. Both men were soon all red, but Dearsley Sahib was much more red than the other. Seeing this, and fearing for his life—because we greatly loved him—some fifty of us made shift to rush upon the red-coats. But a certain man—very black as to the hair, and in no way to be confused with the small man, or the fat man who fought—that man, we affirm, ran upon us, and of us he embraced some ten or fifty in both arms, and beat our heads together, so that our livers turned to water, and we ran away. It is not good to interfere in the fightings of white men. After that Dearsley Sahib fell and did not rise, these men jumped upon his stomach and despoiled him of all his money, and attempted to fire the pay-shed, and departed. Is it true that Dearsley Sahib makes no complaint of these latter things having been done? We were senseless with fear, and do not at all remember. There was no palanquin near the pay-shed. What do we know about palanquins? Is it true that Dearsley Sahib does not return to this place, on account of his sickness, for ten days? This is the fault of those bad men in the red coats, who should be severely punished; for Dearsley Sahib is both our father and mother, and we love him much. Yet, if Dearsley Sahib does not return to this place at all, we will speak the truth. There was a palanquin, for the up-keep of which we were forced to pay nine-tenths of our monthly wage. On such mulctings Dearsley Sahib allowed us to make obeisance to him before the palanquin. What could we do? We were poor men. He took a full half of our wages. Will the Government repay us those moneys? Those three men in red coats bore the palanquin upon their shoulders and departed. All the money that Dearsley Sahib had taken from us was in the cushions of that palanquin. Therefore they stole it. Thousands of rupees were there—all our money. It was our bank-box, to fill which we cheerfully contributed to Dearsley Sahib three-sevenths of our monthly wage. Why does the white man look upon us with the eye of disfavour? Before God, there was a palanquin, and now there is no palanquin; and if they send the police here to make inquisition, we can only say that there never has been any palanquin. Why should a palanquin be near these works? We are poor men, and we know nothing.'

Such is the simplest version of the simplest story connected with the descent upon Dearsley. From the lips of the coolies I received it. Dearsley himself was in no condition to say anything, and Mulvaney preserved a massive silence, broken only by the occasional licking of the lips. He had seen a fight so gorgeous that even his power of speech was taken from him. I respected that reserve until, three days after the affair, I discovered in a disused stable in my quarters a palanquin of unchastened splendour—evidently in past days the litter of a queen. The pole whereby it swung between the shoulders of the bearers was rich with the painted *papier-maché* of Cashmere. The shoulder-pads were of yellow sick. The panels of the litter itself were ablaze with the loves of all the gods and goddesses of the Hindu Pantheon—lacquer on cedar. The cedar sliding doors were fitted with hasps of translucent Jaipur enamel and ran in grooves shod with silver. The cushions were of brocaded Delhi silk, and the curtains which once hid any glimpse of the beauty of the king's palace were stiff with gold. Closer investigation showed that the entire fabric was everywhere rubbed and discoloured by time and wear; but even thus it was sufficiently gorgeous to deserve housing on the threshold of a royal zenana. I found no fault with it, except that it was in my stable. Then, trying to lift it by the silver-shod shoulder-pole, I laughed. The road from Dearsley's pay-shed to the cantonment was a narrow and uneven one, and, traversed by three very inexperienced palanquin-bearers, one of whom was sorely battered about the head, must have been a path of torment. Still I did not quite recognise the right of the three musketeers to turn me into a 'fence' for stolen property.

'I'm askin' you to warehouse ut,' said Mulvaney when he was brought to consider the question. 'There's no steal in ut. Dearsley tould us we cud have ut if we fought. Jock fought—an', oh, sorr, when the throuble was at uts finest an' Jock was bleedin' like a stuck pig, an' little Orth'ris was shquealin' on one leg chewin' big bites out av Dearsley's watch, I wud ha' given my place at the fight to have had you see wan round. He tuk Jock, as I suspicioned he would, an' Jock was deceptive. Nine roun's they were even matched, an' at the tenth—— About that palanquin now. There's not the least throuble in the world, or we wud not ha' brought ut here. You will ondherstand that the Queen—God bless her!—does not reckon for a privit soldier to kape elephints an' palanquins an' sich in barricks. Afther we had dhragged ut down from Dearsley's through that cruel scrub that near broke Orth'ris's heart, we set ut in the ravine for a night; an' a thief av a porcupine an' a civet-cat av a jackal roosted in ut, as well we knew in the mornin'. I put ut to you, sorr, is an elegint palanquin, fit for the princess, the natural abidin' place av all the vermin in cantonmints? We brought ut to you, afther dhark, and put ut in your shtable. Do not let your conscience prick. Think av the rejoicin' men in the pay-shed yonder—lookin' at Dearsley wid his head tied up in a towel—an' well knowin' that they can dhraw their pay ivry month widout stoppages for riffles. Indirectly, sorr, you have rescued from an onprincipled son av a night-hawk the peasanthry av a numerous village. An' besides, will I let that sedan-chair rot on our hands? Not I. 'Tis not every day a piece av pure joolry comes into the market. There's not a king widin these forty miles'—he waved his hand round the dusty horizon—'not a king wud not be glad to buy ut. Some day meself, whin I have leisure, I'll take ut up along the road an' dishpose av ut.'

'How?' said I, for I knew the man was capable of anything.

'Get into ut, av coorse, and keep wan eye open through the curtains. Whin I see a likely man av the native persuasion, I will descind blushin' from my canopy and say, "Buy a palanquin, ye black scutt?" I will have to hire four men to carry me first, though; and that's impossible till next pay-day.'

Curiously enough, Learoyd, who had fought for the prize, and in the winning secured the highest pleasure life had to offer him, was altogether disposed to undervalue it, while Ortheris openly said it would be better to break the thing up. Dearsley, he argued, might be a many-sided man, capable, despite his magnificent fighting qualities, of setting in motion the machinery of the civil law—a thing much abhorred by the soldier. Under any circumstances their fun had come and passed, the next pay-day was close at hand, when there would be beer for all. Wherefore longer conserve the painted palanquin?

'A first-class rifle-shot an' a good little man av your inches you are,' said Mulvaney. 'But you niver had a head worth a soft-boiled egg. 'Tis me has to lie awake av nights schamin' an' plottin' for the three av us. Orth'ris, me son, 'tis no matther av a few gallons av beer—no, nor twenty gallons—but tubs an' vats an' firkins in that sedan-chair. Who ut was, an' what ut was, an' how ut got there, we do not know; but I know in my bones that you an' me an' Jock wid his sprained thumb will get a fortune thereby. Lave me alone, an' let me think.'

Meantime the palanquin stayed in my stall, the key of which was in Mulvaney's hands.

Pay-day came, and with it beer. It was not in experience to hope that Mulvaney, dried by four weeks' drought, would avoid excess. Next morning he and the palanquin had disappeared. He had taken the precaution of getting three days' leave 'to see a friend on the railway,' and the colonel, well knowing that the seasonal outburst was near, and hoping it would spend its force beyond the limits of his jurisdiction, cheerfully gave him all he demanded. At this point Mulvaney's history, as recorded in the mess-room, stopped.

Ortheris carried it not much further. 'No, 'e wasn't drunk,' said the little man loyally, 'the liquor was no more than feelin' its way round inside of 'im; but 'e went an' filled that 'ole bloomin' palanquin with bottles 'fore 'e went off. 'E's gone an' 'ired six men to carry 'im, an' I 'ad to 'elp 'im into 'is nupshal couch, 'cause 'e wouldn't 'ear reason. 'E's gone off in 'is shirt an' trousies, swearin' tremenjus—gone down the road in the palanquin, wavin' 'is legs out o' windy.'

'Yes,' said I, 'but where?'

'Now you arx me a question. 'E said 'e was goin' to sell that palanquin, but from observations what happened when I was stuffin' 'im through the door, I fancy 'e's gone to the new embankment to mock at Dearsley. 'Soon as Jock's off duty I'm goin' there to see if 'e's safe—not Mulvaney, but t'other man. My saints, but I pity 'im as 'elps Terence out o' the palanquin when 'e's once fair drunk!'

'He'll come back without harm,' I said.

''Corse 'e will. On'y question is, what 'll 'e be doin' on the road? Killing Dearsley, like as not. 'E shouldn't 'a gone without Jock or me.'

Reinforced by Learoyd, Ortheris sought the foreman of the coolie-gang. Dearsley's head was still embellished with towels. Mulvaney, drunk or sober, would have struck no man in that condition, and Dearsley indignantly denied that he would have taken advantage of the intoxicated brave.

'I had my pick o' you two,' he explained to Learoyd, 'and you got my palanquin—not before I'd made my profit on it. Why'd I do harm when everything's settled? Your man *did* come here—drunk as Davy's sow on a frosty night—came a-purpose to mock me—stuck his head out of the door an' called me a crucified hodman. I made him drunker, an' sent him along. But I never touched him.'

To these things, Learoyd, slow to perceive the evidences of sincerity, answered only, 'If owt comes to Mulvaaney 'long o' you, I'll gripple you, clouts or no clouts on your ugly head, an' I'll draw t' throat twistyways, man. See there now.'

The embassy removed itself, and Dearsley, the battered, laughed alone over his supper that evening.

Three days passed—a fourth and a fifth. The week drew to a close and Mulvaney did not return. He, his royal palanquin, and his six attendants, had vanished into air. A very large and very tipsy soldier, his feet sticking out of the litter of a reigning princess, is not a thing to travel along the ways without comment. Yet no man of all the country round had seen any such wonder. He was, and he was not; and Learoyd suggested the immediate smashment of Dearsley as a sacrifice to his ghost. Ortheris insisted that all was well, and in the light of past experience his hopes seemed reasonable.

'When Mulvaney goes up the road,' said he, ' 'e's like to go a very long ways up, specially when 'e's so blue drunk as 'e is now. But what gits me is 'is not bein' 'eard of pullin' wool off the niggers somewheres about. That don't look good. The drink must ha'. died out in 'im by this, unless 'e's broke a bank, an' then—Why don't 'e come back? 'E didn't ought to ha' gone off without us.'

Even Ortheris's heart sank at the end of the seventh day, for half the regiment were out scouring the countryside, and Learoyd had been forced to fight two men who hinted openly that Mulvaney had deserted. To do him justice, the colonel laughed at the notion, even when it was put forward by his much-trusted adjutant.

'Mulvaney would as soon think of deserting as you would,' said he. 'No; he's either fallen into a mischief among the villagers—and yet that isn't likely, for he'd blarney himself out of the Pit; or else he is engaged on urgent private affairs—some stupendous devilment that we shall hear of at mess after it has been the round of the barrack-rooms. The worst of it is that I shall have to give him twenty-eight days' confinement at least for being absent without leave, just when I most want him to lick the new batch of recruits into shape. I never knew a man who could put a polish on young soldiers as quickly as Mulvaney can. How does he do it?'

'With blarney and the buckle-end of a belt, sir,' said the adjutant. 'He is worth a couple of non-commissioned officers when we are dealing with an Irish draft, and the London lads seem to adore him. The worst of it is that if he goes to the cells the other two are neither to hold nor to bind till he comes out again. I believe Ortheris preaches mutiny on those occasions, and I know that the mere presence of Learoyd mourning for Mulvaney kills all the cheerfulness of his room. The sergeants tell me that he allows no man to laugh when he feels unhappy. They are a queer gang.'

'For all that, I wish I had a few more of them. I like a well-conducted regiment, but these pasty-faced, shifty-eyed, mealy-mouthed young slouchers from the depot worry me sometimes with their offensive virtue. They don't seem to have backbone enough to do anything but play cards and prowl round the married quarters. I believe I'd forgive that old villain on the spot if he turned up with any sort of explanation that I could in decency accept.'

'Not likely to be much difficulty about that, sir,' said the adjutant. 'Mulvaney's explanations are only one degree less wonderful than his performances. They say that when he was in the Black Tyrone, before he came to us, he was discovered on the banks of the Liffey trying to sell his colonel's charger to a Donegal dealer as a perfect lady's hack. Shackbolt commanded the Tyrone then.'

'Shackbolt must have had apoplexy at the thought of his ramping war-horses answering to that description. He used to buy unbacked devils, and tame them on some pet theory of starvation. What did Mulvaney say?'

'That he was a member of the Society for the Prevention of Cruelty to Animals, anxious to "sell the poor baste where he would get something to fill out his dimples." Shackbolt laughed, but I fancy that was why Mulvaney exchanged to ours.'

'I wish he were back,' said the colonel; 'for I like him and believe he likes me.'

That evening, to cheer our souls, Learoyd, Ortheris, and I went into the waste to smoke out a porcupine. All the dogs attended, but even their clamour—and they began to discuss the shortcomings of porcupines before they left cantonments—could not take us out of ourselves. A large, low moon turned the tops of the plume-grass to silver, and the stunted camelthorn bushes and sour tamarisks into the likenesses of trooping devils. The smell of the sun had not left the earth, and little aimless winds blowing across the rose-gardens to the southward brought the scent of dried roses and water. Our fire once started, and the dogs craftily disposed to wait the dash of the porcupine, we climbed to the top of a rain-scarred hillock of earth, and looked across the scrub seamed with cattle paths, white with the long grass, and dotted with spots of level pond-bottom, where the snipe would gather in winter.

'This,' said Ortheris, with a sigh, as he took in the unkempt desolation of it all, 'this is sanguinary. This is unusually sanguinary. Sort o' mad country. Like a grate when the fire's put out by the sun.' He shaded his eyes against the moonlight. 'An' there's a loony dancin' in the middle of it all. Quite right. I'd dance too if I wasn't so downheart.'

There pranced a Portent in the face of the moon—a huge and ragged spirit of the waste, that flapped its wings from afar. It had risen out of the earth; it was coming towards us, and its outline was never twice the same. The toga, table-cloth, or dressing-gown, whatever the creature wore, took a hundred shapes. Once it stopped on a neighbouring mound and flung all its legs and arms to the winds.

'My, but that scarecrow 'as got 'em bad!' said Ortheris. 'Seems like if 'e comes any furder we'll 'ave to argify with 'im.'

Learoyd raised himself from the dirt as a bull clears his flanks of the wallow. And as a bull bellows, so he, after a short minute at gaze, gave tongue to the stars.

'MULVAANEY! MULVAANEY! A-hoo!'

Oh then it was that we yelled, and the figure dipped into the hollow, till, with a crash of rending grass, the lost one strode up to the light of the fire and disappeared to the waist in a wave of joyous dogs! Then Learoyd and

Ortheris gave greeting, bass and falsetto together, both swallowing a lump in the throat.

'You damned fool!' said they, and severally pounded him with their fists.

'Go easy!' he answered; wrapping a huge arm round each. 'I would have you to know that I am a god, to be treated as such—tho', by my faith, I fancy I've got to go to the guard-room just like a privit soldier.'

The latter part of the sentence destroyed the suspicions raised by the former. Any one would have been justified in regarding Mulvaney as mad. He was hatless and shoeless, and his spirit and trousers were dropping off him. But he wore one wondrous garment—a gigantic cloak that fell from collar-bone to heel—of pale pink silk, wrought all over in cunningest needle-work of hands long since dead, with the loves of the Hindu gods. The monstrous figures leaped in and out of the light of the fire as he settled the folds round him.

Ortheris handled the stuff respectfully for a moment while I was trying to remember where I had seen it before. Then he screamed, 'What 'ave you done with the palanquin? You're wearin' the linin'.'

'I am,' said the Irishman, 'an' by the same token the 'broidery is scrapin' my hide off. I've lived in this sumpshus counterpane for four days. Me son, I begin to ondherstand why the naygur is no use. Widout me boots, an' me trousies like an openwork stocking on a gyurl's leg at a dance, I begin to feel like a naygur-man—all fearful an' timoreous. Give me a pipe an' I'll tell on.'

He lit a pipe, resumed his grip of his two friends, and rocked to and fro in a gale of laughter.

'Mulvaney,' said Ortheris sternly, ' 'tain't no time for laughin'. You've given Jock an' me more trouble than you're worth. You 'ave been absent without leave an' you'll go into cells for that; an' you 'ave come back dis-gustin'ly dressed an' most improper in the linin' o' that bloomin' palanquin. Instid of which you laugh. An' we thought you was dead all the time.'

'Bhoys,' said the culprit, still shaking gently, 'whin I've done my tale you may cry if you like, an' little Orth'ris here can thrample my inside out. Ha' done an' listen. My performinces have been stupenjus: my luck has been the blessed luck av the British Army—an' there's no betther than that. I went out dhrunk an' dhrinkin' in the palanquin, and I have come back a pink god. Did any of you go to Dearsley afther my time was up? He was at the bottom of ut all.'

'Ah said so,' murmured Learoyd. 'To-morrow ah'll smash t' face in upon his heead.'

'Ye will not. Dearsley's a jool av a man. Afther Ortheris had put me into the palanquin an' the six bearer-men were gruntin' down the road, I tuk thought to mock Dearsley for that fight. So I tould thim, "Go to the em-bankmint," and there, bein' most amazin' full, I shtuck my head out av the concern an' passed compliments wid Dearsley. I must ha' miscalled him out-rageous, for whin I am that way the power av the tongue comes on me. I can bare remimber tellin' him that his mouth opened endways like the mouth av a skate, which was thrue afther Learoyd had handled ut; an' I clear remimber his takin' no manner nor matter av offence, but givin' me a big dhrink of beer. 'Twas the beer did the thrick, for I crawled back into the palanquin, steppin' on me right ear wid me left foot, an' thin I slept like the dead. Wanst I half-roused, an' begad the noise in my head was tremenjus—roarin' and rattlin' an' poundin' such as was quite new to me. "Mother av Mercy," thinks I, "phwat a concertina I will have on my shoulders whin I wake! An' wid that I curls mysilf up to sleep before ut should get hould on me. Bhoys, that noise was not dhrink, 'twas the rattle av a thrain!'

There followed an impressive pause.

'Yes, he had put me on a thrain—put me, palanquin an' all, an' six black assassins av his own coolies that was in his nefarious confidence, on the flat av a ballast-thruck, and we were rowlin' an' bowlin' along to Benares. Glory be that I did not wake up thin an' introjuce mysilf to the coolies. As I was sayin', I slept for the betther part av a day an' a night. But remimber you, that that man Dearsley had packed me off on wan av his material-thrains to Benares, all for to make me overstay my leave an' get me into the cells.'

The explanation was an eminently rational one. Benares lay at least ten hours by rail from the cantonments, and nothing in the world could have saved Mulvaney from arrest as a deserter had he appeared there in the apparel of his orgies. Dearsley had not forgotten to take revenge. Learoyd, drawing back a little, began to place soft blows over selected portions of Mulvaney's body. His thoughts were away on the embankment, and they meditated evil for Dearsley. Mulvaney continued—

'Whin I was full awake the palanquin was set down in a street, I sus-picioned, for I cud hear people passin' an' talkin'. But I knew well I was far from home. There is a queer smell upon our cantonments—a smell av dried earth and brick-kilns wid whiffs av cavalry stable-litter. This place smelt marigold flowers an' bad water, an' wanst somethin' alive came an' blew heavy with his muzzle at the chink av the shutter. "It's in a village I am," thinks I to mysilf, "an' the parochial buffalo is investigatin' the palanquin." But anyways I had no desire to move. Only lie still whin you're in foreign parts an' the standin' luck av the British Army will carry ye through. That is an epigram. I made ut.

'Thin a lot av whishperin' divils surrounded the palanquin. "Take ut up," sez wan man. "But who'll pay us?" sez another. "The Maharanee's minister, av coorse," sez the man. "Oho!" sez I to mysilf, "I'm a quane in me own right, wid a minister to pay me expenses. I'll be an emperor if I lie still long enough; but this is no village I've found." I lay quiet, but I gummed me right eye to a crack av the shutters, an' I saw that the whole street was crammed wid palanquins an' horses, an' a sprinklin' av naked priests all yellow powder an' tigers' tails. But I may tell you, Orth'ris, an' you, Learoyd, that av all the palanquins ours was the most imperial an' magnificent. Now a palanquin means a native lady all the world over, except whin a soldier av the Quane happens to be takin' a ride. "Women an' priests!" sez I. "Your father's son is in the right pew this time, Terence. There will be proceedin's." Six black divils in pink muslin tuk up the palanquin, an' oh! but the rowlin' an' the rockin' made me sick. Thin we got fair jammed among the palanquins —not more than fifty av them—an' we grated an' bumped like Queenstown potato-smacks in a runnin' tide. I cud hear the women gigglin' and squirkin' in their palanquins, but mine was the royal equipage. They made way for ut, an', begad, the pink muslin men o' mine were howlin', "Room for the Maharanee av Gokral-Seetarun." Do you know aught av the lady, sorr?'

'Yes,' said I. 'She is a very estimable old queen of the Central Indian States, and they say she is fat. How on earth could she go to Benares without all the city knowing her palanquin?'

' 'Twas the eternal foolishness av the naygur-man. They saw the palanquin lying loneful an' forlornsome, an' the beauty av ut, after Dearsley's men had dhropped ut and gone away, an' they gave ut the best name that occurred to thim. Quite right too. For aught we know the ould lady was thravellin' *incog*—like me. I'm glad to hear she's fat. I was no light weight mysilf, an' my men were mortial anxious to dhrop me under a great big archway promiscuously ornamented wid the most improper carvin's an' cuttin's I iver saw. Begad! they made me blush—like a—like a Maharanee.'

'The temple of Prithi-Devi,' I murmured, remembering the monstrous horrors of that sculptured archway at Benares.

'Pretty Devilskins, savin' your presence, sorr! There was nothin' pretty about ut, except me. 'Twas all half dhark, an' whin the coolies left they shut a big black gate behind av us, an' half a company av fat yellow priests began pully-haulin' the palanquins into a dharker place yet—a big stone hall full av pillars, an' gods, an' incense, an' all manner av similar thruck. The gate disconcerted me, for I perceived I wud have to go forward to get out, my retreat bein' cut off. By the same token a good priest makes a bad palanquin-coolie. Begad! they nearly turned me inside out draggin' the palanquin to the temple. Now the disposishin av the forces inside was this way. The Maharanee av Gokral-Seetarun—that was me—lay by the favour av Providence on the far left flank behind the dhark av a pillar carved with elephints' heads. The remainder av the palanquins was in a big half circle facing in to the biggest, fattest, an' most amazin' she-god that iver I dreamed av. Her head ran up into the black above us, an' her feet stuck out in the light av a little fire av melted butter that a priest was feedin' out av a butter-dish. Thin a man began to sing an' play on somethin' back in the dhark, an' 'twas a queer song. Ut made my hair lift on the back av my neck. Thin the doors av all the palanquins slid back, an' the women bundled out. I saw what I'll niver see again. 'Twas more glorious than thransformations at a pantomime, for they was in pink an' blue an' silver an' red an' grass green, wid di'monds an' im'ralds an' great red rubies all over thim. But that was the least part av the glory. O bhoys, they were more lovely than the like av any loveliness in hiven; ay, their little bare feet were betther than the white hands av a lord's lady, an' their mouths were like puckered roses, an' their eyes were bigger an' dharker than the eyes av any livin' women I've seen. Ye may laugh, but I'm speakin' truth. I niver saw the like, an' niver I will again.'

'Seeing that in all probability you were watching the wives and daughters of most of the kings of India, the chances are that you won't,' I said, for it was dawning on me that Mulvaney had stumbled upon a big Queens' Praying at Benares.

'I niver will,' he said mournfully. 'That sight doesn't come twist to any man. It made me ashamed to watch. A fat priest knocked at my door. I didn't think he'd have the insolince to disturb the Maharanee av Gokral-Seetarun, so I lay still. "The old cow's asleep," sez he to another. "Let her be," sez that. "'Twill be long before she has a calf!' I might ha' known before he spoke that all a woman prays for in Injia—an' for matter o' that in England too—is childher. That made me more sorry I'd come, me bein', as you well know, a childless man.'

He was silent for a moment, thinking of his little son, dead many years ago.

'They prayed, an' the butter-fires blazed up an' the incense turned everything blue, an' between that an' the fires the women looked as tho' they were all ablaze an' twinklin'. They took hold av the she-god's knees, they cried out an' they threw themselves about, an' that world-without-end-amen music was dhrivin' thim mad. Mother av Hiven! how they cried, an' the ould she-god grinnin' above thim all so scornful! The dhrink was dyin' out in me fast, an' I was thinkin' harder than the thoughts wud go through my head—thinkin' how to get out, an' all manner of nonsense as well. The women were rockin' in rows, their di'mond belts clickin', an' the tears runnin' out betune their hands, an' the lights were goin' lower an' dharker. Thin there was a blaze like lightnin' from the roof, an' that showed me the inside av the palanquin, an' at the end where my foot was, stood the livin' spit an' image o' mysilf worked on the linin'. This man here, ut was.'

He hunted in the folds of his pink cloak, ran a hand under one, and thrust into the firelight a foot-long embroidered presentment of the great god Krishna, playing on a flute. The heavy jowl, the staring eye, and the blue-black moustache of the god made up a far-off resemblance to Mulvaney.

'The blaze was gone in a wink, but the whole schame came to me thin. I believe I was mad too. I slid the off-shutter open an' rowled out into the dhark behind the elephint-head pillar, tucked up my trousies to my knees, slipped off my boots an' tuk a general hould av all the pink linin' av the palanquin. Glory be, ut ripped out like a woman's dhriss whin you tread on ut at a sergeants' ball, an' a bottle came with ut. I tuk the bottle an' the next minut I was out av the dhark av the pillar, the pink linin' wrapped round me most graceful, the music thunderin' like kettledrums, an' a could draft blowin' round my bare legs. By this hand that did ut, I was Khrishna tootlin' on the flute—the god that the rig'mental chaplain talks about. A sweet sight I must ha' looked. I knew my eyes were big, and my face was wax-white, an' at the worst I must ha' looked like a ghost. But they took me for the livin' god. The music stopped, and the women were dead dumb an' I crooked my legs like a shepherd on a china basin, an' I did the ghost-waggle with my feet as I had done ut at the rig'mental theatre many times, an' I slid acrost the width av that temple in front av the she-god tootlin' on the beer bottle.'

'Wot did you toot?' demanded Ortheris the practical.

'Me? Oh!' Mulvaney sprang up, suiting the action to the word, and sliding gravely in front of us, a dilapidated but imposing deity in the half light. 'I sang—

> 'Only say
> You'll be Mrs. Brallaghan.
> Don't say nay,
> Charmin' Judy Callaghan.

I didn't know me own voice when I sang. An' oh! 'twas pitiful to see the women. The darlin's were down on their faces. Whin I passed the last wan I cud see her poor little fingers workin' one in another as if she wanted to touch my feet. So I dhrew the tail av this pink overcoat over her head for the greater honour, an' I slid into the dhark on the other side av the temple, and fetched up in the arms av a big fat priest. All I wanted was to get away clear. So I tuk him by his greasy throat an' shut the speech out av him. "Out!" sez I. "Which way, ye fat heathen?"—"Oh!" sez he. "Man," sez I. "White man, soldier man, common soldier man. Where in the name av confusion is the back door?" The women in the temple were still on their faces, an' a young priest was holdin' out his arms above their heads.

' "This way," sez my fat friend, duckin' behind a big bull-god an' divin' into a passage. Thin I remimbered that I must ha' made the miraculous reputation av that temple for the next fifty years. "Not so fast," I sez, an' I held out both my hands wid a wink. That ould thief smiled like a father. I tuk him by the back av the neck in case he should be wishful to put a knife into me unbeknownst, an' I ran him up an' down the passage twice to collect his sensibilities! "Be quiet," sez he, in English. "Now you talk sense," I sez. "Fwhat 'll you give me for the use av that most iligant palanquin I have no time to take away?"—"Don't tell," sez he. "Is ut like?" sez I. "But ye might give me my railway fare. I'm far from home an' I've done you a service." Bhoys, 'tis a good thing to be a priest. The ould man niver throubled himself to dhraw from a bank. As I will prove to you subsequint, he philandered all round the slack av his clothes an' began dribblin' ten-rupee notes, old gold mohurs, and rupees into my hand till I could hould no more.'

'You lie!' said Ortheris. 'You're mad or sunstrook. A native don't give coin unless you cut it out o' 'im. 'Tain't nature.'

'Then my lie an' my sunstroke is concealed under that lump av sod yonder,' retorted Mulvaney unruffled, nodding across the scrub. 'An' there's a dale more in nature than your squidgy little legs have iver taken you to, Orth'ris, me son. Four hundred an' thirty-four rupees by my reckonin', *an'* a big fat gold necklace that I took from him as a remimbrancer, was our share in that business.'

'An' e' give it you for love?' said Ortheris.

'We were alone in that passage. Maybe I was a trifle too pressin', but considher fwhat I had done for the good av the temple and the iverlastin' joy av those women. 'Twas cheap at the price. I wud ha' taken more if I cud ha' found ut. I turned the ould man upside down at the last, but he was milked dhry. Thin he opened a door in another passage an' I found mysilf up to my knees in Benares river-water, an' bad smellin' ut is. More by token I had come out on the river-line close to the burnin' ghat and contagious to a cracklin' corpse. This was in the heart av the night, for I had been four hours in the temple. There was a crowd av boats tied up, so I tuk wan an' wint across the river. Thin I came home acrost country, lyin' up by day.'

'How on earth did you manage?' I said.

'How did Sir Frederick Roberts get from Cabul to Candahar? He marched an' he niver tould how near he was to breakin' down. That's why he is fwhat he is. An' now—' Mulvaney yawned portentously. 'Now I will go an' give myself up for absince widout leave. It's eight an' twenty days an' the rough end of the colonel's tongue in orderly room, any way you look at ut. But 'tis cheap at the price.'

'Mulvaney,' said I softly. 'If there happens to be any sort of excuse that the colonel can in any way accept, I have a notion that you'll get nothing more than the dressing-gown. The new recruits are in, and——'

'Not a word more, sorr. Is ut excuses the old man wants? 'Tis not my way, but he shall have thim. I'll tell him I was engaged in financial operations connected wid a church,' and he flapped his way to cantonments and the cells, singing lustily—

> 'So they sent a corp'ril's file,
> And they put me in the gyard-room
> For conduck unbecomin' of a soldier.'

And when he was lost in the midst of the moonlight we could hear the refrain—

> Bang upon the big drum, bash upon the cymbals,
> As we go marchin along, boys, oh!
> For although in this campaign
> There's no whisky nor champagne,
> We'll keep our spirits goin' with a song, boys!'

Therewith he surrendered himself to the joyful and almost weeping guard, and was made much of by his fellows. But to the colonel he said that he had been smitten with sunstroke and had lain insensible on a villager's cot for untold hours; and between laughter and goodwill the affair was smoothed over, so that he could, next day, teach the new recruits how to 'Fear God, Honour the Queen, Shoot Straight, and Keep Clean.'

'RIKKI-TIKKI-TAVI'

At the hole where he went in
Red-Eye called to Wrinkle-Skin
Hear what little Red-Eye saith:—
'Nag, come up and dance with death!'
Eye to eye and head to head
    (*Keep the measure, Nag*).
This shall end when one is dead
    (*At thy pleasure, Nag*).
Turn for turn and twist for twist
    (*Run and hide thee, Nag*).
Hah! The hooded Death has missed!
    (*Woe betide thee, Nag!*)

THIS is the story of the great war that Rikki-tikki-tavi fought single-handed, through the bath-rooms of the big bungalow in Segowlee cantonment. Darzee, the tailor-bird, helped him, and Chuchundra, the musk-rat, who never comes out into the middle of the floor, but always creeps round by the wall, gave him advice; but Rikki-tikki did the real fighting.

He was a mongoose, rather like a little cat in his fur and his tail, but quite like a weasel in his head and his habits. His eyes and the end of his restless nose were pink; he could scratch himself anywhere he pleased with any leg, front or back, that he chose to use; he could fluff up his tail till it looked like a bottle-brush, and his war-cry as he scuttled through the long grass was: *Rikk-tikk-tikki-tikki-tchk!*

One day, a high summer flood washed him out of the burrow where he lived with his father and mother, and carried him, kicking and clucking, down a roadside ditch. He found a little wisp of grass floating there, and clung to it till he lost his senses. When he revived, he was lying in the hot sun on the middle of a garden path, very draggled indeed, and a small boy was saying: 'Here's a dead mongoose. Let's have a funeral.'

'No,' said his mother; 'let's take him in and dry him. Perhaps he isn't really dead.'

They took him into the house, and a big man picked him up between his finger and thumb and said he was not dead but half choked; so they wrapped him in cotton-wool, and warmed him over a little fire, and he opened his eyes and sneezed.

'Now,' said the big man (he was an Englishman who had just moved into the bungalow); 'don't frighten him, and we'll see what he'll do.'

It is the hardest thing in the world to frighten a mongoose, because he is eaten up from nose to tail with curiosity. The motto of all the mongoose family is, 'Run and find out'; and Rikki-tikki was a true mongoose. He looked at the cotton-wool, decided that it was not good to eat, ran all round the table, sat up and put his fur in order, scratched himself, and jumped on the small boy's shoulder.

'Don't be frightened, Teddy,' said his father. 'That's his way of making friends.'

'Ouch! He's tickling under my chin,' said Teddy.

Rikki-tikki looked down between the boy's collar and neck, snuffed at his ear, and climbed down to the floor, where he sat rubbing his nose.

'Good gracious,' said Teddy's mother, 'and that's a wild creature! I suppose he's so tame because we've been kind to him.'

'All mongooses are like that,' said her husband. 'If Teddy doesn't pick him up by the tail, or try to put him in a cage, he'll run in and out of the house all day long. Let's give him something to eat.'

They gave him a little piece of raw meat. Rikki-tikki liked it immensely, and when it was finished he went out into the veranda and sat in the sunshine and fluffed up his fur to make it dry to the roots. Then he felt better.

'There are more things to find out about in this house,' he said to himself, 'than all my family could find out in all their lives. I shall certainly stay and find out.'

He spent all that day roaming over the house. He nearly drowned himself in the bath-tubs; put his nose into the ink on a writing-table, and burnt it on the end of the big man's cigar, for he climbed up in the big man's lap to see how writing was done. At nightfall he ran into Teddy's nursery to watch how kerosene lamps were lighted, and when Teddy went to bed Rikki-tikki climbed up too; but he was a restless companion, because he had to get up and attend to every noise all through the night, and find out what made it. Teddy's mother and father came in, the last thing, to look at their boy, and Rikki-tikki was awake on the pillow. 'I don't like that,' said Teddy's mother; 'he may bite the child.' 'He'll do no such thing,' said the father. 'Teddy's safer with that little beast than if he had a bloodhound to watch him. If a snake came into the nursery now——'

But Teddy's mother wouldn't think of anything so awful.

Early in the morning Rikki-tikki came to early breakfast in the veranda riding on Teddy's shoulder, and they gave him banana and some boiled egg; and he sat on all their laps one after the other, because every well-brought-up mongoose always hopes to be a house-mongoose some day and have rooms to run about in; and Rikki-tikki's mother (she used to live in the General's house at Segowlee) had carefully told Rikki what to do if ever he came across white men.

Then Rikki-tikki went out into the garden to see what was to be seen. It was a large garden, only half cultivated, with bushes, as big as summer-houses, of Marshal Niel roses; lime and orange trees, clumps of bamboos, and thickets of high grass. Rikki-tikki licked his lips. 'This is a splendid hunting-ground,' he said, and his tail grew bottle-brushy at the thought of it, and he scuttled up and down the garden, snuffing here and there till he heard very sorrowful voices in a thorn-bush. It was Darzee, the tailor-bird, and his wife. They had made a beautiful nest by pulling two big leaves together and stitching them up the edges with fibres, and had filled the hollow with cotton and downy fluff. The nest swayed to and fro, as they sat on the rim and cried.

'What is the matter?' asked Rikki-tikki.

'We are very miserable,' said Darzee. 'One of our babies fell out of the nest yesterday and Nag ate him.'

'H'm!' said Rikki-tikki, 'that is very sad—but I am a stranger here. Who is Nag?'

Darzee and his wife only cowered down in the nest without answering, for from the thick grass at the foot of the bush there came a low hiss—a horrid cold sound that made Rikki-tikki jump back two clear feet. Then inch by inch out of the grass rose up the head and spread hood of Nag, the big black cobra, and he was five feet long from tongue to tail. When he had lifted one-third of himself clear of the ground, he stayed balancing to and fro exactly as a dandelion-tuft balances in the wind, and he looked at Rikki-tikki with the wicked snake's eyes that never change their expression, whatever the snake may be thinking of.

'Who is Nag,' said he. 'I am Nag. The great God Brahm put his mark upon all our people, when the first cobra spread his hood to keep the sun off Brahm as he slept. Look, and be afraid!'

He spread out his hood more than ever, and Rikki-tikki saw the spectacle-mark on the back of it that looks exactly like the eye part of a hook-

and-eye fastening. He was afraid for the minute; but it is impossible for a mongoose to stay frightened for any length of time, and though Rikki-tikki had never met a live cobra before, his mother had fed him on dead ones, and he knew that all a grown mongoose's business in life was to fight and eat snakes. Nag knew that too and, at the bottom of his cold heart, he was afraid.

'Well,' said Rikki-tikki, and his tail began to fluff up again, 'marks or no marks, do you think it is right for you to eat fledglings out of a nest?'

Nag was thinking to himself, and watching the least little movement in the grass behind Rikki-tikki. He knew that mongooses in the garden meant death sooner or later for him and his family; but he wanted to get Rikki-tikki off his guard. So he dropped his head a little, and put it on one side.

'Let us talk,' he said. 'You eat eggs. Why should not I eat birds?'

'Behind you! Look behind you!' sang Darzee.

Rikki-tikki knew better than to waste time in staring. He jumped up in the air as high as he could go, and just under him whizzed by the head of Nagaina, Nag's wicked wife. She had crept up behind him as he was talking, to make an end of him; and he heard her savage hiss as the stroke missed. He came down almost across her back, and if he had been an old mongoose he would have known that then was the time to break her back with one bite; but he was afraid of the terrible lashing return-stroke of the cobra. He bit, indeed, but did not bite long enough, and he jumped clear of the whisking tail, leaving Nagaina torn and angry.

'Wicked, wicked Darzee!' said Nag, lashing up as high as he could reach toward the nest in the thorn-bush; but Darzee had built it out of reach of snakes, and it only swayed to and fro.

Rikki-tikki felt his eyes growing red and hot (when a mongoose's eyes grow red, he is angry), and he sat back on his tail and hind legs like a little kangaroo, and looked all round him, and chattered with rage. But Nag and Nagaina had disappeared into the grass. When a snake misses its stroke, it never says anything or gives any sign of what it means to do next. Rikki-tikki did not care to follow them, for he did not feel sure that he could manage two snakes at once. So he trotted off to the gravel path near the house, and sat down to think. It was a serious matter for him. If you read the old books of natural history, you will find they say that when the mongoose fights the snake and happens to get bitten, he runs off and eats some herb that cures him. That is not true. The victory is only a matter of quickness of eye and quickness of foot,—snake's blow against the mongoose's jump,—and as no eye can follow the motion of a snake's head when it strikes, this makes things much more wonderful than any magic herb. Rikki-tikki knew he was a young mongoose, and it made him all the more pleased to think that he had managed to escape a blow from behind. It gave him confidence in himself, and when Teddy came running down the path, Rikki-tikki was ready to be petted. But just as Teddy was stooping, something wriggled a little in the dust, and a tiny voice said: 'Be careful. I am Death?' It was Karait, the dusty brown snakeling that lies for choice on the dusty earth; and his bite is as dangerous as the cobra's. But he is so small that nobody thinks of him, and so he does the more harm to people.

Rikki-tikki's eyes grew red again, and he danced up to Karait with the peculiar rocking, swaying motion that he had inherited from his family. It looks very funny, but it is so perfectly balanced a gait that you can fly off from it at any angle you please; and in dealing with snakes this is an advantage. If Rikki-tikki had only known, he was doing a much more dangerous thing than fighting Nag, for Karait is so small, and can turn so quickly, that unless Rikki bit him close to the back of the head, he would get the return-stroke in his eye or his lip. But Rikki did not know: his eyes were all red, and he rocked back and forth, looking for a good place to hold. Karait struck out, Rikki jumped sideways and tried to run in, but the wicked little dusty gray head lashed within a fraction of his shoulder, and he had to jump over the body, and the head followed his heels close.

Teddy shouted to the house: 'Oh, look here! Our mongoose is killing a snake'; and Rikki-tikki heard a scream from Teddy's mother. His father ran out with a stick, but by the time he came up, Karait had lunged out once too far, and Rikki-tikki had sprung, jumped on the snake's back, dropped his head far between his fore-legs, bitten as high up the back as he could get hold, and rolled away. That bite paralysed Karait, and Rikki-tikki was just going to eat him up from the tail, after the custom of his family at dinner, when he remembered that a full meal makes a slow mongoose, and if he wanted all his strength and quickness ready, he must keep himself thin. He went away for a dust-bath under the castor-oil bushes, while Teddy's father beat the dead Karait. 'What is the use of that?' thought Rikki-tikki; 'I have settled it all'; and then Teddy's mother picked him up from the dust and hugged him, crying that he had saved Teddy from death, and Teddy's father said that he was a providence, and Teddy looked on with big scared eyes. Rikki-tikki was rather amused at all the fuss, which, of course, he did not understand. Teddy's mother might just as well have petted Teddy for playing in the dust. Rikki was thoroughly enjoying himself.

That night at dinner, walking to and fro among the wine-glasses on the table, he might have stuffed himself three times over with nice things; but he remembered Nag and Nagaina, and though it was very pleasant to be patted and petted by Teddy's mother, and to sit on Teddy's shoulder, his eyes would get red from time to time, and he would go off into his long war-cry of *Rikk-tikk-tikki-tikki-tchk!*

Teddy carried him off to bed, and insisted on Rikki-tikki's sleeping under his chin. Rikki-tikki was too well bred to bite or scratch, but as soon as Teddy was asleep he went off for his nightly walk round the house, and in the dark he ran up against Chuchundra, the musk-rat, creeping round by the wall. Chuchundra is a broken-hearted little beast. He whimpers and cheeps all night, trying to make up his mind to run into the middle of the room; but he never gets there.

'Don't kill me,' said Chuchundra, almost weeping. 'Rikki-tikki, don't kill me!'

'Do you think a snake-killer kills musk-rats?' said Rikki-tikki scornfully.

'Those who kill snakes get killed by snakes,' said Chuchundra, more sorrowfully than ever. 'And how am I to be sure that Nag won't mistake me for you some dark night?'

'There's not the least danger,' said Rikki-tikki; 'but Nag is in the garden, and I know you don't go there.'

'My cousin Chua, the rat, told me——' said Chuchundra, and then he stopped.

'Told you what?'

'H'sh! Nag is everywhere, Rikki-tikki. You should have talked to Chua in the garden.'

'I didn't—so you must tell me. Quick, Chuchundra, or I'll bite you!'

Chuchundra sat down and cried till the tears rolled off his whiskers. 'I am a very poor man,' he sobbed. 'I never had spirit enough to run out into the middle of the room. H'sh! I mustn't tell you anything. Can't you *hear*, Rikki-tikki?'

Rikki-tikki listened. The house was as still as still, but he thought he could just catch the faintest *scratch-scratch* in the world,—a noise as faint as that of a wasp walking on a window-pane,—the dry scratch of a snake's scales on brickwork.

'That's Nag or Nagaina,' he said to himself; 'and he is crawling into the bath-room sluice. You're right, Chuchundra; I should have talked to Chua.'

He stole off to Teddy's bath-room, but there was nothing there, and then to Teddy's mother's bath-room. At the bottom of the smooth plaster wall there was a brick pulled out to make a sluice for the bath-water, and as Rikki-tikki stole in by the masonry curb where the bath is put, he heard Nag and Nagaina whispering together outside in the moonlight.

'When the house is emptied of people,' said Nagaina to her husband, '*he* will have to go away, and then the garden will be our own again. Go in quietly, and remember that the big man who killed Karait is the first one to bite. Then come out and tell me, and we will hunt for Rikki-tikki together.'

'But are you sure that there is anything to be gained by killing the people?' said Nag.

'Everything. When there were no people in the bungalow, did we have any mongoose in the garden? So long as the bungalow is empty, we are king and queen of the garden; and remember that as soon as our eggs in the melon-bed hatch (as they may to-morrow), our children will need room and quiet.'

'I had not thought of that,' said Nag. 'I will go, but there is no need that we should hunt for Rikki-tikki afterward. I will kill the big man and his wife, and the child if I can, and come away quietly. Then the bungalow will be empty, and Rikki-tikki will go.'

Rikki-tikki tingled all over with rage and hatred at this, and then Nag's head came through the sluice, and his five feet of cold body followed it. Angry as he was, Rikki-tikki was very frightened as he saw the size of the big cobra. Nag coiled himself up, raised his head, and looked into the bath-room in the dark, and Rikki could see his eyes glitter.

'Now, if I kill him here, Nagaina will know; and if I fight him on the open floor, the odds are in his favour. What am I to do?' said Rikki-tikki-tavi.

Nag waved to and fro, and then Rikki-tikki heard him drinking from the biggest water-jar that was used to fill the bath. 'That is good,' said the snake. 'Now, when Karait was killed, the big man had a stick. He may have that stick still, but when he comes in to bathe in the morning he will not have a stick. I shall wait here till he comes. Nagaina—do you hear me?—I shall wait here in the cool till daytime.'

There was no answer from outside, so Rikki-tikki knew Nagaina had gone away. Nag coiled himself down, coil by coil, round the bulge at the bottom of the water-jar, and Rikki-tikki stayed still as death. After an hour he began to move, muscle by muscle, towards the jar. Nag was asleep, and Rikki-tikki looked at his big back, wondering which would be the best place for a good hold. 'If I don't break his back at the first jump,' said Rikki, 'he can still fight; and if he fights—O Rikki!' He looked at the thickness of the neck below the hood, but that was too much for him; and a bite near the tail would only make Nag savage.

'It must be the head,' he said at last; 'the head above the hood; and, when I am once there, I must not let go.'

Then he jumped. The head was lying a little clear of the water-jar, under the curve of it; and, as his teeth met, Rikki braced his back against the bulge of the red earthenware to hold down the head. This gave him just one second's purchase, and he made the most of it. Then he was battered to and fro as a rat is shaken by a dog—to and fro on the floor, up and down, and round in great circles, but his eyes were red and he held on as the body cartwhipped over the floor, upsetting the tin dipper and the soap-dish and the flesh-brush, and banged against the tin side of the bath. As he held he closed his jaws tighter and tighter, for he made sure he would be banged to death, and, for the honour of his family, he preferred to be found with his teeth locked. He was dizzy, aching, and felt shaken to pieces when something went off like a thunderclap just behind him; a hot wind knocked him senseless and red fire singed his fur. The big man had been wakened by the noise, and had fired both barrels of a shot-gun into Nag just behind the hood.

Rikki-tikki held on with his eyes shut, for now he was quite sure he was dead; but the head did not move, and the big man picked him up and said: 'It's the mongoose again, Alice; the little chap has saved *our* lives now.'

Then Teddy's mother came in with a very white face, and saw what was left of Nag, and Rikki-tikki dragged himself to Teddy's bedroom and spent half the rest of the night shaking himself tenderly to find out whether he really was broken into forty pieces, as he fancied.

When morning came he was very stiff, but well pleased with his doings. 'Now I have Nagaina to settle with, and she will be worse than five Nags, and there's no knowing when the eggs she spoke of will hatch. Goodness! I must go and see Darzee,' he said.

Without waiting for breakfast, Rikki-tikki ran to the thorn-bush where Darzee was singing a song of triumph at the top of his voice. The news of Nag's death was all over the garden, for the sweeper had thrown the body on the rubbish-heap.

'Oh, you stupid tuft of feathers!' said Rikki-tikki angrily. 'Is this the time to sing?'

'Nag is dead—is dead—is dead!' sang Darzee. 'The valiant Rikki-tikki caught him by the head and held fast. The big man brought the bang-stick, and Nag fell in two pieces! He will never eat my babies again.'

'All that's true enough; but where's Nagaina?' said Rikki-tikki, looking carefully round him.

'Nagaina came to the bath-room sluice and called for Nag,' Darzee went on; 'and Nag came out on the end of a stick—the sweeper picked him up on the end of a stick and threw him upon the rubbish-heap. Let us sing about the great, the red-eyed Rikki-tikki!' and Darzee filled his throat and sang.

'If I could get up to your nest, I'd roll your babies out!' said Rikki-tikki. 'You don't know when to do the right thing at the right time. You're safe enough in your nest there, but it's war for me down here. Stop singing a minute, Darzee.'

'For the great, beautiful Rikki-tikki's sake I will stop,' said Darzee. 'What is it, O Killer of the terrible Nag?'

'Where is Nagaina, for the third time?'

'On the rubbish-heap by the stables, mourning for Nag. Great is Rikki-tikki with the white teeth.'

'Bother my white teeth! Have you ever heard where she keeps her eggs?'

'In the melon-bed, on the end nearest the wall, where the sun strikes nearly all day. She hid them there weeks ago.'

'And you never thought it worth while to tell me? The end nearest the wall, you said?'

'Rikki-tikki, you are not going to eat her eggs?'

'Not eat exactly; no. Darzee, if you have a grain of sense you will fly off to the stables and pretend that your wing is broken, and let Nagaina chase you away to this bush? I must get to the melon-bed, and if I went there now she'd see me.'

Darzee was a feather-brained little fellow who could never hold more than one idea at a time in his head; and just because he knew that Nagaina's children were born in eggs like his own, he didn't think at first that it was fair to kill them. But his wife was a sensible bird, and she knew that cobra's eggs meant young cobras later on; so she flew off from the nest, and left Darzee to keep the babies warm, and continue his song about the death of Nag. Darzee was very like a man in some ways.

She fluttered in front of Nagaina by the rubbish-heap, and cried out, 'Oh, my wing is broken! The boy in the house threw a stone at me and broke it.' Then she fluttered more desperately than ever.

Nagaina lifted up her head and hissed, 'You warned Rikki-tikki when I would have killed him. Indeed and truly, you've chosen a bad place to be lame in.' And she moved toward Darzee's wife, slipping along over the dust.

'The boy broke it with a stone!' shrieked Darzee's wife.

'Well! It may be some consolation to you when you're dead to know that I shall settle accounts with the boy. My husband lies on the rubbish-heap this morning, but before night the boy in the house will lie very still. What is the use of running away? I am sure to catch you. Little fool, look at me!'

Darzee's wife knew better than to do *that*, for a bird who looks at a snake's eyes gets so frightened that she cannot move. Darzee's wife fluttered on, piping sorrowfully, and never leaving the ground, and Nagaina quickened her pace.

Rikki-tikki heard them going up the path from the stables, and he raced for the end of the melon-patch near the wall. There, in the warm litter above the melons, very cunningly hidden, he found twenty-five eggs, about the size of a bantam's eggs, but with whitish skins instead of shells.

'I was not a day too soon,' he said; for he could see the baby cobras curled up inside the skin, and he knew that the minute they were hatched they could each kill a man or a mongoose. He bit off the tops of the eggs as fast as he could, taking care to crush the young cobras, and turned over the litter from time to time to see whether he had missed any. At last there were only three eggs left, and Rikki-tikki began to chuckle to himself, when he heard Darzee's wife screaming:

Rikki-tikki, I led Nagaina toward the house, and she has gone into the veranda, and—oh, come quickly—she means killing!'

Rikki-tikki smashed two eggs, and tumbled backward down the melon-bed with the third egg in his mouth, and scuttled to the veranda as hard as he could put foot to the ground. Teddy and his mother and father were there at early breakfast; but Rikki-tikki saw that they were not eating anything. They sat stone-still, and their faces were white. Nagaina was coiled up on the matting by Teddy's chair, within easy striking distance of Teddy's bare leg, and she was swaying to and fro, singing a song of triumph.

'Son of the big man that killed Nag,' she hissed, 'stay still. I am not ready yet. Wait a little. Keep very still, all you three! If you move I strike, and if you do not move I strike. Oh, foolish people, who killed my Nag!'

Teddy's eyes were fixed on his father, and all his father could do was to whisper, 'Sit still, Teddy. You mustn't move. Teddy, keep still.'

Then Rikki-tikki came up and cried: 'Turn round, Nagaina; turn and fight!'

'All in good time,' said she, without moving her eyes. 'I will settle my account with *you* presently. Look at your friends, Rikki-tikki. They are still and white. They are afraid. They dare not move, and if you come a step nearer I strike.'

'Look at your eggs,' said Rikki-tikki, 'in the melon-bed near the wall. Go and look, Nagaina!'

The big snake turned half round, and saw the egg on the veranda. 'Ah-h! Give it to me,' she said.

Rikki-tikki put his paws one on each side of the egg, and his eyes were blood-red. 'What price for a snake's egg? For a young cobra? For a young king-cobra? For the last—the very last of the brood? The ants are eating all the others down by the melon-bed.'

Nagaina spun clear round, forgetting everything for the sake of the one egg; and Rikki-tikki saw Teddy's father shoot out a big hand, catch Teddy by the shoulder, and drag him across the little table with the tea-cups, safe and out of reach of Nagaina.

'Tricked! Tricked! Tricked! *Rikk-tck-tck!*' chuckled Rikki-tikki. 'The boy is safe, and it was I—I—I—that caught Nag by the hood last night in the bath-room.' Then he began to jump up and down, all four feet together, his head close to the floor. 'He threw me to and fro, but he could not shake me off. He was dead before the big man blew him in two. I did it! *Rikki-tikki-tck-tck!* Come then, Nagaina. Come and fight with me. You shall not be a widow long.'

Nagaina saw that she had lost her chance of killing Teddy, and the egg lay between Rikki-tikki's paws. 'Give me the egg, Rikki-tikki. Give me the last of my eggs, and I will go away and never come back,' she said, lowering her hood.

'Yes, you will go away, and you will never come back; for you will go to the rubbish-heap with Nag. Fight, widow! The big man has gone for his gun! Fight!'

Rikki-tikki was bounding all round Nagaina, keeping just out of reach of her stroke, his little eyes like hot coals. Nagaina gathered herself together, and flung out at him. Rikki-tikki jumped up and backwards. Again and again and again she struck, and each time her head came with a whack on the matting of the veranda and she gathered herself together like a watch-spring. Then Rikki-tikki danced in a circle to get behind her, and Nagaina spun round to keep her head to his head, so that the rustle of her tail on the matting sounded like dry leaves blown along by the wind.

He had forgotten the egg. It still lay on the veranda, and Nagaina came nearer and nearer to it, till at last, while Rikki-tikki was drawing breath, she caught it in her mouth, turned to the veranda steps, and flew like an arrow down the path, with Rikki-tikki behind her. When the cobra runs for her life, she goes like a whip-lash flicked across a horse's neck. Rikki-tikki knew that he must catch her, or all the trouble would begin again. She headed straight for the long grass by the thorn-bush, and as he was running Rikki-tikki heard Darzee still singing his foolish little song of triumph. But Darzee's wife was wiser. She flew off her nest as Nagaina came along, and flapped her wings about Nagaina's head. If Darzee had helped they might have turned her; but Nagaina only lowered her hood and went on. Still, the instant's delay brought Rikki-tikki up to her, and as she plunged into the rat-hole where she and Nag used to live, his little white teeth were clenched on her tail, and he went down with her—and very few mongooses, however wise and old they may be, care to follow a cobra into its hole. It was dark in the hole; and Rikki-tikki never knew when it might open out and give Nagaina room to turn and strike at him. He held on savagely, and stuck out his feet to act as brakes on the dark slope of the hot, moist earth. Then the grass by the mouth of the hole stopped waving, and Darzee said: 'It is all over with Rikki-tikki! We must sing his death-song. Valiant Rikki-tikki is dead! For Nagaina will surely kill him underground.'

So he sang a very mournful song that he made up on the spur of the minute, and just as he got to the most touching part the grass quivered again, and Rikki-tikki, covered with dirt, dragged himself out of the hole leg by leg, licking his whiskers. Darzee stopped with a little shout. Rikki-tikki shook some of the dust out of his fur and sneezed. 'It is all over,' he said. 'The widow will never come out again.' And the red ants that live between the grass stems heard him, and began to troop down one after another to see if he had spoken the truth.

Rikki-tikki curled himself up in the grass and slept where he was— slept and slept till it was late in the afternoon, for he had done a hard day's work.

'Now,' he said, when he awoke, 'I will go back to the house. Tell the Coppersmith, Darzee, and he will tell the garden that Nagaina is dead.'

The Coppersmith is a bird who makes a noise exactly like the beating of a little hammer on a copper pot; and the reason he is always making it is because he is the town-crier to every Indian garden, and tells all the news to everybody who cares to listen. As Rikki-tikki went up the path, he heard his 'attention' notes like a tiny dinner-gong; and then the steady 'Ding-dong-tock! Nag is dead—dong! Nagaina is dead! Ding-dong-tock!' That set all the birds in the garden singing, and the frogs croaking; for Nag and Nagaina used to eat frogs as well as little birds.

When Rikki got to the house, Teddy and Teddy's mother (she looked very white still, for she had been fainting) and Teddy's father came out and almost cried over him; and that night he ate all that was given him till he could eat no more, and went to bed on Teddy's shoulder, where Teddy's mother saw him when she came to look late at night.

'He saved our lives and Teddy's life,' she said to her husband. 'Just think, he saved all our lives.'

Rikki-tikki woke up with a jump, for the mongooses are light sleepers.

'Oh, it's you,' said he. 'What are you bothering for? All the cobras are dead; and if they weren't, I'm here.'

Rikki-tikki had a right to be proud of himself; but he did not grow too proud, and he kept that garden as a mongoose should keep it, with tooth and jump and spring and bite, till never a cobra dared show its head inside the walls.

DARZEE'S CHAUNT

(SUNG IN HONOUR OF RIKKI-TIKKI-TAVI)

SINGER and tailor am I—
    Doubled the joys that I know—
Proud of my lilt to the sky,
    Proud of the house that I sew.
Over and under, so weave I my music—so weave I the house that I sew.

Sing to your fledglings again,
    Mother, O lift up your head!
Evil that plagued us is slain,
    Death in the garden lies dead.
Terror that hid in the roses is impotent—flung on the dunghill and dead!

Who has delivered us, who?
    Tell me his nest and his name.
Rikki, the valiant, the true,
    Tikki, with eyeballs of flame—
Rikk-tikki-tikki, the ivory-fanged, the hunter with eyeballs of flame!

Give him the Thanks of the Birds,
    Bowing with tail-feathers spread,
Praise him with nightingale words—
    Nay, I will praise him instead.
Hear! I will sing you the praise of the bottle-tailed Rikki with eyeballs of red!

(*Here Rikki-tikki interrupted, so the rest of the song is lost.*)

SOMETHING
OF MYSELF

SOMETHING OF MYSELF

I. A VERY YOUNG PERSON

1865–1878

Give me the first six years of a child's life and you can have the rest.

◄§ LOOKING back from this my seventieth year, it seems to me that every card in my working life has been dealt me in such a manner that I had but to play it as it came. Therefore, ascribing all good fortune to Allah the Dispenser of Events, I begin:—

My first impression is of daybreak, light and colour and golden and purple fruits at the level of my shoulder. This would be the memory of early morning walks to the Bombay fruit market with my *ayah* and later with my sister in her perambulator, and of our returns with our purchases piled high on the bows of it. Our *ayah* was a Portuguese Roman Catholic who would pray—I beside her—at a wayside Cross. Meeta, my Hindu bearer, would sometimes go into little Hindu temples where, being below the age of caste, I held his hand and looked at the dimly seen, friendly Gods.

Our evening walks were by the sea in the shadow of palm-groves which, I think, were called the Mahim Woods. When the wind blew the great nuts would tumble, and we fled—my *ayah* and my sister in her perambulator—to the safety of the open. I have always felt the menacing darkness of tropical eventides, as I have loved the voices of night-winds through palm or banana leaves, and the song of the tree-frogs.

There were far-going Arab dhows on the pearly waters, and gaily dressed Parsees wading out to worship the sunset. Of their creed I knew nothing, nor did I know that near our little house on the Bombay Esplanade were the Towers of Silence, where their Dead are exposed to the waiting vultures on the rim of the towers, who scuffle and spread wings when they see the bearers of the Dead below. I did not understand my mother's distress when she found 'a child's hand' in our garden, and said I was not to ask questions about it. I wanted to see that child's hand. But my *ayah* told me.

In the afternoon heats before we took our sleep, she or Meeta would tell us stories and Indian nursery songs all unforgotten, and we were sent into the dining-room after we had been dressed, with the caution 'Speak English now to Papa and Mamma.' So one spoke 'English,' haltingly translated out of the vernacular idiom that one thought and dreamed in. The Mother sang wonderful songs at a black piano and would go out to Big Dinners. Once she came back, very quickly, and told me, still awake, that 'the big Lord Sahib' had been killed and there was to be no Big Dinner. This was Lord Mayo, assassinated by a native. Meeta explained afterwards that he had been 'hit with a knife.' Meeta unconsciously saved me from any night terrors or dread of the dark. Our *ayah*, with a servant's curious mixture of deep affection and shallow device, had told me that a stuffed leopard's head on the nursery wall was there to see that I went to sleep. But Meeta spoke of it scornfully as 'the head of an animal,' and I took it off my mind as a fetish, good or bad, for it was only some unspecified 'animal.'

Far across green spaces round the house was a marvellous place filled with smells of paints and oils, and lumps of clay with which I played. That was the atelier of my Father's School of Art, and a Mr. 'Terry Sahib' his assistant, to whom my small sister was devoted, was our great friend. Once, on the way there alone, I passed the edge of a huge ravine a foot deep, where a winged monster as big as myself attacked me, and I fled and wept. My Father drew for me a picture of the tragedy with a rhyme beneath:—

> There was a small boy in Bombay
> Who once from a hen ran away.
>   When they said: 'You're a baby,'
>   He replied: 'Well, I may be:
> But I don't like these hens of Bombay.'

This consoled me. I have thought well of hens ever since.

Then those days of strong light and darkness passed, and there was a time in a ship with an immense semi-circle blocking all vision on each side of her. (She must have been the old paddle-wheel P. & O. *Ripon*.) There was a train across a desert (the Suez Canal was not yet opened) and a halt in it, and a small girl wrapped in a shawl on the seat opposite me, whose face stands out still. There was next a dark land, and a darker room full of cold, in one wall of which a white woman made naked fire, and I cried aloud with dread, for I had never before seen a grate.

Then came a new small house smelling of aridity and emptiness, and a parting in the dawn with Father and Mother, who said that I must learn quickly to read and write so that they might send me letters and books.

I lived in that house for close on six years. It belonged to a woman who took in children whose parents were in India. She was married to an old Navy Captain, who had been a midshipman at Navarino, and had afterwards been entangled in a harpoon-line while whale-fishing, and dragged down till he miraculously freed himself. But the line had scarred his ankle for life—a dry, black scar, which I used to look at with horrified interest.

The house itself stood in the extreme suburbs of Southsea, next to a Portsmouth unchanged in most particulars since Trafalgar—the Portsmouth of Sir Walter Besant's *By Celia's Arbour*. The timber for a Navy that was only experimenting with iron-clads such as the *Inflexible* lay in great booms in the Harbour. The little training-brigs kept their walks opposite Southsea Castle, and Portsmouth Hard was as it had always been. Outside these things lay the desolation of Hayling Island, Lumps Fort, and the isolated hamlet of Milton. I would go for long walks with the Captain, and once he took me to see a ship called the *Alert* (or *Discovery*) returned from Arctic explorations, her decks filled with old sledges and lumber, and her spare rudder being cut up for souvenirs. A sailor gave me a piece, but I lost it. Then the old Captain died, and I was sorry, for he was the only person in that house as far as I can remember who ever threw me a kind word.

It was an establishment run with the full vigour of the Evangelical as revealed to the Woman. I had never heard of Hell, so I was introduced to it in all its terrors—I and whatever luckless little slavey might be in the house, whom severe rationing had led to steal food. Once I saw the Woman beat such a girl who picked up the kitchen poker and threatened retaliation. Myself I was regularly beaten. The Woman had an only son of twelve or thirteen as religious as she. I was a real joy to him, for when his mother had finished with me for the day he (we slept in the same room) took me on and roasted the other side.

If you cross-examine a child of seven or eight on his day's doings (specially when he wants to go to sleep) he will contradict himself very satisfactorily. If each contradiction be set down as a lie and retailed at breakfast, life is not easy. I have known a certain amount of bullying, but this was calculated torture—religious as well as scientific. Yet it made me give attention to the lies I soon found it necessary to tell: and this, I presume, is the foundation of literary effort.

But my ignorance was my salvation. I was made to read without explanation, under the usual fear of punishment. And on a day that I remember it came to me that 'reading' was not 'the Cat lay on the Mat,' but a means to everything that would make me happy. So I read all that came within my reach. As soon as my pleasure in this was known, deprivation from reading was added to my punishments. I then read by stealth and the more earnestly.

There were not many books in that house, but Father and Mother as soon as they heard I could read sent me priceless volumes. One I have still, a bound copy of *Aunt Judy's Magazine* of the early 'seventies, in which appeared Mrs. Ewing's *Six to Sixteen*. I owe more in circuitous ways to that tale than I can tell. I knew it, as I know it still, almost by heart. Here was a history of real people and real things. It was better than Knatchbull-Hugesson's *Tales at Tea-time*, better even than *The Old Shikarri* with its steel engravings of charging pigs and angry tigers. On another plane was an old magazine with Wordsworth's 'I climbed the dark brow of the mighty

Helvellyn.' I knew nothing of its meaning but the words moved and pleased. So did other extracts from the poems of 'A. Tennyson.'

A visitor, too, gave me a little purple book of severely moral tendency called *The Hope of the Katzikopfs*—about a bad boy made virtuous, but it contained verses that began, 'Farewell Rewards and Fairies,' and ended with an injunction 'To pray for the "noddle" of William Churne of Staffordshire.' This bore fruit afterwards.

And somehow or other I came across a tale about a lion-hunter in South Africa who fell among lions who were all Freemasons, and with them entered into a confederacy against some wicked baboons. I think that, to, lay dormant until the *Jungle Books* began to be born.

There comes to my mind here a memory of two books of verse about child-life which I have tried in vain to identify. One—blue and fat—described 'nine white wolves' coming 'over the wold' and stirred me to the deeps; and also certain savages who 'thought the name of England was something that could not burn.'

The other book—brown and fat—was full of lovely tales in strange metres. A girl was turned into a water-rat 'as a matter of course'; an Urchin cured an old man of gout by means of a cool cabbage-leaf, and somehow 'forty wicked Goblins' were mixed up in the plot; and a 'Darling' got out on the house-leads with a broom and tried to sweep stars off the skies. It must have been an unusual book for that age, but I have never been able to recover it, any more than I have a song that a nursemaid sang at low-tide in the face of the sunset on Littlehampton Sands when I was less than six. But the impression of wonder, excitement and terror and the red bars of failing light is as clear as ever.

Among the servants in the House of Desolation was one from Cumnor, which name I associated with sorrow and darkness and a raven that 'flapped its wings.' Years later I identified the lines: 'And thrice the Raven flapped her wing Around the towers of Cumnor Hall.' But how and where I first heard the lines that cast the shadow is beyond me—unless it be that the brain holds everything that passes within reach of the senses, and it is only ourselves who do not know this.

When my Father sent me a *Robinson Crusoe* with steel engravings I set up in business alone as a trader with savages (the wreck parts of the tale never much interested me), in a mildewy basement room where I stood my solitary confinements. My apparatus was a cocoanut shell strung on a red cord, a tin trunk, and a piece of packing-case which kept off any other world. Thus fenced about, everything inside the fence was quite real, but mixed with the smell of damp cupboards. If the bit of board fell, I had to begin the magic all over again. I have learned since from children who play much alone that this rule of 'beginning again in a pretend game' is not uncommon. The magic, you see, lies in the ring or fence that you take refuge in.

Once I remember being taken to a town called Oxford and a street called Holywell, where I was shown an Ancient of Days who, I was told, was the Provost of Oriel; wherefore I never understood, but conceived him to be some sort of idol. And twice or thrice we went, all of us, to pay a day-long visit to an old gentleman in a house in the country near Havant. Here everything was wonderful and unlike my world, and he had an old lady sister who was kind, and I played in hot, sweet-smelling meadows and ate all sorts of things.

After such a visit I was once put through the third degree by the Woman and her son, who asked me if I had told the old gentleman that I was much fonder of him than was the Woman's son. It must have been the tail-end of some sordid intrigue or other—the old gentleman being of kin to that unhappy pair—but it was beyond my comprehension. My sole concern had been a friendly pony in the paddock. My dazed attempts to clear myself were not accepted and, once again, the pleasure that I was seen to have taken was balanced by punishments and humiliation—above all humiliation. That alternation was quite regular. I can but admire the infernal laborious ingenuity of it all. *Exempli gratia.* Coming out of church once I smiled. The Devil-Boy demanded why. I said I didn't know, which was child's truth. He replied that I *must* know. People didn't laugh for nothing. Heaven knows what explanation I put forward; but it was duly reported to the Woman as a 'lie.' Result, afternoon upstairs with the Collect to learn. I learned most of the Collects that way and a great deal of the Bible. The son after three or four years went into a Bank and was generally too tired on his return to torture me, unless things had gone wrong with him. I learned to know what was coming from his step into the house.

But, for a month each year I possessed a paradise which I verily believe saved me. Each December I stayed with my Aunt Georgy, my mother's sister, wife of Sir Edward Burne-Jones, at The Grange, North End Road. At first I must have been escorted there, but later I went alone, and arriving at the house would reach up to the open-work iron bell-pull on the wonderful gate that let me into all felicity. When I had a house of my own, and The Grange was emptied of meaning, I begged for and was given that bell-pull for my entrance, in the hope that other children might also feel happy when they rang it.

At The Grange I had love and affection as much as the greediest, and I was not very greedy, could desire. There were most wonderful smells of paints and turpentine whiffing down from the big studio on the first floor where my Uncle worked; there was the society of my two cousins, and a sloping mulberry tree which we used to climb for our plots and conferences. There was a rocking-horse in the nursery and a table that, titled up on two chairs, made a toboggan-slide of the best. There were pictures finished or half finished of lovely colours; and in the rooms chairs and cupboards such as the world had not yet seen, for William Morris (our Deputy 'Uncle Topsy') was just beginning to fabricate these things. There was an incessant come and go of young people and grown-ups all willing to play with us—except an elderly person called 'Browning' who took no proper interest in the skirmishes which happened to be raging on his entry. Best of all, immeasurably, was the beloved Aunt herself reading us *The Pirate* or *The Arabian Nights* of evenings, when one lay out on the big sofas sucking toffee, and calling our cousins 'Ho, Son,' or 'Daughter of my Uncle' or 'O True Believer.'

Often the Uncle, who had a 'golden voice,' would assist in our evening play, though mostly he worked at black and white in the middle of our riots. He was never idle. We made a draped chair in the hall serve for the seat of 'Norna of the Fitful Head' and addressed her questions till the Uncle got inside the rugs and gave us answers which thrilled us with delightul shivers, in a voice deeper than all the boots in the world. And once he descended in broad daylight with a tube of 'Mummy Brown' in his hand, saying that he had discovered it was made of dead Pharaohs and we must bury it accordingly. So we all went out and helped—according to the rites of Mizraim and Memphis, I hope—and—to this day I could drive a spade within a foot of where that tube lies.

At bedtime one hastened along the passages, where unfinished cartoons lay against the walls. The Uncle often painted in their eyes first, leaving the rest in charcoal—a most effective presentation. Hence our speed to our own top-landing, where we could hang over the stairs and listen to the loveliest sound in the world—deep-voiced men laughing together over dinner.

It was a jumble of delights and emotions culminating in being allowed to blow the big organ in the studio for the beloved Aunt, while the Uncle worked, or 'Uncle Topsy' came in full of some business of picture-frames or stained glass or general denunciations. Then it was hard to keep the little lead weight on its string below the chalk mark, and if the organ ran out in squeals the beloved Aunt would be sorry. Never, *never* angry!

As a rule Morris took no notice of anything outside what was in his mind at the moment. But I remember one amazing exception. My cousin Margaret and I, then about eight, were in the nursery eating pork-dripping on brown bread, which is a dish for the Gods, when we heard 'Uncle Topsy' in the hall calling, as he usually did, for 'Ned' or 'Georgie.' The matter was outside our world. So we were the more impressed when, not finding the grown-ups, he came in and said he would tell us a story. We settled ourselves under the table which we used for a toboggan-slide and he, gravely as ever, climbed on to our big rocking-horse. There, slowly surging back and forth while the poor beast creaked, he told us a tale full of fascinating horrors, about a man who was condemned to dream bad dreams. One of them took the shape of a cow's tail waving from a heap of dried fish. He went away as abruptly as he had come. Long afterwards, when I was old enough to know a maker's pains, it dawned on me that we must have heard the Saga of Burnt Njal, which was then interesting him. In default of grown-ups, and pressed by need to pass the story between his teeth and clarify it, he had used us.

But on a certain day—one tried to fend off the thought of it—the delicious dream would end, and one would return to the House of Desolation, and for the next two or three mornings there cry on waking up. Hence more punishments and cross-examinations.

Often and often afterwards, the beloved Aunt would ask me why I had never told anyone how I was being treated. Children tell little more than animals, for what comes to them they accept as eternally established. Also, badly-treated children have a clear notion of what they are likely to get if they betray the secrets of a prison-house before they are clear of it.

In justice to the Woman I can say that I was adequately fed. (I remember a gift to her of some red 'fruit' called 'tomatoes' which, after long consideration, she boiled with sugar; and they were very beastly. The tinned meat of those days was Australian beef with a crumbly fat, and string-boiled mutton, hard to get down.) Nor was my life an unsuitable preparation for my future, in that it demanded constant wariness, the habit of observation, and attendance on moods and tempers; the noting of discrepancies between speech and action; a certain reserve of demeanour; and automatic suspicion of sudden favours. Brother Lippo Lippi, in his own harder case, as a boy discovered:—

> Why, soul and sense of him grow sharp alike,
> He learns the look of things and none the less
> For admonition.

So it was with me.

My troubles settled themselves in a few years. My eyes went wrong, and I could not well see to read. For which reason I read the more and in bad lights. My work at the terrible little day-school where I had been sent suffered in consequence, and my monthly reports showed it. The loss of 'reading-time' was the worst of my 'home' punishments for bad school-work. One report was so bad that I threw it away and said that I had never received it. But this is a hard world for the amateur liar. My web of deceit was swiftly exposed—the Son spared time after banking-hours to help in the auto-da-fé— and I was well beaten and sent to school through the streets of Southsea with the placard 'Liar' between my shoulders. In the long run these things, and many more of the like, drained me of any capacity for real, personal hate for the rest of my days. So close must any life-filling passion lie to its opposite. 'Who having known the Diamond will concern himself with glass?'

Some sort of nervous breakdown followed for I imagined I saw shadows and things that were not there, and they worried me more than the Woman. The beloved Aunt must have heard of it, and a man came down to see me as to my eyes and reported that I was half-blind. This, to, was supposed to be 'showing-off,' and I was segregated from my sister—another punishment— as a sort of moral leper. Then—I do not remember that I had any warning —the Mother returned from India. She told me afterwards that when she first came up to my room to kiss me good-night, I flung up an arm to guard off the cuff that I had been trained to expect.

I was taken at once from the House of Desolation, and for months ran wild in a little farmhouse on the edge of Epping Forest, where I was not encouraged to refer to my guilty past. Except for my spectacles, which were uncommon in those days, I was completely happy with my Mother and the local society, which included for me a gipsy of the name of Saville, who told me tales of selling horses to the ignorant; the farmer's wife; her niece Patty who turned a kind blind eye on our raids into the dairy; the postman; and the farm-boys. The farmer did not approve of my teaching one of his cows to stand and be milked in the field. My Mother drew the line at my return to meals red-booted from assisting at the slaughter of swine, or reeking after the exploration of attractive muck-heaps. These were the only restrictions I recall.

A cousin, afterwards to be a Prime Minister, would come down on visits. The farmer said that we did each other 'no good.' Yet the worst I can remember was our self-sacrificing war against a wasp's nest on a muddy islet in a most muddy pond. Our only weapons were switches of broom, but we defeated the enemy unscathed. The trouble at home centred round an enormous current roly-poly—a 'spotted dog' a foot long. We took it away to sustain us in action and we heard a great deal about it from Patty in the evening.

Then we went to London and stayed for some weeks in a tiny lodging-house in the semi-rural Brompton Road, kept by an ivory-faced, lordly-whiskered ex-butler and his patient wife. Here, for the first time, it happened that the night got into my head. I rose up and wandered about that still house till daybreak, when I slipped out into the little brick-walled garden and saw the dawn break. All would have been well but for Pluto, a pet toad brought back from Epping Forest, who lived mostly in one of my pockets. It struck me that he might be thirsty, and I stole into my Mother's room and would have given him a drink from a water-jug. But it slipped and broke and very much was said. The ex-butler could not understand why I had stayed awake all night. I did not know then that such night-wakings would be laid upon me through my life; or that my fortunate hour would be on the turn of sunrise, with a sou'-west breeze afoot.

The sorely tried Mother got my sister and me season-tickets for the old South Kensington Museum which was only across the road. (No need in those days to caution us against the traffic.) Very shortly we two, on account of our regular attendance (for the weather had turned wet), owned that place and one policeman in special. When we came with any grown-ups he saluted us magnificently. From the big Buddha with the little door in his back, to the towering dull-gilt ancient coaches and carven chariots in a long dark corridors—even the places marked 'private' where fresh treasures were always being unpacked—we roved at will, and divided the treasures child-fashion. There were instruments of music inlaid with lapis, beryl and ivories; glorious gold-fretted spinets and clavichords; the bowels of the great Glastonbury clock; mechanical models; steel- and silver-butted pistols, daggers and arquebusses—the labels alone were an education; a collection of precious stones and rings—we quarrelled over those—and a big bluish book which was the manuscript of one of Dickens' novels. That man seemed to me to have written very carelessly; leaving out lots which he had to squeeze in between the lines afterwards.

These experiences were a soaking in colour and design with, above all, the proper Museum smell; and it stayed with me. By the end of that long holiday I understood that my Mother had written verses, that my Father 'wrote things' also; that books and pictures were among the most important affairs in the world; that I could read as much as I chose and ask the meaning of things from anyone I met. I had found out, too, that one could take pen and set down what one thought, and that nobody accused one of 'showing off' by so doing. I read a good deal; *Sidonia the Sorceress*; Emerson's poems; and Bret Harte's stories; and I learned all sorts of verses for the pleasure of repeating them to myself in bed.

II. THE SCHOOL BEFORE ITS TIME

1878–1882

◄§ THEN came school at the far end of England. The Head of it was a lean, slow-spoken, bearded, Arab-complexioned man whom till then I had known as one of my Deputy-Uncles at The Grange—Cormell Price, otherwise 'Uncle Crom.' My mother, on her return to India, confided my sister and me to the care of three dear ladies who lived off the far end of Kensington High Street over against Addison Road, in a house filled with books, peace, kindliness, patience and what to-day would be called 'culture.' But it was natural atmosphere.

One of the ladies wrote novels on her knee, by the fireside, sitting just outside the edge of conversation, beneath two clay pipes tied with black ribbon, which once Carlyle had smoked. All the people one was taken to see either wrote or painted pictures or, as in the case of a Mr. and Miss de Morgan, ornamented tiles. They let me play with their queer, sticky paints. Somewhere in the background were people called Jean Ingelow and Christina Rossetti, but I was never lucky enough to see those good spirits. And there was a choice in the walls of bookshelves of anything one liked from *Firmilian* to *The Moonstone* and *The Woman in White* and, somehow, all Wellington's Indian Despatches, which fascinated me.

These treasures were realised by me in the course of the next few years. Meantime (Spring of '78), after my experience at Southsea, the prospect of school did not attract. The United Services College was in the nature of a company promoted by poor officers and the like for the cheap education of their sons, and set up at Westward Ho! near Bideford. It was largely a caste-school—some seventy-five per cent of us had been born outside England and hoped to follow their fathers in the Army. It was but four or five years old when I joined, and had been made up under Cormell Price's hand by drafts from Haileybury, whose pattern it followed, and, I think, a percentage of 'hard cases' from other schools. Even by the standards of those days, it was primitive in its appointments, and our food would now raise a mutiny in Dartmoor. I remember no time, after home-tips had been spent, when we would not eat dry bread if we could steal it from the trays in the basement before tea. Yet the sick-house was permanently empty except for lawful accidents; I remember not one death of a boy; and only one epidemic—of chicken-pox. Then the Head called us together and con-doled with us in such fashion that we expected immediate break-up and began to cheer. But he said that, perhaps, the best thing would be to take no notice of the incident, and that he would 'work us lightly' for the rest of the term. He did and it checked the epidemic.

Naturally, Westward Ho! was brutal enough, but, setting aside the foul speech that a boy ought to learn early and put behind him by his seventeenth year, it was clean with a cleanliness that I have never heard of in any other school. I remember no cases of even suspected perversion, and am inclined to the theory that if masters did not suspect them, and show that they suspected, there would not be quite so many elsewhere. Talking things over with Cormell Price afterwards, he confessed that his one prophylactic against certain unclean microbes was to 'send us to bed dead tired.' Hence the wideness of our bounds, and his deaf ear towards our incessant riots and wars between the Houses.

At the end of my first term, which was horrible, my parents could not reach England for the Easter holidays, and I had to stay up with a few big boys reading for Army Exams. and a batch of youngsters whose people were very far away. I expected the worst, but when we survivors were left in the echoing form-rooms after the others had driven cheering to the station, life suddenly became a new thing (thanks to Cormell Price). The big remote seniors turned into tolerant elder brothers, and let us small fry rove far out of bounds; shared their delicacies with us at tea; and even took an interest in our hobbies. We had no special work to do and enjoyed ourselves hugely. On the return of the school 'all smiles stopped together,' which was right and proper. For compensation I was given a holiday when my Father came home, and with him went to the Paris Exhibition of '78, where he was in charge of Indian Exhibits. He allowed me, at twelve years old, the full freedom and that spacious and friendly city, and the run of the Exhibition grounds and buildings. It was an education in itself; and set my life-long love for France. Also, he saw to it that I should learn to read French at least for my own amusement, and gave me Jules Verne to begin with. (French as an accomplishment was not well-seen at English schools in my time, and knowledge of it connoted leanings towards immorality. For myself:—

> I hold it truth with him who sung
> Unpublished melodies,
> Who wakes in Paris, being young,
> O' summer, wakes in Paradise.

For those who may be still interested in such matters, I wrote of this part of my life in some *Souvenirs of France*, which are very close to the facts of that time.

My first year and a half was not pleasant. The most persistent bullying comes not less from the bigger boys, who merely kick and pass on, than from young devils of fourteen acting in concert against one butt. Luckily for me I was physically some years in advance of my age, and swimming in the big open sea baths, or off the Pebble Ridge, was the one accomplishment that brought me any credit. I played footer (Rugby Union), but here again my sight hampered me. I was not even in the Second Fifteen.

After my strength came suddenly to me about my fourteenth year, there was no more bullying; and either my natural sloth or past experience did not tempt me to bully in my turn. I had by then found me two friends with whom, by a carefully arranged system of mutual aids, I went up the school on co-operative principles.

How we—the originals of Stalky, M'Turk, and Beetle—first came together I do not remember, but our Triple Alliance was well established before we were thirteen. We had been oppressed by a large toughish boy who raided our poor little lockers. We took him on in a long, mixed rough-and-tumble, just this side of the real thing. At the end we were all-out (we worked by pressure and clinging, much as bees 'ball' a Queen) and he never troubled us again.

Turkey possessed an invincible detachment—far beyond mere insolence —towards all the world: and a tongue, when he used it, dipped in some Irish-blue acid. Moreover, he spoke, sincerely, of the masters as 'ushers,' which was not without charm. His general attitude was that of Ireland in English affairs at that time.

For executive capacity, the organisation of raids, reprisals, and retreats, we depended on Stalky, our Commander-in-Chief and Chief of his own Staff. He came of a household with a stern head, and, I fancy, had training in the holidays. Turkey never told us much about his belongings. He turned up, usually a day or two late, by the Irish packet, aloof, inscrutable, and contra-dictious. On him lay the burden of decorating our study, for he served a strange God called Ruskin. We fought among ourselves 'regular an' faithful as man an' wife,' but any debt which we owed elsewhere was faithfully paid by all three of us.

Our 'socialisation of educational opportunities' took us unscathed up the school, till the original of Little Hartopp, asking one question too many, disclosed that I did not know what a co-sine was and compared me to 'brute beasts.' I taught Turkey all he ever knew of French, and he tried to make Stalky and me comprehend a little Latin. There is much to be said for this system, if you want a boy to learn anything, because he will remember what he gets from an equal where his master's words are forgotten. Similarly, when it was necessary to Stalky that I should get into the Choir, he taught me how to quaver 'I know a maiden fair to see' by punching me in the kidneys all up and down the cricket-field. (But some small trouble over a solitaire marble pushed from beneath the hem of a robe down the choir-steps into the tiled aisle ended that venture.)

I think it was his infernal impersonality that swayed us all in our wars and peace. He saw not only us but himself from the outside, and in later life, as we met in India and elsewhere, the gift persisted. At long last, when with an equipment of doubtful Ford cars and a collection of most-mixed troops, he put up a monumental bluff against the Bolsheviks somewhere in Armenia (it is written in his *Adventures of Dunsterforce*) and was as nearly as possible destroyed, he wrote to the authorities responsible. I asked him what happened. 'They told me they had no more use for my services,' said he. Naturally I condoled. 'Wrong as usual,' said the ex-Head of Number Five study. 'If any officer under *me* had written what I did to the War Office, I'd have had him broke in two-twos.' That fairly sums up the man—and the boy who commanded us. I think I was a buffer state between his drivings and his tongue-lootings and his campaigns in which we were powers; and the acrid, devastating Turkey who, as I have written, 'lived and loved to destroy illusions' yet reached always after beauty. They took up room on tables that I wanted for writing; they broke into my reveries; they mocked my Gods; they stole, pawned or sold my outlying or neglected possessions; and—I could not have gone on a week without them nor they without me.

But my revenge was ample. I have said I was physically precocious. In my last term I had been thrusting an unlovely chin at C—— in form. At last he blew up, protested he could no longer abide the sight, and ordered me to shave. I carried this word to my House-master. He, who had long looked on me as a cultivated sink of iniquities, brooded over his confirmation of his suspicions, and gave me a written order on a Bideford barber for a razor, etc. I kindly invited my friends to come and help, and lamented for three miles the burden of compulsory shaving. There were no *ripostes*. There was no ribaldy. But why Stalky and Turkey did not cut their throats experimenting with the apparatus I do not understand.

We will now return to the savage life in which all these prodigious events 'transpired.'

We smoked, of course, but the penalties of discovery were heavy because the Prefects, who were all of the 'Army Class' up for the Sandhurst or Woolrich Preliminary, were allowed under restrictions to smoke pipes. If any of the rank and file were caught smoking, they came up before the Prefects, not on moral grounds, but for usurping the privileges of the Ruling Caste. The classic phrase was: 'You esteem yourself to be a Prefect, do you? *All* right. Come to my study at six, please.' This seemed to work better than religious lectures and even expulsions which some establishments used to deal out for this dread sin.

Oddly enough 'fagging' did not exist, though the name 'fag' was regularly used as a term of contempt and sign of subordination against the Lower School. If one needed a 'varlet' to clean things in a study or run errands, that was a matter of private bargaining in our only currency—food. Sometimes such service gave protection, in the sense that it was distinct cheek to oppress an accredited 'varlet.' I never served thus, owing to my untidyness; but our study entertained one sporadically, and to him we three expounded all housewifely duties. But, as a rule, Turkey would tidy up like the old maid to whom we always compared him.

Games were compulsory unless written excuse were furnished by competent authority. The penalty for wilful shirking was three cuts with a ground ash from the Prefect of Games. One of the most difficult things to explain to some people is that a boy of seventeen or eighteen can thus beat a boy barely a year his junior, and on the heels of the punishment go for a walk with him; neither party bearing malice or pride.

So too in the War of '14 to '18 young gentlemen found it hard to understand that the Adjutant who poured vitriol on their heads at Parade, but was polite and friendly at Mess, was not sucking up to them to make amends for previous rudeness.

Except in the case of two House-masters I do not recall being lectured or preached at on morals or virtue. It is not always expedient to excite a growing youth's religious emotions, because one set of nerves seems to communicate with others, and Heaven knows what mines a 'pi-jaw' may touch off. But there were no doors to our bare windy dormitories, nor any sort of lock on the form-rooms. Our masters, with one exception who lived outside, were unmarried. The school buildings, originally cheap lodging-houses, made one straight bar against a hillside, and the boys circulated up and down in front of it. A penal battalion could not have been more perfectly policed, though we did not realise. Mercifully we knew little outside the immediate burden of the day and the necessity for getting into the Army. I think, then, that when we worked we worked harder than most schools.

My House-master was deeply conscious and cumbered about with many cares of his charges. What he accomplished thereby I know not. His errors sprang from pure and excessive goodness. Me and my companions he always darkly and deeply suspected. Realising this, we little beasts made him sweat, which he did on slight provocation.

My main interest as I grew older was C——, my English and Classics Master, a rowing-man of splendid physique, and a scholar who lived in secret hope of translating Theocritus worthily. He had a violent temper, no disadvantage in handling boys used to direct speech, and a gift of schoolmaster's 'sarcasm' which must have been a relief to him and was certainly a treasure-trove to me. Also he was a good and House-proud House-master. Under him I came to feel that words could be used as weapons, for he did me the honour to talk at me plentifully; and our year-in year-out form-room bicker-ings gave us both something to play with. One learns more from a good scholar in a rage than from a score of lucid and laborious drudges; and to be made the butt of one's companions in full form is no bad preparation for later experiences. I think this 'approach' is now discouraged for fear of hurting the soul of youth, but in essence it is no more than rattling tins or firing squibs under a colt's nose. I remember nothing save satisfaction or envy when C—— broke his precious ointments over my head.

I tried to give a pale rendering of his style when heated in a 'Stalky' tale, 'Regulus,' but I wish I could have presented him as he blazed forth once on the great Cleopatra Ode—the 27th of the Third Book. I had detonated him by a very vile construe of the first few lines. Having slain me, he charged over my corpse and delivered an interpretation of the rest of the Ode unequalled for power and insight. He held even the Army Class breathless.

There must be still masters of the same sincerity; and gramophone records of such good men, on the brink of profanity, struggling with a Latin form, would be more helpful to education than bushels of printed books. C—— taught me to loathe Horace for two years; to forget him for twenty, and then to love him for the rest of my days and through many sleepless nights.

After my second year at school, the tide of writing set in. In my holidays the three ladies listened—it was all I wanted—to anything I had to say. I drew on their books, from *The City of Dreadful Night* which shook to my unformed core, Mrs. Gatty's *Parables from Nature*, which I imitated and thought I was original, and scores of others. There were few atrocities of form or metre that I did not perpetrate and I enjoyed them all.

I discovered, also, that personal and well-pointed limericks on my companions worked well, and I and a red-nosed boy of uncertain temper exploited the idea—not without dust and heat; next, that the metre of *Hiawatha* saved one all bother about rhyme: and that there had been a man called Dante who, living in a small Italian town at general issue with his neighbours, had invented for most of them lively torments in a nine-ringed Hell, where he exhibited them to after-ages. C—— said, 'He must have made himself infernally unpopular.' I combined my authorities.

I bought a fat, American cloth-bound note-book, and set to work on an Inferno, into which I put, under appropriate torture, all my friends and most of the masters. This was really remunerative because one could chant his future doom to a victim walking below the windows of the study which I with my two companions now possessed. Then, 'as rare things will,' my book vanished, and I lost interest in the *Hiawatha* metre.

Tennyson and *Aurora Leigh* came in the way of nature to me in the holidays, and C—— in form once literally threw *Men and Women* at my head. Here I found 'The Bishop orders his Tomb,' 'Love among the Ruins'

and 'Fra Lippo Lippi,' a not too remote—I dare to think—ancestor of
mine.

Swinburne's poems I must have come across first at the Aunt's. He
did not strike my very young mind as 'anything in particular' till I read
Atalanta in Calydon, and one verse of verses which exactly set the time for
my side-stroke when I bathed in the big rollers off the Ridge. As thus:—

> *Who shall* seek—*who shall* bring
> *Who restore us the* day [half roll]
> *When the* dove *dipped her* wing
> *And the* oars *won their* way [other half roll]
> *Where the labouring Symplegades whiten*
> *The Straits of Propontis with spray?* [carry on with the impetus]

If you can time the last line of it to end with a long roller crashing on your
head, the cadence is complete. I even forgave Bret Harte, to whom I owed
many things, for taking that metre in vain in his *Heathen Chinee*. But I
never forgave C—— for bringing the fact to my notice.

Not till years later—talking things over with my 'Uncle Crom'—did I
realise that injustices of this sort were not without intention. 'You needed
a tight hand in those days,' he drawled. 'C—— gave it to you.' 'He did,'
said I, 'and so did H——,' the married master whom the school thoroughly
feared.

'I remember *that*,' Crom answered. 'Yes, that was me too.' This had
been an affair of an Essay—'A Day in the Holidays,' or something of
that nature. C—— had set it but the papers were to be marked by H——.
My essay was of variegated but constant vileness modelled, I fancy, on
holiday readings of a journal called *The Pink 'Un*. Even I had never done
anything worse. Normally H——'s markings would have been sent in to
C—— without comment. On this occasion, however (I was in Latin form
at the time), H—— entered and asked for the floor. C—— yielded it to
him with a grin. H—— then told me off before my delighted companions
in his best style, which was acid and contumelious. He wound up by a few
general remarks about dying as a 'scurrilous journalist.' (I think now that
H—— too may have read *The Pink 'Un*.) The tone, matter, and setting of
his discourse were as brutal as they were meant to be—brutal as the necessary
wrench on the curb that fetches up a too-flippant colt. C—— added a rider
or two after H—— had left.

(But it pleased Allah to afflict H—— in after years. I met him in
charge of a 'mixed' College in New Zealand, where he taught a class of
young ladies Latinity. 'And when they make false quantities, like *you* used
to, they make—eyes at me!' I thought of my chill mornings at Greek Testa-
ment under his ready hand, and pitied him from the bottom of my soul.)

Yes—I must have been 'nursed' with care by Crom and under his
orders. Hence, when he saw I was irretrievably committed to the ink-pot,
his order that I should edit the School Paper and have the run of his

Library Study. Hence, I presume, C——'s similar permission, granted and withdrawn as the fortunes of our private war varied. Hence the Head's idea that I should learn Russian with him (I got as far as some of the cardinal numbers) and, later, *précis*-writing. This latter meant severe compassion of dry-as-dust material, no essential fact to be omitted. The whole was sweetened with reminiscences of the men of Crom's youth, and throughout the low, soft drawl and the smoke of his perpetual Vevey he shed light on the handling of words. Heaven forgive me! I thought these privileges were due to my transcendent personal merits.

Many of us loved the Head for what he had done for us, but I owed him more than all of them put together; and I think I loved him even more than they did. There came a day when he told me that a fortnight after the close of the summer holidays of '82, I would go to India to work on a paper in Lahore, where my parents lived, and would get one hundred silver rupees a month! At term-end he most unjustly devised a prize poem—subject 'The Battle of Assaye' which, there being no competitor, I won in what I conceived was the metre of my latest 'infection'—Joaquin Miller. And when I took the prize-book Trevelyan's *Competition Wallah*, Crom Price said that if I went on I might be heard of again.

I spent my last few days before sailing with the beloved Aunt in the little cottage that the Burne-Jones' had bought for a holiday house at Rottingdean. There I looked across the village green and the horse-pond at a house called 'The Elms' behind a flint wall, and at a church opposite; and—had I known it—at 'The bodies of those to be In the Houses of Death and of Birth.'

III. SEVEN YEARS' HARD

I am poor Brother Lippo by your leave.
You need not clap your torches to my face.

FRA LIPPO LIPPI

SO, AT sixteen years and nine months, but looking four or five years older, and adorned with real whiskers which the scandalised Mother abolished within one hour of beholding, I found myself at Bombay where I was born, moving among sights and smells that made me deliver in the vernacular sentences whose meaning I knew not. Other Indian-born boys have told me how the same thing happened to them.

There were yet three or four days' rail to Lahore, where my people lived. After these, my English years fell away, nor ever, I think, came back in full strength.

That was a joyous home-coming. For—consider!—I had returned to a

Father and Mother of whom I had seen but little since my sixth year. I might have found my Mother 'the sort of woman I don't care for,' as in one terrible case that I know; and my Father intolerable. But the Mother proved more delightful than all my imaginings or memories. My Father was not only a mine of knowledge and help, but a humorous, tolerant, and expert fellow-craftsman. I had my own room in the house; my servant, handed over to me by my father's servant, whose son he was, with the solemnity of a marriage-contract; my own horse, cart, and groom; my own office-hours and direct responsibilities; and—oh joy!—my own office-box, just like my Father's, which he took daily to the Lahore School of Art and Museum. I do not remember the smallest friction in any detail of our lives. We delighted more in each other's society than in that of strangers; and when my sister came out, a little later, our cup was filled to the brim. Not only were we happy, but we knew it.

But the work was heavy. I represented fifty per cent of the 'editorial staff' of the one daily paper of the Punjab—a small sister of the great *Pioneer* at Allahabad under the same proprietorship. And a daily paper comes out every day even though fifty per cent of the staff have fever.

My Chief took me in hand, and for three years or so I loathed him. He had to break me in, and I knew nothing. What he suffered on my account I cannot tell; but the little that I ever acquired of accuracy, the habit of trying at least to verify references, and some knack of sticking to desk-work, I owed wholly to Stephen Wheeler.

I never worked less than ten hours and seldom more than fifteen per diem; and as our paper came out in the evening did not see the midday sun except on Sundays. I had fever too, regular and persistent, to which I added for a while chronic dysentery. Yet I discovered that a man can work with a temperature of 104, even though next day he has to ask the office who wrote the article. Our native Foreman, on the News side, Mian Rukn Din, a Muhammedan gentleman of kind heart and infinite patience, whom I never saw unequal to a situation, was my loyal friend throughout. From the modern point of view I suppose the life was not fit for a dog, but my world was filled with boys, but a few years older than I, who lived utterly alone, and died from typhoid mostly at the regulation age of twenty-two. As regarding ourselves at home, if there were any dying to be done, we four were together. The rest was in the day's work, with love to sweeten all things.

Books, plays, pictures, and amusements, outside what games the cold weather allowed, there were none. Transport was limited to horses and such railways as existed. This meant that one's normal radius of travel would be about six miles in any direction, and—one did not meet new white faces at every six miles. Death was always our near companion. When there was an outbreak of eleven cases of typhoid in our white community of seventy, and professional nurses had not been invented, the men sat up with the men and the women with the women. We lost four of our invalids and thought we had done well. Otherwise, men and women dropped where they stood. Hence our custom of looking up any one who did not appear at our daily gatherings.

The dead of all times were about us—in the vast forgotten Moslem cemeteries round the Station, where one's horse's hoof of a morning might break through to the corpse below; skulls and bones tumbled out of our mud garden walls, and were turned up among the flowers by the Rains; and at every point were tombs of the dead. Our chief picnic rendezvous and some of our public offices had been memorials to desired dead women; and Fort Lahore, where Dunjit Singh's wives lay, was a mausoleum of ghosts.

This was the setting in which my world revolved. Its centre for me—a member at seventeen—was the Punjab Club, where bachelors, for the most part, gathered to eat meals of no merit among men whose merits they knew well. My Chief was married and came there seldom, so it was mine to be told every evening of the faults of that day's issue in very simple language. Our native compositors 'followed copy' without knowing one word of English. Hence glorious and sometimes obscene misprints. Our proof-readers (sometimes we had a brace of them) drank, which was expected; but systematic and prolonged D.T. on their part gave me more than my share of their work. And in that Club and elsewhere I met none except picked men at their definite work—Civilians, Army, Education, Canals, Forestry, Engineering, Irrigation, Railways, Doctors, and Lawyers—samples of each branch and each talking his own shop. It follows then that that 'show of technical knowledge' for which I was blamed later came to me from the horse's mouth, even to boredom.

So soon as my paper could trust me a little, and I had behaved well at routine work, I was sent out, first for local reportings; then to race-meetings which included curious nights in the lottery-tent. (I saw one go up in flame once, when a heated owner hove an oil-lamp at the handicapper on the night the owner was coming up for election at the Club. That was the first and last time I had seen every available black ball expended and members begging for more.) Later I described openings of big bridges and such-like, which meant a night or two with the engineers; floods on railways—more nights in the wet with wretched heads of repair gangs; village festivals and consequent outbreaks of cholera or small-pox; communal riots under the shadow of the Mosque of Wazir Khan, where the patient waiting troops lay in timber-yards or side-alleys till the order came to go in and hit the crowds on the feet with the gun-butt (killing in Civil Administration was then reckoned confession of failure), and the growling, flaring, creed-drunk city would be brought to hand without effusion of blood, or the appearance of any agitated Viceroy; visits of Viceroys to neighbouring Princes on the edge of the great Indian Desert, where a man might have to wash his raw hands and face in soda-water; reviews of Armies expecting to move against Russia next week; receptions of an Afghan Potentate, with whom the

Indian Government wished to stand well (this included a walk into the Khyber, where I was shot at, but without malice, by a rapparee who disapproved of his ruler's foreign policy); murder and divorce trials, and (a really filthy job) an inquiry into the percentage of lepers among the butchers who supplied beef and mutton to the European community of Lahore. (Here I first learned that crude statements of crude facts are not well seen by responsible official authorities.) It was Squeers' method of instruction, but how could I fail to be equipped with more than all I might need? I was saturated with it, and if I tripped over detail, the Club attended to me.

My first bribe was offered to me at the age of nineteen when I was in a Native State where, naturally, one concern of the Administration was to get more guns of honour added to the Ruler's official salute when he visited British India, and even a roving correspondent's good word might be useful. Hence in the basket of fruits (*dali* is its name) laid at my tent door each morning, a five-hundred-rupee note and a Cashmere shawl. As the sender was of high caste I returned the gift at the hands of the camp-sweeper who was not. Upon this my servant, responsible to his father, and mine, for my well-being, said without emotion: 'Till we get home you eat and drink from my hands.' This I did.

On return to work I found my Chief had fever, and I was in sole charge. Among his editorial correspondence was a letter from this Native State setting forth the record during a few days' visit of 'your reporter, a person called Kipling'; who had broken, it seemed, the Decalogue in every detail from rape to theft. I wrote back that as Acting-Editor I had received the complaints and would investigate, but they must expect me to be biassed because I was the person complained of.

I visited the State more than once later, and there was not a cloud on our relations. I had dealt with the insult *more Asiatico*—which *they* understood; the ball had been returned *more Asiatico*—which *I* understood; and the incident had been closed.

My second bribe came when I worked under Stephen Wheeler's successor, Kay Robinson, brother of Phil Robinson who wrote *In My Indian Garden*. With him, thanks to his predecessor having licked me into some shape, my relations were genial. It was the old matter of gun-salutes again; the old machinery of the basket of fruit and shawls and money for us both, but this time left impudently on the office verandah. Kay and I wasted a happy half-hour pricking '*Timeo Danaos et dona ferentes*' into the currency notes, mourned that we could not take the shawls, and let the matter go.

My third and most interesting bribe was when reporting a divorce case in Eurasian society. An immense brown woman penned me in a corner and offered 'if I would but keep her name out of it' to give me most intimate details, which she began at once to do. I demanded her name before bargaining. 'Oah! I am the Respondent. Thatt is why I ask you.' It is hard to report some dramas without Ophelias if not Hamlets. But I was repaid for her anger when Counsel asked her if she had ever expressed a desire to dance on her husband's grave. Till then she had denied everything. 'Yess,' she hissed, 'and I jolly-damn-well *would* too.'

A soldier of my acquaintance had been sentenced to life-imprisonment for a murder which, on evidence not before the court, seemed to me rather justified. I saw him later in Lahore gaol at work on some complicated arrangement of nibs with different coloured inks, stuck into a sort of loom which, drawn over paper, gave the ruling for the blank forms of financial statements. It seemed wickedly monotonous. But the spirit of man is un-defeatable. 'If I made a mistake of an eighth of an inch in spacing these lines, I'd throw out *all* the accounts of the Upper Punjab,' said he.

As to our reading public, they were at the least as well educated as fifty per cent of our 'staff'; and by force of their lives could not be stampeded or much 'thrilled.' Double headlines we had never heard of, nor special type, and I fear that the amount of 'white' in the newspapers to-day would have struck us as common cheating. Yet the stuff we dealt in would have furnished modern journals of enterprise with almost daily sensations.

My legitimate office-work was sub-editing, which meant eternal cuttings down of unwieldy contributions—such as discourses on abstruse questions of Revenue and Assessment from a great and wise Civilian who wrote the vilest hand that even our compositors ever saw; literary articles about Milton. (And how was I to know that the writer was a relative of one of our pro-prietors, who thought our paper existed to air his theories?) Here Crom Price's training in *précis*-work helped me to get swiftly at what meat there might be in the disorderly messes. There were newspaper exchanges from Egypt to Hong-Kong to be skimmed nearly every morning and, once a week, the English papers on which one drew in time of need; local corre-spondence from out-stations to vet for possible libels in their innocent allusions; 'spoofing'-letters from Subalterns to be guarded against (twice I was trapped here); always, of course, the filing of cables, and woe betide an error then! I took them down from the telephone—a primitive and mysterious power whose native operator broke every word into monosyl-lables. One cut-and-come-again affliction was an accursed Muscovite paper, the *Novoie Vremya*, written in French which, for weeks and weeks, pub-lished the war diaries of Alikhanoff, a Russian General then harrying the Central Russian Khanates. He gave the name of every camp he halted at, and regularly reported that his troops warmed themselves at fires of *sax-aul*, which I suppose is perhaps sage-brush. A week after I had translated the last of the series every remembrance of it passed from my normal memory.

Ten or twelve years later, I fell sick in New York and passed through a long delirium which, by ill-chance, I remembered when I returned to life. At one stage of it I led an enormous force of cavalry mounted on red horses with brand-new leather saddles, under the glare of a green moon, across steppes so vast that they revealed the very curve of earth. We would halt at one of the camps named by Alikhanoff in his diary (I would see the name of it heaving up over the edge of the planet), where we warmed ourselves at fires of *sax-aul*, and where, scorched on one side and frozen on the other, I sat till my infernal squadrons went on again to the next fore-known halt; and so through the list.

In 1885 a Liberal Government had come into power at Home and was acting on liberal 'principle,' which so far as I have observed ends not seldom in bloodshed. Just then, it was a matter of principle that Native Judges should try white women. Native in this case meant overwhelmingly Hindu; and the Hindu's idea of women is not lofty. No one had asked for any such measure—least of all the Judiciary concerned. But principle is principle, though the streets swim. The European community were much annoyed. They went to the extremity of revolt—that is to say even the officials of the Service and their wives very often would not attend the functions and levées of the then Viceroy, a circular and bewildered recluse of religious tendencies. A pleasant English gentleman called C. P. Ilbert had been imported to father and god-father the Bill. I think he, too, was a little bewildered. Our paper, like most of the European Press, began with stern disapproval of the measure, and, I fancy, published much comment and correspondence which would now be called 'disloyal.'

One evening while putting the paper to bed, I looked as usual over the leader. It was the sort of false-balanced, semi-judicial stuff that some English journals wrote about the Indian White Paper from 1932 to '34, and like them it furnished a barely disguised exposition of the Government's high ideals. In after-life one got to know that touch better, but it astonished me at the time, and I asked my Chief what it all meant. He replied, as I should have done in his place: 'None of your dam' business,' and, being married, went to his home. I repaired to the Club which, remember, was the whole of my outside world.

As I entered the long, shabby dining-room where we all sat at one table, everyone hissed. I was innocent enough to ask: 'What's the joke? Who are they hissing?' 'You,' said the man at my side. 'Your dam' rag has ratted over the Bill.'

It is not pleasant to sit still when one is twenty while all your universe hisses you. Then uprose a Captain, our Adjutant of Volunteers, and said: 'Stop that! The boy's only doing what he's paid to do.' The demonstration tailed off, but I had seen a great light. The Adjutant was entirely correct. I was a hireling, paid to do what I was paid to do, and—I did not relish the idea. Someone said kindly: 'You damned young ass! Don't you know that your paper has the Government printing-contract? I *did* know it, but I had never before put two and two together.

A few months later one of my two chief proprietors received the decoration that made him a Knight. Then I began to take much interest in certain smooth Civilians, who had seen good in the Government measure and had somehow been shifted out of the heat to billets in Simla. I followed under shrewd guidance, often native, the many pretty ways by which a

Government can put veiled pressure on its employees in a land where every circumstance *and* relation of a man's life is public property. So, when the great and epoch-making India Bill turned up fifty years later, I felt as one re-treading the tortuous by-ways of his youth. One recognised the very phrases and assurances of the old days still doing good work, and waited, as in a dream, for the very slightly altered formulas in which those who were parting with their convictions, excused themselves. Thus: 'I may act as a brake, you know. At any rate I'm keeping a more extreme man out of the game.' 'There's no sense running counter to the inevitable,'—and all the other Devil-provided camouflage for the sinner-who-faces-both-ways.

In '85 I was made a Freemason by dispensation (Lodge Hope and Perseverance 782 E.C.) being under age, because the Lodge hoped for a good Secretary. They did not get him, but I helped, and got the Father to advise, in decorating the bare walls of the Masonic Hall with hangings after the prescription of Solomon's Temple. Here I met Muslims, Hindus, Sikhs, members of the Araya and Brahmo Samaj, and a Jew tyler, who was priest and butcher to his little community in the city. So yet another world opened to me which I needed.

My Mother and Sister would go up to the Hills for the hot weather, and in due course my Father too. My own holiday came when I could be spared. Thus I often lived alone in the big house, where I commanded by choice native food, as less revolting than meat-cookery, and so added indigestion to my more intimate possessions.

In those months—mid-April to mid-October—one took up one's bed and walked about with it from room to room, seeking for less heated air; or slept on the flat roof with the waterman to throw half-skinfuls of water on one's parched carcase. This brought on fever but saved heat-stroke.

Often the night got into my head as it had done in the boarding-house in the Brompton Road, and I would wander till dawn in all manner of odd places—liquor-shops, gambling and opium-dens, which are not a bit mysterious, wayside entertainments such as puppet-shows, native dances; or in and about the narrow gullies under the Mosque of Wazir Khan for the sheer sake of looking. Sometimes, the Police would challenge, but I knew most of their officers, and many folk in some quarters knew me for the son of my Father, which in the East more than anywhere else is useful. Otherwise, the word 'Newspaper' sufficed; though I did not supply my paper with many accounts of these prowls. One would come home, just as the light broke, in some night-hawk of a hired carriage which stank of hookah-fumes, jasmine-flowers, and sandal wood; and if the driver were moved to talk, he told one a good deal. Much of real Indian life goes on in the hot weather nights. That is why the native staff of the offices are not much use next morning. All native offices aestivate from May at least till September. Files and correspondence are then as a matter of course pitched unopened into corners, to be written up or faked when the weather gets cooler. But the English who go Home on leave, having imposed the set hours of a northern working day upon the children of children, are surprised that India does not work as they do. This is one of the reasons why autonomous India will be interesting.

And there were 'wet' nights too at the Club or one Mess, when a table-full of boys, half-crazed with discomfort, but with just sense enough to stick to beer and bones which seldom betray, tried to rejoice and somehow succeeded. I remember one night when we ate tinned haggis with cholera in the cantonments 'to see what would happen,' and another when a savage stallion in harness was presented with a very hot leg of roast mutton, as he snapped. Theoretically this is a cure for biting, but it only made him more of a cannibal.

I got to meet the soldiery of those days in visits to Fort Lahore and, in a less degree, at Mian Mir Cantonments. My first and best beloved Battalion was the 2nd Fifth Fusiliers, with whom I dined in awed silence a few weeks after I came out. When they left I took up with their successors, the 30th East Lancashire, another north-country regiment; and, last, with the 31st East Surrey—a London recruited confederacy of skilful dog-stealers, some of them my good and loyal friends. There were ghostly dinners too with Subalterns in charge of the Infantry Detachment at Fort Lahore, where, all among marble-inlaid, empty apartments of dead Queens, or under the domes of old tombs, meals began with the regulation thirty grains of quinine in the sherry, and ended—as Allah pleased!

I am, by the way, one of the few civilians who have turned out a Quarter-Guard of Her Majesty's troops. It was on a chill winter morn, about 2 A.M. at the Fort, and though I suppose I had been given the countersign on my departure from the Mess, I forgot it ere I reached the Main Guard, and when challenged announced myself spaciously as 'Visiting Rounds.' When the men had clattered out I asked the Sergeant if he had ever seen a finer collection of scoundrels. That cost me beer by the gallon, but it was worth it.

Having no position to consider, and my trade enforcing it, I could move at will in the fourth dimension. I came to realise the bare horrors of the private's life, and the unnecessary torments he endured on account of the Christian doctrine which lays down that 'the wages of sin is death.' It was counted impious that bazaar prostitutes should be inspected; or that the men should be taught elementary precautions in their dealings with them. This official virtue cost our Army in India nine thousand expensive white men a year always laid up from venereal disease. Visits to Lock Hospitals made me desire, as earnestly as I do to-day, that I might have six hundred priests—Bishops of the Establishment for choice—to handle for six months precisely as the soldiers of my youth were handled.

Heavens knows the men died fast enough from typhoid, which seemed to have something to do with water, but we were not sure; or from cholera, which was manifestly a breath of the Devil that could kill all on one side of a barrack-room and spare the others; from seasonal fever; or from what was described as 'blood-poisoning.'

Lord Roberts, at that time Commander-in-Chief in India, who knew my people, was interested in the men, and—I had by then written one or two stories about soldiers—the proudest moment of my young life was when I rode up Simla Mall beside him on his usual explosive red Arab, while he asked me what the men thought about their accommodation, entertainment-rooms and the like. I told him, and he thanked me as gravely as though I had been a full Colonel.

My month's leave at Simla, or whatever Hill Station my people went to, was pure joy—every golden hour counted. It began in heat and discom-fort, by rail and road. It ended in the cool evening, with a wood fire in one's bedroom, and next morn—thirty more of them ahead!—the early cup of tea, the Mother who brought it in, and the long talks of us all together again. One had leisure to work, too, at whatever play-work was in one's head, and that was usually full.

Simla was another new world. There the Hierarchy lived, and one saw and heard the machinery of administration stripped bare. There were the Heads of the Viceregal and Military staffs and their Aides-de-Camp; and playing whist with Great Ones, who gave him special news, was the Cor-respondent of our big sister-paper the *Pioneer*, then a power in the land.

The dates, but not the pictures, of those holidays are blurred. At one time our little world was full of the aftermaths of Theosophy as taught by Madame Blavatsky to her devotees. My Father knew the lady and, with her, would discuss wholly secular subjects; she being, he told me, one of the most interesting and unscrupulous impostors he had ever met. This, with his experience, was a high compliment. I was not so fortunate, but came across queer, bewildered, old people, who lived in an atmosphere of 'mani-festations' running about their houses. But the earliest days of Theosophy devastated the *Pioneer*, whose Editor became a devout believer, and used the paper for propaganda to an extent which got on the nerves not only of the public but of a proof-reader, who at last moment salted an im-passioned leader on the subject with, in brackets: '*What do you bet this is a dam' lie?*' The Editor was most untheosophically angry!

On one of my Simla leaves—I had been ill with dysentery again—I was sent off for rest along the Himalaya-Thibet road in the company of an invalid officer and his wife. My equipment was my servant—he from whose hands I had fed in the Native State before-mentioned; Dorothea Darbishoff, *alias* Dolly Bobs, a temperamental she-pony; and four baggage-coolies who were recruited and changed at each stage. I knew the edge of the great Hills both from Simla and Dalhousie, but had never marched any distance into them. They were to me a revelation of 'all might, majesty, dominion, and power, henceforth and for ever,' in colour, form, and substance inde-scribable. A little of what I realised then came back to me in *Kim*.

On the day I turned back for Simla—my companions were going

further—my servant embroiled himself with a new quartette of coolies and managed to cut the eye of one of them. I was a few score miles from the nearest white man, and did not wish to be hailed before any little Hill Rajah, knowing as I did that the coolies would unitedly swear that I had directed the outrage. I therefore paid blood-money, and strategically withdrew—on foot for the most part because Dolly Bobs objected to every sight and most of the smells of the landscape. I had to keep the coolies who, like the politicians, would not stay put, in front of me on the six-foot-wide track, and, as is ever the case when one is in difficulties, it set in to rain. My urgent business was to make my first three days' march in one—a matter of thirty odd miles. My coolies wanted to shy off to their village and spend their ill-gotten silver. On me developed the heart-breaking job of shepherding a retreat. I do not think my mileage that day could have been much less than forty miles of sheer up-hill and down-dale slogging. But it did me great good, and enabled me to put away bottles of strong Army beer at the wet evening's end in the resthouse. On our last day, a thunderstorm, which had been at work a few thousand feet below us, rose to the level of the ridge we were crossing and exploded in our midst. We were all flung on our faces, and when I was able to see again I observed the half of a well-grown pine, as neatly split lengthwise as a match by a penknife, in the act of hirpling down the steep hillside by itself. The thunder drowned everything, so that it seemed to be posturing in dumb show, and when it began to hop—horrible vertical hops—the effect was of pure D.T. My coolies, however, who had had the tale of my misdeeds from their predecessors, argued that if the local Gods missed such a sitting shot as I had given them, I could not be altogether unlucky.

It was on this trip that I saw a happy family of four bears out for a walk together, all talking at the tops of their voices; and also—the sun on his wings, a thousand feet below me—I stared long at a wheeling eagle, himself thousands of feet above the map-like valley he was quartering.

On my return I handed my servant over to his father, who dealt faithfully with him for having imperilled my Father's son. But what I did not tell him was that my servant, a Punjabi Muslim, had in his first panic embraced the feet of the injured hill-coolie, a heathen, and begged him to 'show mercy.' A servant, precisely because he is a servant, has his *izzat*—his honour—or, as the Chinese say, his 'face.' Save that, and he is yours. One should never rate one's man before others; nor, if he knows that you know the implication of the words that you are using on him, should you ever use certain words and phrases. But to a young man raw from England, or to an old one in whose service one has grown grey, anything is permitted. In the first case: 'He is a youngster. He slangs as his girl has taught him,' and the man keeps his countenance even though his master's worst words are inflected woman-fashion. In the second case, the aged servitor and deputy-conscience says: 'It is naught. We were young men together. Ah! you should have heard him then!'

The reward for this very small consideration is service of a kind that one accepted as a matter of course—till one was without it. My man would go monthly to the local Bank and draw my pay in coined rupees, which he would carry home raw in his waist-band, as the whole bazaar knew, and decant into an old wardrobe, whence I would draw for my needs till there remained no more.

Yet, it was necessary to his professional honour that he should present me monthly a list of petty disbursements on my personal behalf—such as oil for the buggy-lamps, bootlaces, thread for darning my socks, buttons replaced and the like—all written out in bazaar-English by the letter-writer at the corner of the road. The total rose, of course, with my pay, and on each rupee of this bill my man took the commission of the East, say one-sixteenth or perhaps one-tenth of each rupee.

For the rest, till I was in my twenty-fourth year, I no more dreamed of dressing myself than I did of shutting an inner door or—I was going to say turning a key in a lock. But we had no locks. I gave myself indeed the trouble of stepping into the garments that were held out to me after my bath, and out of them as I was assisted to do. And—luxury of which I dream still—I was shaved before I was awake!

One must set these things against the taste of fever in one's mouth, and the buzz of quinine in one's ears; the temper frayed by heat to breaking-point but for sanity's sake held back from the break; the descending darkness of intolerable dusks; and the less supportable dawns of fierce, stale heat through half of the year.

When my people were at the Hills and I was alone, my Father's butler took command. One peril of solitary life is going to seed in details of living. As our numbers at the Club shrank between April and mid-September, men grew careless, till at last our conscience-stricken Secretary, himself an offender, would fetch us up with a jerk, and forbid us dining in little more than singlet and riding breeches.

This temptation was stronger in one's own house, though one knew if one broke the ritual of dressing for the last meal one was parting with a sheet-anchor. (Young gentlemen of larger views to-day consider this 'dress-for-dinner' business as an affectation ranking with 'the old school tie.' I would give some months' pay for the privilege of enlightening them.) Here the butler would take charge. 'For the honour of the house there must be a dinner. It is long since the Sahib has bidden friends to eat.' I would protest like a fretful child. He would reply: 'Except for the names of the Sahibs to be invited all things are on *my* head.' So one dug up four or five companions in discomfort; the pitiful, scorched marigold blooms would appear on the table and, to a full accompaniment of glass, silver, and napery, the ritual would be worked through, and the butler's honour satisfied for a while.

At the Club, sudden causeless hates flared up between friends and died down like straw fires; old grievances were recalled and brooded over aloud; the complaint-book bristled with accusations and inventions. All of which came to nothing when the first Rains fell, and after a three days' siege of creeping and crawling things, whose bodies stopped our billiards and almost put out the lamps they sizzled in, life picked up in the blessed cool.

But it was a strange life. Once, suddenly, in the Club ante-room a man asked a neighbour to pass him the newspaper. 'Get it yourself,' was the hot-weather answer. The man rose but on his way to the table dropped and writhed in the first grip of cholera. He was carried to his quarters, the Doctor came, and for three days he went through all the stages of the disease even to the characteristic baring of discoloured gums. Then he returned to life and, on being condoled with, said: 'I remember getting up to get the paper, but after that, give you my word, I don't remember a thing till I heard Lawrie say that I was coming out of it.' I have heard since that oblivion is some-times vouchsafed.

Though I was spared the worst horrors, thanks to the pressure of work, a capacity for being able to read, and the pleasure of writing what my head was filled with, I felt each succeeding hot weather more and more, and cowered in my soul as it returned.

This is fit place for a 'pivot' experience to be set side by side with the affair of the Adjutant of Volunteers at the Club. It happened one hot-weather evening, in '86 or thereabouts, when I felt that I had come to the edge of all endurance. As I entered my empty house in the dusk there was no more in me except the horror of a great darkness, that I must have been fighting for some days. I came through that darkness alive, but how I do not know. Late at night I picked up a book by Walter Besant which was called *All in a Garden Fair*. It dealt with a young man who desired to write; who came to realise the possibilities of common things seen, and who eventually suc-ceeded in his desire. What its merits may be from to-day's 'literary' stand-point I do not know. But I *do* know that that book was my salvation in sore personal need, and with the reading and re-reading it became to me a revela-tion, a hope and strength. I was certainly, I argued, as well equipped as the hero and—and—after all, there was no need for me to stay here for ever. I could go away and measure myself against the doorsills of London as soon as I had money. Therefore I would begin to save money, for I perceived there was absolutely no reason outside myself why I should not do exactly what to me seemed good. For proof of my revelation I did, sporadically but sincerely, try to save money, and I built up in my head—always with the book to fall back upon—a dream of the future that sustained me. To Walter Besant singly and solely do I owe this—as I told him when we met, and he laughed, rolled in his chair, and seemed pleased.

In the joyous reign of Kay Robinson, my second Chief, our paper changed its shape and type. This took up for a week or so all hours of the twenty-four and cost me a breakdown due to lack of sleep. But we two were proud of the results. Our new feature was a daily 'turnover'—same as the little pink *Globe* at Home—of one column and a quarter. Naturally, the 'office' had to supply most of them and once more I was forced to 'write short.'

All the queer outside world would drop into our workshop sooner or later—say a Captain just cashiered for horrible drunkenness, who reported his fall with a wry, appealing face, and then—disappeared. Or a man old enough to be my father, on the edge of tears because he had been overpassed for Honours in the *Gazette*. Or three troopers of the Ninth Lancers, one of whom was an old schoolmate of mine who became a General with an expedition of his own in West Africa in the Great War. The other two also were gentlemen-rankers who rose to high commands. One met men going up and down the ladder in every shape of misery and success.

There was a night at the Club when some silly idiot found a half-dead viper and brought it to dinner in a pickle-bottle. One man of the company kept messing about with the furious little beast on the table-cloth till he had to be warned to take his hands away. A few weeks after, some of us realised it would have been better had he accomplished what had been in his foreboding mind that night.

But the cold weather brought ample amends. The family were together again and—except for my Mother's ukase against her men bringing bound volumes of the *Illustrated London News* to meals (a survival of hot-weather savagery)—all was bliss. So, in the cold weather of '85 we four made up a Christmas annual called *Quartette*, which pleased us a great deal and attracted a certain amount of attention. (Later, much later, it became a 'collector's piece' in the U.S. book-market, and to that extent smudged the happy memories of its birth.) In '85 I began a series of tales in the *Civil and Military Gazette* which were called *Plain Tales from the Hills*. They came in when and as padding was needed. In '86 also I published a collection of newspaper verses on Anglo-Indian life, called *Departmental Ditties*, which, dealing with things known and suffered by many people, were well received. I had been allowed, further, to send stuff that we, editorially, had no use for, to far-off Calcutta papers, such as the *Indigo Planters' Gazette*, and elsewhere. These things were making for me the beginnings of a name even unto Bengal.

But mark how discreetly the cards were being dealt me. Up till '87 my performances had been veiled in the decent obscurity of the far end of an outlying province, among a specialised community, who did not interest any but themselves. I was like a young horse entered for small, up-country events where I could get used to noise and crowds, fall about till I found my feet, and learn to keep my head with the hoofs drumming behind me. Better than all, the pace of my office work was 'too good to inquire,' and its nature—that I should realise all sorts and conditions of men and make others realise them —gave me no time to 'realise' myself.

Here was my modest notion of my own position at the end of my five years' Viceroyalty on the little *Civil and Military Gazette*. I was still fifty per cent of the editorial staff, though for a while I rose to have a man under me. But—just are the Gods!—that varlet was 'literary' and must needs write

Elia-like 'turnovers' instead of sticking to the legitimate! Any fool, I knew to my sorrow, could write. My job was to sub-edit him or her into some sort of shape. Any other fool could review; (I myself on urgent call have reviewed the later works of a writer called Browning, and what my Father said about *that* was unpublishable). Reporting was a minor 'feature' although we did not use that word. I myself *qua* reporter could turn in stuff one day and *qua* sub-editor knock it remorselessly into cocked hats the next. The difference, then, between me and the vulgar herd who 'write for papers' was, as I saw it, the gulf that divides the beneficed clergyman from ladies and gentlemen who contribute pumpkins and dahlias to Harvest Festival decorations. To say that I magnified my office is to understate. But this may have saved me from magnifying myself beyond decency.

In '87 orders came for me to serve on the *Pioneer*, our big sister-paper at Allahabad, hundreds of miles to the southward, where I should be one of four at least and a new boy at a big school.

But the North-West Provinces, as they were then, being largely Hindu, were strange 'air and water' to me. My life had lain among Muslims, and a man leans one way or other according to his first service. The large, well-appointed Club, where Poker had just driven out Whist and men gambled seriously, was full of large-bore officials, and of a respectability all new. The Fort where troops were quartered had its points; but one bastion jutted out into a most holy river. Therefore, partially burned corpses made such a habit of stranding just below the Subalterns' quarters that a special expert was entertained to pole them off and onward. In Fort Lahore we dealt in nothing worse than ghosts.

Moreover, the *Pioneer* lived under the eye of its chief proprietor, who spent several months of each year in his bungalow over the way. It is true that I owed him my chance in life, but when one has been second in command of even a third-class cruiser, one does not care to have one's Admiral permanently moored at a cable's length. His love for his paper, which his single genius and ability had largely created, led him sometimes to 'give the boys a hand.' On those hectic days (for he added and subtracted to the last minute) we were relieved when the issue caught the down-country mail.

But he was patient with me, as were the others, and through him again I got a wider field for 'outside stuff.' There was to be a weekly edition of the *Pioneer* for Home consumption. Would I edit it, additional to ordinary work? Would I not? There would be fiction—syndicated serial-matter bought by the running foot from agencies at home. That would fill one whole big page. The 'sight of means to do ill deeds' had the usual effect. Why buy Bret Harte, I asked, when I was prepared to supply home-grown fiction on the hoof? And I did.

My editing of the *Weekly* may have been a shade casual—it was but a re-hash of news and views after all. My head was full of, to me, infinitely more important material. Henceforth no mere twelve-hundred Plain Tales jammed into rigid frames, but three- or five-thousand word-cartoons once a week. So did young Lippo Lippi, whose child I was, look on the blank walls of his monastery when he was bidden decorate them! ' 'Twas ask and have, Choose for more's ready,' with a vengeance.

I fancy my change of surroundings and outlook precipitated the rush. At the beginning of it I had an experience which, in my innocence, I mistook for the genuine motions of my Daemon. I must have been loaded more heavily than I realised with 'Gyp,' for there came to me in scenes as stereoscopically clear as those in the crystal an Anglo-Indian *Autour du Mariage*. My pen took charge and I, greatly admiring, watched it write for me far into the nights. The result I christened *The Story of the Gadsbys*, and when it first appeared in England I was complimented on my 'knowledge of the world.' After my indecent immaturity came to light, I heard less of these gifts. Yet, as the Father said loyally: 'It wasn't *all* so dam' bad, Ruddy.'

At any rate it went into the *Weekly*, together with soldier tales, Indian tales, and tales of the opposite sex. There was one of this last which, because of a doubt, I handed up to the Mother, who abolished it and wrote me: *Never you do that again*. But I did and managed to pull off, not unhandily, a tale called 'A Wayside Comedy,' where I worked hard for a certain 'economy of implication,' and in one phrase of less than a dozen words believed I had succeeded. More than forty years later a Frenchman, browsing about some of my old work, quoted this phrase as the *clou* of the tale and the key to its method. It was a belated 'workshop compliment' that I appreciated. Thus, then, I made my own experiments in the weights, colours, perfumes, and attributes of words in relation to other words, either as read aloud so that they may hold the ear, or, scattered over the page, draw the eye. There is no line of my verse or prose which has not been mouthed till the tongue has made all smooth, and memory, after many recitals, has mechanically skipped the grosser superfluities.

These things occupied and contented me, but—outside of them—I felt that I did not quite fit the *Pioneer's* scheme of things and that my superiors were of the same opinion. My work on the *Weekly* was not legitimate journalism. My flippancy in handling what I was trusted with was not well seen by the Government or the departmental officialism, on which the *Pioneer* rightly depended for advance and private news, gathered in at Simla or Calcutta by our most important Chief Correspondent. I fancy my owners thought me safer on the road than in my chair; for they sent me out to look at Native State mines, mills, factories and the like. Here I think they were entirely justified. My proprietor at Allahabad has his own game to play (it brought him his well-deserved knighthood in due course) and, to some extent, my vagaries might have embarrassed him. One, I know, did. The *Pioneer* editorially, but cautiously as a terrier drawing up to a porcupine, had hinted that some of Lord Roberts's military appointments at that time verged on nepotism. It was a regretful and well-balanced allocution. My rhymed comment (and why my Chief passed it I know not!) said just the same thing, but not quite so augustly. All I remember of it are the last two flagrant lines:

> And if the *Pioneer* is wrath
> Oh Lord, *what must* you *be!*

I don't think Lord Roberts was pleased with it, but I know he was not half so annoyed as my Chief Proprietor.

On my side I was ripe for change and, thanks always to *All in a Garden Fair*, had a notion now of where I was heading. My absorption in the *Pioneer Weekly* stories, which I wanted to finish, had put my plans to the back of my head, but when I came out of that furious spell of work towards the end of '88 I rearranged myself. I wanted money for the future. I counted my assets. They came to one book of verse; one ditto prose; and—thanks to the *Pioneer's* permission—a set of six small paper-backed railway bookstall volumes embodying most of my tales in the *Weekly*—copyright of which the *Pioneer* might well have claimed. The man who then controlled the Indian railway bookstalls came of an imaginative race, used to taking chances. I sold him the six paper-backed books for £200 and a small royalty. *Plain Tales from the Hills* I sold for £50, and I forget how much the same publisher gave me for *Departmental Ditties*. (This was the first and last time I ever dealt direct with publishers.)

Fortified with this wealth, and six months' pay in lieu of notice, I left India for England by way of the Far East and the United States, after six and a half years of hard work and a reasonable amount of sickness. My Godspeed came from the managing director, a gentleman of sound commercial instincts, who had never concealed his belief that I was grossly overpaid, and who, when he paid me my last wages, said: 'Take it from me, you'll never be worth more than four hundred rupees a month to anyone.' Common pride bids me tell that at that time I was drawing seven hundred a month.

Accounts were squared between us curiously soon. When my notoriety fell upon me, there was a demand for my old proofs, signed and unsigned stuff not included in my books, and a general turning out of refuse-bins for private publication and sale. This upset my hopes of editing my books decently and responsibly, and wrought general confusion. But I was told later that the *Pioneer* had made as much out of its share in this remnant-traffic as it had paid me in wages since I first landed. (Which shows how one cannot get ahead of gentlemen of sound commercial instincts.)

Yet a man must needs love anything that he has worked and suffered under. When, at long last, the *Pioneer*—India's greatest and most important paper which used to pay twenty-seven per cent to its shareholders—fell on evil days and, after being bedevilled and bewitched, was sold to a syndicate, and I received a notification beginning: 'We think you may be interested to know that,' etc., I felt curiously alone and unsponsored. But my first mistress and most true love, the little *Civil and Military Gazette* weathered the storm. Even if I wrote them, these lines are true:—

> Try as he will, no man breaks wholly loose
> From his first love, no matter who she be.

> Oh, was there ever sailor free to choose,
>   That didn't settle somewhere near the sea?

> Parsons in pulpits, tax-payers in pews,
>   Kings on your thrones, you know as well as me,
> We've only one virginity to lose,
>   And where we lost it there our hearts will be!

And, besides, there is, or was, a tablet in my old Lahore office asserting that here I 'worked.' And Allah knows that is true also!

IV. THE INTERREGNUM

> The youth who daily further from the East
> Must travel . . .
>
> WORDSWORTH

  AND, in the autumn of '89, I stepped into a sort of waking dream when I took, as a matter of course, the fantastic cards that Fate was pleased to deal me.

The ancient landmarks of my boyhood still stood. There were the beloved Aunt and Uncle, the little house of the Three Old Ladies, and in one corner of it the quiet figure by the fireplace composedly writing her next novel on her knee. It was at the quietest of tea-parties, in this circle, that I first met Mary Kingsley, the bravest woman of all my knowledge. We talked a good deal over the cups, and more while walking home afterwards—she of West African cannibals and the like. At last, the world forgetting, I said: 'Come up to my rooms and we'll talk it out there.' She agreed, as a man would, then suddenly remembering said: 'Oh, I forgot I was a woman. 'Fraid I mustn't.' So I realised that my world was all to explore again.

A few—a very few—people in it had died, but no one expected to do so for another twenty years. White women stood and waited on one behind one's chair. It was all whirlingly outside my comprehension.

But my small stock-in-trade of books had become known in certain quarters; and there was an evident demand for my stuff. I do not recall that I stirred a hand to help myself. Things happened to me. I went, by invitation, to Mowbray Morris the editor of *Macmillan's Magazine*, who asked me how old I was and, when I told him I hoped to be twenty-four at the end of the year, said: 'Good God!' He took from me an Indian tale and some verses, which latter he wisely edited a little. They were both published in the same number of the *Magazine*—one signed by my name and the other 'Yussuf.' All of this confirmed the feeling (which has come back at intervals through my life), 'Lord ha' mercy on me, this is none of I.'

Then more tales were asked for, and the editor of the St. James's Gazette wanted stray articles, signed and unsigned. My 'turnover' training on the Civil and Military made this easy for me, and somehow I felt easier with a daily paper under my right elbow.

About this time was an interview in a weekly paper, where I felt myself rather on the wrong side of the counter and that I ought to be questioning my questioner. Shortly after, that same weekly made me a proposition which I could not see my way to accept, and then announced that I was 'feeling my oats,' of which, it was careful to point out, it had given me my first sieveful. Since, at that time, I was overwhelmed, not to say scared, by the amazing luck that had come to me, the pronouncement gave me confidence. If that was how I struck the external world—good! For naturally I considered the whole universe was acutely interested in me only—just as a man who strays into a skirmish is persuaded he is the pivot of the action.

Meantime, I had found me quarters in Villiers Street, Strand, which forty-six years ago was primitive and passionate in its habits and population. My rooms were small, not over-clean or well-kept, but from my desk I could look out of my window through the fan-light of Gatti's Music-Hall entrance, across the street, almost on to its stage. The Charing Cross trains rumbled through my dreams on one side, the boom of the Strand on the other, while, before my windows, Father Thames under the Shot Tower walked up and down with his traffic.

At the outset I had so muddled and mismanaged my affairs that, for a while, I found myself with some money owing me for work done, but no funds in hand. People who ask for money, however justifiably, have it remembered against them. The beloved Aunt, or any one of the Three Old Ladies, would have given to me without question; but that seemed too like confessing failure at the outset. My rent was paid; I had my dress-suit; I had nothing to pawn save a collection of unmarked shirts picked up in all the ports; so I made shift to manage on what small cash I had in pocket.

My rooms were above an establishment of Harris the Sausage King who, for tuppence, gave as much sausage and mash as would carry one from breakfast to dinner when one dined with nice people who did not eat sausage for a living. Another tuppence found me a filling supper. The excellent tobacco of those days was, unless you sank to threepenny 'Shag' or soared to sixpenny 'Turkish,' tuppence the half-ounce: and fourpence, which included a pewter of beer or porter, was the price of admission to Gatti's.

It was here, in the company of an elderly but upright barmaid from a pub near by, that I listened to the observed and compelling songs of the Lion and Mammoth Comiques, and the shriller strains—but equally 'observed'—of the Bessies and Bellas, whom I could hear arguing beneath my window with their cab-drivers, as they sped from Hall to Hall. One lady sometimes delighted us with viva-voce versions of—'what 'as just 'appened to me outside 'ere, if you'll believe it.' Then she would plunge into brilliant improvisations. Oh, we believed! Many of us had, perhaps, taken part in the tail of that argument at the doors, ere she stormed in.

Those monologues I could never hope to rival, but the smoke, the roar, and the good-fellowship of relaxed humanity at Gatti's 'set' the scheme for a certain sort of song. The Private Soldier in India I thought I knew fairly well. His English brother (in the Guards mostly) sat and sang at my elbow any night I chose; and, for Greek chorus, I had the comments of my barmaid —deeply and dispassionately versed in all knowledge of evil as she had watched it across the zinc she was always swabbing off. (Hence, some years later, verses called 'Mary, pity Women,' based on what she told me about 'a friend o' mine 'oo was mistook in 'er man.') The outcome was the first of some verses called *Barrack-Room Ballads* which I showed to Henley of the *Scots*, later *National Observer*, who wanted more; and I became for a while one of the happy company who used to gather in a little restaurant off Leicester Square and regulate all literature till all hours of the morning.

I had the greatest admiration for Henley's verse and prose and, if such things be merchandise in the next world, will cheerfully sell a large proportion of what I have written for a single meditation—illumination—inspiration or what you please—that he wrote on the *Arabian Nights* in a tiny book of Essays and Reviews.

As regards his free verse I—plus some Chianti—once put forward the old notion that free verse was like fishing with barbless hooks. Henley replied volcanically. It was, said he, 'the cadences that did it.' That was true; but he alone, to my mind, could handle them aright, being a Master Craftsman who had paid for his apprenticeship.

Henley's demerits were, of course, explained to the world by loving friends after his death. I had the fortune to know him only as kind, generous, and a jewel of an editor, with the gift of fetching the very best out of his cattle, with words that would astonish oxen. He had, further, an organic loathing of Mr. Gladstone and all Liberalism. A Government Commission of Enquiry was sitting in those days on some unusually blatant traffic in murder among the Irish Land Leaguers; and had white-washed the whole crowd. Whereupon, I wrote some impolite verses called 'Cleared' which at first *The Times* seemed ready to take but on second thoughts declined. I was recommended to carry them to a monthly review of sorts edited by a Mr. Frank Harris, whom I discovered to be the one human being that I could on no terms get on with. He, too, shied at the verses, which I referred to Henley, who, having no sense of political decency, published them in his *Observer* and—after a cautious interval—*The Times* quoted them in full. This was rather like some of my experiences in India, and gave me yet more confidence.

To my great pride I was elected a Member of the Savile—'the little Savile' then in Piccadilly—and, on my introduction, dined with no less than Hardy and Walter Besant. My debts to the latter grew at once, and you may remember that I owed him much indeed. He had his own views on publishers, and was founding, or had just founded, the Authors' Society. He

advised me to entrust my business to an agent and sent me to his own—
A. P. Watt, whose son was about my own age. The father took hold of my
affairs at once and most sagely; and on his death his son succeeded. In the
course of forty odd years I do not recall any difference between us that three
minutes' talk could not clear up. This, also, I owed to Besant.

Nor did his goodness halt there. He would sit behind his big, frosted
beard and twinkling spectacles, and deal me out wisdom concerning this new
incomprehensible world. One heard very good talk at the Savile. Much of it
was the careless give-and-take of the atelier when the models are off their
stands, and one throws bread-pellets at one's betters, and makes hay of all
schools save one's own. But Besant saw deeper. He advised me to 'keep out
of the dog-fight.' He said that if I were 'in with one lot' I would have to be
out with another; and that, at least, 'things would get like a girls' school
where they stick out their tongues at each other when they pass.' That was
true too. One heard men vastly one's seniors wasting energy and good oaths
in recounting 'intrigues' against them, and of men who had 'their knife into'
their work, or whom they themselves wished to 'knife.' (This reminded me
somehow of the elderly officials who opened their hearts in my old office
when they were disappointed over anticipated Honours.) It seemed best to
stand clear of it all. For that reason, I have never directly or indirectly criti-
cised any fellow-craftsman's output, or encouraged any man or woman to do
so; nor have I approached any persons that they might be led to comment
on my output. My acquaintance with my contemporaries has from first to
last been very limited.

At 'the little Savile' I remember much kindness and toleration. There
was Gosse, of course, sensitive as a cat to all atmospheres, but utterly fearless
when it came to questions of good workmanship; Hardy's grave and bitter
humour; Andrew Lang, as detached to all appearances as a cloud but—one
learned to know—never kinder in your behalf than when he seemed least
concerned with you; Eustace Balfour, a large, lovable man, and one of the
best of talkers, who died too soon: Herbert Stephen, very wise and very funny
when he chose: Rider Haggard, to whom I took at once, he being of the
stamp adored by children and trusted by men at sight; and he could tell tales,
mainly against himself, that broke up the tables: Saintsbury, a solid rock of
learning and geniality whom I revered all my days; profoundly a scholar and
versed in the art of good living. There was a breakfast with him and Walter
Pollock of the *Saturday Review* in the Albany, when he produced some
specially devilish Oriental delicacy which we cooked by the light of our
united ignorances. It was splendid! Why those two men took the trouble to
notice me, I never knew; but I learned to rely on Saintsbury's judgment in
the weightier matters of the Laws of Literature. At his latter end he gave me
inestimable help in a little piece of work called 'Proofs of Holy Writ,' which
without his books could never have been handled. I found him at Bath,
compiling with erudition equal to his earnestness, the Cellar-book of the
Queen's Doll's House. He produced a bottle of real Tokay, which I tasted,

and lost my number badly by saying that it reminded me of some medicinal wine. It is true he merely called me a blasphemer of the worst, but what he thought I do not care to think!

There were scores of other good men at the Savile, but the tones and the faces of those I have named come back clearest.

My home life—it was a far cry from Piccadilly to Villiers Street—was otherwise, through the months of amazement which followed my return to England. That period was all, as I have said, a dream, in which it seemed that I could push down walls, walk through ramparts and stride across rivers. Yet I was so ignorant, I never guessed when the great fogs fell that trains could take me to light and sunshine a few miles outside London. Once I faced the reflection of my own face in the jet-black mirror of the window-panes for five days. When the fog thinned, I looked out and saw a man standing opposite the pub where the barmaid lived. Of a sudden his breast turned dull red like a robin's, and he crumpled, having cut his throat. In a few minutes—seconds it seemed—a hand-ambulance arrived and took up the body. A pot-boy with a bucket of steaming water sluiced the blood off into the gutter, and what little crowd had collected went its way.

One got to know that ambulance (it lived somewhere at the back of St. Clement Danes) as well as the Police of the E. Division, and even as far as Piccadilly Circus where, any time after 10.30 P.M., the forces might be found at issue with 'real ladies.' And through all this shifting, shouting brotheldom the pious British householder and his family bored their way back from the theatres, eyes-front and fixed, as though not seeing.

Among my guests in chambers was a Lion Comique from Gatti's—an artist with sound views on art. According to him, 'it was all right to keep on knockin' 'em' ('puttin' it across' came later) 'but, outside o' *that*, a man wants something to lay *hold* of. I'd ha' got it, I think, but for this dam' whisky. But, take it from me, life's all a bloomin' kick-up.' Certainly my life was; but, to some extent, my Indian training served to ballast me.

I was plentifully assured, *viva voce* and in the Press cuttings—which is a drug that I do not recommend to the young—that 'nothing since Dickens' compared with my 'meteoric rise to fame,' etc. (But I was more or less inoculated, if not immune, to the coarser sorts of print.) And there was my portrait to be painted for the Royal Academy as a notoriety. (But I had a Muhammedan's objection to having my face taken, as likely to draw the Evil Eye. So I was not too puffed up.) And there were letters and letters of all sorts of tendencies. (But if I answered them all I might as well be back at my old table.) And there were proposals from 'certain people of importance,' insistent and unscrupulous as horse-copers, telling me how 'the ball was at my feet' and that I had only to kick it—by repeating the notes I had already struck and trailing characters I had already 'created' through impossible scenes—to achieve all sorts of desirable things. But I had seen men as well as horses foundered in my lost world behind me. One thing only stood fast through this welter. I was making money—much more than four hundred rupees a month—and when my Bank-book told me I had one thousand whole pounds saved, the Strand was hardly wide enough for my triumph. I had intended a book 'to take advantage of the market.' This I had just sense enough to countermand. What I most needed was that my people should come over and see what had overtaken their son. This they did on a flying visit, and then my 'kick-up' had some worth.

As always, they seemed to suggest nothing and interfere nowhere. But they were there—my Father and his sage Yorkshire outlook and wisdom; my Mother, all Celt and three-parts fire—both so entirely comprehending that except in trivial matters we had hardly need of words.

I think I can with truth say that those two made for me the only public for whom then I had any regard whatever till their deaths, in my forty-fifth year. Their arrival simplified things, and 'set' in my head a notion that had been rising at the back of it. It seemed easy enough to 'knock 'em'—but to what end beyond the heat of the exercise? (That both my grandfathers had been Wesleyan Ministers did not strike me till I was, familiarly, reminded of it.) I had been at work on the rough of a set of verses called later 'The English Flag' and had boggled at a line which had to be a key-line but persisted in going 'soft.' As was the custom between us, I asked into the air: 'What am I trying to get *at*?' Instantly the Mother, with her quick flutter of the hands: 'You're *trying* to say: "What do they know of England who only England know." ' The Father confirmed. The rest of the rhetoric came away easily; for it was only pictures seen, as it were, from the deck of a long fourteen-footer, a craft that will almost sail herself.

In the talks that followed, I exposed my notion of trying to tell to the English something of the world outside England—not directly but by implication.

They understood. Long before the end the Mother, summarising, said: 'I see. "Unto them did he discover His swan's nest among the reeds." Thank you for telling us, dear.' That settled that; and when Lord Tennyson (whom alas! I never had the good fortune to meet) expressed his approval of the verses when they appeared, I took it for a lucky sign. Most men properly broke to a trade pick up some sort of workshop facility which gives them an advantage over their untrained fellows. My office-work had taught me to think out a notion in detail, pack it away in my head, and work on it by snatches in any surroundings. The lurch and surge of the old horse-drawn buses made a luxurious cradle for such ruminations. Bit by bit, my original notion grew into a vast, vague conspectus—Army and Navy Stores List if you like—of the whole sweep and meaning of things and effort and origins throughout the Empire. I visualised it, as I do most ideas, in the shape of a semi-circle of buildings and temples projecting into a sea—of dreams. At any rate, after I had got it straight in my head, I felt there need be no more 'knockin' 'em' in the abstract.

Likewise, in my wanderings beyond Villiers Street, I had met several men and an occasional woman, whom I by no means loved. They were overly soft-spoken or blatant, and dealt in pernicious varieties of safe sedition. For the most part they seemed to be purveyors of luxuries to the 'Aristocracy,' whose destruction by painful means they loudly professed to desire. They derided my poor little Gods of the East, and asserted that the British in India spent violent lives 'oppressing' the Native. (This in a land where white girls of sixteen, at twelve or fourteen pounds per annum, hauled thirty and forty pounds weight of bath-water at a time up four flights of stairs!)

The more subtle among them had plans, which they told me, for 'snatching away England's arms when she isn't looking—just like a naughty child—so that when she wants to fight she'll find she can't.' (We have come far on that road since.) Meantime, their aim was peaceful, intellectual penetration and the formation of what to-day would be called 'cells' in unventilated corners. Collaborating with these gentry was a mixed crowd of wide-minded, wide-mouthed Liberals, who darkened council with pious but disintegrating catch-words, and took care to live very well indeed. Somewhere, playing up to them, were various journals, not at all badly written, with a most enviable genius for perverting or mistaking anything that did not suit their bilious doctrine. The general situation, as I saw it, promised an alluring 'dog-fight,' in which I had no need to take aggressive part because, as soon as the first bloom had faded off my work, my normal output seemed to have the gift of *arriding per se* the very people I most disliked. And I had the additional luck not to be taken seriously for some time. People talked, quite reasonably, of rockets and sticks; and that genius, J. K. S., brother to Herbert Stephen, dealt with Haggard and me in some stanzas which I would have given much to have written myself. They breathed a prayer for better days when:—

> The world shall cease to wonder
>   At the genius of an Ass,
> And a boy's eccentric blunder
>   Shall not bring success to pass:
>
> When there stands a muzzled stripling,
>   Mute, beside a muzzled bore:
> When the Rudyards cease from Kipling
>   And the Haggards Ride no more.

It ran joyously through all the papers. It still hangs faintly in the air and, as I used to warn Haggard, may continue as an aroma when all but our two queer names are forgotten.

Several perfectly good reviewers also helped me by demonstrating how I had arrived at my effects by a series of happy accidents. One kind man even went to some trouble, including a good dinner, to discover personally whether I had 'ever read much.' I could not do less than confirm his worst suspicions, for I had been 'taken on' in that way at the Punjab Club, till my examiner found out that I was pulling his leg, and chased me all round the compound.

(The greatest reverence is due to the young. They have, when irritated, little of their own.)

But in all this jam of work done or devising, demands, distractions, excitements, and promiscuous confusions, my health cracked again. I had broken down twice in India from straight overwork, plus fever and dysentery, but this time the staleness and depression came after a bout of real influenza, when all my Indian microbes joined hands and sang for a month in the darkness of Villiers Street.

So I took ship to Italy, and there chanced to meet Lord Dufferin, our Ambassador, who had been Viceroy of India and had known my people. Also, I had written some verses called 'The Song of the Women' about Lady Dufferin's maternity work for women in India, which both she and he liked. He was kindness itself, and made me his guest at his Villa near Naples where, one evening between lights, he talked—at first to me directly, then sliding into a reverie—of his work in India, Canada, and the world at large. I had seen administrative machinery from beneath, all stripped and overheated. This was the first time I had listened to one who had handled it from above. And unlike the generality of Viceroys, Lord Dufferin *knew*. Of all his revelations and reminiscences, the sentence that stays with me is: 'And so, you see, there can be no room' (or was it 'allowance'?) 'for good intentions in one's work.'

Italy, however, was not enough. My need was to get clean away and re-sort myself. Cruises were then unknown; but my dependence was Cook. For the great J. M. himself—the man with the iron mouth and domed brow—had been one of my Father's guests at Lahore, when he was trying to induce the Indian Government to let him take over the annual pilgrimage to Mecca as a business proposition. Had he succeeded some lives, and perhaps a war or two, might have been saved. His home offices took friendly interest in my plans and steamer connections.

I sailed first to Cape Town in a gigantic three-thousand-ton liner called *The Moor*, not knowing I was in the hands of Fate. Aboard her, I met a Navy Captain going to a new Command at Simons Town. At Madeira he desired to lay in wine for his two-year commission. I assisted him through a variegated day and fluctuating evening, which laid the foundations of life-long friendship.

Cape Town in '91 was a sleepy, unkempt little place, where the stoeps of some of the older Dutch houses still jutted over the pavement. Occasional cows strolled up the main streets, which were full of coloured people of the sort that my *ayah* had pointed out to me were curly-haired (*hubshees*) who slept in such posture as made it easy for the devils to enter their bodies. But there were also many Malays who were Muslims of a sort and had their own Mosques, and whose flamboyantly-attired women sold flowers on the curb, and took in washing. The dry, spiced smell of the land and the smack of the clean sunshine were health-restoring. My Navy Captain introduced me to the Naval society of Simons Town, where the south-easter blows five days a week, and the Admiral of the Cape Station lived in splendour, with at least a brace of live turtles harnessed to the end of a little wooden jetty, swimming about till due to be taken up for turtle soup. The Navy Club there and the tales of the junior officers delighted me beyond words. There I witnessed one of the most comprehensive 'rags' I had ever seen. It rose out of a polite suggestion to a newly-appointed Lieutenant-Commander that the fore-topmast of his tiny gunboat 'wanted staying forward.' It went on till all the furniture was completely rearranged all over the room. (How was I to guess that in a few years I should know Simons Town like the inside of my own pocket, and should give much of my life and love to the glorious land around it.)

We parted, my Captain and I, after a farewell picnic, among white, blowing sand where natives were blasting and where, of a sudden, a wrathful baboon came down the rock-face and halted waist-deep in a bed of arum-lilies. 'We'll meet again,' said my Captain, 'and if ever you want a cruise, let me know.'

A day or so before my departure for Australia, I lunched at an Adderley Street restaurant next to three men. One of them, I was told, was Cecil Rhodes, who had made the staple of our passengers' talk on *The Moor* coming out. It never occurred to me to speak to him; and I have often wondered why. . . .

Her name was *The Doric*. She was almost empty, and she spent twenty-four consecutive days and nights trying, all but successfully, to fill her boats at one roll and empty them down the saloon skylight the next. Sea and sky were equally grey and naked on that weary run to Melbourne. Then I found myself in a new land with new smells and among people who insisted a little too much that they also were new. But there are no such things as new people in this very old world.

The leading paper offered me the most distinguished honour of describing the Melbourne Cup, but I had reported races before and knew it was not in my line. I was more interested in the middle-aged men who had spent their lives making or managing the land. They were direct of speech among each other, and talked a political slang new to me. One learned, as one always does, more from what they said to each other or took for granted in their talk, than one could have got at from a hundred questions. And on a warm night I attended a Labour Congress, where Labour debated whether some much-needed life-boats should be allowed to be ordered from England, or whether the order should be postponed till life-boats could be built in Australia under Labour direction at Labour prices.

Hereafter my memories of Australian travel are mixed up with trains transferring me, at unholy hours, from one too-exclusive State gauge to another; of enormous skies and primitive refreshment rooms, where I drank hot tea and ate mutton, while now and then a hot wind, like the *loo* of the Punjab, boomed out of the emptiness. A hard land, it seemed to me, and made harder for themselves by the action of its inhabitants, who—it may have been the climate—always seemed a bit on edge.

I went also to Sydney, which was populated by leisured multitudes all in their shirt-sleeves and all picnicking all the day. They volunteered that they were new and young, but would do wonderful things some day, which promise they more than kept. Then to Hobart, in Tasmania, to pay my respects to Sir Edward Grey who had been Governor at Cape Town in the days of the Mutiny, and on his own responsibility had diverted to India troop-ships filled with troops intended for some native war that had flared up behind him in the colony. He was very old, very wise and fore-seeing, with the gentleness that accompanies a certain sort of strength.

Then came New Zealand by steamer (one was always taking small and rickety coast-wise craft across those big seas), and at Wellington I was met, precisely where warned to expect him, by 'Pelorus Jack,' the big, white-marked shark, who held it his duty to escort shipping up the harbour. He enjoyed a special protection of the Legislature proclaiming him sacred, but, years later, some animal shot and wounded him and he was no more seen. Wellington opened another world of kindly people, more homogeneous, it struck me, than the Australian, large, long-eyelashed, and extraordinarily good-looking. Maybe I was prejudiced, because no less than ten beautiful maidens took me for a row in a big canoe by moonlight on the still waters of Wellington Harbour, and everyone generally put aside everything for my behoof, instruction, amusement, and comfort. So, indeed, it has always been. For which reason I deserve no credit when my work happens to be accurate in detail. A friend long ago taxed me with having enjoyed the 'income of a Prince and the treatment of an Ambassador,' and with not appreciating it. He even called me, among other things, 'an ungrateful hound.' But what, I ask you, could I have done except go on with my work and try to add to the pleasure of those that had found it pleasant? One cannot repay the unrepayable by grins and handshakes.

From Wellington I went north towards Auckland in a buggy with a small grey mare, and a most taciturn driver. It was bush country after rain. We crossed a rising river twenty-three times in one day, and came out on great plains where wild horses stared at us, and caught their feet in long blown manes as they stamped and snorted. At one of our halts I was given for dinner a roast bird with a skin like pork crackling, but it had no wings nor trace of any. It was a kiwi—an apteryx. I ought to have saved its skeleton, for few men have eaten apteryx. Hereabouts my driver—I had seen the like happen in lonely places before—exploded, as sometimes solitaries will. We passed a horse's skull beside the track, at which he began to swear horribly but without passion. He had, he said, driven and ridden past that skull for a very long time. To him it meant the lock on the chain of his bondage to circumstance, and why the hell did I come along talking about all those foreign, far places I had seen? Yet he made me go on telling him.

I had had some notion of sailing from Auckland to visit Robert Lewis Stevenson at Samoa, for he had done me the honour to write me about some of my tales; and moreover I was Eminent Past Master R.L.S. Even to-day I would back myself to take seventy-five per cent marks in written or *viva-voce* examination on *The Wrong Box* which, as the Initiated know, is the Test Volume of that Degree. I read it first in a small hotel in Boston in '89, when the negro waiter nearly turned me out of the dining-room for spluttering over my meal.

But Auckland, soft and lovely in the sunshine, seemed the end of organised travel; for the captain of a fruit-boat, which might or might not go to Samoa at some time or other, was so devotedly drunk that I decided to turn south, and work back to India. All I carried away from the magic town of Auckland was the face and voice of a woman who sold me beer at a little hotel there. They stayed at the back of my head till ten years later when, in a local train of the Cape Town suburbs, I heard a petty officer from Simon's Town telling a companion about a woman in New Zealand who 'never scrupled to help a lame duck or put her foot on a scorpion.' Then—precisely as the removal of the key-log in a timber-jam starts the whole pile—those words gave me the key to the face and voice at Auckland, and a tale called 'Mrs. Bathurst' slid into my mind, smoothly and orderly as floating timber on a bank-high river.

The South Island, mainly populated by Scots, their sheep, and the Devil's own high winds, I tackled in another small steamer, among colder and increasing seas. We cleared it at the Last Lamp-post in the World—Invercargill—on a boisterous dark evening, when General Booth of the Salvation Army came on board. I saw him walking backward in the dusk over the uneven wharf, his cloak blown upwards, tulip-fashion, over his grey head, while he beat a tambourine in the face of the singing, weeping, praying crowd who had come to see him off.

We stood out, and at once took the South Atlantic. For the better part of a week we were swept from end to end, our poop was split, and a foot or two of water smashed through the tiny saloon. I remember no set meals. The General's cabin was near mine, and in the intervals between crashes overhead and cataracts down below he sounded like a wound elephant; for he was in every way a big man.

I saw no more of him till I had picked up my P. & O. which also happened to be his for Colombo at Adelaide. Here all the world came out in paddle-boats and small craft to speed him on his road to India. He spoke to them from our upper deck, and one of his gestures—an imperative, repeated, downward sweep of the arm—puzzled me, till I saw that a woman crouching on the paddle-box of a crowded boat had rucked her petticoats well up to her knees. In those days righteous woman ended at the neck and instep. Presently, she saw what was troubling the General. Her skirts were adjusted and all was peace and piety. I talked much with General Booth during that voyage. Like the young ass I was, I expressed my distaste at his appearance on Invercargill wharf. 'Young feller,' he replied, bending great brows at me, 'if I thought I could win *one* more soul to the Lord by walking on my head and playing the tambourine with my toes, I'd—I'd learn how.'

He had the right of it ('if by any means I can save some') and I had decency enough to apologise. He told me about the beginnings of his mission, and how surely he would be in gaol were his accounts submitted to any sort of official inspection; and how his work *must* be a one-man despotism with only the Lord for supervisor. (Even so spoke Paul and, I am well sure, Muhammed.)

'Then why,' I asked, 'can't you stop your Salvation lassies from going out to India and living alone native-fashion among natives?' I told him something of village conditions in India. The despot's defence was very human. 'But what *am* I to do?' he demanded. 'The girls *will* go, and one *can't* stop 'em.'

I think this first flare of enthusiasm was rationalised later, but not before some good lives had been expended. I conceived great respect and admiration for this man with the head of Isaiah and the fire of the Prophet, but, like the latter, rather at sea among women. The next time I met him was at Oxford when Degrees were being conferred. He strode across to me in his Doctor's robes, which magnificently became him, and, 'Young feller,' said he, 'how's your soul?'

I have always liked the Salvation Army, of whose work outside England I have seen a little. They are, of course, open to all the objections urged against them by science and the regular creeds: but it seems to me that when a soul conceives itself as being reborn it may go through agonies both unscientific and unregulated. Haggard, who had worked with him and for the Army on several occasions, told me that for sheer luxury of attendance, kindliness, and good-will, nothing compared with travel under their care.

From Colombo I crossed over to the India of the extreme south which I did not know, and for four days and four nights in the belly of the train could not understand one word of the speech around me. Then came the open north and Lahore, where I was snatching a few days' visit with my people. They were coming 'Home' for good soon: so this was my last look round the only real home I had yet known.

V. THE COMMITTEE OF WAYS AND MEANS

❧ THEN down to Bombay where my *ayah*, so old but so unaltered, met me with blessings and tears; and then to London to be married in January '92 in the thick of an influenza epidemic, when the undertakers had run out of black horses and the dead had to be content with brown ones. The living were mostly abed. (We did not know then that this epidemic was the first warning that the plague—forgotten for generations—was on the move out of Manchuria.)

All of which touched me as much as it would any other young man under like circumstances. My concern was to get out of the pest-house as soon as might be. For was I not a person of substance? Had I not several— more than two at least—thousand pounds in Fixed Deposits? Had not my own Bank's Manager himself suggested that I might invest some of my 'capital' in, say, indigo? But I preferred to invest once more in Cook's tickets —for two—on a voyage round the world. It was all arranged beyond any chance of failure.

So we were married in the church with the pencil-pointed steeple at Langham Place—Gosse, Henry James, and my cousin Ambrose Poynter being all the congregation present—and we parted at the church door to the scandal of the Beadle, my wife to administer medicine to her mother, and I to a wedding breakfast with Ambrose Poynter; after which, on returning to collect my wife, I saw, pinned down by weights on the rainy pavement as was the custom of those untroubled days, a newspaper poster announcing my marriage, which made me feel uncomfortable and defenceless.

And a few days afterwards we were on our magic carpet which was to take us round the earth, beginning with Canada deep in snow. Among our wedding gifts was a generous silver flask filled with whisky, but of incontinent habit. It leaked in the valise where it lay with flannel shirts. And it scented the entire Pullman from end to end ere we arrived at the cause. But by that time all our fellow-passengers were pitying that poor girl who had linked her life to this shameless inebriate. Thus in a false atmosphere all of our innocent own, we came to Vancouver, where with an eye to the future and for proof of wealth we bought, or thought we had, twenty acres of a wilderness called North Vancouver, now part of the City. But there was a catch in the thing as we found many years later when, after paying taxes on it for ever so long, we discovered it belonged to someone else. All the consolation we got then from the smiling people of Vancouver was: 'You bought that from Steve, did you? Ah-ah, Steve! You hadn't ought to ha' bought from Steve. No! Not from Steve.' And thus did the good Steve cure us of speculating in real estate.

Then to Yokohama, where we were treated with all the kindliness in the world by a man and his wife on whom we had no shadow of any claim. They made us more than welcome in their house, and saw to it that we should see Japan in wistaria and peony time. Here an earthquake (prophetic as it turned out) overtook us one hot break of dawn, and we fled out into the garden, where a tall cryptomeria waggled its insane head back and forth with an 'I told you so' expression; though not a breath was stirring. A little later I went to the Yokohama branch of my Bank on a wet forenoon to draw some of my solid wealth. Said the Manager to me: 'Why not take more? It will be just as easy.' I answered that I did not care to have too much cash at one time in my careless keeping, but that when I had looked over my accounts I might come again in the afternoon. I did so; but in that little space my Bank, the notice on its shut door explained, had suspended payment. (Yes, I should have done better to have invested my 'capital' as its London Manager had hinted.)

I returned with my news to my bride of three months and a child to be born. Except for what I had drawn that morning—the Manager had sailed as near to the wind as loyalty permitted—and the unexpended Cook vouchers, and our personal possessions in our trunks, we had nothing whatever. There was an instant Committee of Ways and Means, which advanced our understanding of each other more than a cycle of solvent matrimony. Retreat —flight, if you like—was indicated. What would Cook return for the tickets, not including the price of lost dreams? 'Every pound you've paid, of course,' said Cook of Yokohama. 'These things are all luck and—here's your refund.'

Back again, then, across the cold North Pacific, through Canada on the heels of the melting snows, and to the outskirts of a little New England town where my wife's paternal grandfather (a Frenchman) had made his home and estate many years before. The country was large-boned, mountainous, wooded, and divided into farms of from fifty to two hundred barren acres. Roads, sketched in dirt, connected white, clap-boarded farmhouses, where the older members of the families made shift to hold down the eating mortgages. The younger folk had gone elsewhere. There were many abandoned houses too; some decaying where they stood; others already reduced to a stone chimney-stack or mere green dimples still held by an undefeated lilac-bush. On one small farm was a building known as the Bliss Cottage, generally inhabited by a hired man. It was of one storey and a half; seventeen feet high to the roof-tree; seventeen feet deep and, including the kitchen and woodshed, twenty-seven feet wide over all. Its water-supply was a single half-inch lead pipe connecting with a spring in the neighbourhood. But it was habitable, and it stood over a deep if dampish cellar. Its rent was ten dollars or two pounds a month.

We took it. We furnished it with a simplicity that foreran the hire-purchase system. We bought, second or third-hand, a huge, hot-air stove which we installed in the cellar. We cut generous holes in our thin floors for its eight-inch tin pipes (why we were not burned in our beds each week of the winter I never can understand) and we were extraordinarily and self-centredly content.

As the New England summer flamed into autumn I piled cut spruce boughs all round the draughty cottage sill, and helped to put up a tiny roofless verandah along one side of it for future needs. When winter shut down and sleigh-bells rang all over the white world that tucked us in, we counted ourselves secure. Sometimes we had a servant. Sometimes she would find the solitude too much for her and flee without warning, one even leaving her trunk. This troubled us not at all. There are always two sides to a plate, and the cleaning of frying- and saucepans is as little a mystery as the making of comfortable beds. When our lead pipe froze, we would slip on our coon-skin coats and thaw it out with a lighted candle. There was no space in the attic bedroom for a cradle, so we decided that a trunk-tray would be just as good. We envied no one—not even when skunks wandered into our cellar and, knowing the nature of the beasts, we immobilised ourselves till it should please them to depart.

But our neighbours saw no humour in our proceedings. Here was a stranger of an unloved race, currently reported to 'make as much as a hundred dollars out of a ten-cent bottle of ink,' and who had 'pieces in the papers' about him, who had married a 'Balestier girl.' Did not her grandmother still live on the Balestier place, where 'old Balestier' instead of farming had built a large house, and there had dined late in special raiment, and drunk red wines after the custom of the French instead of decent whisky? And behold this Britisher, under pretext of having lost money, had settled his wife down 'right among her own folk' in the Bliss Cottage. It was not seemly on the face of it; so they watched as secretively as the New England or English peasant can, and what toleration they extended to the 'Britisher' was solely for the sake of 'the Balestier girl.'

But we had received the first shock of our young lives at the first crisis in them. The Committee of Ways and Means passed a resolution, never rescinded, that henceforth, at any price, it must own its collective self.

As money came in from the sale of books and tales, the first use we made of it was to buy back *Departmental Ditties*, *Plain Tales*, and the six paperbacked books that I had sold to get me funds for leaving India in '89. They cost something, but, owning them, the Bliss Cottage breathed more comfortably.

Not till much later did we realise the terrible things that 'folks thought of your doin's.' From their point of view they were right. Also, they were practical as the following will show.

One day a stranger drove up to the Bliss Cottage. The palaver opened thus:—

'Kiplin', ain't ye?'

That was admitted.

"Write, don't ye?"

That seemed accurate. (Long pause.)

'Thet bein' so, you've got to live to please folk, hain't ye?'

That indeed was the raw truth. He sat rigid in the buggy and went on.

'Thet bein' so, you've got to please to live, I reckon?'

It was true. (I thought of my Adjutant of Volunteers at Lahore.)

'Puttin' it thet way,' he pursued, 'we'll 'low that, by and by, ye *can't* please. Sickness—accident—any darn thing. *Then*—what's liable to happen ye—both of ye?'

I began to see, and he to fumble in his breast pocket.

'Thet's where Life Insurance comes in. Naow, I represent,' etc. etc. It was beautiful salesmanship. The Company was reputable, and I effected my first American Insurance, Leuconoë agreeing with Horace to trust the future as little as possible.

Other visitors were not so tactful. Reporters came from papers in Boston, which I presume believed itself to be civilised, and demanded interviews. I told them I had nothing to say. 'If ye hevn't, guess we'll *make* ye say something.' So they went away and lied copiously, their orders being to 'get the story.' This was new to me at the time; but the Press had not got into its full free stride of later years.

My workroom in the Bliss Cottage was seven feet by eight, and from December to April the snow lay level with its window-sill. It chanced that I had written a tale about Indian Forestry work which included a boy who had been brought up by wolves. In the stillness, and suspense, of the winter of '92 some memory of the Masonic Lions of my childhood's magazine, and a phrase in Haggard's *Nada the Lily*, combined with the echo of this tale. After blocking out the main idea in my head, the pen took charge, and I watched it begin to write stories about Mowgli and animals, which later grew into the *Jungle Books*.

Once launched there seemed no particular reason to stop, but I had learned to distinguish between the peremptory motions of my Daemon, and the 'carry-over' or induced electricity, which comes of what you might call mere 'frictional' writing. Two tales, I remember, I threw away and was better pleased with the remainder. More to the point, my Father thought well of the workmanship.

My first child and daughter was born in three foot of snow on the night of December 29th, 1892. Her Mother's birthday being the 31st and mine the 30th of the same month, we congratulated her on her sense of the fitness of things, and she throve in her trunk tray in the sunshine on the little plank verandah. Her birth brought me into contact with the best friend I made in New England—Dr. Conland.

It seemed that the Bliss Cottage might be getting a little congested, so, in the following spring, the Committee of Ways and Means 'considered a field and bought it'—as much as ten whole acres—on a rocky hillside looking across a huge valley to Wantastiquet, the wooded mountain across the Connecticut river.

That summer there came out of Quebec Jean Pigeon with nine other *habitants* who put up a wooden shed for their own accommodation in what seemed twenty minutes, and then set to work to build us a house which we called 'Naulahka.' Ninety feet was the length of it and thirty the width, on a high foundation of solid mortared rocks which gave us an airy and a skunk-proof basement. The rest was wood, shingled, roof and sides, with dull green hand-split shingles, and the windows were lavish and wide. Lavish too was the long open attic, as I realised when too late. Pigeon asked me whether I would have it finished in ash or cherry. Ignorant that I was, I chose ash, and so missed a stretch of perhaps the most satisfying interior wood that is grown. Those were opulent days, when timber was nothing regarded, and the best of cabinet work could be had for little money.

Next, we laid out a long drive to the road. This needed dynamite to soften its grades and a most mellow plumber brought up many sticks of it all rattling about under his buggy-seat among the tamping-rods. We dived, like wood-chucks, into the nearest deepest hole. Next, needing water, we sunk a five-inch shaft three hundred foot into the New England granite, which nowhere was less than three, though some say thirty, thousand foot thick. Over that we set a windmill, which gave us not enough water and moaned and squeaked o' nights. So we knocked out its lowest bolts, hitched on two yoke of bullocks, and overthrew it, as it might have been the Vendôme Column: thus spiritually recouping ourselves for at least half the cost of erection. A low-power atmospheric pump, which it was my disgustful duty to oil, was its successor. These experiences gave us both a life-long taste for playing with timber, stone, concrete and such delightful things.

Horses were an integral part of our lives, for the Bliss Cottage was three miles from the little town, and half a mile from the house in building. Our permanent servitor was a big, philosophical black called Marcus Aurelius, who waited in the buggy as cars wait to-day, and when weary of standing up would carefully lie down and go to sleep between his shafts. After we had finished with him, we tied his reins short and sent him in charge of the buggy alone down the road to his stable-door, where he resumed his slumbers till someone came to undress him and put him to bed. There was a small mob of other horses about the landscape, including a meek old stallion with a permanently lame leg, who passed the evening of his days in a horse-power machine which cut wood for us.

I tried to give something of the fun and flavour of those days in a story called 'A Walking Delegate' where all the characters are from horse-life.

The wife's passion, I discovered, was driving trotters. It chanced that our first winter in 'Naulahka' she went to look at the new patent safety heating-stove, which blew flame in her face and burnt it severely. She recovered slowly, and Dr. Conland suggested that she needed a tonic. I had been in treaty for a couple of young, seal-brown, full brother and sister Morgans, good for a three-mile clip, and, on Conland's hint, concluded the deal. When I told the wife, she thought it would console her to try them and, that same afternoon, leaving one eye free of the bandages, she did so in three foot of snow and a failing light, while I suffered beside her. But Nip and Tuck were perfect roadsters and the 'tonic' succeeded. After that they took us all over the large countryside.

It would be hard to exaggerate the loneliness and sterility of life on the farms. The land was denuding itself of its accustomed inhabitants, and their places had not yet been taken by the wreckage of Eastern Europe or the wealthy city folk who later bought 'pleasure farms.' What might have become characters, powers and attributes perverted themselves into that desolation as cankered trees throw out branches akimbo, and strange faiths and cruelties, born of solitude to the edge of insanity, flourished like lichen on sick bark.

One day-long excursion up the flanks of Wantastiquet, our guardian mountain across the river, brought us to a farmhouse where we were welcomed by the usual wild-eyed, flat-fronted woman of the place. Looking over sweeps of emptiness, we saw our 'Naulahka' riding on its hillside like a little boat on the flank of a far wave. Said the woman, fiercely: 'Be you the new lights 'crost the valley yonder? Ye don't know what a comfort they've been to me this winter. Ye aren't ever goin' to shroud 'em up—or be ye?' So, as long as we lived there, that broad side of 'Naulahka' which looked her-ward was always nakedly lit.

In the little town where we shopped there was another atmosphere. Vermont was by tradition a 'Dry' State. For that reason, one found in almost every office the water-bottle and thick tooth-glass displayed openly, and in discreet cupboards or drawers the whisky bottle. Business was conducted and concluded with gulps of raw spirit, followed by a pledget of ice-cold water. Then, both parties chewed cloves, but whether to defeat the Law, which no one ever regarded, or to deceive their women-folk of whom they went in great fear (they were mostly educated up to College age by spinsters) I do not know.

But a promising scheme for a Country Club had to be abandoned because many men who would by right belong to it could not be trusted with a full whisky bottle. On the farms, of course, men drank cider, of various strengths, and sometimes achieved almost maniacal forms of drunkenness. The whole business seemed to me as unwholesomely furtive and false as many aspects of American life at that time.

Administratively, there was unlimited and meticulous legality, with a multiplication of semi-judicial offices and titles; but of law-abidingness, or of any conception of what that implied, not a trace. Very little in business, transportation, or distribution, that I had to deal with, was sure, punctual, accurate, or organised. But this they neither knew nor would have believed though angels affirmed it. Ethnologically, emigrants were coming into the States at about a million head a year. They supplied the cheap—almost slave—labour, lacking which all wheels would have stopped, and they were handled with a callousness that horrified me. The Irish had passed out of the market into 'politics' which suited their instincts of secrecy, plunder, and anonymous denunciation. The Italians were still at work, laying down trams, but were moving up, via small shops and curious activities, to the dominant position which they now occupied in well-organised society. The German, who had preceded even the Irish, counted himself a full-blooded American, and looked down gutturally on what he called 'foreign trash.' Somewhere in the background, though he did not know it, was the 'representative' American, who traced his blood through three or four generations and who, controlling nothing and affecting less, protested that the accepted lawlessness of life was not 'representative' of his country, whose moral, aesthetic, and literary champion he had appointed himself. He said too, almost automatically, that all foreign elements could and would soon be 'assimilated' into 'good Americans.' And not a soul cared what he said or how he said it! They were making or losing money.

The political background of the land was monotonous. When the people looked, which was seldom, outside their own borders, England was still the dark and dreadful enemy to be feared and guarded against. The Irish, whose other creed is Hate; the history books in the Schools; the Orators; the eminent Senators; and above all the Press; saw to that. Now John Hay, one of the very few American Ambassadors to England with two sides to their heads, had his summer house a few hours north by rail from us. On a visit to him, we discussed the matter. His explanation was convincing. I quote the words which stayed textually in my memory. 'America's hatred of England is the hoop round the forty-four (as they were then) staves of the Union.' He said it was the only standard possible to apply to an enormously variegated population. 'So—when a man comes up out of the sea, we say to him: "See that big bully over there in the East? He's England! Hate him, and you're a good American."'

On the principle, 'if you can't keep a love affair going, start a row,' this is reasonable. At any rate the belief lifted on occasion the overwhelming vacuity of the national life into some contact with imponderable externals.

But how thoroughly the doctrine was exploited I did not realise till we visited Washington in '96, where I met Theodore Roosevelt, then Under Secretary (I never caught the name of the Upper) to the U.S. Navy. I liked him from the first and largely believed in him. He would come to our hotel, and thank God in a loud voice that he had not one drop of British blood in him; his ancestry being Dutch, and his creed conforming-Dopper, I think it is called. Naturally I told him nice tales about his Uncles and Aunts in South Africa—only I called them Ooms and Tanties—who esteemed themselves the sole lawful Dutch under the canopy and dismissed Roosevelt's stock for 'Verdomder Hollanders.' Then he became really eloquent, and we would go off to the Zoo together, where he talked about grizzlies that he had met. It was laid on him, at that time, to furnish his land with an adequate Navy; the existing collection of unrelated types and casual purchases being worn out. I asked him how he proposed to get it, for the American people did not love taxation. 'Out of *you*,' was the disarming reply. And so—to some extent—it was. The obedient and instructed Press explained how England—treacherous and jealous as ever—only waited round the corner to descend on the unprotected coasts of Liberty, and to that end was preparing, etc. etc. etc. (This in '96 when England had more than enough hay on her own trident to keep her busy!) But the trick worked, and all the Orators and Senators gave tongue, like the Hannibal Chollops that they were. I remember the wife of a Senator who, apart from his politics, was very largely civilised, invited me to drop into the Senate and listen to her spouse 'twisting the Lion's tail.' It seemed an odd sort of refreshment to offer a visitor. I could not go, but I read his speech. [At the present time (autumn '35) I have also read with interest the apology offered by an American Secretary of State to Nazi Germany for unfavourable comments on that land by a New York Police Court Judge.] But those were great and spacious and friendly days in Washington which—politics apart—Allah had not altogether deprived of a sense of humour; and the food was a thing to dream of.

Through Roosevelt I met Professor Langley of the Smithsonian, an old man who had designed a model aeroplane driven—for petrol had not yet arrived—by a miniature flash-boiler engine, a marvel of delicate craftsmanship. It flew on trial over two hundred yards, and drowned itself in the waters of the Potomac, which was cause of great mirth and humour to the Press of his country. Langley took it coolly enough and said to me that, though he would never live till then, I should see the aeroplane established.

The Smithsonian, specially on the ethnological side, was a pleasant place to browse in. Every nation, like every individual, walks in a vain show— else it could not live with itself—but I never got over the wonder of a people who, having extirpated the aboriginals of their continent more completely than any modern race had ever done, honestly believed that they were a godly little New England community, setting examples to brutal mankind. This wonder I used to explain to Theodore Roosevelt, who made the glass cases of Indian relics shake with his rebuttals.

The next time I met him was in England, not long after his country had acquired the Philippines, and he—like an elderly lady with one babe— yearned to advise England on colonial administration. His views were sound enough, for his subject was Egypt as it was beginning to be then, and his text 'Govern or get out.' He consulted several people as to how far he could go. I assured him that the English would take anything from him, but were racially immune to advice.

I never met him again, but we corresponded through the years when he 'jumped' Panama from a brother-President there whom he described as 'Pithecanthropoid,' and also during the War, in the course of which I met two of his delightful sons. My own idea of him was that he was a much bigger man than his people understood or, at that time, knew how to use, and that he and they might have been better off had he been born twenty years later.

Meantime, our lives went on at the Bliss Cottage and, so soon as it was built, at Naulahka. To the former one day came Sam McClure, credited with being the original of Stevenson's Pinkerton in *The Wrecker*, but himself, far more original. He had been everything from a pedlar to a tintype photographer along the highways, and had held intact his genius and simplicity. He entered, alight with the notion for a new Magazine to be called 'McClure's.' I think the talk lasted some twelve—or it may have been seventeen—hours, before the notion was fully hatched out. He, like Roosevelt, was in advance of his age, for he looked rather straightly at practices and impostures which were in the course of being sanctified because they paid. People called it 'muck-raking' at the time, and it seemed to do no sort of good. I liked and admired McClure more than a little, for he was one of the few with whom three and a half words serve for a sentence, and as clean and straight as spring water. Nor did I like him less when he made a sporting offer to take all my output for the next few years at what looked like fancy rates. But the Committee of Ways and Means decided that futures were not to be dealt in. (I here earnestly commend to the attention of the ambitious young a text in the thirty-third chapter of Ecclesiasticus which runs: 'So long as thou livest and has breath in thee, give not thyself over to any.')

To 'Naulahka,' on a wet day, came from Scribner's of New York a large young man called Frank Doubleday, with a proposal, among other things, for a complete edition of my then works. One accepts or refuses things that really matter on personal and illogical grounds. We took to that young man at sight, and he and his wife became of our closest friends. In due time, when he was building up what turned into the great firm of Doubleday, Page & Co., and later Doubleday, Doran & Co., I handed over the American side of my business to him. Whereby I escaped many distractions for the rest of my life. Thanks to the large and intended gaps in the American Copyright law, much could be done by the enterprising not only to steal, which was natural, but to add to and interpolate and embellish the thefts with stuff I had never written. At first this annoyed me, but later I laughed; and Frank Doubleday chased the pirates up with cheaper and cheaper editions, so that their thefts became less profitable. There was no more pretence to morality in these gentlemen than in their brethren, the bootleggers of later years. As a pillar of the Copyright League (even he could not see the humour of it) once said, when I tried to bring him to book for a more than usually flagrant trespass: 'We thought there was money in it, so we did it.' It was, you see, his religion. By and large I should say that American pirates have made say half as many dollars out of my stuff as I am occasionally charged with having 'made' out of the legitimate market in that country.

Into this queer life the Father came to see how we fared, and we two went wandering into Quebec where, the temperature being 95 and all the world dressed all over after the convention of those days, the Father was much amazed. Then we visited at Boston his old friend, Charles Eliot Norton of Harvard, whose daughters I had known at The Grange in my boyhood and since. They were Brahmins of the Boston Brahmins, living delightfully, but Norton himself, full of forebodings as to the future of his land's soul, felt the established earth sliding under him, as horses feel coming earth-tremors.

He told us a tale of old days in New England. He and another Professor, wandering round the country in a buggy and discussing high and moral matters, halted at the farm of an elderly farmer well known to them who, in the usual silence of New England, set about getting the horse a bucket of water. The two men in the buggy went on with their discussion, in the course of which one of them said: 'Well, according to Montaigne,' and gave a quotation. Voice from the horse's head, where the farmer was holding the bucket: ' 'Tweren't Montaigne said that. 'Twere Montes-ki-ew.' And 'twas.

That, said Norton, was in the middle or late 'seventies. We two wandered about the back of Shady Hill in a buggy, but nothing of that amazing kind befell us. And Norton spoke of Emerson and Wendell Holmes and Longfellow and the Alcotts and other influences of the past as we returned to his library, and he browsed aloud among his books; for he was a scholar among scholars.

But what struck me, and he owned to something of the same feeling, was the apparent waste and ineffectiveness in the face of the foreign inrush, of all the indigenous effort of the past generation. It was then that I first began to wonder whether Abraham Lincoln had not killed rather too many autochthonous 'Americans' in the Civil War, for the benefit of their hastily imported Continental supplanters. This is black heresy, but I have since met men and women who have breathed it. The weakest of the old-type immigrants had been sifted and salted by the long sailing-voyage of those days. But steam began in the later 'sixties and early 'seventies, when human cargoes could be delivered with all their imperfections and infections in a fortnight or so. And one million more-or-less acclimatised Americans had been killed.

Somehow or other, between '92 and '96 we managed to pay two flying visits to England, where my people were retired and lived in Wiltshire; and we learned to loathe the cold North Atlantic more and more. On one trip our steamer came almost atop of a whale, who submerged just in time to clear us, and looked up into my face with an unforgettable little eye the size of a bullock's. Eminent Masters R.L.S. will remember what William Dent Pitman saw of 'haughty and indefinable' in the hairdresser's waxen model. When I was illustrating the *Just So Stories*, I remembered and strove after that eye.

We went once or twice to Gloucester, Mass., on a summer visit, when I attended the annual Memorial Service to the men drowned or lost in the cod-fishing schooners fleet. Gloucester was then the metropolis of that industry.

Now our Dr. Conland had served in that fleet when he was young. One thing leading to another, as happens in this world, I embarked on a little book which was called *Captains Courageous*. My part was the writing; his the details. This book took us (he rejoicing to escape from the dread respectability of our little town) to the shore-front, and the old T-wharf of Boston Harbour, and to queer meals in sailors' eating-houses, where he renewed his youth among ex-shipmates or their kin. We assisted hospitable tug-masters to help haul three- and four-stick schooners of Pocahontas coal all around the harbour; we boarded every craft that looked as if she might be useful, and we delighted ourselves to the limit of delight. Charts we got—old and new—and the crude implements of navigation such as they used off the Banks, and a battered boat-compass, still a treasure with me.

(Also, by pure luck, I had sight of the first sickening uprush and vomit of iridescent coal-dusted water into the hold of a ship, a crippled iron hulk, sinking at her moorings.) And Conland took large cod and the appropriate knives with which they are prepared for the hold, and demonstrated anatomically and surgically so that I could make no mistake about treating them in print. Old tales, too, he dug up, and the lists of dead and gone schooners whom he had loved, and I revelled in profligate abundance of detail—not necessarily for publication but for the joy of it. And he sent me—may he be forgiven!—out on a pollock-fisher, which is ten times fouler than any cod-schooner, and I was immortally sick, even though they tried to revive me with a fragment of unfresh pollock.

As though this were not enough, when, at the end of my tale, I desired that some of my characters should pass from San Francisco to New York in record time, and wrote to a railway magnate of my acquaintance asking what he himself would do, that most excellent man sent a fully worked-out time-table, with watering halts, changes of engine, mileage, track conditions and climates, so that a corpse could not have gone wrong in the schedule. My characters arrived triumphantly; and, then, a real live railway magnate was so moved after reading the book that he called out his engines and called out his men, hitched up his own private car, and set himself to beat *my* time on paper over the identical route, and succeeded. Yet the book was not all reporterage. I wanted to see if I could catch and hold something of a rather beautiful localised American atmosphere that was already beginning to fade. Thanks to Conland I came near this.

A million—or it may have been only forty—years later, a Super-film Magnate was in treaty with me for the film rights of this book. At the end of the sitting, my Daemon led me to ask if it were proposed to introduce much 'sex appeal' into the great work. 'Why, certainly,' said he. Now a happily married lady cod-fish lays about three million eggs at one confinement. I told him as much. He said: 'Is that so?' And went on about 'ideals.' . . . Conland had been long since dead, but I prayed that wherever he was, he might have heard.

And so, in this unreal life, indoors and out, four years passed, and a good deal of verse and prose saw the light. Better than all, I had known a corner of the United States as a householder, which is the only way of getting at a country. Tourists may carry away impressions, but it is the seasonal detail of small things and doings (such as putting up fly-screens and stove-pipes, buying yeast-cakes and being lectured by your neighbours) that bite in the lines of mental pictures. They were an interesting folk, but behind their desperate activities lay always, it seemed to me, immense and unacknowledged boredom—the dead-weight of material things passionately worked up into Gods, that only bored their worshippers more and worse and longer. The intellectual influences of their Continental immigrants were to come later. At this time they were still more or less connected with the English tradition and schools, and the Semitic strain had not yet been uplifted in a too-much-at-ease Zion. So far as I was concerned, I felt the atmosphere was to some extent hostile. The idea seemed to be that I was 'making money' out of America—witness the new house and the horses— and was not sufficiently grateful for my privileges. My visits to England and the talk there persuaded me that the English scene might be shifting to some new developments, which would be worth watching. A meeting of the Committee of Ways and Means came to the conclusion that Naulahka, desirable as it was, meant only 'a house' and not 'The House' of our dreams. So we loosed hold and, with another small daughter, born in the early spring snows and beautifully tanned in a sumptuous upper verandah, we took ship for England, after clearing up all our accounts. As Emerson wrote:

> *Would'st thou seal up the Avenues of ill?*
> *Pay every debt as though God wrote the bill.*

The end of '96 saw us in Torquay, where we found a house for our heads that seemed almost too good to be true. It was large and bright, with big rooms each and all open to the sun, the grounds embellished with great trees and the warm land dipping southerly to the clean sea under the Marychurch cliffs. It had been inhabited for thirty years by three old maids. We took it hopefully. Then we made two notable discoveries. Everybody was learning to ride things called 'bicycles.' In Torquay there was a circular cinder-track where, at stated hours, men and women rode solemnly round and round on them. Tailors supplied special costumes for this sport. Some-one—I think it was Sam McClure from America—had given us a tandem-bicycle, whose double steering-bars made good dependence for continuous domestic quarrel. On this devil's toast-rack we took exercise, each believing that the other liked it. We even rode it through the idle, empty lanes, and would pass or overtake without upset several carts in several hours. But, one fortunate day, it skidded, and decanted us on to the road-metal. Almost before we had risen from our knees, we made mutual confession of our common loathing of wheels, pushed the Hell-Spider home by hand, and rode it no more.

The other revelation came in the shape of a growing depression which enveloped us both—a gathering blackness of mind and sorrow of the heart, that each put down to new, soft climate and, without telling the other, fought against for long weeks. It was the Feng-shui—the Spirit of the house itself—that darkened the sunshine and fell upon us every time we entered, checking the very words on our lips.

A talk about a doubtful cistern brought another mutual confession. 'But I thought *you* liked the place?' 'But I made sure *you* did,' was the burden of our litanies. Using the cistern for a stalking-horse, we paid forfeit and fled. More than thirty years later on a motor-trip we ventured down the steep little road to that house, and met, almost unchanged, the gardener and his wife in the large, open, sunny stable-yard, and, quite unchanged, the same brooding Spirit of deep, deep Despondency within the open, lit rooms.

But while we were at Torquay there came to me the idea of beginning some tracts or parables on the education of the young. These, for reasons honestly beyond my control, turned themselves into a series of tales called *Stalky & Co.* My very dear Headmaster, Cormell Price, who had now turned into 'Uncle Crom' or just 'Crommy,' paid a visit at the time and we discussed school things generally. He said, with the chuckle that I had reason to know, that my tracts would be some time before they came to their own. On their appearance they were regarded as irreverent, not true to life, and rather 'brutal.' This led me to wonder, not for the first time, at which end of their carcasses grown men keep their school memories.

Talking things over with 'Crommy,' I reviled him for the badness and scantiness of our food at Westward Ho! To which he replied: 'We-el! For one thing, we were all as poor as church mice. Can you remember anyone who had as much as a bob a week pocket money? *I* can't. For another, a boy who is always hungry is more interested in his belly than in anything else.' (In the Boer War I learned that the virtue in a battalion living on what is known as 'Two and a half'—Army biscuits—a day is severe.) Speaking of sickness and epidemics, which were unknown to us, he said: 'I expect you were healthy because you lived in the open almost as much as Dartmoor ponies.' *Stalky & Co.* became the illegitimate ancestor of several stories of school-life whose heroes lived through experiences mercifully denied to me. It is still read ('35) and I maintain it is a truly valuable collection of tracts.

Our flight from Torquay ended almost by instinct at Rottingdean where the beloved Aunt and Uncle had their holiday house, and where I spent my very last days before sailing for India fourteen years back. In 1882 there had been but one daily bus from Brighton, which took forty minutes; and when a stranger appeared on the village green the native young would stick out their tongues at him. The Downs poured almost direct into the one village street and lay out eastward unbroken to Russia Hill above Newhaven. It was little altered in '96. My cousin, Stanley Baldwin, had married the eldest daughter of the Ridsdales out of the Dene—the big house that flanked one side of the green. My Uncle's 'North End House' commanded the other, and a third house opposite the church was waiting to be taken according to the decrees of Fate. The Baldwin marriage, then, made us free of the joyous young brotherhood and sisterhood of the Dene, and its friends.

The Aunt and the Uncle had said to us: 'Let the child that is coming to you be born in our house,' and had effaced themselves till my son John arrived on a warm August night of '97, under what seemed every good omen. Meantime, we had rented by direct interposition of Fate that third house opposite the church on the green. It stood in a sort of little island behind flint walls which we then thought were high enough, and almost beneath some big ilex trees. It was small, none too well built, but cheap, and so suited us who still remembered a little affair at Yokohama. Then there grew up great happiness between 'The Dene,' 'North End House' and 'The Elms.' One could throw a cricket ball from any one house to the other, but, beyond turning out at 2 A.M. to help a silly foxhound puppy who had stuck in a drain, I do not remember any violent alarms and excursions other than packing farm-carts filled with mixed babies—Stanley Baldwin's and ours— and despatching them into the safe clean heart of the motherly Downs for jam-smeared picnics. Those Downs moved me to write some verses called 'Sussex.' To-day, from Rottingdean to Newhaven is almost fully developed suburb, of great horror.

When the Burne-Jones' returned to their own 'North End House,' all was more than well. My Uncle's world was naturally not mine, but his heart and brain were large enough to take in any universe, and in the matter of doing one's own work in one's own way he had no doubts. His golden laugh, his delight in small things, and the perpetual war of practical jokes that waged between us, was refreshment after working hours. And when we cousins, Phil, his son, Stanley Baldwin and I, went to the beach and came back with descriptions of fat bathers, he would draw them, indescribably swag-bellied, wallowing in the surf. Those were exceedingly good days, and one's work came easily and fully.

Now even in the Bliss Cottage I had a vague notion of an Irish boy, born in India and mixed up with native life. I went as far as to make him the son of a private in an Irish Battalion, and christened him 'Kim of the 'Rishti'—short, that is, for Irish. This done, I felt like Mr. Micawber that I had as good as paid that I. O. U. on the future, and went after other things for some years.

In the meantime my people had left India for good, and were established in a small stone house near Tisbury, Wilts. It possessed a neat little stone-walled stable with a shed or two, all perfectly designed for clay and plaster of Paris works, which are not desired indoors. Later, the Father put up a tin tabernacle which he had thatched, and there disposed his drawing portfolios, big photo and architectural books, gravers, modelling-tools, paints, siccatives, varnishes, and the hundred other don't-you-touch-'ems that every right-minded man who works with his hands naturally collects. (These matters are detailed because they all come into the story.)

Within short walk of him lay Fonthill, the great house of Arthur Morrison, millionaire and collector of all manner of beautiful things, his wife contenting herself with mere precious and sub-precious stones. And my Father was free of all these treasures, and many others in such houses as 'Clouds,' where the Wyndhams lived, a few miles away. I think that both he and my Mother were happy in their English years, for they knew exactly what they did not want; and I knew that when I came over to see them I had no need to sing: 'Backward, turn backward, O Time in thy flight.'

In a gloomy, windy autumn *Kim* came back to me with insistence, and I took it to be smoked over with my Father. Under our united tobaccos it grew like the Djinn released from the brass bottle, and the more we explored its possibilities the more opulence of detail did we discover. I do not know what proportion of an iceberg is below waterline, but *Kim* as it finally appeared was about one-tenth of what the first lavish specification called for.

As to its form there was but one possible to the author, who said that what was good enough for Cervantes was good enough for him. To whom the Mother: 'Don't you stand in your wool-boots hiding behind Cervantes with *me!* You *know* you couldn't make a plot to save your soul.'

So I went home much fortified and *Kim* took care of himself. The only trouble was to keep him within bounds. Between us, we knew every step, sight and smell on his casual road, as well as all the persons he met. Once only, as I remember, did I have to bother the India Office, where there are four acres of books and documents in the basements, for a certain work on Indian magic which I always sincerely regret that I could not steal. They fuss about receipts there.

At 'The Elms,' Rottingdean, the sou'wester raged day and night, till the silly windows jiggled their wedges loose. (Which was why the Committee vowed never to have a house of their own with up-and-down windows. Cf. Charles Reade on that subject.) But I was quite unconcerned. I had my Eastern sunlight and if I wanted more I could get it at 'The Gables,' Tisbury. At last I reported *Kim* finished. 'Did *it* stop, or you?' the Father asked. And when I told him that it was *It*, he said: 'Then it oughn't to be too bad.'

He would take no sort of credit for any of his suggestions, memories or confirmations—not even for that single touch of the low-driving sunlight which makes luminous every detail in the picture of the Grand Trunk Road at eventide. The Himalayas I painted *all* by myself, as the children say. So also the picture of the Lahore Museum of which I had once been Deputy Curator for six weeks—unpaid but immensely important. And there was a half-chapter of the Lama sitting down in the blue-green shadows at the foot of a glacier, telling Kim stories out of the Jatakas, which was truly beautiful but, as my old Classic master would have said, 'otiose,' and it was removed almost with tears.

But the crown of the fun came when (in 1902) was issued an illustrated edition of my works, and the Father attended to *Kim*. He had the notion of making low-relief plaques and photographing them afterwards. Here it was needful to catch the local photographer, who, till then, had specialised in privates of the Line with plastered hair and skin-tight uniforms, and to lead him up the strenuous path of photographing dead things so that they might show a little life. The man was a bit bewildered at first, but he had a teacher of teachers, and so grew to understand. The incidental muck-heaps in the stable-yard were quite noticeable, though a loyal housemaid fought them broom-and-bucket, and Mother allowed messy half-born 'sketches' to be dumped by our careless hands on sofas and chairs. Naturally when he got his final proofs he was sure that 'it all ought to be done again from the beginning,' which was rather how I felt about the letterpress, but, if it be possible, he and I will do that in a better world, and on a scale to amaze Archangels.

There is one picture that I remember of him in the tin tabernacle, hunting big photos of Indian architecture for some utterly trivial detail in a corner of some plaque. He looked up as I came in and, rubbing his beard and carrying on his own thought, quoted: 'If you get simple beauty and naught else, You get about the best thing God invents.' It is the greatest of my many blessings that I was given grace to know them at the time, instead of having them brought to my remorseful notice too late.

I expect that is why I am perhaps a little impatient over the High Cannibalism as practised to-day.

And so much for *Kim* which has stood up for thirty-five years. There was a good deal of beauty in it, and not a little wisdom; the best in both sorts being owed to my Father.

A great, but frightening, honour came to me when I was thirty-three (1897) and was elected to the Athenaeum under Rule Two, which provides for admitting distinguished persons without ballot. I took council with Burne-Jones as to what to do. 'I don't dine there often,' said he. 'It frightens *me* rather, but we'll tackle it together.' And on a night appointed we went to that meal. So far as I recall we were the only people in that big dining-room, for in those days the Athenaeum, till one got to know it, was rather like a cathedral between services. But at any rate I had dined there, and hung my hat on Peg 33. (I have shifted it since.) Before long I realised that if one wanted to know anything from forging an anchor to forging antiquities one would find the world's ultimate expert in the matter at lunch. I managed to be taken into a delightful window-table, pre-empted by an old General, who had begun life as a Middy in the Crimea before he entered the Guards. In his later years he was a fearless yachtsman, as well as several other things, and he dealt faithfully with me when I made technical errors in any tale of mine that interested him. I grew very fond of him, and of four or five others who used that table.

One afternoon, I remember, Parsons of the *Turbinia* asked if I would care to see a diamond burned. The demonstration took place in a room crammed with wires and electric cells (I forget what their aggregate voltage was) and all went well for a while. The diamond's tip bubbled like cauliflower *au gratin*. Then there was a flash and a crash, and we were on the floor in darkness. But, as Parsons said, that was not the diamond's fault.

Among other pillars of the dear, dingy, old downstairs billiard-room was Hercules Ross, of the British Museum on the Eastern Antiquities side. Externally, he was very handsome, but his professional soul was black, even for that of a Curator—and my Father had been a Curator. (Note. It is entirely right that the English should mistrust and disregard all the Arts and most of the Sciences, for on that indifference rests their moral grandeur, but their starvation in their estimates is sometimes too marked.)

At this present age I do not lunch very often at the Athenaeum, where it has struck me that the bulk of the members are scandalously young, whether elected under Rule Two or by ballot of their fellow-infants. Nor do I relish persons of forty calling me 'Sir.'

My life made me grossly dependent on Clubs for my spiritual comfort. Three English ones, The Athenaeum, Carlton, and Beefsteak, met my wants, but the Beefsteak gave me most. Our company there was unpredictable, and one could say what one pleased at the moment without being taken at the foot of the letter. Sometimes one would draw a full house of five different professions, from the Bench to the Dramatic Buccaneer. Otherwhiles, three of a kind, chance-stranded in town, would drift into long, leisurely talk that ranged half earth over, and separate well pleased with themselves and their table-companions. And once, when I feared that I might have to dine alone, there entered a member whom I had never seen before, and have never met since, full of bird-preservation. By the time we parted what I did not know about bird sanctuaries was scarcely worth knowing. But it was best when of a sudden someone or something plunged us all in what you might call a general 'rag,' each man's tongue guarding his own head.

There is no race so dowered as the English with the gift of talking real, rich, allusive, cut-in-and-out 'skittles.' Americans are too much anecdotards; the French too much orators for this light-handed game, and neither race delivers itself so unreservedly to mirth as we do.

When I lived in Villiers Street, I picked up with the shore-end of a select fishing club, which met in a tobacconist's back-parlour. They were mostly small tradesmen, keen on roach, dace and such, but they too had that gift, as I expect their forbears had in Addison's time.

The late Doctor Johnson once observed that 'we shall receive no letters in the grave.' I am perfectly sure, though Boswell never set it down, that he lamented the lack of Clubs in that same place.

VI. SOUTH AFRICA

⊷§ BUT at the back of my head there was an uneasiness, based on things that men were telling me about affairs outside England. (The inhabitants of that country never looked further than their annual seaside resorts.) There was trouble too in South Africa after the Jameson Raid which promised, men wrote me, further trouble. Altogether, one had a sense of 'a sound of a going in the tops of the mulberry trees'—of things moving into position as troops move. And into the middle of it all came the Great Queen's Diamond Jubilee, and a certain optimism that scared me. The outcome, as far as I was concerned, took the shape of a set of verses called

'Recessional,' which were published in *The Times* in '97 at the end of the Jubilee celebrations. It was more in the nature of a *nuzz ur-wattu* (an averter of the Evil Eye), and—with the conservatism of the English—was used in choirs and places where they sing long after our Navy and Army alike had in the name of 'peace' been rendered innocuous. It was written just before I went off on Navy manœuvres with my friend Captain Bagley. When I returned it seemed to me that the time was ripe for its publication, so, after making one or two changes in it, I gave it to *The Times*. I say 'gave' because for this kind of work I did not take payment. It does not much matter what people think of a man after his death, but I should not like the people whose good opinion I valued to believe that I took money for verses on Joseph Chamberlain, Rhodes, Lord Milner or any of my South African verse in *The Times*.

It was this uneasiness of mine which led us down to the Cape in the winter of '97, taking the Father with us. There we lived in a boarding-house at Wynberg, kept by an Irishwoman, who faithfully followed the instincts of her race and spread miseries and discomforts round her in return for good monies. But the children throve, and the colour, light, and half-oriental manners of the land bound chains round our hearts for years to come.

It was here that I first met Rhodes to have any talk with. He was as inarticulate as a school-boy of fifteen. Jameson and he, as I perceived later, communicated by telepathy. But Jameson was not with him at that time. Rhodes had a habit of jerking out sudden questions as disconcerting as those of a child—or the Roman Emperor he so much resembled. He said to me apropos of nothing in particular: 'What's your dream?' I answered that he was part of it, and I think I told him that I had come down to look at things. He showed me some of his newly established fruit-farms in the peninsula, wonderful old Dutch houses, stalled in deep peace, and lamented the difficulty of getting sound wood for packing-cases and the shortcomings of native labour. But it was his wish and his will that there should be a fruit-growing industry in the Colony, and his chosen lieutenants made it presently come to pass. The Colony then owed no thanks to any Dutch Ministry in that regard. The racial twist of the Dutch (they had taken that title to themselves and called the inhabitants of the Low Countries 'Hollanders') was to exploit everything they could which was being done for them, to put every obstacle in the way of any sort of development, and to take all the cash they could squeeze out of it. In which respect they were no better and no worse than many of their brethren. It was against their creed to try and stamp out cattle-plagues, to dip their sheep, or to combat locusts, which in a country overwhelmingly pastoral had its drawbacks. Cape Town, as a big distributing centre, was dominated in many ways by rather nervous shop-keepers, who wished to stand well with their customers up-country, and who served as Mayors and occasional public officials. And the aftermath of the Jameson Raid had scared many people.

During the South African War my position among the rank and file came to be unofficially above that of most Generals. Money was wanted to procure small comforts for the troops at the Front and, to this end, the *Daily Mail* started what must have been a very early 'stunt.' It was agreed that I should ask the public for subscriptions. That paper charged itself with the rest. My verses ('The Absent-Minded Beggar') had some elements of direct appeal but, as was pointed out, lacked 'poetry.' Sir Arthur Sullivan wedded the words to a tune guaranteed to pull teeth out of barrel-organs. Anybody could do what they chose with the result, recite, sing, intone or reprint, etc., on condition that they turned in all fees and profits to the main account—'The Absend-minded Beggar Fund'—which closed at about a quarter of a million. Some of this was spent in tobacco. Men smoked pipes more than cigarettes at that epoch, and the popular brand was a cake— chewable also—called 'Hignett's True Affection.' My note-of-hand at the Cape Town depot was good for as much as I cared to take about with me. The rest followed. My telegrams were given priority by sweating R.E. sergeants from all sorts of congested depots. My seat in the train was kept for me by British Bayonets in their shirt-sleeves. My small baggage was fought for and servilely carried by Colonial details, who are not normally meek, and I was *persona gratissima* at certain Wynberg Hospitals where the nurses found I was good for pyjamas. Once I took a bale of them to the wrong nurse (the red capes confused me) and, knowing the matter to be urgent, loudly announced: 'Sister, I've got your pyjamas.' That one was neither grateful nor very polite.

My attractions led to every sort of delightful or sometimes sorrowful wayside intimacies with all manner of men: and only once did I receive a snub. I was going up to Bloemfontein just after its capture in a carriage taken from the Boers, who had covered its floors with sheep's guts and onions, and its side with caricatures of 'Chamberlain' on a gallows. Other- wise, there was nothing much except woodwork. Behind us was an open truck of British troops whom the Company wag was entertaining by mimick- ing their officers telling them how to pile horseshoes. As evening fell, I got from him a couple of three-wicked, signal-lamp candles, which gave us at least light to eat by. I naturally wanted to know how he had come by these desirable things. He replied: 'Look 'ere, Guv'nor, *I* didn't ask *you* 'ow you come by the baccy you dished out just now. *Can't* you bloody well leave me alone?'

In this same ghost-train an Indian officer's servant (Muhammedan) was worried on a point of conscience. 'Would this Government-issued tin of bully-beef be lawful food for a Muslim?' I told him that, when Islam wars with unbelievers, the Koran permits reasonable latitude of ceremonial obligations; and he need not hesitate. Next dawn, he was at my bunk-side with Anglo-India's morning cup of tea. (He must have stolen the hot water from the engine, for there was not a drop in the landscape.) When I asked how the miracle had come about, he replied, with the smile of my own Kadir Buksh: 'Millar, Sahib,' signifying that he had found (or 'made') it.

My Bloemfontein trip was on Lord Roberts' order to report and do what I was told. This was explained at the station by two strangers, who grew into my friends for life, H. A. Gwynne, then Head Correspondent of Reuter's, and Perceval Landon of *The Times*. 'You've got to help us edit a paper for the troops,' they said, and forthwith inducted me into the newly-captured 'office,' for Bloemfontein had fallen—Boer fashion—rather like an outraged Sunday School a few days before.

The compositors and the plant were also captives of our bow and spear and rather cross about it—especially the ex-editor's wife, a German with a tongue. When one saw a compositor, one told him to compose Lord Roberts' Official Proclamation to the deeply injured enemy. I had the satisfaction of picking up from the floor a detailed account of how Her Majesty's Brigade of Guards had been driven into action by the fire of our artillery; and a proof of a really rude leader about myself.

There was in that lull a large trade in proclamations—and butter at half a crown the pound. We used all the old stereos, advertising long-since-exhausted comestibles, coal and groceries (face-powder I think was the only surviving commodity in the Bloemfontein shops), and we enlivened their interstices with our own contributions, supplemented by the works of dusty men, who looked in and gave us very fine copy—mostly libellous.

Julian Ralph, the very best of Americans, was a co-editor also. And he had a grown son who went down with a fever unpleasantly like typhoid. We searched for a competent doctor, and halted a German who, so great was the terror of our arms after the 'capture,' demanded haughtily: 'But who shall pay me for my trouble if I come?' No one seemed to know, but several men explained who would pay him if he dallied on the way. He took one look at the boy's stomach, and said happily: 'Of *course* it is typhoid.' Then came the question how to get the case over to hospital, which was rank with typhoid, the Boers having cut the water supply. The first thing was to fetch down the temperature with an alcohol swabbing. Here we were at a standstill till some genius—I think it was Landon—said: 'I've noticed there's an officer's wife in the place who's wearing a fringe.' On this hint a man went forth into the wide dusty streets, and presently found her, fringe and all. Heaven knows how she had managed to wangle her way up, but she was a sportswoman of purest water. 'Come to my room,' said she, and in passing over the priceless bottle, only sighed: 'Don't use it *all*— unless you have to.' We ran the boy down from 103 to a generous 99 and pushed him into hospital, where it turned out that it was not typhoid after all but only bad veldt-fever.

First and last there were, I think, eight thousand cases of typhoid in Bloemfontein. Often to my knowledge both 'ceremonial' Union Jacks in a battalion would be 'in use' at the same time. Extra corpses went to the grave under the service blanket.

Our own utter carelessness, officialdom and ignorance were responsible for much of the death-rate. I have seen a Horse Battery 'dead to the wide' come in at midnight in raging rain and be assigned, by some idiot saving himself trouble, the site of an evacuated typhoid-hospital. Result—thirty cases after a month. I have seen men drinking raw Modder-River a few yards below where the mules were staling; and the organisation and siting of latrines seemed to be considered 'nigger-work.' The most important medical office in any Battalion ought to be Provost-Marshal of Latrines.

To typhoid was added dysentery, the smell of which is even more depressing than the stench of human carrion. One could wind the dysentery tents a mile off. And remember that, till we planted disease, the vast sun-baked land was antiseptic and sterilised—so much so that a clean abdominal Mauser-wound often entailed no more than a week of abstention from solid food. I found this out on a hospital-train, where I had to head off a mob of angry 'abdominals' from regular rations. That was when we were picking up casualties after a small affair called Paardeberg, and the lists—really about two thousand—were carefully minimised to save the English public from 'shock.' During this work I happened to fall unreservedly, in darkness, over a man near the train, and filled my palms with gravel. He explained in an even voice that he was 'fractured 'ip, sir. 'Ope you ain't 'urt yourself, sir.' I never got at this unknown Philip Sydney's name. They were wonderful even in the hour of death—these men and boys—lodge-keepers and ex-butlers of the Reserve and raw town-lads of twenty.

But to return to Bloemfontein. In an interval of our editorial labours, I went out of the town and presently met the 'solitary horseman' of the novels. He was a Conductor—Commissariat Sergeant—who reported that the 'flower of the British Army' had been ambushed and cut up at a place called 'Sanna's Post,' and passed on obviously discomposed. I had imagined the flower of that Army to be busied behind me reading our paper; but, a short while after, I met an officer who, in the old Indian days, was nick-named 'the Sardine.' He was calm, but rather fuzzy as to the outlines of his uniform, which was frayed and ripped by bullets. Yes, there had been trouble where he came from, but he was fuller for the moment of professional admiration.

'What was it like? They got us in a donga. Just like going into a theatre. "Stalls left, dress-circle right," don't you know? We just dropped into the trap, and it was "Infantry this way, please. Guns to the right, if you please." Beautiful bit of work! How many did they get of us? About twelve hundred, I think, and four—maybe six—guns. Expert job they made of it. That's the result of bill-stickin' expeditions.' And with more compliments to the foe, he too passed on.

By the time I returned to Bloemfontein the populace had it that eighty thousand Boers were closing in on the town at once, and the Press Censor (Lord Stanley, now Derby) was besieged with persons anxious to telegraph to Cape Town. To him a non-Aryan pushed a domestic wire 'weather here changeable.' Stanley, himself a little worried for the fate of some of his friends in that ambuscaded column, rebuked the gentleman.

The Sardine was right about the 'bill-sticking' expeditions. Wandering columns had been sent round the country to show how kind the British desired to be to the misguided Boer. But the Transvaal Boer, not being a town-bird, was unimpressed by the 'fall' of the Free State Capital, and ran loose on the veldt with his pony and Mauser.

So there had to be a battle, which was called the Battle of Kari Siding. All the staff of the *Bloemfontein Friend* attended. I was put in a Cape cart, with native driver containing most of the drinks, and with me was a well-known war-correspondent. The enormous pale landscape swallowed up seven thousand troops without a sign, along a front of seven miles. On our way we passed a collection of neat, deep and empty trenches well undercut for shelter on the shrapnel-side. A young Guards officer, recently promoted to *Brevet*-Major—and rather sore with the paper that we had printed it *Branch*—studied them interestedly. They were the first dim lines of the dug-out, but his and our eyes were held. The Hun had designed them *secundum artem*, but the Boer had preferred the open within reach of his pony. At last we came to a lone farmhouse in a vale adorned with no less than five white flags. Beyond the ridge was a sputter of musketry and now and then the whoop of a field-piece. 'Here,' said my guide and guardian, 'we get out and walk. Our driver will wait for us at the farm-house.' But the driver loudly objected. 'No, sar. They shoot. They shoot me.' 'But they are white-flagged all over,' we said. 'Yess, sar. That *why*,' was his answer, and he preferred to take his mules down into a decently remote donga and wait our return.

The farm-house (you will see in a little why I am so detailed) held two men and, I think, two women, who received us disinterestedly. We went on into a vacant world full of sunshine and distances, where now and again a single bullet sang to himself. What I most objected to was the sensation of being under aimed fire—being, as it were, required as a head. 'What are they doing this for?' I asked my friend. 'Because they think we are the Something Light Horse. They ought to be just under this slope.' I prayed that the particularly Something Light Horse would go elsewhere, which they presently did, for the aimed fire slackened and a wandering Colonial, bored to extinction, turned up with news from a far flank. 'No; nothing doing and no one to see.' Then more cracklings and a most cautious move forward to the lip of a large hollow where sheep were grazing. Some of them began to drop and kick. 'That's both sides trying sighting-shots,' said my companion. 'What range do you make it?' I asked. 'Eight hundred, at the nearest. That's close quarters nowadays. You'll never see anything closer than this. Modern rifles make it impossible. We're hung up till something cracks somewhere.' There was a decent lull for meals on both sides, interrupted now and again by sputters. Then one indubitable shell—ridiculously like a pip-squeak in that vastness but throwing up much dirt. 'Krupp! Four or six pounder at extreme range,' said the expert. 'They still think we're the—Light Horse. They'll come to be fairly regular from now on.' Sure enough, every twenty minutes or so, one judgmatic shell pitched on our slope. We waited, seeing nothing in the emptiness, and hearing only a faint murmur as of wind along gas-jets, running in and out of the unconcerned hills.

Then pom-poms opened. These were nasty little one-pounders, ten in a belt (which usually jammed about the sixth round). On soft ground they merely thudded. On rock-face the shell breaks up and yowls like a cat. My friend for the first time seemed interested. 'If these are *their* pom-poms, it's Pretoria for us,' was his diagnosis. I looked behind me—the whole length of South Africa down to Cape Town—and it seemed very far. I felt that I could have covered it in five minutes under fair conditions, but— *not* with those aimed shots up my back. The pom-poms opened again at a bare rock-reef that gave the shells full value. For about two minutes a file of racing ponies, their tails and their riders' heads well down, showed and vanished northward. 'Our pom-poms,' said the correspondent. 'Le Gallais, I expect. *Now* we shan't be long.' All this time the absurd Krupp was faithfully feeling for us, *vice*—Light Horse, and, given a few more hours, might perhaps hit one of us. Then to the left, almost under us, a small piece of hanging woodland filled and fumed with our shrapnel much as a man's moustache fills with cigarette-smoke. It was most impressive and lasted for quite twenty minutes. Then silence; then a movement of men and horses from our side up the slope, and the hangar our guns had been hammering spat steady fire at them. More Boer ponies on more skylines; a last flurry of pom-poms on the right and a little frieze of far-off meek-tailed ponies, already out of rifle range.

'*Maffeesh*,' said the correspondent, and fell to writing on his knee. 'We've shifted 'em.'

Leaving our infantry to follow men on pony-back towards the Equator, we returned to the farm-house. In the donga where he was waiting someone squibbed off a rifle just after we took our seats, and our driver flogged out over the rocks to the danger of our sacred bottles.

Then Bloemfontein, and Gwynne storming in late with his accounts complete—one hundred and twenty-five casualties, and the general opinion that 'French was a bit of a butcher' and a tale of the General commanding the cavalry who absolutely refused to break up his horses by galloping them across raw rock—'not for any dam' Boer.'

Months later, I got a cutting from an American paper, on information from Geneva—even then a pest-house of propaganda—describing how I and some officers—names, date, and place correct—had entered a farm-house where we found two men and three women. We had dragged the women from under the bed where they had taken refuge (I assure you that no Tantie Sannie of that day could bestow herself beneath any known bed) and, giving them a hundred yards' start, had shot them down as they ran.

Even then, the beastliness struck me as more comic than significant. But by that time I ought to have known that it was the Hun's reflection of his own face as he spied at our back-windows. He had thrown in the 'hundred yards' start' touch as a tribute to our national sense of fair play.

From the business point of view the war was ridiculous. We charged ourselves step by step with the care and maintenance of all Boerdom—women and children included. Whence horrible tales of our atrocities in the concentration-camps.

One of the most widely exploited charges was our deliberate cruelty in making prisoners' tents and quarters open to the north. A Miss Hobhouse among others was loud in this matter, but she was to be excused.

We were showing off our newly-built 'Woolsack' to a great lady on her way up-country, where a residence was being built for her. At the larder the wife pointed out that it faced south—that quarter being the coldest when one is south of the Equator. The great lady considered the heresy for a moment. Then, with the British sniff which abolishes the absurd, 'Hmm. I shan't allow *that* to make any difference to *me*.'

Some Army and Navy Stores Lists were introduced into the prisoners' camps, and the women returned to civil life with a knowledge of corsets, stockings, toilet-cases, and other accessories frowned upon by their clergymen and their husbands. *Qua* women they were not very lovely, but they made their men fight, and they knew well how to fight on their own lines.

In the give-and-take of our work our troops got to gauge the merits of the commando-leaders they were facing. As I remember the scale, De Wet, with two hundred and fifty men, was to be taken seriously. With twice that number he was likely to fall over his own feet. Smuts (of Cambridge) warring, men assured me, in a black suit, trousers rucked to the knees, and a top-hat, could handle five hundred but, beyond that, got muddled. And so with the others. I had the felicity of meeting Smuts as a British General, at the Ritz during the Great War. Meditating on things seen and suffered, he said that being hunted about the veldt on a pony made a man think quickly, and that perhaps Mr. Balfour (as he was then) would have been better for the same experience.

Each commando had its own reputation in the field, and the grizzlier their beards the greater our respect. There was an elderly contingent from Wakkerstroom which demanded most cautious handling. They shot, as you might say, for the pot. The young men were not so good. And there were foreign contingents who insisted on fighting after the manner of Europe. These the Boers wisely put in the forefront of the battle and kept away from. In one affair the Zarps—the Transvaal Police—fought brilliantly and were nearly all killed. But they were Swedes for the most part, and we were sorry.

Occasionally foreign prisoners were gathered in. Among them I remember a Frenchman who had joined for pure logical hatred of England, but, being a professional, could not resist telling us how we ought to wage the war. He was quite sound but rather cantankerous.

The 'war' became an unpleasing composte of 'political considerations,' social reform, and housing; maternity-work and variegated absurdities. It is possible, though I doubt it, that first and last we may have killed four thousand Boers. Our own casualties, mainly from preventible disease, must have been six times as many.

The junior officers agreed that the experience ought to be a 'first-class dress-parade for Armageddon,' but their practical conclusions were mis-leading. Long-range, aimed rifle-fire would do the work of the future: troops would never get nearer each other than half a mile, and Mounted Infantry would be vital. This was because, having found men on foot cannot overtake men on ponies, we created eighty thousand of as good Mounted Infantry as the world had seen. For these Western Europe had no use. Artillery preparation of wire-works, such as were not at Magersfontein, was rather overlooked in the reformers' schemes, on account of the difficulty of bringing up ammunition by horse-power. The pom-poms, and Lord Dundonald's galloping light-gun carriages, ate up their own weight in shell in three or four minutes.

In the ramshackle hotel at Bloemfontein, where the Correspondents lived and the Officers dropped in, one heard free and fierce debate as points came up, but—since no one dreamt of the internal-combustion engine that was to stand the world on its thick head, and since our wireless apparatus did not work in those landscapes—we were all beating the air.

Eventually the 'war' petered out on political lines. Brother Boer—and all ranks called him that—would do everything except die. Our men did not see why they should perish chasing stray commandos, or festering in block-houses, and there followed a sort of demoralising 'handy-pandy' of alternate surrenders complicated by exchange of Army tobacco for Boer brandy which was bad for both sides.

At long last, we were left apologising to a deeply-indignant people, whom we had been nursing and doctoring for a year or two; and who now expected, and received, all manner of free gifts and appliances for the farming they had never practised. We put them in a position to uphold and expand their primitive lust for racial domination, and thanked God we were 'rid of a knave.'

*   *   *   *   *

Into these shifts and changes we would descend yearly for five or six months from the peace of England to the deeper peace of the 'Woolsack,' and life under the oak-trees overhanging the patio, where mother-squirrels taught their babies to climb, and in the stillness of hot afternoons the fall of an acorn was almost like a shot. To one side of us was a pine and euca-lyptus grove, heavy with mixed scent; in front our garden, where anything one planted out in May became a blossoming bush by December. Behind all, tiered the flank of Table Mountain and its copses of silver-trees, flanking scarred ravines. To get to Rhodes's house, 'Groote Schuur,' one used a path through a ravine set with hydrangeas, which in autumn (England's spring) were one solid packed blue river. To this Paradise we moved each year-end from 1900 to 1907—a complete equipage of governess, maids and children, so that the latter came to know and therefore, as children will, to own the Union Castle Line—stewards and all: and on any change of governess to instruct the new hand how cabins were set away for a long voyage and 'what went where.' Incidentally we lost two governesses and one loved cook by marriage, the tepid seas being propitious to such things.

Ship-board life, going and coming, was a mere prolongation of South Africa and its interests. There were Jews a plenty from the Rand; Pioneers; Native Commissioners dealing with Basutos or Zulus; men of the Matabele Wars and the opening of Rhodesia; prospectors; politicians of all stripes, all full of their business; Army officers also, and from one of these, when I expected no such jewel, I got a tale called 'Little Foxes'—so true in detail that an awed Superintendent of Police wrote me out of Port Sudan, demanding how I had come to know the very names of the hounds in the very pack to which he had been Whip in his youth. But, as I wrote him back, I had been talking with the Master.

Jameson, too, once came home with us, and disgraced himself at the table which we kept for ourselves. A most English lady with two fair daughters had been put there our first day out, and when she rightly enough objected to the quality of the food, and called it prison fare, Jameson said: 'Speaking as one of the criminal classes, I assure you it is worse.' At the next meal the table was all our own.

But the outward journey was the great joy because it always included Christmas near the Line, where there was no room for memories; seasonable inscriptions written in soap on the mirrors by skilly stewards; and a glorious fancy-dress ball. Then, after the Southern Cross had well risen above the bows, the packing away of heavy kit, secure it would not be needed till May, the friendly, well-known Mountain and the rush to the garden to see what had happened in our absence; the flying barefoot visit to our neighbours the Strubens at Strubenheim, where the children were regularly and lovingly spoiled; the large smile of the Malay laundress, and the easy pick-up-again of existence.

Life went well then, and specially for the children, who had all the beasts on the Rhodes estate to play with. Uphill lived the lions, Alice and Jumbo, whose morning voices were the signal for getting up. The zebra paddock, which the emus also used, was immediately behind the 'Woolsack' —a slope of scores of acres. The zebras were always play-fighting like Lions and Unicorns on the Royal Arms; the game being to grab the other's fore-leg below the knee if it could not snatch it away. No fence could hold them when they cared to shift. Jameson and I once saw a family of three returning from an excursion. A heavy sneeze-wood-post fence and wires lay in the path, blind-tight except where the lowest wire spanned a small ditch. Here Papa kneeled, snouted under the wire till it slid along his withers, hove it up, and so crawled through. Mamma and Baby followed in the same fashion. At this, an aged lawn-mower pony who was watching conceived he might also escape, but got no further than backing his fat hind-quarters against one of the posts, and turning round from time to time in wonder that it had not given way. It was, as Jameson said, the complete allegory of the Boer and the Briton.

In another paddock close to the house lived a spitting llama, whose peculiarity the children learned early. But their little visitors did not, and, if they were told to stand close to the fence and make noises, they did—once. You can see the rest.

But our most interesting visitor was a bull-kudu of some eighteen hands. He would jump the seven-foot fence round our little peach orchard, hook a loaded branch in the great rings of his horns, rend it off with a jerk, eat the peaches, leaving the stones, and lift himself over the wires, like a cloud, up the flank of Table Mountain. Once, coming home after dinner, we met him at the foot of the garden, gigantic in the moonlight, and fetched a compass round him, walking delicately, the warm red dust in our shoes: because we knew that a few days before the keepers had given him a dose of small shot in his stern for chasing somebody's cook.

The children's chaperon on their walks was a bulldog—Jumbo—of terrific aspect, to whom all Kaffirs gave full right of way. There was a legend that he had once taken hold of a native and, when at last removed, came away with his mouth full of the native. Normally, he lay about the house and apologised abjectly when anyone stepped on him. The children fed him with currant buns and then, remembering that currants were indigestible, would pick them out of his back teeth while he held his dribbling jaws carefully open.

A baby lion was another of our family for one winter. His mother, Alice, desiring to eat him when born, he was raked out with broomsticks from her side and then to 'Groote Schuur' where, in spite of the unwilling attentions of a she-dog foster-mother (he had of course the claws of a cat) he pined. The wife hinted that, with care, he might recover. 'Very good,' said Rhodes. 'I'll send him over to the "Woolsack" and you can try.' He came, with corrugated-iron den and foster-mother complete. The latter the wife dismissed; went out and bought stout motor-gloves, and the largest of babies' bottles, and fed him forthwith. He highly approved of this, and ceased not to pull at the bottle till it was all empty. His tummy was then slapped, as it might have been a water-melon, to be sure that it rang full, and he went to sleep. Thus he lived and throve in his den, which the children were forbidden to enter, lest their caresses should injure him.

When he was about the size of a large rabbit, he cut little pins of teeth, and made coughing noises which he was persuaded were genuine roars. Later, he developed rickets, and I was despatched to an expert at Cape Town to ask for a cure. 'Too much milk,' said the expert. 'Give him real, not cold-storage, boiled mutton-broth.' This at first he refused to touch in the saucer, but was induced to lick the wife's dipped finger, whence he removed the skin. His ears were boxed, and he was left alone with the saucer to learn table-manners. He wailed all night, but in the morning lapped like a lion among Christians, and soon got rid of his infirmity. For three months he was at large among us, incessantly talking to himself as he wandered about the house or in the garden where he stalked butterflies. He dozed on the stoep, I noticed, due north and south, looking with slow eyes up the length of Africa—always a little aloof, but obedient to the children, who at that time wore little more than one garment apiece. We returned him in perfect condition on our departure for England, and he was then the size of a bull-terrier but not so high. Rhodes and Jameson were both away. He was put in a cage, fed, like his family, on imperfectly thawed cold-storage meats fouled in the grit of his floor, and soon died of colic. But M'slibaan, which we made Matabele for 'Sullivan,' as fitted his Matabele ancestry, was always honoured among the many kind ghosts that inhabited the 'Woolsack.'

Lions, as pets, are hardly safe after six months old; but here is an exception. A man kept a lioness up-country till she was a full year old. Then, with deep regret on both sides, sent her to Rhodes's Zoo. Six months later he came down, and with a girl who did not know what fear was entered her cage, where she received him fawning, rolling, crooning—almost weeping with love and delight. Theoretically, of course, he and the girl ought to have been killed, but they took no hurt at all.

During the war, by some luck our water-supply had not been restricted, and our bath was of the type you step down into and soak in at full length. Hence also Gwynne, filthy after months of the veldt, standing afar off like a leper. ('I say, I want a bath and—there's my kit in the garden. No, I haven't left it on the stoep. It's crawling.') Many came. As the children put it: 'There's always lots of dirty ones.'

When Rhodes was hatching his scheme of the Scholarships, he would come over and, as it were, think aloud or discuss, mainly with the wife, the expense side of the idea. It was she who suggested that £250 a year was not enough for scholars who would have to carry themselves through the long intervals of an Oxford 'year.' So he made it three hundred. My use to him was mainly as a purveyor of words; for he was largely inarticulate. After the idea had been presented—and one had to know his code for it—he would say: 'What am I trying to express? Say it, *say* it.' So I would say it, and if the phrase suited not, he would work it over, chin a little down, till it satisfied him.

The order of his life at 'Groote Schuur' was something like this. The senior guest allotted their rooms to men who wished to 'see' him. They did not come except for good reason connected with their work, and they stayed till Rhodes 'saw' them, which might be two or three days. His heart compelled him to lie down a good deal on a huge couch on the marble-flagged verandah facing up Table Mountain towards the four-acre patch of hydrangeas, which lay out like lapis-lazuli on the lawns. He would say: 'Well, So-and-so. I see you. What is it?' And the case would be put.

There was a man laying the Cape-to-Cairo telegraph, who had come to a stretch of seventy miles beside a lake, where the ladies of those parts esteemed copper above gold, and took it from the poles for their adornment. What to do? When he had finished his exposition Rhodes, turning heavily on his couch, said: 'You've got some sort of lake there, haven't you? Lay it like a cable. Don't bother me with a little thing like that.' Palaver done set, and at his leisure the man returned.

One met interesting folk at 'Groote Schuur' meals which often ended in long talks of the days of building up Rhodesia.

During the Matabele War Rhodes, with some others, under a guide, had wandered on horseback beyond the limits of safety, and had to take refuge in some caves. The situation was eminently unhealthy, and in view of some angry Matabeles hunting them they had to spur out of it. But the guide, just when the party were in the open, was foolish enough to say something to the effect that Rhodes's 'valuable life' was to be considered. Upon which Rhodes pulled up and said: 'Let's get this straight before we go on. You led us into this mess, didn't you?' 'Yes, sir, yes. But *please* come on.' 'No. Wait a minute. Consequently you're running to save your own hide, aren't you?' 'Yes, sir. We all are.' 'That's all right. I only wanted to have it settled. *Now* we'll come on.' And they did, but it was a close shave. I heard this at his table, even as I heard his delayed reply to a query by a young officer who wished to know what Rhodes thought of him and his career. Rhodes postponed his answer till dinner and then, in his characteristic voice, laid down that the young man would eminently succeed but only to a certain point, because he was always thinking of his career and not of the job he was doing. Thirty later years proved the truth of his verdict.

VII. THE VERY-OWN HOUSE

How can I turn from any fire
On any man's hearth-stone?
I know the wonder and desire
That went to build my own.
                    THE FIRES

⤷ ALL this busy while the Committee of Ways and Means kept before them the hope of a house of their very own—a real House in which to settle down for keeps—and took trains on rails and horsed carriages of the age to seek it. Our adventures were many and sometimes grim—as when a 'comfortable nursery' proved to be a dark padded cell at the end of a discreet passage! Thus we quested for two or three years, till one summer day a friend cried at our door: 'Mr. Harmsworth has just brought round one of those motor-car things. Come and try it!'

It was a twenty-minute trip. We returned white with dust and dizzy with noise. But the poison worked from that hour. Somehow, an enterprising Brighton agency hired us a Victoria-hooded, carriage-sprung, carriage-braked, single-cylinder, belt-driven, fixed-ignition Embryo which, at times, could cover eight miles an hour. Its hire, including 'driver,' was three and a half guineas a week. The beloved Aunt, who feared nothing created, said 'Me too!' So we three house-hunted together taking risks of ignorance that made me shudder through after-years. But we went to Arundel and back, which was sixty miles, and returned in the same ten-hour day! We, and a few other desperate pioneers, took the first shock of outraged public opinion. Earls stood up in their belted barouches and cursed us. Gipsies, governess-carts, brewery waggons—all the world except the poor patient horses who would have been quite quiet if left alone joined in the commination service, and *The Times* leaders on 'motor-cars' were eolithic in outlook.

Then I bought me a steam-car called a 'Locomobile,' whose nature and attributes I faithfully drew in a tale called 'Steam Tactics.' She reduced us to the limits of fatigue and hysteria, all up and down Sussex. Next came the earliest Lanchester whose springing, even at that time, was perfect. But no designer, manufacturer, owner, nor chauffeur knew anything about anything. The heads of the Lanchester firm would, after furious telegrams, visit us as friends (we were all friends in those days) and sit round our hearth speculating Why What did That. Once, the proud designer—she was his newest baby—took me as far as Worthing, where she fainted opposite a vacant building-lot. This we paved completely with every other fitting that she possessed ere we got at her trouble. We then re-assembled her, a two hours' job. After which, she spat boiling water over our laps, but we stuffed a rug into the geyser and so spouted home.

But it was the heart-breaking Locomobile that brought us to the house called 'Bateman's.' We had seen an advertisement of her, and we reached her down an enlarged rabbit-hole of a lane. At very first sight the Committee of Ways and Means said: 'That's her! The Only She! Make an honest woman of her—quick!' We entered and felt her Spirit—her Feng-shui—to be good. We went through every room and found no shadow of ancient regrets, stifled miseries, nor any menace, though the 'new' end of her was three hundred years old. To our woe the Owner said: 'I've just let it for twelve months.' We withdrew, each repeatedly telling the other that no sensible person would be found dead in the stuffy little valley where she stood. We lied thus while we pretended to look at other houses till, a year later, we saw her advertised again, and got her.

When all was signed and sealed, the seller said: 'Now I can ask you something. How are you going to manage about getting to and from the station? It's nearly four miles, and I've used up two pair of horses on the hill here.' 'I'm thinking of using this sort of contraption,' I replied from my seat in—Jane Cakebread Lanchester, I think, was her dishonourable name. 'Oh! *Those* things haven't come to stay!' he returned. Years afterwards I met him, and he confided that had he known what I had guessed, he would have asked twice the money. In three years from our purchase the railway station had passed out of our lives. In seven, I heard my chauffeur say to an underpowered visiting sardine-tin: 'Hills? There ain't any hills on the London road.'

The House was not of a type to present to servants by lamp or candle-light. Hence electricity, which in 1902 was a serious affair. We chanced, at a week-end visit, to meet Sir William Willcocks, who had designed the Assouan Dam—a trifling affair on the Nile. Not to be over-crowed, we told him of our project for de-clutching the water-wheel from an ancient mill at the end of our garden, and using its microscopical mill-pond to run a turbine. That was enough! 'Dam?' said he. '*You* don't know anything about dams or turbines. *I'll* come and look.' That Monday morn he came with us, explored the brook and the mill-sluit, and foretold truly the exact amount of horse-power that we should get out of our turbine—'Four and a half and no more.' But he called me Egyptian names for the state of my brook, which, till then, I had deemed picturesque. 'It's all messed up with tree and bushes. Cut 'em down and slope the banks to one in three.' 'Lend me a couple of Fellahîn Battalions and I'll begin,' I said.

He said also: 'Don't run your light cable on poles. Bury it.' So we got a deep-sea cable which had failed under test at twelve hundred volts—our voltage being one hundred and ten—and laid him in a trench from the Mill to the house, a full furlong, where he worked for a quarter of a century. At the end of that time he was a little fatigued, and the turbine had worn as much as one-sixteenth of an inch on her bearings. So we gave them both honourable demission—and never again got anything so faithful.

Of the little one-street village up the hill we only knew that, according to the guide-books, they came of a smuggling, sheep-stealing stock, brought more or less into civilisation within the past three generations. Those of them who worked for us, and who I presume would to-day be called 'Labour,' struck for higher pay than they had agreed on as soon as we were committed to our first serious works. My foreman and general contractor, himself of their race, and soon to become our good friend, said: 'They think they've got ye. They think there's no harm in tryin' it.' There was not. I had sense enough to feel that most of them were artists and craftsmen, either in stone or timber, or wood-cutting, or drain-laying or—which is a gift—the aesthetic disposition of dirt; persons of contrivance who could conjure with any sort of material. As our electric-light campaign developed, a London contractor came down to put a fifteen-inch eduction-pipe through the innocent-seeming mill-dam. His imported gang came across a solid core of ancient brickwork about as work-able as obsidian. They left, after using very strong words. But every other man of 'our folk' had known exactly where and what that core was, and when

'Lunnon' had sufficiently weakened it, they 'conjured' the pipe quietly through what remained.

The only thing that ever shook them was when we cut a little under the Mill foundations to fix the turbine; and found that she sat on a crib or raft of two-foot-square elm logs. What we took came out, to all appearance, as untouched as when it had been put under water. Yet, in an hour, the great baulk, exposed to air, became silver dust, and the men stood round marvelling. There was one among them, close upon seventy when we first met, a poacher by heredity and instinct, a gentleman who, when his need to drink was on him, which was not too often, absented himself and had it out alone; and he was more 'one with Nature' than whole parlours full of poets. He became our special stay and councillor. Once we wanted to shift a lime and a witch-elm into the garden proper. He said not a word till we talked of getting a tree-specialist from London. 'Have it *as* you're minded. I dunno as I should if I was you,' was his comment. But this we understood that he would take charge when the planets were favourable. Presently, he called up four of his own kin (also artists) and brushed us aside. The trees came away kindly. He placed them, with due regard for their growth for the next two or three generations; supported them, throat and bole, with stays and stiffenings, and bade us hold them thus for four years. All fell out as he had foretold. The trees are now close on forty foot high and have never flinched. Equally, a well-grown witch-elm that needed discipline, he climbed into and topped, and she carries to this day the graceful dome he gave her. In his later years—he lived to be close on eighty-five—he would, as I am doing now, review his past, which held incident enough for many unpublishable volumes. He spoke of old loves, fights, intrigues, anonymous denunciations 'by such folk as knew writing,' and vindictive conspiracies carried out with oriental thoroughness. Of poaching he talked in all its branches, from buying *Cocculus Indicus* for poisoning fish in ponds, to the art of making silk-nets for trout-brooks—mine among them, and he left a specimen to me; and of pitched battles (guns barred) with heavy-handed keepers, in the old days in Lord Ashburnham's woods where a man might pick up a fallow-deer. His sags were lighted with pictures of Nature, as he, indeed, knew her; night-pieces and dawn-breakings; stealthy returns and the thinking out of alibis, all naked by the fire, while his clothes dried; and of the face and temper of the next twilight under which he stole forth to follow his passion. His wife, after she had known us for ten years, would range through a past that accepted magic, witchcraft and love-philtres, for which last there was a demand as late as the middle 'sixties.

She described one midnight ritual at the local 'wise woman's' cottage, when a black cock was killed with curious rites and words, and '*all* de time dere was, like, *someone* trying to come *through* at ye from outside in de dark. Dunno as I believe so much in such things *now*, but when I was a maid I—I justabout *did!*' She died well over ninety, and to the last carried the tact, manner and presence, for all she was so small, of an old-world Duchess.

There were interesting and helpful outsiders, too. One was a journeyman bricklayer who, I remember, kept a store of gold sovereigns loose in his pocket, and kindly built us a wall; but so leisurely that he came to be almost part of the establishment. When we wished to sink a well opposite some cottages, he said he had the gift of water-finding, and I testify that, when he held one fork of the hazel Y and I the other, the thing bowed itself against all the grip of my hand over an unfailing supply.

Then, out of the woods that know everything and tell nothing, came two dark and mysterious Primitives. They had heard. The would sink that well, for they had the 'gift.' Their tools were an enormous wooden trug, a portable windlass whose handles were curved, and smooth as ox-horns, and a short-handled hoe. They made a ring of brickwork on the bare ground and, with their hands at first, grubbed out the dirt beneath it. As the ring sank they heightened it, course by course, grubbing out with the hoe, till the shaft, true as a rifle-barrel, was deep enough to call for their Father of Trugs, which one brother down below would fill, and the other haul up on the magic wind-lass. When we stopped, at twenty-five feet, we had found a Jacobean tobacco-pipe, a worn Cromwellian latten spoon and, at the bottom of all, the bronze cheek of a Roman horse-bit.

In cleaning out an old pond which might have been an ancient marl-pit or mine-head, we dredged two intact Elizabethan 'sealed quarts' that Christopher Sly affected, all pearly with the patina of centuries. Its deepest mud yielded us a perfectly polished Neolithic axe-head with but one chip on its still venomous edge.

These things are detailed that you may understand how, when my cousin, Ambrose Poynter, said to me: 'Write a yarn about Roman times here,' I was interested. 'Write,' said he, 'about an old Centurion of the Occupation telling his experiences to his children.' 'What is his name?' I demanded, for I move easiest from a given point. 'Parnesius,' said my cousin; and the name stuck in my head. I was then on Committee of Ways and Means (which had grown to include Public Works and Communications) but, in due season, the name came back—with seven other inchoate devils. I went off Committee, and began to 'hatch,' in which state I was 'a brother to dragons and a companion to owls.' Just beyond the west fringe of our land, in a little valley running from Nowhere to Nothing-at-all, stood the long, over-grown slap-heap of a most ancient forge, supposed to have been worked by the Phoenicians and Romans and, since then, uninterruptedly till the middle of the eighteenth century. The bracken and rush-patches still hid stray pigs of iron, and if one scratched a few inches through the rabbit-shaven turf, one came on the narrow mule-tracks of peacock-hued furnace-slag laid down in Elizabeth's day. The ghost of a road climbed up out of this dead arena, and crossed our fields, where it was known as 'The Gunway,' and popularly connected with Armada times. Every foot of that little corner was alive with ghosts and shadows. Then, it pleased our children to act for us, in the open, what they remembered of A Midsummer-Night's Dream. Then a friend gave them a real birch-bark canoe, drawing at least three inches, in which they went adventuring on the brook. And in a near pasture of the water-meadows lay out an old and unshifting Fairy Ring.

You see how patiently the cards were stacked and dealt into my hands? The Old Things of our Valley glided into every aspect of our outdoor works. Earth, Air, Water and People had been—I saw it at last—in full conspiracy to give me ten times as much as I could compass, even if I wrote a complete history of England, as that might have touched or reached our Valley.

I went off at score—not on Parnesius, but a story told in a fog by a petty Baltic pirate, who had brought his galley to Pevensey and, off Beachy Head—where in the War we heard merchant-ships being torpedoed—had passed the Roman fleet abandoning Britain to her doom. That tale may have served as a pipe-opener, but one could not see its wood for its trees, so I threw it away.

I carried the situation to the little house in Wiltshire, where my Father and Mother were installed; and smoked it over with the Father, who said—not for the first time: 'Most things in this world are accomplished by judicious leaving alone.' So we played cribbage (he had carved a perfect Lama and a little Kim for my two pegs), while the Mother worked beside us, or, each taking a book, lapsed into the silence of entire mutual comprehension. One night, apropos of nothing at all, the Father said: 'And you'll have to look up your references rather more carefully, won't you?' That had *not* been my distinction on the little *Civil and Military*.

This led me on another false scent. I wrote a tale told by Daniel Defoe in a brickyard (we had a real one of our own at that time where we burned bricks for barns and cottages to the exact tints we desired) of how he had been sent to stampede King James II, then havering about Thames mouth, out of an England where no party had any use for him. It turned out a painstaken and meritorious piece of work, overloaded with verified references, with about as much feeling to it as a walking-stick. So it also was discarded, with a tale of Doctor Johnson telling the children how he had once thrown his spurs out of a boat in Scotland, to the amazement of one Boswell. Evidently my Daemon would not function in brickyards or schoolrooms. Therefore, like Alice in Wonderland, I turned my back on the whole thing and walked the other way. Therefore, the whole thing set and linked itself. I fell first upon Normans and Saxons. Parnesius came later, directly out of a little wood above the Phoenician forge; and the rest of the tales in *Puck of Pook's Hill* followed in order. The Father came over to see us and, hearing 'Hal o' the Draft,' closed in with fore-reaching pen, presently ousted me from my table, and inlaid the description of Hal's own drawing-knife. He liked that tale, and its companion piece 'The Wrong Thing' (*Rewards and Fairies*) which latter he embellished, notably in respect to an Italian fresco-worker, whose work never went 'deeper than the plaster.' He said that 'judicious leaving alone' did not apply between artists.

Of 'Dymchurch Flit,' with which I was always unashamedly content, he asked: 'Where did you get that lighting from?' It had come of itself. *Qua* workmanship, that tale and two night-pieces in 'Cold Iron' (*Rewards and*

Fairies) are the best in that kind I have ever made, but somehow 'The Treasure and the Law' (*Puck of Pook's Hill*) always struck me as too heavy for its frame.

Yet that tale brought me a prized petty triumph. I had put a well into the wall of Pevensey Castle *circa* A.D. 1100, because I needed it there. Archeologically, it did not exist till this year (1935) when excavators brought such a well to light. But that I maintain was a reasonable gamble. Self-contained castles must have self-contained water supplies. A longer chance that I took in my Roman tales was when I quartered the Seventh Cohort of the Thirtieth (Ulpia Victrix) Legion on the Wall, and asserted that there Roman troops used arrows against the Picts. The first shot was based on honest 'research'; the second was legitimate inference. Years after the tale was told, a digging-party on the Wall sent me some heavy four-sided, Roman made, 'killing' arrows found *in situ* and—most marvellously—a rubbing of a memorial-tablet to the Seventh Cohort of the Thirtieth Legion! Having been brought up in a suspicious school, I suspected a 'leg-pull' here, but was assured that the rubbing was perfectly genuine.

I embarked on *Rewards and Fairies*—the second book—in two minds. Stories a plenty I had to tell, but how many would be authentic and how many due to 'induction'? There was moreover the old Law: 'As soon as you find you can do anything, do something you can't.'

My doubt cleared itself with the first tale 'Cold Iron,' which gave me my underwood: 'What else could I have done?'—the plinth of all structures. Yet, since the tales had to be read by children, before people realised that they were meant for grown-ups; and since they had to be a sort of balance to, as well as a seal upon, some aspects of my 'Imperialistic' output in the past, I worked the material in three or four overlaid tints and textures, which might or might not reveal themselves according to the shifting light of sex, youth, and experience. It was like working lacquer and mother o' pearl, a natural combination, into the same scheme as niello and grisaille, and trying not to let the joins show.

So I loaded the book up with allegories and allusions, and verified references until my old Chief would have been almost pleased with me; put in three or four really good sets of verses; the bones of one entire historical novel for any to clothe who cared; and even slipped in a cryptogram, whose key I regret I must have utterly forgotten. It was glorious fun; and I knew it must be very good or very bad because the series turned itself off just as *Kim* had done.

Among the verses in *Rewards* was one set called 'If,' which escaped from the book, and for a while ran about the world. They were drawn from Jameson's character, and contained councils of perfection most easy to give. Once started, the mechanisation of the age made them snowball themselves in a way that startled me. Schools, and places where they teach, took them for the suffering Young—which did me no good with the Young when I met them later. ('Why did you write that stuff? I've had to write it out twice as an impot.') They were printed as cards to hang up in offices and bedrooms; illuminated text-wise and anthologised to weariness. Twenty-seven of the Nations of the Earth translated them into their seven-and-twenty tongues, and printed them on every sort of fabric.

Some years after the War a kind friend hinted that my two innocent little books might have helped towards begetting the 'Higher Cannibalism' in biography. By which I understood him to mean the exhumation of scarcely cold notorieties, defenceless females for choice, and tricking them out with sprightly inferences and 'sex'-deductions to suit the mood of the market. It was an awful charge, and anyway I felt that others had qualified as Chief Morticians to that trade.

For rest and refreshment and dearly-loved experiments and anxieties, during the six months or so of each year that we stayed in England, there was always the House and the land, and on occasion the Brook at the foot of our garden, which would flood devastatingly. As she supplied the water for our turbine, and as the little weir which turned her current into the little mill-race was of a frail antiquity, one had to attend to her often and at once, and always at the most inconvenient moment.

Undiscerning folks would ask: 'What do you find to *do* in the country?' Our answer was: 'Everything except time to do it.'

We began with tenants—two or three small farmers on our very few acres—from whom we learned that farming was a mixture of farce, fraud, and philanthropy that stole the heart out of the land. After many, and some comic experiences, we fell back on our own county's cattle—the big, red, Sussex breed who make beef and not milk. One got something at least for one's money from the mere sight of them, and they did not tell lies. Rider Haggard would visit us from time to time and give of his ample land-wisdom. I remember I planted some new apple-trees in an old orchard then rented by an Irishman, who at once put in an agile and hungry goat. Haggard met the combination suddenly one morning. He had gifts of speech, and said very clearly indeed that one might as well put Satan in an orchard as a goat. I forget what—though I acted on it—he said about tenants. His comings were always a joy to us and the children, who followed him like hounds in the hope of 'more South African stories.' Never was a better tale-teller or, to my mind, a man with a more convincing imagination. We found by accident that each could work at ease in the other's company. So he would visit me, and I him, with work in hand; and between us we could even hatch out tales together—a most exacting test of sympathy.

I was honoured till he died by the friendship of a Colonel Wemyss Feilden, who moved into the village to inherit a beautiful little William and Mary house on the same day as we came to take over 'Bateman's.' He was in soul and spirit Colonel Newcome; in manner as diffident and retiring as an old maid out of *Cranford*; and up to his eighty-second year could fairly walk me off my feet, and pull down pheasants from high heaven. He had begun life in the Black Watch with whom, outside Delhi during the Mutiny, he heard one morning as they were all shaving that a 'little fellow called Roberts' had captured single-handed a rebel Standard and was coming through the Camp. 'We all turned out. The boy was on horseback looking rather pleased with himself, and his mounted Orderly carried the Colour behind him. We cheered him with the lather on our faces.'

After the Mutiny he sold out, and having interests in Natal went awhile to South Africa. Next, he ran the blockade of the U.S. Civil War, and wedded his Southern wife in Richmond with a ring hammered out of an English sovereign 'because there wasn't any gold in Richmond just then.' Mrs. Feilden at seventy-five was in herself fair explanation of all the steps he had taken—and forfeited.

He came to be one of Lee's aides-de-camp, and told me how once on a stormy night, when he rode in with despatches, Lee had ordered him to take off his dripping cloak and lie by the fire; and how when he waked from badly needed sleep, he saw the General on his knees before the flame drying the cloak. 'That was just before the surrender,' said he. 'We had finished robbing the grave, and we'd begun on the cradle. For those last three months I was with fifteen thousand boys under seventeen, and I don't remember any one of them even smiling.'

Bit by bit I came to understand that he was a traveller and an Arctic explorer, in possession of the snow-white Polar ribbon; a botanist and naturalist of reputation; and himself above all.

When Rider Haggard heard these things, he rested not till he had made the Colonel's acquaintance. They cottoned to each other on sight and sound; South Africa in the early days being their bond. One evening, Haggard told us how his son had been born on the edge of Zulu, I think, territory, the first white child in those parts. 'Yes,' said the Colonel, quietly out of his corner. 'I and'—he named two men—'rode twenty-seven miles to look at him. We hadn't seen a white baby for some time.' Then Haggard remembered that visit of strangers.

And once there came to us with her married daughter the widow of a Confederate Cavalry leader; both of them were what you might call 'unre-constructed' rebels. Somehow, the widow mentioned a road and a church beside a river in Georgia. 'It's still there, then?' said the Colonel, giving it its name. 'Why do you ask?' was the quick reply. 'Because, if you look in such-and-such a pew, you might find my initials. I cut them there the night ——'s Cavalry stabled their horses there.' There was a pause. ' 'Fore God, then, *who* are you?' she gasped. He told her. 'You knew my husband?' 'I served under him. He was the only man in our corps who wore a white collar.' She pelted him with questions, and the names of the old dead. 'Come away,' whispered her daughter to me. 'They don't want *us*.' Nor did they for a long hour.

Sooner or later, all sorts of men cast up at our house. From India naturally; from the Cape increasingly after the Boer War and our half-yearly visits there; from Rhodesia when that province was in the making; from Australia, with schemes for emigration which one knew Organised Labour would never allow to pass its legislatures; from Canada, when 'Imperial Preference' came to the fore, and Jameson, after one bitter experience, cursed 'that dam' dancing-master (Laurier) who had bitched the whole show'; and from off main-line Islands and Colonies—men of all makes, each with his life-tale, grievance, idea, ideal, or warning.

There was an ex-Governor of the Philippines, who had slaved his soul out for years to pull his charge into some sort of shape and—on a turn of the political wheel at Washington—had been dismissed at literally less notice than he would have dared to give a native orderly. I remembered not a few men whose work and hope had been snatched from under their noses, and my sympathy was very real. His account of Filipino political 'leaders,' writing and shouting all day for 'independence' and running round to him after dark to be assured that there was no chance of the dread boon bein granted—'because then we shall most probably all be killed'—was cheeringly familiar.

The difficulty was to keep these interests separate in the head; but the grind of adjusting the mental eye to new perspectives was good for the faculties. Besides this *viva voca*, there was always heavy written work, three-fourths of which was valueless, but for the sake of the possibly worth-while residue all had to be gone through. This was specially the case during the three years before the War, when warnings came thick and fast, and the wise people to whom I conveyed them said: 'Oh, but you're *so-o*—extreme.'

Blasts of extravagant publicity alternated with my officework. In the late summer of '06, for example, we took ship to Canada, which I had not seen in any particularity for many years, and of which I had been told that it was coming out of its spiritual and material subjection to the United States. Our steamer was an Allen Liner with the earliest turbines and wireless. In the wireless-room, as we were feeling our way blind throught the straits of Belle Isle, a sister ship, sixty miles ahead, morsed that the fog with her was even thicker. Said a young engineer in the doorway: 'Who's yon talking, Jock? Ask him if he's done drying his socks.' And the old professional jest crackled out through the smother. It was my first experience of practical wireless.

At Quebec we met Sir William Van Horne, head of the whole C.P.R. system, but, on our wedding trip fifteen years before, a mere Divisional Superintendent who had lost a trunk of my wife's and had stood his Division on its head to find it. His deferred, but ample revenge was to give us one whole Pullman car with coloured porter complete, to take and use and hitch on to and declutch from any train we chose, to anywhere we fancied, for as long as we liked. We took it, and did all those things to Vancouver and back again. When we wished to sleep in peace, it slid off into still, secret freight-yards till morning. When we would eat, *chefs* of the great mail trains, which it had honoured by its attachment, asked us what we would like. (It was the season of blueberries and wild duck.) If we even looked as though we wanted anything, that thing would be waiting for us a few score miles up the line. In this manner and in such state we progressed, and the procession and the progress was meat and drink to the soul of William the coloured porter, our Nurse, Valet, Seneschal, and Master of Ceremonies. (More by token, the wife understood coloured folk, and that put William all at ease.) Many people would come aboard to visit us at halting-places, and there were speeches of sorts to be prepared and delivered at the towns. In the first case: ''Nother depytation, Boss,' from William behind enormous flower-pieces; '*and* more bo-kays for de Lady.' In the second: 'Dere's a speech doo at ——. You go right ahaid with what you're composin', Boss. Jest put your feets out an' I'll shine 'em meanwhile.' So, brushed up and properly shod, I was ushered into the public eye by the immortal William.

In some ways it was punishing 'all out' work, but in all ways worth it. I had been given an honorary degree, my first, by the McGill University at Montreal. That University received me with interest, and after I had delivered a highly moral discourse, the students dumped me into a fragile horse-vehicle, which they hurtled through the streets. Said one nice child sitting in the hood of it: 'You gave us a dam' dull speech. Can't you say anything amusin' now?' I could but express my fears for the safety of the conveyance, which was disintegrating by instalments.

In '15 I met some of the those boys digging trenches in France.

No words of mine can give any notion of the kindness and good-will lavished on us through every step of our road. I tried, and failed to do so in a written account of it. (*Letters to the Family*.) And always the marvel—to which the Canadians seemed insensible—was that on one side of an imaginary line should be Safety, Law, Honour, and Obedience, and on the other frank, brutal decivilisation; and that, despite this, Canada should be impressed by any aspect whatever of the United States. Some hint of this too I strove to give in my *Letters*.

Before we parted, William told us a tale of a friend of his who was consumed with desire to be a Pullman porter 'bekase he had watched me doin' it, an' thought he could do it—jest by watchin' me.' (This was the burden of his parable, like a deep-toned, locomotive bell.) Overborne at last, William wangled for his friend the coveted post—'next car ahaid to mine . . . I got *my* folks to baid early 'kase I guessed he'd be needin' me soon. . . . But *he* thought he could do it. And den all *his* folk in *his* car, dey all wanted to go to baid at de same time—like dey allus do. An' he tried—Gawd knows he tried—to 'commodate 'em all de same time an' he couldn't. He jes' couldn't. . . . He didn't know haow. He thought he did bekase he had,' etc. etc. 'An' den he quit . . . he jes' quit.' A long pause.

'Jumped out of window?' we demanded.

'No. Oh no. Dey wasn't no jump to him dat night. He went into de broom-closet—'kase I found him dar—an' he cried, an' all his folks slammin' on de broom-house door an' cussin' him 'kase dey wanted to go to baid. An' he couldn't put 'em dar. He couldn't put 'em. He thought,' etc. etc. 'An' den? Why o' course I jes' whirled in an' put 'em to baid for him an' when I told 'em how t'wuz with dat sorerful cryin' nigger, dey laughed. Dey laughed heaps an' heaps. . . . But he thought he could do it by havin' watched me do it.'

A few weeks after we returned from the wonderful trip, I was notified that I had been awarded the Nobel Prize of that year for Literature. It was a very great honour, in all ways unexpected.

It was necessary to go to Stockholm. Even while we were on the sea, the old King of Sweden died. We reached the city, snow-white under sun, to find all the world in evening dress, the official mourning which is curiously impressive. Next afternoon, the prize-winners were taken to be presented to the new King. Winter darkness in those latitudes fall at three o'clock, and it was snowing. One half of the vast acreage of the Palace sat in darkness, for there lay the dead King's body. We were conveyed along interminable corridors looking out into black quadrangles, where snow whitened the cloaks of the sentries, the breeches of old-time cannon, and the shot-piles alongside of them. Presently, we reached a living world of more corridors and suites all lighted up, but wrapped in that Court hush which is like no other silence on earth. Then, in a great lit room, the weary-eyed, over-worked, new King, saying to each the words appropriate to the occasion. Next, the Queen, in marvellous Mary Queen of Scots mourning, a few words, and the return piloted by soft-footed Court officials through a stillness so deep that one heard the click of the decorations on their uniforms. They said that the last words of the old King had been: 'Don't let them shut the theatres for me.' So Stockholm that night went soberly about her pleasures, all dumbed down under the snow.

Morning did not come till ten o'clock, and one lay abed in thick dark, listening to the blunted grind of the trams speeding the people to their workday's work. But the ordering of their lives was reasonable, thought out, and most comfortable for all classes in the matters of food, housing, the lesser but more desirable decencies, and the consideration given to the Arts. I had only known the Swede as a first-class immigrant in various parts of the earth. Looking at his native land I could guess whence he drew his strength and directness. Snow and frost are no bad nurses.

At that epoch staid women attached to the public wash-houses washed in a glorious lather of soap, worked up with big bunches of finest pine-shavings (when you think of it, a sponge is almost as dirty a tool as the permanent tooth-brush of the European), men desirous of the most luxurious bath known to civilisation. But foreigners did not always catch the idea. Hence this tale told to me at a winter resort in the deep, creamy contralto of the North by a Swedish lady who took, and pronounced, her English rather biblically. The introit you can imagine for yourself. Here is the finale: 'And then she—the old woman com-ed—came—in to wash that man. But he was angered—angry. He wented—he went dee-ep into the water and he say-ed—said—"Go a-way!" And she sayed, "But I comm to wash you, sare." And she made to do that. But he tur-ned over up-on his fa-ace, and wa-ved his legs in the airs and he sayed: "Go a-dam-way away!" So she went to the Direktor and she say-ed: "Comm he-ere. There are a mads in my bath, which will not let me wash of him." But the Direktor say-ed to her: "Oh, that are not a mads. That are an Englishman. He will himself—he will wash himself." '

VIII. WORKING-TOOLS

EVERY man must be his own law in his own work, but it is a poor-spirited artist in any craft who does not know how the other man's work should be done or could be improved. I have heard as much criticism among hedgers and ditchers and woodmen of a companion's handling of spade, bill-hook, or axe, as would fill a Sunday paper. Carters and cattleman are even more meticulous, since they must deal with temperaments and seasonal instabilities. We had once on the farms a pair of brothers between ten and twelve. The younger could deal so cunningly with an intractable cart-mare who rushed her gates, and for choice diagonally, that he was called in to take charge of her as a matter of course. The elder, at eleven, could do all that his strength allowed, and the much more than ancestral craft had added, with any edged tool or wood. Modern progress has turned them into meritorious menials.

One of my cattleman had a son who at eight could appraise the merits and character of any beast in his father's care, and was on terms of terrifying familiarity with the herd-bull, whom he would slap on the nose to make him walk disposedly before us when visitors came. At eighteen, he would have been worth two hundred a year to begin with on any ranch in the Dominions. But he was 'good at his books,' and is now in a small grocery, but wears a black coat on the Sabbath. Which things are a portent.

I have told what my early surroundings were, and how richly they furnished me with material. Also, how rigorously newspaper spaces limited my canvasses and, for the reader's sake, prescribed that within these limits must be some sort of beginning, middle, and end. My ordinary reporting, leader- and note-writing carried the same lesson, which took me an impatient while to learn. Added to this, I was almost nightly responsible for my output to visible and often brutally voluble critics at the Club. They were not concerned with my dreams. They wanted accuracy and interest, but first of all accuracy.

My young head was in a ferment of new things seen and realised at every turn and—that I might in any way keep abreast of the flood—it was necessary that every word should tell, carry, weigh, taste and, if need were, smell. Here the Father helped me incomparably by his 'judicious leaving alone.' 'Make your own experiments,' said he. 'It's the only road. If I helped, I'd hinder.' So I made my own experiments and, of course, the viler they were the more I admired them.

Mercifully, the mere act of writing was, and always has been, a physical pleasure to me. This made it easier to throw away anything that did not turn out well: and to practise, as it were, scales.

Verse, naturally, came first, and here the Mother was at hand, with now and then some shrivelling comment that infuriated me. But, as she said: 'There's no Mother in Poetry, my dear.' It was she, indeed, who had collected and privately printed verses written at school up to my sixteenth year, which I faithfully sent out from the little House of the Dear Ladies. Later, when the notoriety came, 'in they broke, those people of importance,' and the innocent thing 'came on to the market,' and Philadelphia lawyers, a breed by itself, wanted to know, because they had paid much money for an old copy, what I remembered about its genesis. They had been first written in a stiff, marble-backed MS. book, the front page of which the Father had inset with a scandalous sepia-sketch of Tennyson and Browning in procession, and a spectacled school-boy bringing up the rear. I gave it, when I left school, to a woman who returned it to me many years later—for which she will take an even higher place in Heaven than her natural goodness ensures—and I burnt it, lest it should fall into the hands of 'lesser breeds without the (Copyright) law.'

I forget who started the notion of my writing a series of Anglo-Indian tales, but I remember our council over the naming of the series. They were originally much longer than when they appeared, but the shortening of them, first to my own fancy after rapturous re-readings, and next to the space available, taught me that a tale from which pieces have been raked out is like a fire that has been poked. One does not know that the operation has been performed, but everyone feels the effect. Note, though, that the excised stuff must have been honestly written for inclusion. I found that when, to save trouble, I 'wrote short' *ab initio* much salt went out of the work. This supports the theory of the chimaera which, having bombinated and been removed, *is* capable of producing secondary causes *in vacuo*.

This leads me to the higher Editing. Take of well-ground Indian Ink as much as suffices and a camel-hair brush proportionate to the interspaces of your lines. In an auspicious hour, read your final draft and consider faithfully every paragraph, sentence and word, blacking out where requisite. Let it lie by to drain as long as possible. At the end of that time, re-read and you should find that it will bear a second shortening. Finally, read it aloud alone and at leisure. Maybe a shade more brushwork will then indicate or impose itself. If not, praise Allah and let it go, and 'when thou hast done, repent not.' The shorter the tale, the longer the brushwork and, normally, the shorter the lie-by, and *vice versa*. The longer the tale, the less brush but the longer lie-by. I have had tales by me for three or five years which shortened themselves almost yearly. The magic lies in the Brush and the Ink. For the Pen, when it is writing, can only scratch; and bottle ink is not to compare with the ground Chinese stick. *Experto crede.*

Let us now consider the Personal Daemon of Aristotle and others, of whom it has been truthfully written, though not published:

This is the doom of the Makers—their Daemon lives in their pen.
If he be absent or sleeping, they are even as other men.
But if he be utterly present, and they swerve not from his behest,
The word that he gives shall continue, whether in earnest or jest.

Most men, and some most unlikely, keep him under an alias which varies with their literary or scientific attainments. Mine came to me early when I sat bewildered among other notions, and said: 'Take this and no other.' I obeyed, and was rewarded. It was a tale in the little Christmas Magazine *Quartette* which we four wrote together, and it was called 'The Phantom Rickshaw.' Some of it was weak, much was bad and out of key; but it was my first serious attempt to think in another man's skin.

After that I learned to lean upon him and recognise the sign of his approach. If ever I held back, Ananias fashion, anything of myself (even though I had to throw it out afterwards) I paid for it by missing what I *then* knew the tale lacked. As an instance, many years later I wrote about a mediaeval artist, a monastery, and the premature discovery of the microscope. ('The Eye of Allah.') Again and again it went dead under my hand, and for the life of me I could not see why. I put it away and waited. Then said my Daemon —and I was meditating something else at the time—'Treat it as an illuminated manuscript.' I had ridden off on hard black-and-white decoration, instead of pumicing the whole thing ivory-smooth, and loading it with thick colour and gilt. Again, in a South African, post-Boer War tale called 'The Captive,' which was built up round the phrase 'a first-class dress parade for Armageddon,' I could not get my lighting into key with the tone of the monologue. The background insisted too much. My Daemon said at last: 'Paint the background first once for all, as hard as a public-house sign, and leave it alone.' This done, the rest fell into place with the American accent and outlook of the teller.

My Daemon was with me in the *Jungle Books, Kim,* and both Puck books, and good care I took to walk delicately, lest he should withdraw. I know that he did not, because when those books were finished they said so themselves with, almost, the water-hammer click of a tap turned off. One of the clauses in our contract was that I should never follow up 'a success,' for by this sin fell Napoleon and a few others. *Note here.* When your Daemon is in charge, do not try to think consciously. Drift, wait, and obey.

I am afraid that I was not much impressed by reviews. But my early days in London were unfortunate. As I got to know literary circles and their critical output, I was struck by the slenderness of some of the writers' equipment. I could not see how they got along with so casual a knowledge of French work and, apparently, of much English grounding that I had supposed indispensable. Their stuff seemed to be a day-to-day traffic in generalities, hedged by trade considerations. Here I expect I was wrong, but, making my own tests (the man who had asked me out to dinner to discover what I had read gave me the notion), I would ask simple questions, misquote or misattribute my quotations; or (once or twice) invent an author. The result did not increase my reverence. Had they been newspaper men in a hurry, I should have understood; but the gentlemen were presented to me as Priests and Pontiffs. And the generality of them seemed to have followed other trades—in banks or offices—before coming to the Ink; whereas I was free born. It was pure snobbism on my part, but it served to keep me inside myself, which is what snobbery is for.

I would not to-day recommend any writer to concern himeslf overly with reviews. London is a parish, and the Provincial Press has been syndicated, standardised, and smarmed down out of individuality. But there remains still a little fun in that fair. In Manchester was a paper called *The Manchester Guardian*. Outside the mule-lines I had never met anything that could kick or squeal so continuously, or so completely round the entire compass of things. It suspected me from the first, and when my 'Imperialistic' iniquities were established after the Boer War, it used each new book of mine for a shrill recount of my previous sins (exactly as C—— used to do) and, I think, enjoyed itself. In return I collected and filed its more acid but uncommonly well-written leaders for my own purposes. After many years, I wrote a tale ('The Wish House') about a woman of what was called 'temperament' who loved a man and who also suffered from a cancer on her leg—the exact situation carefully specified. The review came to me with a gibe on the margin from a faithful friend: 'You threw up a catch *that* time!' The review said that I had revived Chaucer's Wife of Bath even to the 'mormal on her shinne.' And it looked just like that too! There was no possible answer so, breaking my rule not to have commerce with any paper, I wrote to *The Manchester Guardian* and gave myself 'out—caught to leg.' The reply came from an evident human being (I had thought red-hot linotypes composed their staff) who was pleased with the tribute to his knowledge of Chaucer.

Per contra, I have had miraculous escapes in technical matters, which make me blush still. Luckily the men of the seas and the engine-room do not write to the Press, and my worst slip is still underided.

The nearest shave that ever missed me was averted by my Daemon. I was at the moment in Canada, where a young Englishman gave me, as a personal experience, a story of a body-snatching episode in deep snow, perpetrated in some lonely prairie-town and culminating in purest horror. To get it out of the system I wrote it detailedly, and it came away just a shade too good; too well-balanced; too slick. I put it aside, not that I was actively uneasy about it, but I wanted to make sure. Months passed, and I started a tooth which I took to the dentist in the little American town near 'Naulahka.' I had to wait a while in his parlour, where I found a file of bound *Harper's Magazines*—say six hundred pages to the volume—dating from the 'fifties. I picked up one, and read as undistractedly as the tooth permitted. There I found my tale, identical in every mark—frozen ground, frozen corpse stiff in its fur robes in the buggy—the inn-keeper offering it a drink—and so on to the ghastly end. Had I published that tale, what could have saved me from the charge of deliberate plagiarism? *Note here.* Always, in our trade, look a gift horse at both ends and in the middle. He may throw you.

But here is a curious case. In the late summer, I think, of '13, I was invited to Manœuvres round Frensham Ponds at Aldershot. The troops were from the Eighth Division of the coming year—Guardsmen, Black Watch, and the rest, down to the horsed maxims—two per battalion. Many of the officers had been juniors in the Boer War, known to Gwynne, one of the guests, and some to me. When the sham fight was developing, the day turned blue-hazy, the sky lowered, and the heat struck like the Karroo, as one scuttled among the heaths, listening to the uncontrolled clang of the musketry fire. It came over me that anything might be afoot in such weather, pom-poms for instance, half heard on a flank, or the glint of a helio through a cloud-drift. In short I conceived the whole pressure of our dead of the Boer War flickering and re-forming as the horizon flickered in the heat; the galloping feet of a single horse, and a voice once well-known that passed chanting ribaldry along the flank of a crack battalion. ('But Winnie is one of the lost—poor dear!' was that song, if any remember it or its Singer in 1900-1901.) In an interval, while we lay on the grass, I told Gwynne what was in my head; and some officers also listened. The finale was to be Manœuvres abandoned and a hurried calling-off of all arms by badly frightened Commandants—the men themselves sweating with terror though they knew not why.

Gwynne played with the notion, and added details of Boer fighting that I did not know; and I remember a young Duke of Northumberland, since dead, who was interested. The notion so obsessed me that I wrote out the beginning at once. But in cold blood it seemed more and more fantastic and absurd, unnecessary and hysterical. Yet, three or four times I took it up and, as many, laid it down. After the War I threw the draft away. It would have done no good, and might have opened the door, and my mail, to unprofitable discussion. For there is a type of mind that dives after what it calls 'psychical experiences.' And I am in no way 'psychic.' Dealing as I have done with large, superficial areas of incident and occasion, one is bound to make a few lucky hits or happy deductions. But there is no need to drag in the 'clairvoyance,' or the rest of the modern jargon. I have seen too much evil and sorrow and wreck of good minds on the road to Endor to take one step along that perilous track. Once only was I sure that I had 'passed beyond the bounds of ordinance.' I dreamt that I stood, in my best clothes, which I do not wear as a rule, one in a line of similarly habited men, in some vast hall, floored with rough-jointed stone slabs. Opposite me, the width of the hall, was another line of persons and the impression of a crowd behind them. On my left some ceremony was taking place that I wanted to see, but could not unless I stepped out of my line because the fat stomach of my neighbour on my left barred my vision. At the ceremony's close, both lines of spectators broke up and moved forward and met, and the great space filled with people. Then a man came up behind me, slipped his hand beneath my arm, and said: 'I want a word with you.' I forget the rest: but it had been a perfectly clear dream, and it stuck in my memory. Six weeks or more later, I attended in my capacity of a Member of the War Graves Commission a ceremony at Westminster Abbey, where the Prince of Wales dedicated a plaque to 'The Million Dead' of the Great War. We Commissioners lined up facing, across the width of the Abbey Nave, more members of the Ministry and a big body of the public behind them, all in black clothes. I could see nothing of the ceremony because the stomach of the man on my left barred my vision. Then, my eye was caught by the cracks of the stone flooring, and I said to myself: 'But here is where I have been!' We broke up, both lines flowed forward and met, and the Nave filled with a crowd, through which a man came up and slipped his hand upon my arm saying: 'I want a word with you, please.' It was about some utterly trivial matter that I have forgotten.

But how, and why, had I been shown an unreleased roll of my life-film? For the sake of the 'weaker brethren'—and sisters—I made no use of the experience.

In respect to verifying one's references, which is a matter in which one can help one's Daemon, it is curious how loath a man is to take his own medicine. Once, on a Boxing Day, with hard frost coming greasily out of the ground, my friend, Sir John Bland-Sutton, the head of the College of Surgeons, came down to 'Bateman's' very full of a lecture which he was to deliver on 'gizzards.' We were settled before the fire after lunch, when he volunteered that So-and-so had said that if you hold a hen to your ear, you can hear the click in its gizzard of the little pebbles that help its digestion. 'Interesting,' said I. 'He's an authority.' 'Oh yes, but'—a long pause—'have you any hens about here, Kipling?' I owned that I had, two hundred yards down a lane, but why not accept So-and-so? 'I can't,' said John simply, 'till I've tried it.' Remorselessly, he worried me into taking him to the hens, who lived in an open shed in front of the gardener's cottage. As we skated over the glairy ground, I saw an eye at the corner of the drawn-down Boxing-Day blind, and knew that my character for sobriety would be blasted all over the farms before nightfall. We caught an outraged pullet. John soothed her for a while (he said her pulse was a hundred and twenty-six), and held her to his ear. 'She clicks all right,' he announced. 'Listen.' I did, and there was click enough for a lecture. 'Now we can go back to the house,' I pleaded. 'Wait a bit. Let's catch that cock. He'll click better.' We caught him after a loud and long chase, and he clicked like a solitaire-board. I went home, my ears alive with parasites, so wrapped up in my own indignation that the fun of it escaped me. It had not been *my* verification, you see.

But John was right. Take nothing for granted if you can check it. Even though that seem waste-work, and has nothing to do with the essentials of things, it encourages the Daemon. There are always men who by trade or calling know the fact or the inference that you put forth. If you are wrong by a hair in this, they argue: 'False in one thing, false in all.' Having sinned, I know. Likewise, never play down to your public—not because some of them do not deserve it, but because it is bad for your hand. All your material is drawn from the lives of men. Remember, then, what David did with the water brought to him in the heat of battle.

And, if it be in your power, bear serenely with imitators. My *Jungle Books* begat Zoos of them. But the genius of all the genii was one who wrote a series called *Tarzan of the Apes*. I read it, but regret I never saw it on the films, where it rages most successfully. He had 'jazzed' the motif of the *Jungle Books* and, I imagine, had thoroughly enjoyed himself. He was reported to have said that he wanted to find out how bad a book he could write and 'get away with,' which is a legitimate ambition.

Another case was verses of the sort that are recited. An Edinburgh taxi-driver in the War told me that they were much in vogue among the shelters and was honoured to meet me, their author. Afterwards, I found that they were running neck-and-neck with 'Gunga Din' in the military go-as-you-pleases and on the Lower Deck, and were always ascribed to my graceful hand. They were called 'The Green Eye of the Little Yellow God.' They described an English Colonel and his daughter at Khatmandhu in Nepal where there was a military Mess; and her lover of the name of 'mad Carew' which rhymed comfortably. The refrain was more or less 'And the green-eyed yellow Idol looking down.' It was luscious and rampant, with a touch, I thought, of the suburban Toilet-Club school favoured by the late Mr. Oscar Wilde. Yet, and this to me with the Devil of it, it carried for one reader an awesome suggestion of 'but for the Grace of God there goes Richard Baxter.' (Refer again to the hairdresser's model which so moved Mr. Dent Pitman.) Whether the author had done it out of his own head, or as an inspired parody of the possibilities latent in a fellow-craftsman, I do not know. But I admired him.

Occasionally one could test a plagiarist. I had to invent a tree, with name to match, for a man who at that time was rather riding in my pocket. In about eighteen months—the time it takes for a 'test' diamond thrown over wires into a field of 'blue' rock to turn up on the Kimberley sorting-tables—my tree appeared in his 'nature-studies'—name as spelt by me and virtues attributed. Since in our trade we be all felons, more or less, I repented when I had caught him, but not too much.

And I would charge you for the sake of your daily correspondence, never to launch a glittering generality, which an older generation used to call 'Tupperism.' Long ago I stated that 'East was East and West was West and never the twain should meet.' It seemed right, for I had checked it by the card, but I was careful to point out circumstances under which cardinal points ceased to exist. Forty years rolled on, and for a fair half of them the excellent and uplifted of all lands would write me, apropos of each new piece of broad-minded folly in India, Egypt, or Ceylon, that East and West *had* met—as, in their muddled minds, I suppose they had. Being a political Calvinist, I could not argue with these condemned ones. But their letters had to be opened and filed.

Again. I wrote a song called 'Mandalay' which, tacked to a tune with a swing, made one of the waltzes of that distant age. A private soldier reviews his loves and, in the chorus, his experiences in the Burma campaign. One of his ladies lives at Moulmein, which is not on the road to anywhere, and he describes the *amour* with some minuteness, but always in his chorus deals with 'the road to Mandalay,' his golden path to romance. The inhabitants of the United States, to whom I owed most of the bother, 'Panamaed' that song (this was before copyright), set it to their own tunes, and sang it in their own national voices. Not content with this, they took to pleasure cruising, and discovered that Moulmein did not command any view of any sun rising across the Bay of Bengal. They must have interfered too with the navigation of the Irrawaddy Flotilla steamers, for one of the Captains S. O. S.-ed me to give him 'something to tell these somethinged tourists about it.' I forget what word I sent, but I hoped it might help.

Had I opened the chorus of the song with 'Oh' instead of 'On the road,' etc., it might have shown that the song was a sort of general mix-up of the singer's Far-Eastern memories against a background of the Bay of Bengal as seen at dawn from a troop-ship taking him there. But 'On' in this case was more singable than 'Oh.' That simple explanation may stand as a warning.

Lastly—and this got under my skin because it touched something that mattered—when, after the Boer War, there seemed an off-chance of introducing conscription into England, I wrote verses called 'The Islanders' which, after a few days' newspaper correspondence, were dismissed as violent, untimely, and untrue. In them I had suggested that it was unwise to 'grudge a year of service to the lordliest life on earth.' In the immediate next lines I described the life to which the year of service was grudged as:

> Ancient, effortless, ordered—cycle on cycle set—
> Life so long untroubled that ye who inherit forget
> It was not made with the mountains; it is not one with the deep.
> Men, not Gods, devised it. Men, not Gods, must keep.

In a very little while it was put about that I had said that 'a year of compulsory service' would be 'effortless, ordered,' etc. etc.—with the rider that I didn't know much about it. This perversion was perversified by a man who ought to have known better; and I, I suppose, should have known that it was part of the 'effortless, ordered' drift towards Armageddon. You ask: 'Why inflict on us legends of your Middle Ages?' Because in life as in literature, its sole enduring record, is no age. Men and Things come round again, eternal as the seasons.

But, attacking or attacked, so long as you have breath, on no provocation explain. What you have said may be justified by things or some man, but never take a hand in a 'dog-fight' that opens: 'My attention has been drawn to,' etc.

I came near to breaking this Law with *Punch*, an institution I always respected for its continuity and its utter Englishdom, and from whose files I drew my modern working history. I had written during the Boer War a set of verses based on unofficial criticisms of many serious junior officers. (Incidentally they contained one jewel of a line that opened 'And which it may subsequently transpire'—a galaxy of words I had long panted to place in the literary firmament.) Nobody loved them, and indeed they were not conciliatory; but *Punch* took them rather hard. This was a pity because *Punch* would have been useful at that juncture. I knew none of its staff but I asked questions and learned that *Punch* on this particular issue was—non-Aryan 'and German at that.' It is true that the Children of Israel are 'people of the Book,' and in the second Surah of the Koran Allah is made to say: 'High above mankind have I raised you.' Yet, later, in the fifth Surah, it is written: 'Oft as they kindle a beacon-fire for war, shall God quench it. And their aim will be to abet disorder on the earth: but God loveth not the abettors of disorder.' More important still, my bearer in Lahore never announced our good little Jew tyler but he spat loudly and openly in the verandah. I swallowed my spittle at once. Israel is a race to leave alone. It abets disorder.

Many years later, during the War, *The Times*, with which I had had no dealings for a dozen years or so, was 'landed' with what purported to be some verses by me, headed 'The Old Volunteer.' They had been sent in by a Sunday mail with some sort of faked postmark and without any covering letter. They were stamped with a rubber-stamp from the village office, they were written on an absolutely straight margin, which is beyond my powers, and in an un-European fist. (I had never since typewriters began sent out press-work unless it was typed.) From my point of view the contribution should not have deceived a messenger-boy. Ninthly and lastly, they were wholly unintelligible.

Human nature being what it is, *The Times* was much more annoyed with me than anyone else, though goodness knows—this, remember, was in '17—I did not worry them about it, beyond hinting that the usual week-end English slackness, when no one is in charge, had made the mess. They took the matter up with the pomp of the Public Institution which they were, and submitted the MS. to experts, who proved that it must be the work of a man who had all but 'spoofed' *The Times* about some fragments of Keats. He happened to be an old friend of mine, and when I told him of his magnified 'characteristic' letters, and the betraying slopes at which they lay—*his*, as I pointed out, 'very C's and U's and T's,' he was wrath and, being a poet, swore a good deal that if he could not have done a better parody of my 'stuff' with his left hand he would retire from business. This I believed, for, on the heels of my modest disclaimer which appeared, none too conspicuously, in *The Times*, I had had a letter in a chaffing vein about 'The Old Volunteer' from a non-Aryan who never much appreciated me; and the handwriting of it, coupled with the subtlety of choosing a week-end (as the Hun had chosen August Bank Holiday of '14) for the work, *plus* the Oriental detachedness and insensitiveness of playing that sort of game in the heart of a life-and-death struggle, made me suspect him more than a little. He is now in Abraham's bosom, so I shall never know. But *The Times* seemed very happy with its enlarged letters, and measurements of the alphabet, and—there really *was* a war on which filled my days and nights. Then *The Times* sent down detectives to my home. I didn't see the drift of this, but naturally was interested. And It was a Detective out of a book, down to the very creaks of Its boots. (On the human side at lunch It knew a lot about second-hand furniture.) Officially, It behaved like all the detectives in the literature of that period. Finally, It settled Its self, back to the light, facing me at my worktable, and told me a long yarn about a man who worried the Police with complaints of anonymous letters addressed to him from unknown sources, all of which, through the perspicacity of the Police, turned out to have been written by himself to himself for the purpose of attracting notoriety. As in the case of the young man on the Canadian train, that tale felt as though it had come out of a magazine of the 'sixties; and I was so interested in its laborious evolution, that I missed its implication till quite the end. Then I got to thinking of the Psychology of the detective, and what a gay life of plots It must tramp through; and of the psychology of *The Times*-in-a-hole, which is where no one shows to advantage; and of how Moberly Bell, whose bows I had crossed in the old days, would have tackled the matter; what Buckle, whom I loved for his sincerity and gentlehood, would have thought of it all. Thus I forgot to defend my 'injured honour.' The thing had passed out of reason into the Higher Hysterics. What could I do but offer It some more sherry and thank It for a pleasant interview?

I have told this at length because Institutions of idealistic tendencies sometimes wait till a man is dead, and then furnish their own evidence. Should this happen, try to believe that in the deepest trough of the War I did not step aside to play with *The Times*, Printing House Square, London, E. C.

In the come-and-go of family talk there was often discussion as to whether I could write a 'real novel.' The Father thought that the setting of my work and life would be against it, and Time justified him.

Now here is a curious thing. At the Paris Exhibition of 1878 I saw, and never forgot, a picture of the death of Manon Lescaut, and asked my Father many questions. I read that amazing 'one book' of the Abbé Prévost, in alternate slabs with Scarron's *Roman Comique*, when I was about eighteen, and it brought up the picture. My theory is that a germ lay dormant till my change of life to London (though that is not Paris) woke it up, and that *The Light That Failed* was a sort of inverted, metagrobolised phantasmagoria based on *Manon*. I was confirmed in my belief when the French took to that *conte* with relish, and I always fancied that it walked better in translation than in the original. But it was only a *conte*—not a built book.

Kim, of course, was nakedly picaresque and plotless—a thing imposed from without.

Yet I dreamed for many years of building a veritable three-decker out of chosen and long-stored timber—teak, green-heart, and ten-year-old oak knees—each curve melting deliciously into the next that the sea might nowhere meet resistance or weakness; the whole suggesting motion even when, her great sails for the moment furled, she lay in some needed haven—a vessel ballasted on ingots of pure research and knowledge, roomy, fitted with delicate cabinet-work below-decks, painted, carved, gilt and wreathed the length of her, from her blazing stern-galleries outlined by bronzy palm-trunks, to her rampant figure-head—an East India man worthy to lie alongside *The Cloister and the Hearth*.

Not being able to do this, I dismissed the ambition as 'beneath the thinking mind.' So does a half-blind man dismiss shooting and golf.

Nor did I live to see the day when the new three-deckers should hoist themselves over the horizon, quivering to their own power, over-loaded with bars, ball-rooms and insistent chromium plumbing; hellishly noisy from the sports' deck to the barber's shop; but serving their generation as the old craft served theirs. The young men were already laying down the lines of them, fondly believing that the old laws of design and construction were for them abrogated.

And with what tools did I work in my own mould-loft? I had always been choice, not to say coquettish in this respect. In Lahore for my *Plain Tales* I used a slim, octagonal-sided, agate penholder with a Waverley nib. It was a gift, and when in an evil hour it snapped I was much disturbed. Then followed a procession of impersonal hirelings each with a Waverley, and next a silver penholder with a quill-like curve, which promised well but did not perform. In Villiers Street I got me an outsize office pewter ink-pot, on which I would gouge the names of the tales and books I wrote out of it. But the housemaids of married life polished those titles away till it grew as faded as a palimpsest.

I then abandoned hand-dipped Waverleys—a nib I never changed—and for years wallowed in the pin-pointed 'stylo' and its successor the 'fountain' which for me meant geyser-pens. In later years I clung to a slim, smooth, black treasure (Jael was her office name) which I picked up in Jerusalem. I tried pump-pens with glass insides, but they were of 'intolerable entrails.'

For my ink I demanded the blackest, and had I been in my Father's house, as once I was, would have kept an ink-boy to grind me Indian-ink. All 'blue-blacks' were an abomination to my Daemon, and I never found a bottled vermilion fit to rubricate initials when one hung in the wind waiting.

My writing-blocks were built for me to an unchanged pattern of large, off-white, blue sheets, of which I was most wasteful. All this old-maiderie did not prevent me when abroad from buying and using blocks, and tackle, in any country.

With a lead pencil I ceased to express—probably because I had to use a pencil in reporting. I took very few notes except of names, dates, and addresses. If a thing didn't stay in my memory, I argued it was hardly worth writing out. But each man has his own method. I rudely drew what I wanted to remember.

Like most men who ply one trade in one place for any while, I always kept certain gadgets on my work-table, which was ten feet long from North to South and badly congested. One was a long, lacquer, canoe-shaped pen-tray full of brushes and dead 'fountains'; a wooden box held clips and bands; another, a tin one, pins; yet another, a bottle-slider, kept all manner of un-needed essentials from emery-paper to small screw-drivers; a paper-weight, said to have been Warren Hastings'; a tiny, weighted fur-seal and a leather crocodile sat on some of the papers; an inky foot-rule and a Father of Pen-wipers which a much-loved housemaid of ours presented yearly, made up the main-guard of these little fetishes.

My treatment of books, which I looked upon as tools of my trade, was popularly regarded as barbarian. Yet I economised on my multitudinous pen-knives, and it did no harm to my fore-finger. There were books which I re-spected because they were put in locked cases. The others, all the house over, took their chances.

Left and right of the table were two big globes, on one of which a great airman had once outlined in white paint those air-routes to the East and Australia which were well in use before my death.

POEMS

POEMS

THE BETROTHED

"You must choose between me and your cigar."
—BREACH OF PROMISE CASE, CIRCA 1885.

Open the old cigar-box, get me a Cuba stout,
For things are running crossways, and Maggie and I are out.

We quarrelled about Havanas—we fought o'er a good cheroot,
And *I* know she is exacting, and she says I am a brute.

Open the old cigar-box—let me consider a space;
In the soft blue veil of the vapour musing on Maggie's face.

Maggie is pretty to look at—Maggie's a loving lass,
But the prettiest cheeks must wrinkle, the truest of loves must pass.

There's peace in a Larranaga, there's calm in a Henry Clay;
But the best cigar in an hour is finished and thrown away—

Thrown away for another as perfect and ripe and brown—
But I could not throw away Maggie for fear o' the talk o' the town!

Maggie, my wife at fifty—grey and dour and old—
With never another Maggie to purchase for love or gold!

And the light of Days that have Been the dark of the Days that Are,
And Love's torch stinking and stale, like the butt of a dead cigar—

The butt of a dead cigar you are bound to keep in your pocket—
With never a new one to light tho' it's charred and black to the socket!

Open the old cigar-box—let me consider a while.
Here is a mild Manila—there is a wifely smile.

Which is the better portion—bondage bought with a ring,
Or a harem of dusky beauties, fifty tied in a string?

Counsellors cunning and silent—comforters true and tried,
And never a one of the fifty to sneer at a rival bride?

Thought in the early morning, solace in time of woes,
Peace in the hush of the twilight, balm ere my eyelids close,

This will the fifty give me, asking nought in return,
With only a *Suttee's* passion—to do their duty and burn.

This will the fifty give me. When they are spent and dead,
Five times other fifties shall be my servants instead.

The furrows of far-off Java, the isles of the Spanish Main,
When they hear my harem is empty will send me my brides again.

I will take no heed to their raiment, nor food for their mouths withal,
So long as the gulls are nesting, so long as the showers fall.

I will scent 'em with best vanilla, with tea will I temper their hides,
And the Moor and the Mormon shall envy who read of the tale of my brides.

For Maggie has written a letter to give me my choice between
The wee little whimpering Love and the great god Nick o' Teen.

And I have been servant of Love for barely a twelvemonth clear,
But I have been Priest of Cabanas a matter of seven year;

And the gloom of my bachelor days is flecked with the cheery light
Of stumps that I burned to Friendship and Pleasure and Work and Fight.

And I turn my eyes to the future that Maggie and I must prove,
But the only light on the marshes is the Will-o'-the-Wisp of Love.

Will it see me safe through my journey or leave me bogged in the mire?
Since a puff of tobacco can cloud it, shall I follow the fitful fire?

Open the old cigar-box—let me consider anew—
Old friends, and who is Maggie that I should abandon *you?*

A million surplus Maggies are willing to bear the yoke;
And a woman is only a woman, but a good Cigar is a Smoke.

Light me another Cuba—I hold to my first-sworn vows.
If Maggie will have no rival, I'll have no Maggie for Spouse!

TO THOMAS ATKINS

PRELUDE TO "BARRACK-ROOM BALLADS" WHICH FOLLOW

I have made for you a song,
And it may be right or wrong,
But only you can tell me if it's true.
I have tried for to explain
Both your pleasure and your pain,
And, Thomas, here's my best respects to you!

O there'll surely come a day
When they'll give you all your pay,
And treat you as a Christian ought to do;
So, until that day comes round,
Heaven keep you safe and sound,
And, Thomas, here's my best respects to you!

DANNY DEEVER

"What are the bugles blowin' for?" said Files-on-Parade.
"To turn you out, to turn you out," the Colour-Sergeant said.
"What makes you look so white, so white?" said Files-on-Parade.
"I'm dreadin' what I've got to watch," the Colour-Sergeant said.
    For they're hangin' Danny Deever, you can hear the Dead March play,
    The Regiment's in 'ollow square—they're hangin' him to-day;
    They've taken of his buttons off an' cut his stripes away,
    An' they're hangin' Danny Deever in the mornin'.

"What makes the rear-rank breathe so 'ard?" said Files-on-Parade.
"It's bitter cold, it's bitter cold," the Colour-Sergeant said.
"What makes that front-rank man fall down?" said Files-on-Parade.
"A touch o' sun, a touch o' sun," the Colour-Sergeant said.
    They are hangin' Danny Deever, they are marchin' of 'im round,
    They 'ave 'alted Danny Deever by 'is coffin on the ground;
    An' 'e'll swing in 'arf a minute for a sneakin' shootin' hound—
    O they're hangin' Danny Deever in the mornin'!

" 'Is cot was right-'and cot to mine," said Files-on-Parade.
" 'E's sleepin' out an' far to-night," the Colour-Sergeant said.
"I've drunk 'is beer a score o' times," said Files-on-Parade.
" 'E's drinkin' beer alone," the Colour-Sergeant said.
    They are hangin' Danny Deever, you must mark 'im to 'is place,

For 'e shot a comrade sleepin'—you must look 'im in the face;
Nine 'undred of 'is county an' the Regiment's disgrace,
While they're hangin' Danny Deever in the mornin'.

"What's that so black agin the sun?" said Files-on-Parade.
"It's Danny fightin' 'ard for life," the Colour-Sergeant said.
"What's that that whimpers over'ead?" said Files-on-Parade.
"It's Danny's soul that's passin' now," the Colour-Sergeant said.
     For they're done with Danny Deever, you can 'ear the quickstep play,
     The Regiment's in column, an' they're marchin' us away;
     Ho! the young recruits are shakin', an' they'll want their beer to-day,
     After hangin' Danny Deever in the mornin'!

"FUZZY-WUZZY"

SOUDAN EXPEDITIONARY FORCE. EARLY CAMPAIGNS

We've fought with many men acrost the seas,
     An' some of 'em was brave an' some was not:
The Paythan an' the Zulu an' Burmese;
     But the Fuzzy was the finest o' the lot.
We never got a ha'porth's change of 'im:
     'E squatted in the scrub an' 'ocked our 'orses,

'E cut our sentries up at Sua*kim*,
   An' 'e played the cat an' banjo with our forces.
      So 'ere's *to* you, Fuzzy-Wuzzy, at your 'ome in the Soudan;
      You're a pore benighted 'eathen but a first-class fightin' man;
      We gives you your certificate, an' if you want it signed
      We'll come an' 'ave a romp with you whenever you're inclined.

We took our chanst among the Kyber 'ills,
   The Boers knocked us silly at a mile,
The Burman gave us Irriwaddy chills,
   An' a Zulu *impi* dished us up in style:
But all we ever got from such as they
   Was pop to what the Fuzzy made us swaller;
We 'eld our bloomin' own, the papers say,
   But man for man the Fuzzy knocked us 'oller.
      Then 'ere's *to* you, Fuzzy-Wuzzy, an' the missis and the kid;
      Our orders was to break you, an' of course we went an' did.
      We sloshed you with Martinis, an' it wasn't 'ardly fair;
      But for all the odds agin' you, Fuzzy-Wuz, you broke the square.

'E 'asn't got no papers of 'is own,
   'E 'asn't got no medals nor rewards,
So *we* must certify the skill 'e's shown
   In usin' of 'is long two-'anded swords:
When 'e's 'oppin' in an' out among the bush
   With 'is coffin-'eaded shield an' shovel-spear,
An 'appy day with Fuzzy on the rush
   Will last an 'ealthy Tommy for a year.
      So 'ere's *to* you, Fuzzy-Wuzzy, an' your friends which are no more,
      If we 'adn't lost some messmates we would 'help you to deplore.
      But give an' take's the gospel, an' we'll call the bargain fair,
      For if you 'ave lost more than us, you crumpled up the square!

'E rushes at the smoke when we let drive,
   An', before we know, 'e's 'ackin' at our 'ead;
'E's all 'ot sand an' ginger when alive,
   An' 'e's generally shammin' when 'e's dead.
'E's a daisy, 'es a ducky, 'e's a lamb!
   'E's a injia-rubber idiot on the spree,
'E's the on'y thing that doesn't give a damn
   For a Regiment o' British Infantree!
      So 'ere's *to* you, Fuzzy-Wuzzy, at your 'ome in the Soudan;
      You're a pore benighted 'eathen but a first-class fightin' man;
      An' 'ere's *to* you, Fuzzy-Wuzzy, with your 'ayrick 'ead of 'air—
      You big black boundin' beggar—for you broke a British square!

GUNGA DIN

You may talk o' gin and beer
When you're quartered safe out 'ere,
An' you're sent to penny-fights an' Aldershot it;
But when it comes to slaughter
You will do your work on water,
An' you'll lick the bloomin' boots of 'im that's got it.
Now in Injia's sunny clime,
Where I used to spend my time
A-servin' of 'Er Majesty the Queen,
Of all them blackfaced crew
The finest man I knew
Was our regimental bhisti, Gunga Din.
      He was "Din! Din! Din!
  "You limpin' lump o' brick-dust, Gunga Din!
     "Hi! Slippy *hitherao!*
     "Water, get it! *Panee lao,*[1]
  "You squidgy-nosed old idol, Gunga Din."

The uniform 'e wore
Was nothin' much before,

[1] Bring water swiftly.

An' rather less than 'arf o' that be'ind,
For a piece o' twisty rag
An' a goatskin water-bag
Was all the field-equipment 'e could find.
When the sweatin' troop-train lay
In a sidin' through the day,
Where the 'eat would make your bloomin' eyebrows crawl,
We shouted "Harry By!"[2]
Till our throats were bricky-dry,
Then we wopped 'im 'cause 'e couldn't serve us all.
   It was "Din! Din! Din!
  "You 'eathen, where the mischief 'ave you been?
   "You put some *juldee*[3] in it
   "Or I'll *marrow*[4] you this minute
  "If you don't fill up my helmet, Gunga Din!"

'E would dot an' carry one
Till the longest day was done;
An' 'e didn't seem to know the use o' fear.
If we charged or broke or cut,
You could bet your bloomin' nut,
'E'd be waitin' fifty paces right flank rear.
With 'is mussick[5] on 'is back,
'E would skip with our attack,
An' watch us till the bugles made "Retire,"
An' for all 'is dirty 'ide
'E was white, clear white, inside
When 'e went to tend the wounded under fire!
   It was "Din! Din! Din!"
  With the bullets kickin' dust-spots on the green.

[2] O brother. [3] Be quick. [4] Hit you. [5] Water-skin.

When the cartridges ran out,
You could hear the front-ranks shout,
"Hi! ammunition-mules an' Gunga Din!"

I shan't forgit the night
When I dropped be'ind the fight
With a bullet where my belt-plate should 'a' been.
I was chokin' mad with thirst,
An' the man that spied me first
Was our good old grinnin', gruntin' Gunga Din.
'E lifted up my 'ead,
An' he plugged me where I bled,
An' 'e guv me 'arf-a-pint o' water green.
It was crawlin' and it stunk,
But of all the drinks I've drunk,
I'm gratefullest to one from Gunga Din.
          It was "Din! Din! Din!
  " 'Ere's a beggar with a bullet through 'is spleen;
       " 'E's chawin' up the ground,
        "An' 'e's kickin' all around:
     "For Gawd's sake git the water, Gunga Din!"

'E carried me away
To where a dooli lay,
An' a bullet come an' drilled the beggar clean.
'E put me safe inside,
An' just before 'e died,
"I 'ope you liked your drink," sez Gunga Din.
So I'll meet 'im later on
At the place where 'e is gone—
Where it's always double drill and no canteen.
'E'll be squattin' on the coals
Givin' drink to poor damned souls,
An' I'll get a swig in hell from Gunga Din!
          Yes, Din! Din! Din!
  You Lazarushian-leather Gunga Din!
       Though I've belted you and flayed you,
       By the livin' Gawd that made you,
  You're a better man than I am, Gunga Din!

THE WIDOW AT WINDSOR

'Ave you 'eard o' the Widow at Windsor
  With a hairy gold crown on 'er 'ead?

She 'as ships on the foam—she 'as millions at 'ome,
   An' she pays us poor beggars in red.
     (Ow, poor beggars in red!)
There's 'er nick on the cavalry 'orses,
   There's 'er mark on the medical stores—
An' 'er troopers you'll find with a fair wind be'ind
   That takes us to various wars.
     (Poor beggars!—barbarious wars!)
       Then 'ere's to the Widow at Windsor,
         An 'ere's to the stores an' the guns,
       The men an' the 'orses what makes up the forces
         O' Missis Victorier's sons.
       (Poor beggars! Victorier's sons!)

Walk wide o' the Widow at Windsor,
   For 'alf o' Creation she owns:
We 'ave bought 'er the same with the sword an' the flame,
   An' we've salted it down with our bones.
     (Poor beggars!—it's blue with our bones!)
Hands off o' the sons o' the Widow,
   Hands off o' the goods in 'er shop,
For the Kings must come down an' the Emperors frown
   When the Widow at Windsor says "Stop!"
     (Poor beggars!—we're sent to say "Stop!")
       Then 'ere's to the Lodge o' the Widow,
         From the Pole to the Tropics it runs—
       To the Lodge that we tile with the rank an' the file,
         An' open in form with the guns.
       (Poor beggars!—it's always they guns!)

We 'ave 'eard o' the Widow at Windsor,
   It's safest to leave 'er alone:
For 'er sentries we stand by the sea an' the land
   Wherever the bugles are blown.
     (Poor beggars!—an' don't we get blown!)
Take 'old o' the Wings o' the Mornin',
   An' flop round the earth till you're dead;
But you won't get away from the tune that they play
   To the bloomin' old rag over'ead.
     (Poor beggars!—it's 'ot over'ead!)
       Then 'ere's to the Sons o' the Widow,
         Wherever, 'owever they roam.
       'Ere's all they desire, an' if they require
         A speedy return to their 'ome.
       (Poor beggars! they'll never see 'ome!)

MANDALAY

By the old Moulmein Pagoda, lookin' lazy at the sea,
There's a Burma girl a-settin', and I know she thinks o' me;
For the wind is in the palm-trees, and the temple-bells they say:
"Come you back, you British soldier; come you back to Mandalay!"
  Come you back to Mandalay,
  Where the old Flotilla lay:
  Can't you 'ear their paddles chunkin' from Rangoon to Mandalay?
  On the road to Mandalay,
  Where the flyin'-fishes play,
  An' the dawn comes up like thunder outer China 'crost the Bay!

'Er petticoat was yaller an' 'er little cap was green,
An' 'er name was Supi-yaw-lat—jes' the same as Theebaw's Queen,
An' I seed her first a-smokin' of a whackin' white cheroot,
An' a-wastin' Christian kisses on an 'eathen idol's foot:
  Bloomin' idol made o' mud—
  Wot they called the Great Gawd Budd—
  Plucky lot she cared for idols when I kissed 'er where she stud!
  On the road to Mandalay . . .

When the mist was on the rice-fields an' the sun was droppin' slow,
She'd git 'er little banjo an' she'd sing "*Kulla-lo-lo!*"
With 'er arm upon my shoulder an' 'er cheek again my cheek
We useter watch the steamers an' the *hathis* pilin' teak.
  Elephints a-pilin' teak
  In the sludgy, squdgy creek,
  Where the silence 'ung that 'eavy you was 'arf afraid to speak!
  On the road to Mandalay . . .

But that's all shove be'ind me—long ago an' fur away,
And there ain't no 'buses runnin' from the Bank to Mandalay;
An' I'm learnin' 'ere in London what the ten-year soldier tells:
"If you've 'eard the East a-callin', you won't never 'eed naught else."
  No! you won't 'eed nothin' else
  But them spicy garlic smells,
  An' the sunshine an' the palm-trees an' the tinkly temple-bells;
  On the road to Mandalay . . .

I am sick o' wastin' leather on these gritty pavin'-stones,
An' the blasted English drizzle wakes the fever in my bones;
Tho' I walks with fifty 'ousemaids outer Chelsea to the Strand,
An' they talks a lot o' lovin', but wot do they understand?
  Beefy face an' grubby 'and—

Law! wot do they understand?
I've a neater, sweeter maiden in a cleaner, greener land!
On the road to Mandalay . . .

Ship me somewheres east of Suez, where the best is like the worst,
Where there aren't no Ten Commandments an' a man can raise a thirst;
For the temple-bells are callin', and' it's there that I would be—
By the old Moulmein Pagoda, looking lazy at the sea;
    On the road to Mandalay,
    Where the old Flotilla lay,
    With our sick beneath the awnings when we went to Mandalay!
    O the road to Mandalay,
    Where the flyin'-fishes play,
    An' the dawn comes up like thunder outer China 'crost the Bay!

THE BALLAD OF EAST AND WEST

1889

Oh, East is East, and West is West, and never the twain shall meet,
Till Earth and Sky stand presently at God's great Judgment Seat,
But there is neither East nor West, Border, nor Breed, nor Birth,
When two strong men stand face to face, though they come from the ends
    of the earth!

Kamal is out with twenty men to raise the Border-side,
And he has lifted the Colonel's mare that is the Colonel's pride.
He has lifted her out of the stable-door between the dawn and the day,
And turned the calkins upon her feet, and ridden her far away.
Then up and spoke the Colonel's son that led a troop of the Guides:
"Is there never a man of all my men can say where Kamal hides?"
Then up and spoke Mohammed Khan, the son of the Ressaldar:
"If ye know the track of the morning-mist, ye know where his pickets are.
"At dust he harries the Abazai—at dawn he is into Bonair,
"But he must go by Fort Bukloh to his own place to fare.
"So if ye gallop to Fort Bukloh as fast as a bird can fly,
"By the favour of God ye may cut him off ere he win to the Tongue of Jagai.
"But if he be past the Tongue of Jagai, right swiftly turn ye then,
"For the length and the breadth of that grisly plain is sown with Kamal's
    men.
"There is rock to the left, and rock to the right, and low lean thorn between,
"And ye may hear a breech-bolt snick where never a man is seen."
The Colonel's son has taken horse, and a raw rough dun was he,

With the mouth of a bell and the heart of Hell and the head of a gallows-tree.
The Colonel's son to the Fort has won, they bid him stay to eat—
Who rides at the tail of a Border thief, he sits not long at his meat.
He's up and away from Fort Bukloh as fast as he can fly,
Till he was aware of his father's mare in the gut of the Tongue of Jagai,
Till he was aware of his father's mare with Kamal upon her back,
And when he could spy the white of her eye, he made the pistol crack.
He has fired once, he has fired twice, but the whistling ball went wide.
"Ye shoot like a soldier," Kamal said. "Show now if ye can ride!"
It's up and over the Tongue of Jagai, as blown dust-devils go,
The dun he fled like a stag of ten, but the mare like a barren doe.
The dun he leaned against the bit and slugged his head above,
But the red mare played with the snaffle-bars, as a maiden plays with a glove.
There was rock to the left and rock to the right, and low lean thorn between,
And thrice he heard a breech-bolt snick tho' never a man was seen.
They have ridden the low moon out of the sky, their hoofs drum up the dawn,
The dun he went like a wounded bull, but the mare like a new-roused fawn.
The dun he fell at a water-course—in a woeful heap fell he,
And Kamal has turned the red mare back, and pulled the rider free.
He has knocked the pistol out of his hand—small room was there to strive,
" 'Twas only by favour of mine," quoth he, "ye rode so long alive:
"There was not a rock for twenty mile, there was not a clump of tree,
"But covered a man of my own men with his rifle cocked on his knee.
"If I had raised my bridle-hand, as I have held it low,
"The little jackals that flee so fast were feasting all in a row.
"If I had bowed my head on my breast, as I have held it high,
"The kite that whistles above us now were gorged till she could not fly."
Lightly answered the Colonel's son: "Do good to bird and beast,
"But count who come for the broken meats before thou makest a feast.
"If there should follow a thousand swords to carry my bones away,
"Belike the price of a jackal's meal were more than a thief could pay.
"They will feed their horse on the standing crop, their men on the garnered
        grain.
"The thatch of the byres will serve their fires when all the cattle are slain.
"But if thou thinkest the price be fair,—thy brethren wait to sup,
"The hound is kin to the jackal-spawn,—howl, dog, and call them up!
"And if thou thinkest the price be high, in steer and gear and stack,
"Give me my father's mare again, and I'll fight my own way back!"
Kamal has gripped him by the hand and set him upon his feet.
"No talk shall be of dogs," said he, "when wolf and grey wolf meet.
"May I eat dirt if thou hast hurt of me in deed or breath;
"What dam of lances brought thee forth to jest at the dawn with Death?"
Lightly answered the Colonel's son: "I hold by the blood of my clan:
"Take up the mare for my father's gift—by God, she has carried a man!"
The red mare ran to the Colonel's son, and nuzzled against his breast;

"We be two strong men," said Kamal then, "but she loveth the younger best.
"So she shall go with a lifter's dower, my turquoise-studded rein,
"My 'broidered saddle and saddle-cloth, and silver stirrups twain."
The Colonel's son a pistol drew, and held it muzzle-end,
"Ye have taken the one from a foe," said he. "Will ye take the mate from
    a friend?"
"A gift for a gift," said Kamal straight; "a limb for the risk of a limb.
"Thy father has sent his son to me, I'll send my son to him!"
With that he whistled his only son, that dropped from a mountain-crest—
He trode the ling like a buck in spring, and he looked like a lance in rest.
"Now here is thy master," Kamal said, "who leads a troop of the Guides,
"And thou must ride at his left side as shield on shoulder rides.
"Till Death or I cut loose the tie, at camp and board and bed,
"Thy life is his—thy fate it is to guard him with thy head.
"So, thou must eat the White Queen's meat, and all her foes are thine,
"And thou must harry thy father's hold for the peace of the Border-line.
"And thou must make a trooper tough and hack thy way to power—
"Belike they will raise thee to Ressaldar when I am hanged in Peshawur!"

They have looked each other between the eyes, and there they found no fault.
They have taken the Oath of the Brother-in-Blood on leavened bread and salt:
They have taken the Oath of the Brother-in-Blood on fire and fresh-cut sod,
On the hilt and the haft of the Khyber knife, and the Wondrous Names of
    God.
The Colonel's son he rides the mare and Kamal's boy the dun,
And two have come back to Fort Bukloh where there went forth but one.
And when they drew to the Quarter-Guard, full twenty swords flew clear—
There was not a man but carried his feud with the blood of the mountaineer.
"Ha' done! ha' done!" said the Colonel's son. "Put up the steel at your sides!
"Last night ye had struck at a Border thief—to-night 'tis a man of the
    Guides!"

Oh, East is East, and West is West, and never the twain shall meet,
Till Earth and Sky stand presently at God's great Judgment Seat;
But there is neither East nor West, Border, nor Breed, nor Birth,
When two strong men stand face to face, though they come from the ends
    of the earth!

A CAROL

"THE TREE OF JUSTICE"—REWARDS AND FAIRIES

Our Lord Who did the Ox command
    To kneel to Judah's King,

He binds His frost upon the land
　　To ripen it for Spring—
To ripen it for Spring, good sirs,
　　According to His Word.
Which well must be as ye can see—
　　And who shall judge the Lord?

When we poor fenmen skate the ice
　　Or shiver on the wold,
We hear the cry of a single tree
　　That breaks her heart in the cold—
That breaks her heart in the cold, good sirs,
　　And rendeth by the board.
Which well must be as ye can see—
　　And who shall judge the Lord?

Her wood is crazed and little worth
　　Excepting as to burn,
　　That we may warm and make our mirth
　　Until the Spring return—
Until the Spring return, good sirs,
　　When Christians walk abroad;
Which well must be as ye can see—
　　And who shall judge the Lord?

God bless the master of this house,
　　And all who sleep therein!
And guard the fens from pirate folk,
　　And keep us all from sin,
To walk in honesty, good sirs,
　　Of thought and deed and word!
Which shall befriend our latter end. . . .
　　And who shall judge the Lord?

THE NEW KNIGHTHOOD

"A DEAL IN COTTON"—ACTIONS AND REACTIONS

　　Who gives him the Bath?
　　"I," said the wet,
　　Rank Jungle-sweat,
　　"I'll give him the Bath!"

Who'll sing the psalms?
"We," said the Palms.
"As the hot wind becalms,
"We'll sing the psalms."

Who lays on the sword?
"I," said the Sun,
"Before he has done,
"I'll lay on the sword."

Who fastens his belt?
"I," said Short-Rations,
"I know all the fashions
"Of tightening a belt!"

Who gives him his spur?
"I," said his Chief,
Exactly and brief,
"I'll give him the spur."

Who'll shake his hand?
"I," said the Fever,
"And I'm no deceiver,
"I'll shake his hand."

Who brings him the wine?
"I," said Quinine,
"It's a habit of mine.
"I'll come with his wine."

Who'll put him to proof?
"I," said All Earth.
"Whatever he's worth,
"I'll put to the proof."

Who'll choose him for Knight?
"I," said his Mother,
"Before any other,
"My very own Knight."

And after this fashion, adventure to seek,
Was Sir Galahad made—as it might be last week!

THE THOUSANDTH MAN

"SIMPLE SIMON"—REWARDS AND FAIRIES

One man in a thousand, Solomon says,
Will stick more close than a brother.
And it's worth while seeking him half your days
If you find him before the other.
Nine hundred and ninety-nine depend
On what the world sees in you,
But the Thousandth Man will stand your friend
With the whole round world agin you.

'Tis neither promise nor prayer nor show
Will settle the finding for 'ee.
Nine hundred and ninety-nine of 'em go
By your looks, or your acts, or your glory.
But if he finds you and you find him.
The rest of the world don't matter;
For the Thousandth Man will sink or swim
With you in any water.

You can use his purse with no more talk
Than he uses yours for his spendings,
And laugh and meet in your daily walk
As though there had been no lendings.
Nine hundred and ninety-nine of 'em call
For silver and gold in their dealings;
But the Thousandth Man he's worth 'em all,
Because you can show him your feelings.

His wrong's your wrong, and his right's your right,
In season or out of season.
Stand up and back it in all men's sight—
With *that* for your only reason!
Nine hundred and ninety-nine can't bide
The shame or mocking or laughter,
But the Thousandth Man will stand by your side
To the gallows-foot—and after!

THE PUZZLER

"THE PUZZLER"—ACTIONS AND REACTIONS

The Celt in all his variants from Builth to Ballyhoo,
His mental processes are plain—one knows what he will do,
And can logically predicate his finish by his start;
But the English—ah, the English!—they are quite a race apart.

Their psychology is bovine, their outlook crude and raw.
They abandon vital matters to be tickled with a straw;
But the straw that they were tickled with—the chaff that they were fed with—
They convert into a weaver's beam to break their foeman's head with.

For undemocratic reasons and for motives not of State,
They arrive at their conclusions—largely inarticulate.
Being void of self-expression they confide their views to none;
But sometimes in a smoking-room, one learns why things were done.

Yes, sometimes in a smoking-room, through clouds of "Ers" and "Ums,"
Obliquely and by inference, illumination comes,
On some step that they have taken, or some action they approve—
Embellished with the *argot* of the Upper Fourth Remove.

In telegraphic sentences, half nodded to their friends,
They hint a matter's inwardness—and there the matter ends.
And while the Celt is talking from Valencia to Kirkwall,
The English—ah, the English!—don't say anything at all.

"A SERVANT WHEN HE REIGNETH"

"For three things the earth is disquieted, and for four which it cannot bear. For a servant when he reigneth, and a fool when he is filled with meat; for an odious woman when she is married, and an handmaid that is heir to her mistress."—PROV. XXX. 21-22-23.

Three things make earth unquiet
And four she cannot brook
The godly Agur counted them
And put them in a book—
Those Four Tremendous Curses
With which mankind is cursed;
But a Servant when He Reigneth
Old Agur entered first.

An Handmaid that is Mistress
We need not call upon.
A Fool when he is full of Meat
Will fall asleep anon.
An Odious Woman Married
May bear a babe and mend;
But a Servant when He Reigneth
Is Confusion to the end.

His feet are swift to tumult,
His hands are slow to toil,
His ears are deaf to reason,
His lips are loud in broil.
He knows no use for power
Except to show his might.
He gives no heed to judgment
Unless it prove him right.

Because he served a master
Before his Kingship came,
And hid in all disaster
Behind his master's name,
So, when his Folly opens
The unnecessary hells,
A Servant when He Reigneth
Throws the blame on some one else.

His vows are lightly spoken,
His faith is hard to bind,
His trust is easy broken,
He fears his fellow-kind.
The nearest mob will move him
To break the pledge he gave—
Oh, a Servant when he Regineth
Is more than ever slave!

IF—

"BROTHER SQUARE-TOES"—REWARDS AND FAIRIES

If you can keep your head when all about you
    Are losing theirs and blaming it on you,
If you can trust yourself when all men doubt you,

But make allowance for their doubting too;
If you can wait and not be tired by waiting,
　Or being lied about, don't deal in lies,
Or being hated, don't give way to hating,
　And yet don't look too good, nor talk too wise:

If you can dream—and not make dreams your master;
　If you can think—and not make thoughts your aim;
If you can meet with Triumph and Disaster
　And treat those two impostors just the same;
If you can bear to hear the truth you've spoken
　Twisted by knaves to make a trap for fools,
Or watch the things you gave your life to, broken,
　And stoop and build 'em up with worn-out tools:

If you can make one heap of all your winnings
　And risk it on one turn of pitch-and-toss,
And lose, and start again at your beginnings
　And never breathe a word about your loss;
If you can force your heart and nerve and sinew
　To serve your turn long after they are gone,
And so hold on when there is nothing in you
　Except the Will which says to them: "Hold on!"

If you can talk with crowds and keep your virtue,
　Or walk with Kings—nor lose the common touch,
If neither foes nor loving friends can hurt you,
　If all men count with you, but none too much;
If you can fill the unforgiving minute
　With sixty seconds' worth of distance run,
Yours is the Earth and everything that's in it,
　And—which is more—you'll be a Man, my son!

"THE POWER OF THE DOG"

"GARM—A HOSTAGE"—ACTIONS AND REACTIONS

There is sorrow enough in the natural way
From men and women to fill our day;
And when we are certain of sorrow in store,
Why do we always arrange for more?
Brothers and Sisters, I bid you beware
Of giving your heart to a dog to tear.

Buy a pup and your money will buy
Love unflinching that cannot lie—
Perfect passion and worship fed
By a kick in the ribs or a pat on the head.
Nevertheless it is hardly fair
To risk your heart for a dog to tear.

When the fourteen years which Nature permits
Are closing in asthma, or tumour, or fits,
And the vet's unspoken prescription runs
To lethal chambers or loaded guns,
Then you will find—it's your own affair—
But . . . you've given your heart to a dog to tear.

When the body that lived at your single will,
With its whimper of welcome, is stilled (how still!)
When the spirit that answered your every mood
Is gone—wherever it goes—for good,
You will discover how much you care,
And will give your heart to a dog to tear.

We've sorrow enough in the natural way,
When it comes to burying Christian clay.

Our loves are not given, but only lent,
At compound interest of cent per cent.
Though it is not always the case, I believe,
That the longer we've kept 'em, the more do we grieve:

For, when debts are payable, right or wrong,
A short-time loan is as bad as a long—
So why in—Heaven (before we are there)
Should we give our hearts to a dog to tear?

MOTHER O' MINE

DEDICATION TO "THE LIGHT THAT FAILED"

If I were hanged on the highest hill,
Mother o' mine, O mother o' mine!
I know whose love would follow me still,
Mother o' mine, O mother o' mine!

If I were drowned in the deepest sea,
Mother o' mine, O mother o' mine!
I know whose tears would come down to me,
Mother o' mine, O mother o' mine!

If I were damned of body and soul,
I know whose prayers would make me whole,
Mother o' mine, O mother o' mine!

DANE-GELD

A.D. 980–1016

It is always a temptation to an armed and agile nation
    To call upon a neighbour and to say:—
"We invaded you last night—we are quite prepared to fight,
    Unless you pay us cash to go away."

And that is called asking for Dane-geld,
    And the people who ask it explain
That you've only to pay 'em the Dane-geld
    And then you'll get rid of the Dane!

It is always a temptation to a rich and lazy nation,
　　To puff and look important and to say:—
"Though we know we should defeat you, we have not the
　　　　time to meet you.
　　We will therefore pay you cash to go away."

And that is called paying the Dane-geld;
　　But we've proved it again and again,
That if once you have paid him the Dane-geld
　　You never get rid of the Dane.

It is wrong to put temptation in the path of any nation,
　　For fear they should succumb and go astray;
So when you are requested to pay up or be molested,
　　You will find it better policy to say:—

"We never pay *any*-one Dane-geld,
　　No matter how trifling the cost;
For the end of that game is oppression and shame,
　　And the nation that plays it is lost!"

THE LINER SHE'S A LADY

1894

The Liner she's a lady, an' she never looks nor 'eeds—
The Man-o'-War's 'er 'usband, an' 'e gives 'er all she needs;
But, oh, the little cargo-boats, that sail the wet seas roun',
They're just the same as you an' me a-plyin' up an' down!

　　Plyin' up an' down, Jenny, 'angin' round the Yard,
　　All the way by Fratton tram down to Portsmouth 'Ard;
　　Anythin' for business, an' we're growin' old—
　　Plyin' up an' down, Jenny, waitin' in the cold!

The Liner she's a lady by the paint upon 'er face,
An' if she meets an accident they count it sore disgrace.
The Man-o'-War's 'er 'usband, and 'e's always 'andy by,
But, oh, the little cargo-boats, they've got to load or die!

The Liner she's a lady, and 'er route is cut an' dried;
The Man-o'-War's 'er 'usband, an' 'e always keeps beside;
But, oh, the little cargo-boats that 'aven't any man,
They've got to do their business first, and make the most they can!

The Liner she's a lady, and if a war should come,
The Man-o'-War's 'er 'usband, and 'e'd bid 'er stay at home;
But, oh, the little cargo-boats that fill with every tide!
'E'd 'ave to go up an' fight for them, for they are England's pride.

The Liner she's a lady, but if she wasn't made,
There still would be the cargo-boats for 'ome an' foreign trade.
The Man-o'-War's 'er 'usband, but if we wasn't 'ere,
'E wouldn't have to fight at all for 'ome an' friends so dear.

> 'Ome an' friends so dear, Jenny, 'angin' round the Yard,
> All the way by Fratton tram down to Portsmouth 'Ard;
> Anythin' for business, an' we're growin' old—
> 'Ome an' friends so dear, Jenny, waitin' in the cold!

"WHEN 'OMER SMOTE 'IS BLOOMIN' LYRE"

INTRODUCTION TO THE BARRACK-ROOM BALLADS IN "THE SEVEN SEAS"

When 'Omer smote 'is bloomin' lyre,
  He'd 'eard men sing by land an' sea;
An' what he thought 'e might require,
  'E went an' took—the same as me!

The market-girls an' fishermen,
  The shepherds an' the sailors, too,
They 'eard old songs turn up again,
  But kep' it quiet—same as you!

They knew 'e stole; 'e knew they knowed.
  They didn't tell, nor make a fuss,
But winked at 'Omer down the road,
  An' 'e winked back—the same as us!

"BACK TO THE ARMY AGAIN"

I'm 'ere in a ticky ulster an' a broken billycock 'at,
A-layin' on to the sergeant I don't know a gun from a bat;
My shirt's doin' duty for jacket, my sock's stickin' out o' my boots,
An' I'm learnin' the damned old goose-step along o' the new recruits!

> Back to Army again, sergeant,
>   Back to the Army again.
> Don't look so 'ard, for I 'aven't no card,
>   I'm back to the Army again!

I done my six years' service. 'Er Majesty sez: "Good day—
You'll please to come when you're rung for, an' 'ere's your 'ole back-pay:
An' fourpence a day for baccy—an' bloomin' gen'rous, too;
An' now you can make your fortune—the same as your orf'cers do."

> Back to the Army again, sergeant,
>   Back to the Army again.
> 'Ow did I learn to do right-about-turn?
>   I'm back to the Army again!

A man o' four-an'-twenty that 'asn't learned of a trade—
Beside "Reserve" agin' him—'e'd better be never made.
I tried my luck for a quarter, an' that was enough for me,
An' I thought of 'Er Majesty's barricks, an' I thought I'd go an' see.

> Back to the Army again, sergeant,
>   Back to the Army again.
> 'Tisn't my fault if I dress when I 'alt—
>   I'm back to the Army again!

The sergeant arst no questions, but 'e winked the other eye,
'E sez to me, " 'Shun!" an' I shunted, the same as in days gone by;
For 'e saw the set o' my shoulders, an' I couldn't 'elp 'oldin' straight
When me an' the other rookies come under the barrick-gate.

> Back to the Army again, sergeant,
>   Back to the Army again.
> 'Oo would ha' thought I could carry an' port?[1]
>   I'm back to the Army again!

I took my bath, an' I wallered—for, Gawd, I needed it so!
I smelt the smell o' the barricks, I 'eard the bugles go.
I 'eard the feet on the gravel—the feet o' the men what drill—
An' I sez to my flutterin' 'eart-strings, I sez to 'em, "Peace, be still!"

> Back to the Army again, sergeant,
>   Back to the Army again.
> 'Oo said I knew when the troopship was due?
>   I'm back to the Army again!

[1] Carry and port his rifle.

I carried my slops to the tailor; I sez to 'im, "None o' your lip!
You tight 'em over the shoulders, an' loose 'em over the 'ip,
For the set o' the tunic's 'orrid." An' 'e sez to me, "Strike me dead,
But I thought you was used to the business!" an' so 'e done what I said.

> Back to the Army again, sergeant,
> Back to the Army again.
> Rather too free with my fancies? Wot—me?
> I'm back to the Army again!

Next week I'll 'ave 'em fitted; I'll buy me a swagger-cane;
They'll let me free o' the barricks to walk on the Hoe again,
In the name o' William Parsons, that used to be Edward Clay,
An'—any pore beggar that wants it can draw my fourpence a day!

> Back to the Army again, sergeant,
> Back to the Army again.
> Out o' the cold an' the rain, sergeant,
> Out o' the cold an' the rain.
> 'Oo's there?

A man that's too good to be lost you,
  A man that is 'andled an' made—
A man that will pay what 'e cost you
  In learnin' the others their trade—parade!
You're droppin' the pick o' the Army
  Because you don't 'elp 'em remain,
But drives 'em to cheat to get out o' the street
  An' back to the Army again!

THE LADIES

> I've taken my fun where I've found it;
>   I've rouged an' I've ranged in my time;
> I've 'ad my pickin' o' sweethearts,
>   An' four o' the lot was prime.
> One was an 'arf-caste widow,
>   One was a woman at Prome,
> One was the wife of a *jemadar-sais*[1]
>   An' one is a girl at 'ome.

[1] Head-groom.

Now I aren't no 'and with the ladies,
   For, takin' 'em all along,
You never can say till you've tried 'em,
   An' then you are like to be wrong.
There's times when you'll think that you mightn't,
   There's times when you'll know that you might;
But the things you will learn from the Yellow an' Brown,
   They'll 'elp you a lot with the White!

I was a young un at 'Oogli,
   Shy as a girl to begin;
Aggie de Castrer she made me,
   An' Aggie was clever as sin;

Older than me, but my first un—
    More like a mother she were—
Showed me the way to promotion an' pay,
    An' I learned about women from 'er!

Then I was ordered to Burma,
    Actin' in charge o' Bazar,
An' I got me a tiddy live 'eathen
    Through buyin' supplies off 'er pa.
Funny an' yellow an' faithful—
    Doll in a teacup she were—
But we lived on the square, like a true-married pair,
    An' I learned about women from 'er!

Then we was shifted to Neemuch
    (Or I might ha' been keepin' 'er now),
An' I took with a shiny she-devil,
    The wife of a nigger at Mhow;
'Taught me the gipsy-folks' *bolee*;[2]
    Kind o' volcano she were,
For she knifed me one night 'cause I wished she was white,
    And I learned about women from 'er!

Then I come 'ome in a trooper,
    'Long of a kid o' sixteen—
'Girl from a convent at Meerut,
    The straightest I ever 'ave seen.
Love at first sight was 'er trouble,
    She didn't know what it were;
An' I wouldn't do such, 'cause I liked 'er too much,
    But—I learned about women from 'er!

I've taken my fun where I've found it,
    An' now I must pay for my fun,
For the more you 'ave known o' the others
    The less will you settle to one;
An' the end of it's sittin' and thinkin',
    An' dreamin' Hell-fires to see;
So be warned by my lot (which I know you will not),
    An' learn about women from me!

    What did the Colonel's Lady think?
        Nobody never knew.
    Somebody asked the Sergeant's Wife,
        An' she told 'em true!

[2] Slang.

When you get to a man in the case,
  They're like as a row of pins—
For the Colonel's Lady an' Judy O'Grady
  Are sisters under their skins!

BILL 'AWKINS

" 'As anybody seen Bill 'Awkins?"
    "Now 'ow in the devil would I know?"
" 'E's taken my girl out walkin',
    An' I've got to tell 'im so—
        Gawd—bless 'im!
    I've got to tell 'im so."

"D'yer know what 'e's like, Bill 'Awkins?"
    "Now what in the devil would I care?"
" 'E's the livin', breathin' image of an organ-grinder's monkey,
    With a pound of grease in 'is 'air—
        Gawd—bless 'im!
    An' a pound o' grease in 'is 'air."

"An' s'pose you met Bill 'Awkins,
    Now what in the devil 'ud ye do?"
"I'd open 'is cheek to 'is chin-strap buckle,
    An' bung up 'is both eyes, too—
        Gawd—bless 'im!
    An' bung up 'is both eyes, too!"

"Look 'ere, where 'e comes, Bill 'Awkins!
    Now, what in the devil will you say?"
"It isn't fit an' proper to be fightin' on a Sunday,
    So I'll pass 'im the time o' day—
        Gawd—bless 'im!
    I'll pass 'im the time o' day!"

"MARY, PITY WOMEN!"

You call yourself a man,
    For all you used to sweat,
An' leave me, as you can,
    My certain shame to bear?

I 'ear! You do not care—
You done the worst you know.
    I 'ate you, grinnin' there. . . .
Ah, Gawd, I love you so!

Nice while it lasted, an' now it is over—
Tear out your 'eart an' good-bye to your lover!
What's the use o' grievin', when the mother that bore you
(Mary, pity women!) knew it all before you?

It aren't no false alarm,
    The finish to your fun;
You—you 'ave brung the 'arm,
    An' I'm the ruined one!
    An' now you'll off an' run
With some new fool in tow.
    Your 'eart? You 'aven't none. . . .
Ah, Gawd, I love you so!

When a man is tired there is naught will bind 'im
All 'e solemn promised 'e will shove be'ind 'im.
What's the good o' prayin' for The Wrath to strike 'im
(Mary, pity women!), when the rest are like 'im?

What 'ope for me or—it?
    What's left for us to do?
I've walked with men a bit,
    But this—but this is you.
    So 'elp me, Christ, it's true!
Where can I 'ide or go?
You coward through and through! . . .
Ah, Gawd, I love you so!

All the more you give 'em the less are they for givin'—
Love lies dead, an' you cannot kiss 'im livin'.
Down the road 'e led you there is no returnin'
(Mary, pity women!), but you're late in learnin'!

You'd like to treat me fair?
    You can't, because we're pore?
We'd starve? What do I care!
    We might, but *this* is shore!
    I want the name—no more—
The name, an' lines to show,
    An' not to be an 'ore. . . .
Ah, Gawd, I love you so!

What's the good o' pleadin', when the mother that bore you
(Mary, pity women!) knew it all before you?
Sleep on 'is promises an' wake to your sorrow
(Mary, pity women!), for we sail to-morrow!

THE WHITE MAN'S BURDEN

1899

THE UNITED STATES AND THE PHILIPPINE ISLANDS

Take up the White Man's burden—
    Send forth the best ye breed—
Go bind your sons to exile
    To serve your captives' need;
To wait in heavy harness
    On fluttered folk and wild—
Your new-caught, sullen peoples,
    Half devil and half child.

Take up the White Man's burden—
    In patience to abide,
To veil the threat of terror
    And check the show of pride;
By open speech and simple,
    An hundred times made plain.
To seek another's profit,
    And work another's gain.

Take up the White Man's burden—
    The savage wars of peace—
Fill full the mouth of Famine
    And bid the sickness cease;
And when your goal is nearest
    The end for others sought,
Watch Sloth and heathen Folly
    Bring all your hope to nought.

Take up the White Man's burden—
    No tawdry rule of kings,
But toil of serf and sweeper—
    The tale of common things.
The ports ye shall not enter,

The roads ye shall not tread,
Go make them with your living,
    And mark them with your dead!

Take up the White Man's burden—
    And reap his old reward:
The blame of those ye better,
    The hate of those ye guard—
The cry of hosts ye humour
    (Ah, slowly!) toward the light:—
"Why brought ye us from bondage,
    "Our loved Egyptian night?"

Take up the White Man's burden—
    Ye dare not stoop to less—
Nor call too loud on Freedom
    To cloak your weariness;
By all ye cry or whisper,
    By all ye leave or do,
The silent, sullen peoples
    Shall weigh your Gods and you.

Take up the White Man's burden—
    Have done with childish days—
The lightly proffered laurel,
    The easy, ungrudged praise.
Comes now, to search your manhood
    Through all the thankless years,
Cold-edged with dear-bought wisdom,
    The judgment of your peers!

CHANT-PAGAN

ENGLISH IRREGULAR, DISCHARGED

Me that 'ave been what I've been—
    Me that 'ave gone where I've gone—
Me that 'ave seen what I've seen—
    'Ow can I ever take on
With awful old England again,
An' 'ouses both sides of the street,
And 'edges two sides of the lane,
And the parson an' gentry between,

An' touchin' my 'at when we meet—
   Me that 'ave been what I've been?

Me that 'ave watched 'arf a world
'Eave up all shiny with dew,
Kopje on kop to the sun,
An' as soon as the mist let 'em through
Our 'elios winkin' like fun—
Three sides of a ninety-mile square,
Over valleys as big as a shire—
"Are ye there? Are ye there? Are ye there?"
An' then the blind drum of our fire . . .
An' I'm rollin' 'is lawns for the Squire,
                                        Me!

Me that 'ave rode through the dark
Forty mile, often, on end,
Along the Ma'ollisberg Range,
With only the stars for my mark
An' only the night for my friend,
An' things runnin' off as you pass,
An' things jumpin' up in the grass,
An' the silence, the shine an' the size
Of the 'igh, unexpressible skies—
I am takin' some letters almost
As much as a mile to the post,
An' "mind you come back with the change!"
                                        Me!

Me that saw Barberton took
When we dropped through the clouds on their 'ead,
An' they 'ove the guns over and fled—
Me that was through Di'mond 'Ill,
An' Pieters an' Springs an' Belfast—
From Dundee to Vereeniging all—
Me that stuck out to the last
(An' five bloomin' bars on my chest)—
I am doin' my Sunday-school best,
By the 'elp of the Squire an' 'is wife
(Not to mention the 'ousemaid an' cook),
To come in an' 'ands up an' be still,
An' honestly work for my bread,
My livin' in that state of life
To which it shall please God to call
                                        Me!

Me that 'ave followed my trade
In the place where the Lightnin's are made;
'Twixt the Rains and the Sun and the Moon—
Me that lay down an' got up
Three years with the sky for my roof—
That 'ave ridden my 'unger an' thirst
Six thousand raw mile on the hoof,
With the Vaal and the Orange for cup,
An' the Brandwater Basin for dish,—
Oh! it's 'ard to be'ave as they wish
(Too 'ard, an' a little too soon),
I'll 'ave to think over it first—

                                        Me!

I will arise an' get 'ence—
I will trek South and make sure
If it's only my fancy or not
That the sunshine of England is pale,
And the breezes of England are stale,
An' there's somethin' gone small with the lot.
For *I* know of a sun an' a wind,
An' some plains and a mountain be'ind,
An' some graves by a barb-wire fence,
An' a Dutchman I've fought 'oo might give
Me a job where I ever inclined
To look in an' offsaddle an' live
Where there's neither a road nor a tree—
But only my Maker an' me,
An I think it will kill me or cure,
So I think I will go there an' see.

                                        Me!

BOOTS

INFANTRY COLUMNS

We're foot—slog—slog—slog—sloggin' over Africa—
Foot—foot—foot—foot—sloggin' over Africa—
(Boots—boots—boots—boots—movin' up an' down again!)
            There's no discharge in the war!

Seven—six—eleven—five—nine-an'-twenty mile to-day—
Four—eleven—seventeen—thirty-two the day before—

(Boots—boots—boots—boots—movin' up an' down again!)
  There's no discharge in the war!

Don't—don't—don't—don't—look at what's in front of you.
(Boots—boots—boots—boots—movin' up an' down again);
Men—men—men—men—men go mad with watchin' em,
  An' there's no discharge in the war!

Try—try—try—try—to think o' something different—
Oh—my—God—keep—me from goin' lunatic!
(Boots—boots—boots—boots—movin' up an' down again!)
  There's no discharge in the war!

Count—count—count—count—the bullets in the bandoliers.
If—your—eyes—drop—they will get atop o' you!
(Boots—boots—boots—boots—movin' up an' down again)—
  There's no discharge in the war!

We—can—stick—out—'unger, thirst, an' weariness,
But—not—not—not—not the chronic sight of 'em—
Boot—boots—boots—boots—movin' up an' down again,
  An' there's no discharge in the war!

'Taint—so—bad—by—day because o' company,
But night—brings—long—strings—o' forty thousand million
Boots—boots—boots—boots—movin' up an' down again.
  There's no discharge in the war!

I—'ave—marched—six—weeks in 'Ell an' certify
It—is—not—fire—devils, dark, or anything,
But boots—boots—boots—boots—movin' up an' down again,
  An' there's no discharge in the war!

THE MARRIED MAN

RESERVIST OF THE LINE

The bachelor 'e fights for one
    As joyful as can be;
But the married man don't call it fun,
    Because 'e fights for three—
For 'Im an' 'Er an' It
    (An' Two an' One make Three)

'E wants to finish 'is little bit,
  An' e' wants to go 'ome to 'is tea!

The bachelor pokes up 'is 'ead
  To see if you are gone;
But the married man lies down instead,
  An' waits till the sights come on,
For 'im an' 'Er an' a hit
  (Direct or ricochee)
'E wants to finish 'is little bit,
  An' 'e wants to go 'ome to 'is tea.

The bachelor will miss you clear
  To fight another day;
But the married man, 'e says "No fear!"
  'E wants you out of the way
Of 'Im an' 'Er an' It
  (An' 'is road to 'is farm or the sea),
'E wants to finish 'is little bit,
  An' 'e wants to go 'ome to 'is tea.

The bachelor 'e fights 'is fight
  An' stretches out an' snores;
But the married man sits up all night—
  For 'e don't like out-o'-doors.
'E'll strain an' listen an' peer
  An' give the first alarm—
For the sake o' the breathin' 'e's used to 'ear,
  An' the 'ead on the thick of 'is arm.

The bachelor may risk 'is 'ide
  To 'elp you when you're downed;
But the married man will wait beside
  Till the ambulance comes round.
'E'll take your 'ome address
  An' all you've time to say,
Or if 'e sees there's 'ope, 'e'll press
  Your art'ry 'alf the day—

For 'Im an' 'Er an' It
  (An' One from Three leaves Two),
For 'e knows you wanted to finish your bit,
  An' 'e knows 'oo's wantin' you.
Yes, 'Im an' 'Er an' It
  (Our 'oly One in Three),

We're all of us anxious to finish our bit,
   An' we want to get 'ome to our tea!

Yes, It an' 'Er an' Im,
   Which often makes me think
The married man must sink or swim
   An'—'e can't afford to sink!
Oh, 'Im an' It an' 'Er
   Since Adam an' Eve began!
So I'd rather fight with the bacheler
   An' be nursed by the married man!

RECESSIONAL

1897

God of our fathers, known of old,
   Lord of our far-flung battle-line,
Beneath whose awful Hand we hold
   Dominion over palm and pine—
Lord God of Hosts, be with us yet,
Lest we forget—lest we forget!

The tumult and the shouting dies;
   The Captains and the Kings depart:
Still stands Thine ancient sacrifice,
   An humble and a contrite heart.
Lord God of Hosts, be with us yet,
Lest we forget—lest we forget!

Far-called, our navies melt away;
   On dune and headland sinks the fire:
Lo, all our pomp of yesterday
   Is one with Nineveh and Tyre!
Judge of the Nations, spare us yet,
Lest we forget—lest we forget!

If, drunk with sight of power, we loose
   Wild tongues that have not Thee in awe,
Such boastings as the Gentiles use,
   Or lesser breeds without the Law—
Lord God of Hosts, be with us yet,
Lest we forget—lest we forget!

For heathen heart that puts her trust
   In reeking tube and iron shard,
All valiant dust that builds on dust,
   And guarding, calls not Thee to guard,
For frantic boast and foolish word—
Thy mercy on Thy People, Lord!

THE SONS OF MARTHA

1907

The Sons of Mary seldom bother, for they have inherited that good part;
But the Sons of Martha favour their Mother of the careful soul and the troubled heart.
And because she lost her temper once, and because she was rude to the Lord her Guest,
Her Sons must wait upon Mary's Sons, world without end, reprieve, or rest.

It is their care in all the ages to take the buffet and cushion the shock.
It is their care that the gear engages; it is their care that the switches lock.
It is their care that the wheels run truly; it is their care to embark and entrain,
Tally, transport, and deliver duly the Sons of Mary by land and main.

They say to mountains, "Be ye removed." They say to the lesser floods, "Be dry."
Under their rods are the rocks reprovèd—they are not afraid of that which is high.
Then do the hill-tops shake to the summit—then is the bed of the deep laid bare,
That the Sons of Mary may overcome it, pleasantly sleeping and unaware.

They finger death at their gloves' end where they piece and repiece the living wires.
He rears against the gates they tend: they feed him hungry behind their fires.
Early at dawn, ere men see clear, they stumble into his terrible stall,
And hale him forth like a haltered steer, and goad and turn him till evenfall.

To these from birth is Belief forbidden; from these till death is Relief afar.
They are concerned with matters hidden—under the earthline their altars are—
The secret fountains to follow up, waters withdrawn to restore to the mouth,
And gather the floods as in a cup, and pour them again at a city's drouth.

They do not preach that their God will rouse them a little before the nuts
   work loose.
They do not teach that His Pity allows them to drop their job when they
   dam'-well choose.
As in the thronged and the lighted ways, so in the dark and the desert they
   stand,
Wary and watchful all their days that their brethren's days may be long in
   the land.

Raise ye the stone or cleave the wood to make a path more fair or flat—
Lo, it is black already with blood some Son of Martha spilled for that!
Not as a ladder from earth to Heaven, not as a witness to any creed,
But simple service simply given to his own kind in their common need.

And the Sons of Mary smile and are blessèd—they know the Angels are on
   their side.
They know in them is the Grace confessèd, and for them are the Mercies
   multiplied.
They sit at the Feet—they hear the Word—they see how truly the Promise
   runs.
They have cast their burden upon the Lord, and—the Lord He lays it on
   Martha's Sons!

THE VIRGINITY

Try as he will, no man breaks wholly loose
   From his first love, no matter who she be.
Oh, was there ever sailor free to choose,
   That didn't settle somewhere near the sea?

Myself, it don't excite me nor amuse
   To watch a pack o' shipping on the sea;
But I can understand my neighbour's views
   From certain things which have occurred to me.

Men must keep touch with things they used to use
   To earn their living, even when they are free;
And so come back upon the least excuse—
   Same as the sailor settled near the sea.

He knows he's never going on no cruise—
   He knows he's done and finished with the sea;
And yet he likes to feel she's there to use—
   If he should ask her—as she used to be.

Even though she cost him all he had to lose,
 Even though she made him sick to hear or see,
Still, what she left of him will mostly choose
 Her skirts to sit by. How comes such to be?

Parsons in pulpits, tax-payers in pews,
 Kings on your thrones, you know as well as me,
We've only one virginity to lose,
 And where we lost it there our hearts will be!

THE FEMALE OF THE SPECIES

1911

When the Himalayan peasant meets the he-bear in his pride,
He shouts to scare the monster, who will often turn aside.
But the she-bear thus accosted rends the peasant tooth and nail.
For the female of the species is more deadly than the male.

When Nag the basking cobra hears the careless foot of man,
He will sometimes wriggle sideways and avoid it if he can.
But his mate makes no such motion where she camps beside the trail.
For the female of the species is more deadly than the male.

When the early Jesuit fathers preached to Hurons and Choctaws,
They prayed to be delivered from the vengeance of the squaws.
'Twas the women, not the warriors, turned those stark enthusiasts pale.
For the female of the species is more deadly than the male.

Man's timid heart is bursting with the things he must not say,
For the Woman that God gave him isn't his to give away;
But when hunter meets with husbands, each confirms the other's tale—
The female of the species is more deadly than the male.

Man, a bear in most relations—worm and savage otherwise,—
Man propounds negotiations, Man accepts the compromise.
Very rarely will he squarely push the logic of a fact
To its ultimate conclusion in unmitigated act.

Fear, or foolishness, impels him, ere he lay the wicked low,
To concede some form of trial even to his fiercest foe.
Mirth obscene diverts his anger—Doubt and Pity oft perplex
Him in dealing with an issue—to the scandal of The Sex!

But the Woman that God gave him, every fibre of her frame
Proves her launched for one sole issue, armed and engined for the same;
And to serve that single issue, lest the generations fail,
The female of the species must be deadlier than the male.

She who faces Death by torture for each life beneath her breast
May not deal in doubt or pity—must not swerve for fact or jest.
These be purely male diversions—not in these her honour dwells.
She the Other Law we live by, is that Law and nothing else.

She can bring no more to living than the powers that make her great
As the Mother of the Infant and the Mistress of the Mate.
And when Babe and Man are lacking and she strides unclaimed to claim
Her right as femme (and baron), her equipment is the same.

She is wedded to convictions—in default of grosser ties;
Her contentions are her children, Heaven help him who denies!—
He will meet no suave discussion, but the instant, white-hot, wild,
Wakened female of the species warring as for spouse and child.

Unprovoked and awful charges—even so the she-bear fights,
Speech that drips, corrodes, and poisons—even so the cobra bites,
Scientific vivisection of one nerve till it is raw
And the victim writhes in anguish—like the Jesuit with the squaw!

So it comes that Man, the coward, when he gathers to confer
With his fellow-braves in council, dare not leave a place for her
Where, at war with Life and Conscience, he uplifts his erring hands
To some God of Abstract Justice—which no woman understands.

And Man knows it! Knows, moreover, that the Woman that God gave him
Must command but may not govern—shall enthral but not enslave him.
And *She* knows, because She warns him, and Her instincts never fail,
That the Female of Her Species is more deadly than the Male.

STUDY OF AN ELEVATION, IN INDIAN INK

This ditty is a string of lies.
But—how the deuce did Gubbins rise?

Potiphar Gubbins, C.E.
Stands at the top of the tree;
And I muse in my bed on the reasons that led
To the hoisting of Potiphar G.

Potiphar Gubbins, C.E.,
Is seven years junior to Me;
Each bridge that he makes either buckles or breaks,
And his work is as rough as he.

Potiphar Gubbins, C.E.,
Is coarse as a chimpanzee;
And I can't understand why you gave him your hand,
Lovely Mehitabel Lee.

Potiphar Gubbins, C.E.,
Is dear to the Powers that Be;
For They bow and They smile in an affable style,
Which is seldom accorded to Me.

Potiphar Gubbins, C.E.,
Is certain as certain can be
Of a highly paid post which is claimed by a host
Of seniors—including Me.

Careless and lazy is he,
Greatly inferior to Me.
What is the spell that you manage so well,
Commonplace Potiphar G.?

Lovely Mehitabel Lee,
Let me inquire of thee,
Should I have riz to where Potiphar is,
Hadst thou been mated to Me?

DELILAH

We have another Viceroy now,—those days are dead and done
Of Delilah Aberyswith and depraved Ulysses Gunne.

Delilah Aberyswith was a lady—not too young—
With a perfect taste in dresses and a badly-bitted tongue,
With a thirst for information, and a greater thirst for praise,
And a little house in Simla in the Prehistoric Days.

By reason of her marriage to a gentleman in power,
Delilah was acquainted with the gossip of the hour;
And many little secrets, of the half-official kind,
Were whispered to Delilah, and she bore them all in mind.

She patronized extensively a man, Ulysses Gunne,
Whose mode of earning money was a low and shameful one.
He wrote for certain papers, which, as everybody knows,
Is worse than serving in a shop or scaring off the crows.

He praised her "queenly beauty" first; and, later on, he hinted
At the "vastness of her intellect" with compliment unstinted.
He went with her a-riding, and his love for her was such
That he lent her all his horses and—she galled them very much.

One day, THEY brewed a secret of a fine financial sort;
It related to Appointments, to a Man and a Report.
'Twas almost worth the keeping,—only seven people knew it—
And Gunne rose up to seek the truth and patiently ensue it.

It was a Viceroy's Secret, but—perhaps the wine was red—
Perhaps an Aged Concillor had lost his aged head—
Perhaps Delilah's eyes were bright—Delilah's whispers sweet—
The Aged Member told her what 'twere treason to repeat.

Ulysses went a-riding, and they talked of love and flowers;
Ulysses went a-calling, and he called for several hours;
Ulysses went a-waltzing, and Delilah helped him dance—
Ulysses let the waltzes go, and waited for his chance.

The summer sun was setting, and the summer air was still,
The couple went a-walking in the shade of Summer Hill.
The wasteful sunset faded out in turkis-green and gold,
Ulysses pleaded softly, and . . . that bad Delilah told!

Next morn, a startled Empire learnt the all-important news;
Next week, the Aged Councillor was shaking in his shoes.
Next month, I met Delilah and she did not show the least
Hesitation in affirming that Ulysses was a "beast."

*   *   *   *   *

We have another Viceroy now, those days are dead and done—
Off, Delilah Aberyswith and most mean Ulysses Gunne!

MY RIVAL

I go to concert, party, ball—
    What profit is in these?
I sit alone against the wall
    And strive to look at ease.
The incense that is mine by right
    They burn before Her shrine;
And that's because I'm seventeen
    And she is forty-nine.

I cannot check my girlish blush,
    My colour comes and goes.
I redden to my finger-tips,
    And sometimes to my nose.
But She is white where white should be,
    And red where red should shine.
The blush that flies at seventeen
    Is fixed at forty-nine.

I wish *I* had her constant cheek:
    I wish that I could sing
All sorts of funny little songs,
    Not quite the proper thing.
I'm very *gauche* and very shy,
    Her jokes aren't in my line;
And, worst of all, I'm seventeen
    While She is forty-nine.

The young men come, the young men go,
    Each pink and white and neat,
She's older than their mothers, but
    They grovel at Her feet.
They walk beside Her 'rickshaw-wheels—
    None ever walk by mine;
And that's because I'm seventeen
    And She is forty-nine.

She rides with half a dozen men
    (She calls them "boys" and "mashes"),
I trot along the Mall alone;
    My prettiest frocks and sashes
Don't help to fill my programme-card,
    And vainly I repine
From ten to two A.M. Ah me!
    Would I were forty-nine.

She calls me "darling," "pet," and "dear,"
    And "sweet retiring maid."
I'm always at the back, I know—
    She puts me in the shade.
She introduces me to men—
    "Cast" lovers, I opine;
For sixty takes to seventeen,
    Nineteen to forty-nine.

But even She must older grow
    And end Her dancing days,
She can't go on for ever so
    At concerts, balls, and plays.
One ray of priceless hope I see
    Before my footsteps shine;
Just think, that She'll be eighty-one
    When I am forty-nine!

L'ENVOI

DEPARTMENTAL DITTIES

The smoke upon your Altar dies,
    The flowers decay,
The Goddess of your sacrifice

Has flown away.
What profit then to sing or slay
The sacrifice from day to day?

"We know the Shrine is void," they said.
   "The Goddess flown—
"Yet wreaths are on the altar laid—
   "The Altar-Stone
"Is black with fumes of sacrifice,
"Albeit She has fled our eyes.

"For, it may be, if still we sing
   "And tend the Shrine,
"Some Deity on wandering wing
   "May there incline;
"And, finding all in order meet,
"Stay while we worship at Her feet."

THE SEA AND THE HILLS

1902

Who hath desired the Sea?—the sight of salt water unbounded—
The heave and the halt and the hurl and the crash of the comber wind-
    hounded?
The sleek-barrelled swell before storm, grey, foamless, enormous, and
    growing—
Stark calm on the lap of the Line or the crazy-eyed hurricane blowing—
His Sea in no showing the same—his Sea and the same 'neath each showing:
        His Sea as she slackens or thrills?
So and no otherwise—so and no otherwise—hillmen desire their Hills!

Who hath desired the Sea?—the immense and contemptuous surges?
The shudder, the stumble, the swerve, as the star-stabbing bow-sprit emerges?
The orderly clouds of the Trades, the ridged, roaring sapphire thereunder—
Unheralded cliff-haunting flaws and the headsail's low-volleying thunder—
His Sea in no wonder the same—his Sea and the same through each wonder:
        His Sea as she rages or stills?
So and no otherwise—so and no otherwise—hillmen desire their Hills.

Who hath desired the Sea? Her menaces swift as her mercies?
The in-rolling walls of the fog and the silver-winged breeze that disperses?
The unstable mined berg going South and the calvings and groans that de-
    clare it—

White water half-guessed overside and the moon breaking timely to bare it—
His Sea as his fathers have dared—his Sea as his children shall dare it:
　　　His Sea as she serves him or kills?
So and no otherwise—so and no otherwise—hillmen desire their Hills.

Who hath desired the Sea? Her excellent loneliness rather
Than forecourts of kings, and her outermost pits than the streets where men
　　　gather
Inland, among dust, under trees—inland where the slayer may slay him—
Inland, out of reach of her arms, and the bosom whereon he must lay him—
His Sea from the first that betrayed—at the last that shall never betray him:
　　　His Sea that his being fulfils?
So and no otherwise—so and no otherwise—hillmen desire their Hills.

THE "MARY GLOSTER"

1894

I've paid for your sickest fancies; I've humoured your crackedest whim—
Dick, it's your daddy, dying; you've got to listen to him!

Good for a fortnight, am I? The doctor told you? He lied.
I shall go under by morning, and—— Put that nurse outside.
'Never seen death yet, Dickie? Well, now is your time to learn,
And you'll wish you held my record before it comes to your turn.
Not counting the Line and the Foundry, the Yards and the village, too,
I've made myself and a million; but I'm damned if I made you.
Master at two-and-twenty, and married at twenty-three—
Ten thousand men on the pay-roll, and forty freighters at sea!
Fifty years between 'em, and every year of it fight,
And now I'm Sir Anthony Gloster, dying, a baronite:
For I lunched with his Royal 'Ighness—what was it the papers had?
"Not the least of our merchant-princes." Dickie, that's me, your dad!
I didn't begin with askings. I took my job and I stuck;
I took the chances they wouldn't, an' now they're calling it luck.
Lord, what boats I've handled—rotten and leaky and old—
Ran 'em, or—opened the bilge-cock, precisely as I was told.
Grub that 'ud bind you crazy, and crews that 'ud turn you grey,
And a big fat lump of insurance to cover the risk on the way.
The others they dursn't do it; they said they valued their life
(They've served me since as skippers). I went, and I took my wife.
Over the world I drove 'em, married at twenty-three,
And your mother saving the money and making a man of me.
I was content to be master, but she said there was better behind;
She took the chances I wouldn't, and I followed your mother blind.
She egged me to borrow the money, an' she helped me to clear the loan,

When we bought half-shares in a cheap 'un and hoisted a flag of our own.
Patching and coaling on credit, and living the Lord knew how,
We started the Red Ox freighters—we've eight-and-thirty now.
And those were the days of clippers, and the freights were clipper-freights,
And we knew we were making our fortune, but she died in Macassar Straits—
By the Little Paternosters, as you come to the Union Bank—
And we dropped her in fourteen fathom: I pricked it off where she sank.
Owners we were, full owners, and the boat was christened for her,
And she died in the *Mary Gloster*. My heart, how young we were!
So I went on a spree round Java and well-nigh ran her ashore,
But your mother came and warned me and I would't liquor no more:
Strict I stuck to my business, afraid to stop or I'd think,
Saving the money (she warned me), and letting the other men drink.
And I met M'Cullough in London (I'd saved five 'undred then),
And 'tween us we started the Foundry—three forges and twenty men.
Cheap repairs for the cheap 'uns. It paid, and the business grew;
For I bought me a steam-lathe patent, and that was a gold mine too.
"Cheaper to build 'em than buy 'em," *I* said, but M'Cullough he shied,
And we wasted a year in talking before we moved to the Clyde.
And the Lines were all beginning, and we all of us started fair,
Building our engines like houses and staying the boilers square.
But M'Cullough 'e wanted cabins with marble and maple and all,
And Brussels an' Utrecht velvet, and baths and a Social Hall,
And pipes for closets all over, and cutting the frames too light,
But M'Cullough he died in the Sixties, and —— Well, I'm dying to-night. . . .
I knew—*I* knew what was coming, when we bid on the *Byfleet's* keel—
They piddled and piffled with iron, I'd given my orders for steel!
Steel and the first expansions. It paid, I tell you, it paid,
When we came with our nine-knot freighters and collared the long-run trade!
And they asked me how I did it, and I gave 'em the Scripture text,
"You keep your light so shining a little in front o' the next!"
They copied all they could follow, but they couldn't copy my mind,
And I left 'em sweating and stealing a year and a half behind.
Then came the armour-contracts, but that was M'Cullough's side;
He was always best in the Foundry, but better, perhaps, he died.
I went through his private papers; the notes was plainer than print;
And I'm no fool to finish if a man'll give me a hint.
(I remember his widow was angry.) So I saw what his drawings meant,
And I started the six-inch rollers, and it paid me sixty per cent.
Sixty per cent *with* failures, and more than twice we could do,
And a quarter-million to credit, and I saved it all for you!
I thought—it doesn't matter—you seemed to favour your ma,
But you're nearer forty than thirty, and I know the kind you are.
Harrer an' Trinity College! I ought to ha' sent you to sea—
But I stood you an education, an' what have you done for me?

The things I knew was proper you wouldn't thank me to give,
And the things I knew was rotten you said was the way to live.
For you muddled with books and pictures, an' china an' etchin's an' fans,
And your rooms at college was beastly—more like a whore's than a man's;
Till you married that thin-flanked woman, as white and as stale as a bone,
An' she gave you your social nonsense; but where's that kid o' your own?
I've seen your carriages blocking the half o' the Cromwell Road,
But never the doctor's brougham to help the missus unload.
(So there isn't even a grandchild, an' the Gloster family's done.)
Not like your mother, she isn't. She carried her freight each run.
But they died, the pore little beggars! At sea she had 'em—they died.
Only you, an' you stood it. You haven't stood much beside.
Weak, a liar, and idle, and mean as a collier's whelp
Nosing for scraps in the galley. No help—my son was no help!
So he gets three 'undred thousand, in trust and the interest paid.
I wouldn't give it you, Dickie—you see, I made it in trade.
You're saved from soiling your fingers, and if you have no child,
It all comes back to the business. 'Gad, won't your wife be wild!
'Calls and calls in her carriage, her 'andkerchief up to 'er eye:
"Daddy! dear daddy's dyin'!" and doing her best to cry.
Grateful? Oh, yes, I'm grateful, but keep her away from here.
Your mother 'ud never ha' stood 'er, and, anyhow, women are queer. . . .
There's women will say I've married a second time. Not quite!
But give pore Aggie a hundred, and tell her your lawyers'll fight.
She was the best o' the boiling—you'll meet her before it ends.
I'm in for a row with the mother—I'll leave you settle my friends.
For a man he must go with a woman, which women don't understand—
Or the sort that say they can see it they aren't the marrying brand.
But I wanted to speak o' your mother that's Lady Gloster still;
I'm going to up and see her, without its hurting the will.
Here! Take your hand off the bell-pull. Five thousand's waiting for you,
If you'll only listen a minute, and do as I bid you do.
They'll try to prove me crazy, and, if you bungle, they can;
And I've only you to trust to! (O God, why ain't it a man?)
There's some waste money on marbles, the same as M'Cullough tried—
Marbles and mausoleums—but I call that sinful pride.
There's some ship bodies for burial—we've carried 'em, soldered and packed,
Down in their wills they wrote it, and nobody called them cracked.
But me—I've too much money, and people might . . . All my fault:
It come o' hoping for grandsons and buying that Wokin' vault. . . .
I'm sick o' the 'ole dam' business. I'm going back where I came.
Dick, you're the son o' my body, and you'll take charge o' the same!
I want to lie by your mother, ten thousand mile away,
And they'll want to send me to Woking; and that's where you'll earn your
    pay.

I've thought it out on the quiet, the same as it ought to be done—
Quiet, and decent, and proper—an' here's your orders, my son.
You know the Line? You don't, though. You write to the Board, and tell
Your father's death has upset you an' you're going to cruise for a spell,
An' you'd like the *Mary Gloster*—I've held her ready for this—
They'll put her in working order and you'll take her out as she is.
Yes, it was money idle when I patched her and laid her aside
(Thank God, I can pay for my fancies!)—the boat where your mother died,
By the Little Paternosters, as you come to the Union Bank,
We dropped her—I think I told you—and I pricked it off where she sank.
['Tiny she looked on the grating—that oily, treacly sea—]
'Hundred and Eighteen East, remember, and South just Three.
Easy bearings to carry—Three South—Three to the dot;
But I gave McAndrew a copy in case of dying—or not.
And so you'll write to McAndrew, he's Chief of the Maori Line;
They'll give him leave, if you ask 'em and say it's business o' mine.
I built three boats for the Maoris, an' very well pleased they were,
An I've known Mac since the Fifties, and Mac knew me—and her.
After the first stroke warned me I sent him the money to keep
Against the time you'd claim it, committin' your dad to the deep;
For you are the son o' my body, and Mac was my oldest friend,
I've never asked 'im to dinner, but he'll see it out to the end.
Stiff-necked Glasgow beggar! I've heard he's prayed for my soul,
But he couldn't lie if you paid him, and he'd starve before he stole.
He'll take the *Mary* in ballast—you'll find her a lively ship;
And you'll take Sir Anthony Gloster, that goes on 'is wedding-trip,
Lashed in our old deck-cabin with all three port-holes wide,
The kick o' the screw beneath him and the round blue seas outside!
Sir Anthony Gloster's carriage—our 'ouse-flag flyin' free—
Ten thousand men on the pay-roll and forty freighters at sea!
He made himself and a million, but this world is a fleetin' show,
And he'll go to the wife of 'is bosom the same as he ought to go—
By the heel of the Paternosters—there isn't a chance to mistake—
And Mac'll pay you the money as soon as the bubbles break!
Five thousand for six weeks' cruising, the staunchest freighter afloat,
And Mac he'll give you your bonus the minute I'm out o' the boat!
He'll take you round to Macassar, and you'll come back alone;
He knows what I want o' the *Mary*. . . . I'll do what I please with my own.
Your mother 'ud call it wasteful, but I've seven-and-thirty more;
I'll come in my private carriage and bid it wait at the door. . . .
For my son 'e was never a credit: 'e muddled with books and art,
And e' lived on Sir Anthony's money and 'e broke Sir Anthony's heart.
There isn't even a grandchild, and the Gloster family's done—
The only one you left me—O mother, the only one!
Harrer and Trinity College—me slavin' early an' late—

An' he thinks I'm dying crazy, and you're in Macassar Strait!
Flesh o' my flesh, my dearie, for ever an' ever amen,
That first stroke come for a warning. I ought to ha' gone to you then.
But—cheap repairs for a cheap 'un—the doctor said I'd do.
Mary, why didn't *you* warn me? I've allus heeded to you,
Excep'—I know—about women; but you are a spirit now;
An', wife, they was only women, and I was a man. That's how.
An' a man 'e must go with a woman, as you *could* not understand;
But I never talked 'em secrets. I paid 'em out o' hand.
Thank Gawd, I can pay for my fancies! Now what's five thousand to me,
For a berth off the Paternosters in the haven where I would be?
I believe in the Resurrection, if I read my Bible plain,
But I wouldn't trust 'em at Wokin'; we're safer at sea again.
For the heart it shall go with the treasure—go down to the sea in ships.
I'm sick of the hired women. I'll kiss my girl on her lips!
I'll be content with my fountain. I'll drink from my own well,
And the wife of my youth shall charm me—an' the rest can go to Hell!
(Dickie, *he* will, that's certain.) I'll lie in our standin'-bed,
An' Mac'll take her in ballast—an' she trims best by the head. . . .
Down by the head an' sinkin', her fires are drawn and cold,
And the water's splashin' hollow on the skin of the empty hold—
Churning an' choking and chuckling, quiet and scummy and dark—
Full to her lower hatches and risin' steady. Hark!
That was the after-bulkhead. . . . She's flooded from stem to stern. . . .
'Never seen death yet, Dickie? . . . Well, now is your time to learn!

THE MERCHANTMEN

1893

King Solomon drew merchantmen,
    Because of his desire
For peacocks, apes, and ivory,
    From Tarshish unto Tyre,
With cedars out of Lebanon
    Which Hiram rafted down;
But we be only sailormen
    That use in London town.

Coastwise—cross-seas—round the world and back again—
  Where the flaw shall head us or the full Trade suits—
Plain-sail—storm-sail—lay your board and tack again—
  And that's the way we'll pay Paddy Doyle for his boots!

We bring no store of ingots,
    Of spice or precious stones,
But what we have we gathered
    With sweat and aching bones:
In flame beneath the Tropics,
    In frost upon the floe,
And jeopardy of every wind
    That does between them go.

And some we got by purchase,
    And some we had by trade,
And some we found by courtesy
    Of pike and carronade—
At midnight, 'mid-sea meetings,
    For charity to keep,
And light the rolling homeward-bound
    That rowed a foot too deep!

By sport of bitter weather
    We're walty, strained, and scarred
From the kentledge on the kelson
    To the slings upon the yard.
Six oceans had their will of us
    To carry all away—
Our galley's in the Baltic,
    And our boom's in Mossel Bay.

We've floundered off the Texel,
   Awash with sodden deals,
We've shipped from Valparaiso
   With the Norther at our heels:
We're ratched beyond the Crossets
   That tusk the Southern Pole,
And dipped our gunnels under
   To the dread Agulhas roll.

Beyond all outer charting
   We sailed where none have sailed,
And saw the land-lights burning
   On islands none have hailed;
Our hair stood up for wonder,
   But, when the night was done,
There danced the deep to windward
   Blue-empty 'neath the sun!

Strange consorts rode beside us
   And brought us evil luck;
The witch-fire climbed our channels,
   And flared on vane and truck,
Till, through the red tornado,
   That lashed us nigh to blind,
We saw The Dutchman plunging,
   Full canvas, head to wind!

We've heard the Midnight Leadsman
   That calls the black deep down—
Ay, thrice we've heard The Swimmer,
   The Thing that may not drown.
On frozen bunt and gasket
   The sleet-cloud drave her hosts,
When, manned by more than signed with us,
   We passed the Isle of Ghosts!

And north, amid the hummocks,
   A biscuit-toss below,
We met the silent shallop
   That frighted whalers know;
For, down a cruel ice-lane,
   That opened as he sped,
We saw dead Hendrick Hudson
   Steer, North by West, his dead.
So dealt God's waters with us

Beneath the roaring skies,
So walked His signs and marvels
All naked to our eyes:
But we were heading homeward
With trade to lose or make—
Good Lord, they slipped behind us
In the tailing of our wake!

Let go, let go the anchors;
Now shamed at heart are we
To bring so poor a cargo home
That had for gift the sea!
Let go the great bow-anchor—
Ah, fools were we and blind—
The worst we stored with utter toil,
The best we left behind!

Coastwise—cross-seas—round the world and back again,
Whither flaw shall fail us or the Trades drive down:
Plain-sail—storm-sail—lay your board and tack again—
And all to bring a cargo up to London Town!

THE SONG OF DIEGO VALDEZ

1902

The God of Fair Beginnings
Hath prospered here my hand—
The cargoes of my lading,
And the keels of my command.
For out of many ventures
That sailed with hope as high,
My own have made the better trade,
And Admiral am I.

To me my King's much honour,
To me my people's love—
To me the pride of Princes
And power all pride above;
To me the shouting cities,
To me the mob's refrain:—
"Who knows not noble Valdez
"Hath never heard of Spain."

But I remember comrades—
   Old playmates on new seas—
Whenas we traded orpiment
   Among the savages—
A thousand leagues to south'ard
   And thirty years removed—
They knew not noble Valdez,
   But me they knew and loved.

Then they that found good liquor,
   They drank it not alone,
And they that found fair plunder,
   They told us every one,
About our chosen islands
   Or secret shoals between,
When, weary from far voyage,
   We gathered to careen.

There burned our breaming-fagots
   All pale along the shore:
There rose our worn pavilions—
   A sail above an oar:
As flashed each yearning anchor
   Through mellow seas afire,
So swift our careless captains
   Rowed each to his desire.

Where lay our loosened harness?
   Where turned our naked feet?
Whose tavern 'mid the palm-trees?
   What quenchings of what heat?
Oh, fountain in the desert!
   Oh, cistern in the waste!
Oh, bread we ate in secret!
   Oh, cup we spilled in haste!

The youth new-taught of longing,
   The widow curbed and wan,
The goodwife proud at season,
   And the maid aware of man—
All souls unslaked, consuming,
   Defrauded in delays,
Desire not more their quittance
   Than I those forfeit days!

I dreamed to wait my pleasure
    Unchanged my spring would bide:
Wherefore, to wait my pleasure,
    I put my spring aside
Till, first in face of Fortune,
    And last in mazed disdain,
I made Diego Valdez
    High Admiral of Spain.

Then walked no wind 'neath Heaven
    Nor surge that did not aid—
I dared extreme occasion,
    Nor ever one betrayed.
They wrought a deeper treason—
    (Led seas that served my needs!)
They sold Diego Valdez
    To bondage of great deeds.

The tempest flung me seaward,
    And pinned and bade me hold
The course I might not alter—
    And men esteemed me bold!
The calms embayed my quarry,
    The fog-wreath sealed his eyes;
The dawn-wind brought my topsails—
    And men esteemed me wise!

Yet, 'spite my tyrant triumphs,
    Bewildered, dispossessed—
My dream held I before me—
    My vision of my rest;
But, crowned by Fleet and People,
    And bound by King and Pope—
Stands here Diego Valdez
    To rob me of my hope.

No prayer of mine shall move him.
    No word of his set free
The Lord of Sixty Pennants
    And the Steward of the Sea.
His will can loose ten thousand
    To seek their loves again—
But not Diego Valdez,
    High Admiral of Spain.

There walks no wind 'neath Heaven
    Nor wave that shall restore
The old careening riot
    And the clamorous, crowded shore—
The fountain in the desert,
    The cistern in the waste,
The bread we ate in secret,
    The cup we spilled in haste.

Now call I to my Captains—
    For council fly the sign—
Now leap their zealous galleys,
    Twelve-oared, across the brine.
To me the straiter prison,
    To me the heavier chain—
To me Diego Valdez,
    High Admiral of Spain!

THE GIPSY TRAIL

The white moth to the closing bine,
    The bee to the opened clover,
And the gipsy blood to the gipsy blood
    Ever the wide world over.

Ever the wide world over, lass,
    Ever the trail held true,
Over the world and under the world,
    And back at the last to you.

Out of the dark of the gorgio camp,
    Out of the grime and the gray
(Morning waits at the end of the world),
    Gipsy, come away!

The wild boar to the sun-dried swamp,
    The red crane to her reed,
And the Romany lass to the Romany lad,
    By the tie of a roving breed.

The pied snake to the rifted rock,
    The buck to the stony plain,
And the Romany lass to the Romany lad,
    And both to the road again.

Both to the road again, again!
　Out on a clean sea-track—
Follow the cross of the gipsy trail
　Over the world and back!

Follow the Romany patteran
　North where the blue bergs sail,
And the bows are grey with the frozen spray,
　And the masts are shod with mail.

Follow the Romany patteran
　Sheer to the Austral Light,
Where the besom of God is the wild South wind,
　Sweeping the sea-floors white.

Follow the Romany patteran
　West to the sinking sun,
Till the junk-sails lift through the houseless drift.
　And the east and west are one.

Follow the Romany patteran
　East where the silence broods
By a purple wave on an opal beach
　In the hush of the Mahim woods.

"The wild hawk to the wind-swept sky,
　The deer to the wholesome wold,
And the heart of a man to the heart of a maid,
　As it was in the days of old."

The heart of a man to the heart of a maid—
　Light of my tents, be fleet.
Morning waits at the end of the world,
　And the world is all at our feet!

THE NATIVE-BORN

1894

We've drunk to the Queen—God bless her!—
　We've drunk to our mothers' land;
We've drunk to our English brother,
　(But he does not understand);

We've drunk to the wide creation,
   And the Cross swings low for the morn,
Last toast, and of Obligation,
   A health to the Native-born!

They change their skies above them,
   But not their hearts that roam!
We learned from our wistful mothers
   To call old England "home";
We read of the English skylark,
   Of the spring in the English lanes,
But we screamed with the painted lories
   As we rode on the dusty plains!

They passed with their old-world legends—
   Their tales of wrong and dearth—
Our fathers held by purchase,
   But we by the right of birth;
Our heart's where they rocked our cradle,
   Our love where we spent our toil,
And our faith and our hope and our honour
   We pledge to our native soil!

I charge you charge your glasses—
   I charge you drink with me
To the men of the Four New Nations,
   And the Islands of the Sea—
To the last least lump of coral
   That none may stand outside,
And our own good pride shall teach us
   To praise our comrade's pride.

To the hush of the breathless morning
   On the thin, tin, crackling roofs,
To the haze of the burned back-ranges
   And the dust of the shoeless hoofs—
To the risk of a death by drowning,
   To the risk of a death by drouth—
To the men of a million acres,
   To the Sons of the Golden South!

To the Sons of the Golden South (*Stand up!*),
   And the life we live and know,
Let a fellow sing o' the little things he cares about,

If a fellow fights for the little things he cares about
With the weight of a single blow!

To the smoke of a hundred coasters,
　To the sheep on a thousand hills,
To the sun that never blisters,
　To the rain that never chills—
To the land of the waiting springtime,
　To our five-meal, meat-fed men,
To the tall, deep-bosomed women,
　And the children nine and ten!

And the children nine and ten (Stand up!),
　And the life we live and know,
Let a fellow sing o' the little things he cares about,
If a fellow fights for the little things he cares about
　With the weight of a two-fold blow!

To the far-flung, fenceless prairie
　Where the quick cloud-shadows trail,
To our neighbours' barn in the offing
　And the line of the new-cut rail;
To the plough in her league-long furrow
　With the grey Lake gulls behind—
To the weight of a half-year's winter
　And the warm wet western wind!

To the home of the floods and thunder,
　To her pale dry healing blue—
To the lift of the great Cape combers,
　And the smell of the baked Karroo.
To the growl of the sluicing stamp-head—
　To the reef and the water-gold,
To the last and the largest Empire,
　To the map that is half unrolled!

To our dear dark foster-mothers,
　To the heathen songs they sung—
To the heathen speech we babbled
　Ere we came to the white man's tongue.
To the cool of our deep verandah—
　To the blaze of our jewelled main,
To the night, to the palms in the moonlight,
　And the fire-fly in the cane!

To the hearth of Our People's People—
    To her well-ploughed windy sea,
To the hush of our dread high-altar
    Where The Abbey makes us We.
To the grist of the slow-ground ages,
    To the gain that is yours and mine—
To the Bank of the Open Credit,
    To the Power-house of the Line!

We've drunk to the Queen—God bless her!
    We've drunk to our mothers' land;
We've drunk to our English brother
    (And we hope he'll understand).
We've drunk as much as we're able,
    And the Cross swings low for the morn;
Last toast—and your foot on the table!—
    A health to the Native-born!

A health to the Native-born (Stand up!),
    We're six white men arow,
All bound to sing o' the little things we care about,
All bound to fight for the little things we care about
    With the weight of a six-fold blow!
By the might of our Cable-tow (Take hands!),
    From the Orkneys to the Horn
All round the world (and a little loop to pull it by),
All round the world (and a little strap to buckle it).
    A health to the Native-born!

THE LOST LEGION

1895

There's a Legion that never was 'listed,
    That carries no colours or crest,
But, split in a thousand detachments,
    Is breaking the road for the rest.
Our fathers they left us their blessing—
    They taught us, and groomed us, and crammed;
But we've shaken the Clubs and the Messes
    To go and find out and be damned
                        (Dear boys!),
    To go and get shot and be damned.

So some of us chivvy the slaver,
   And some of us cherish the black,
And some of us hunt on the Oil Coast,
   And some on the Wallaby track:
And some of us drift to Sarawak,
   And some of us drift up The Fly,
And some share our tucker with tigers,
   And some with the gentle Masai,
                      (Dear boys!),
   Take tea with the giddy Masai.

We've painted The Islands vermilion,
   We've pearled on half-shares in the Bay,
We've shouted on seven-ounce nuggets,
   We've starved on a Seedeeboy's pay;
We've laughed at the world as we found it,—
   Its women and cities and men—
From Sayyid Burgash in a tantrum
   To the smoke-reddened eyes of Loben,
                      (Dear boys!),
   We've a little account with Loben.

The ends of the Earth were our portion,
   The ocean at large was our share.
There was never a skirmish to windward
   But the Leaderless Legion was there:
Yes, somehow and somewhere and always
   We were first when the trouble began,
From a lottery-row in Manila,
   To an I.D.B. race on the Pan
                      (Dear boys!),
   With the Mounted Police on the Pan.

We preach in advance of the Army,
   We skirmish ahead of the Church,
With never a gunboat to help us
   When we're scuppered and left in the lurch.
But we know as the cartridges finish,
   And we're filed on our last little shelves,
That the Legion that never was 'listed
   Will send us as good as ourselves
                    (Good men!),
   Five hundred as good as ourselves!

Then a health (we must drink it in whispers),
   To our wholly unauthorized horde—

To the line of our dusty foreloopers,
   The Gentlemen Rovers abroad—
Yes, a health to ourselves ere we scatter,
   For the steamer won't wait for the train,
And the Legion that never was 'listed
   Goes back into quarters again!
                        'Regards!
Goes back under canvas again.
                        Hurrah!
The swag and the billy again.
                        Here's how!
The trail and the packhorse again.
                        Salue!
The trek and the laager again!

THE LAST OF THE LIGHT BRIGADE

1891

There were thirty million English who talked of England's might,
There were twenty broken troopers who lacked a bed for the night.
They had neither food nor money, they had neither service nor trade;
They were only shiftless soldiers, the last of the Light Brigade.

They felt that life was fleeting; they knew not that art was long,
That though they were dying of famine, they lived in deathless song.
They asked for a little money to keep the wolf from the door;
And the thirty million English sent twenty pounds and four!

They laid their heads together that were scarred and lined and grey;
Keen were the Russian sabres, but want was keener than they;
And an old Troop-Sergeant muttered, "Let us go to the man who writes
The things on Balaclava the kiddies at school recites."

They went without bands or colours, a regiment ten-file strong,
To look for the Master-singer who had crowned them all in his song;
And, waiting his servant's order, by the garden gate they stayed,
A desolate little cluster, the last of the Light Brigade.

They strove to stand to attention, to straighen the toil-bowed back;
They drilled on an empty stomach, the loose-knit files fell slack;
With stooping of weary shoulders, in garments tattered and frayed,
They shambled into his presence, the last of the Light Brigade.

The old Troop-Sergeant was spokesman, and "Beggin' your pardon," he said,
"You wrote o' the Light Brigade, sir. Here's all that isn't dead.
An' it's all come true what you wrote, sir, regardin' the mouth of hell;
For we're all of us nigh to the workhouse, an' we thought we'd call an' tell.

"No, thank you, we don't want food, sir; but couldn't you take an' write
A sort of 'to be continued' and 'see next page' o' the fight?
We think that someone has blundered, an' couldn't you tell 'em how?
You wrote we were heroes once, sir. Please, write we are starving now."

The poor little army departed, limping and lean and forlorn.
And the heart of the Master-singer grew hot with "the scorn of scorn."
And he wrote for them wonderful verses that swept the land like flame,
Till the fatted souls of the English were scourged with the thing called Shame.

O thirty million English that babble of England's might,
Behold there are twenty heroes who lack their food to-night;
Our children's children are lisping to "honour the charge they made—"
And we leave to the streets and the workhouse the charge of the Light
    Brigade!

SUSSEX

1902

God gave all men all earth to love,
    But, since our hearts are small,
Ordained for each one spot should prove
    Belovèd over all;
That, as He watched Creation's birth,
    So we, in godlike mood,
May of our love create our earth
    And see that it is good.

So one shall Baltic pines content,
    As one some Surrey glade,
Or one the palm-grove's droned lament
    Before Levuka's Trade.
Each to his choice, and I rejoice
    The lot has fallen to me
In a fair ground—in a fair ground—
    Yea, Sussex by the sea!

No tender-hearted garden crowns,
    No bosomed woods adorn
Our blunt, bow-headed, whale-backed Downs,
    But gnarled and writhen thorn—
Bare slopes where chasing shadows skim,
    And, through the gaps revealed,
Belt upon belt, the wooded, dim,
    Blue goodness of the Weald.

Clean of officious fence or hedge,
    Half-wild and wholly tame,
The wise turf cloaks the white cliff-edge
    As when the Romans came.
What sign of those that fought and died
    At shift of sword and sword?
The barrow and the camp abide,
    The sunlight and the sward.

Here leaps ashore the full Sou'west
    All heavy-winged with brine,
Here lies above the folded crest
    The Channel's leaden line;
And here the sea-fogs lap and cling,
    And here, each warning each,
The sheep-bells and the ship-bells ring
    Along the hidden beach.

We have no waters to delight
    Our broad and brookless vales—
Only the dewpond on the height
    Unfed, that never fails—
Whereby no tattered herbage tells
    Which way the season flies—
Only our close-bit thyme that smells
    Like dawn in Paradise.

Here through the strong and shadeless days
    The tinkling silence thrills;
Or little, lost, Down churches praise
    The Lord who made the hills:
But here the Old Gods guard their round,
    And, in her secret heart,
The heathen kingdom Wilfrid found
    Dreams, as she dwells, apart.

Though all the rest were all my share,
    With equal soul I'd see
Her nine-and-thirty sisters fair,
    Yet none more fair than she.
Choose ye your need from Thames to Tweed,
    And I will choose instead
Such lands as lie 'twixt Rake and Rye,
    Black Down and Beachy Head.

I will go out against the sun
    Where the rolled scarp retires,
And the Long Man of Wilmington
    Looks naked toward the shires;
And east till doubling Rother crawls
    To find the fickle tide,
By dry and sea-forgotten walls,
    Our ports of stranded pride.

I will go north about the shaws
    And the deep ghylls that breed
Huge oaks and old, the which we hold
    No more than Sussex weed;
Or south where windy Piddinghoe's
    Begilded dolphin veers,
And red beside wide-bankèd Ouse
    Lie down our Sussex steers.

So to the land our hearts we give
    Till the sure magic strike,
And Memory, Use, and Love make live
    Us and our fields alike—
That deeper than our speech and thought,
    Beyond our reason's sway,
Clay of the pit whence we were wrought
    Yearns to its fellow-clay.

God gives all men all earth to love,
    But, since man's heart is small,
Ordains for each one spot shall prove
    Belovèd over all.
Each to his choice, and I rejoice
    The lot has fallen to me
In a fair ground—in a fair ground—
    Yea, Sussex by the sea!

THE VAMPIRE

1897

A fool there was and he made his prayer
(Even as you and I!)
To a rag and a bone and a hank of hair
(We called her the woman who did not care)
But the fool he called her his lady fair—
(Even as you and I!)

Oh, the years we waste and the tears we waste
And the work of our head and hand
Belong to the woman who did not know
(And now we know that she never could know)
And did not understand!

A fool there was and his goods he spent
(Even as you and I!)
Honour and faith and a sure intent
(And it wasn't the least what the lady meant)
But a fool must follow his natural bent
(Even as you and I!)

Oh, the toil we lost and the spoil we lost
And the excellent things we planned
Belong to the woman who didn't know why
(And now we know that she never knew why)
And did not understand!

The fool was stripped to his foolish hide
(Even as you and I!)
Which she might have seen when she threw him aside—
(But it isn't on record the lady tried)
So some of him lived but the most of him died—
(Even as you and I!)

And it isn't the shame and it isn't the blame
That stings like a white-hot brand
It's coming to know that she never knew why
(Seeing, at last, she could never know why)
And never could understand!

WHEN EARTH'S LAST PICTURE IS PAINTED

1892

L'ENVOI TO "THE SEVEN SEAS"

When Earth's last picture is painted and the tubes are twisted and dried,
When the oldest colours have faded, and the youngest critic has died,
We shall rest, and, faith, we shall need it—lie down for an æon or two,
Till the Master of All Good Workmen shall put us to work anew.
And those that were good shall be happy: they shall sit in a golden chair;
They shall splash at a ten-league canvas with brushes of comets' hair.
They shall find real saints to draw from—Magdalene, Peter, and Paul;
They shall work for an age at a sitting and never be tired at all!

And only The Master shall praise us, and only The Master shall blame;
And no one shall work for money, and no one shall work for fame,
But each for the joy of the working, and each, in his separate star,
Shall draw the Thing as he sees It for the God of Things as They are!

THE BALLAD OF THE KING'S MERCY

1889

Abdhur Rahman, the Durani Chief, of him is the story told.
His mercy fills the Khyber hills—his grace is manifold;
He has taken toll of the North and the South—his glory reacheth far,
And they tell the tale of his charity from Balkh to Kandahar.

Before the old Peshawur Gate, where Kurd and Kafir meet,
The Governor of Kabul dealt the Justice of the Street,
And that was strait as running noose and swift as plunging knife,
Tho' he who held the longer purse might hold the longer life.
There was a hound of Hindustan had struck a Yusufzai,
Wherefore they spat upon his face and led him out to die.
It chanced the King went forth that hour when throat was bared to knife;
The Kafir grovelled under-hoof and clamoured for his life.

Then said the King: "Have hope, O friend! Yea, Death disgraced is hard.
"Much honour shall be thine"; and called the Captain of the Guard,
Yar Khan, a bastard of the Blood, so city-babble saith,
And he was honoured of the King—the which is salt to Death;
And he was son of Daoud Shah, the Reiver of the Plains,

And blood of old Durani Lords ran fire in his veins;
And 'twas to tame an Afghan pride nor Hell nor Heaven could bind,
The King would make him butcher to a yelping cur of Hind.

"Strike!" said the King. "King's blood art thou—his death shall be his pride!"
Then louder, that the crowd might catch: "Fear not—his arms are tied!"
Yar Khan drew clear the Khyber knife, and struck, and sheathed again.
"O man, thy will is done," quoth he; "A King this dog hath slain."

> *Abdhur Rahman, the Durani Chief, to the North and the South is sold.*
> *The North and the South shall open their mouth to a Ghilzai flag*
> *unrolled,*
> *When the big guns speak to the Khyber peak, and his dog-Heratis fly:*
> *Ye have heard the song—How long? How long? Wolves of the Abazai!*

That night before the watch was set, when all the streets were clear,
The Governor of Kabul spoke: "My King, hast thou no fear?
"Thou knowest—thou hast heard,"—his speech died at his master's face.
And grimly said the Afghan King: I rule the Afghan race.
"My path is mine—see thou to thine. To-night upon thy bed
"Think who there be in Kabul now that clamour for thy head."

That night when all the gates were shut to City and to throne,
Within a little garden-house the King lay down alone.
Before the sinking of the moon, which is the Night of Night,
Yar Khan came softly to the King to make his honour white.
(The children of the town had mocked beneath his horse's hoofs,
The harlots of the town had hailed him "butcher!" from their roofs.)

But as he groped against the wall, two hands upon him fell,
The King behind his shoulder spake: "Dead man, thou dost not well!
" 'Tis ill to jest with Kings by day and seek a boon by night;
"And that thou bearest in thy hand is all too sharp to write.
"But three days hence, if God be good, and if thy strength remain,
"Thou shalt demand one boon of me and bless me in thy pain.
"For I am merciful to all, and most of all to thee.
"My butcher of the shambles, rest—no knife hast thou for me!"

> *Abdhur Rahman, the Durani Chief, holds hard by the South and the*
> *North;*
> *But the Ghilzai knows, ere the melting snows, when the swollen banks*
> *break forth,*
> *When the red-coats crawl to the sungar wall, and his Usbeg lances fail:*
> *Ye have heard the song—How long? How long? Wolves of the Zukka*
> *Kheyl!*

They stoned him in the rubbish-field when dawn was in the sky,
According to the written word, "See that he do not die."
They stoned him till the stones were piled above him on the plain,
And those the labouring limbs displaced they tumbled back again.
One watched beside the dreary mound that veiled the battered thing,
And him the King with laughter called the Herald of the King.

It was upon the second night, the night of Ramazan,
The watcher leaning earthward heard the message of Yar Khan.
From shattered breast through shrivelled lips broke forth the rattling breath,
"Creature of God, deliver me from agony of Death."

They sought the King among his girls, and risked their lives thereby:
"Protector of the Pitiful, give order that he die!"

"Bid him endure until the day," a lagging answer came;
"The night is short, and he can pray and learn to bless my name."
Before the dawn three times he spoke, and on the day once more:
"Creature of God, deliver me, and bless the King therefor!"
They shot him at the morning prayer, to ease him of his pain,
And when he heard the matchlocks clink, he blessed the King again.
Which thing the singers made a song for all the world to sing
So that the Outer Seas may know the mercy of the King.

> *Abdhur Rahman, the Durani Chief, of him is the story told,*
> *He has opened his mouth to the North and the South, they have stuffed*
>   *his mouth with gold.*
> *Ye know the truth of his tender ruth—and sweet his favours are:*
> *Ye have heard the song—How long? How long?—from Balkh to*
>   *Kandahar.*

THE TRUCE OF THE BEAR

1898

Yearly, with tent and rifle, our careless white men go
By the Pass called Muttianee, to shoot in the vale below.
Yearly by Muttianee he follows our white men in—
Matun, the old blind beggar, bandaged from brow to chin.

Eyeless, noseless, and lipless—toothless, broken of speech,
Seeking a dole at the doorway he mumbles his tale to each;
Over and over the story, ending as he began:
"Make ye no truce with Adam-zad—the Bear that walks like a Man!

"There was a flint in my musket—pricked and primed was the pan,
When I went hunting Adam-zad—the Bear that stands like a Man.
I looked my last on the timber, I looked my last on the snow,
When I went hunting Adam-zad fifty summers ago!

"I knew his times and his seasons, as he knew mine, that fed
By night in the ripened maizefield and robbed my house of bread.
I knew his strength and cunning, as he knew mine, that crept
At dawn to the crowded goat-pens and plundered while I slept.

"Up from his stony playground—down from his well-digged lair—
Out on the naked ridges ran Adam-zad the Bear—
Groaning, grunting, and roaring, heavy with stolen meals,
Two long marches to northward, and I was at his heels!

"Two long marches to northward, at the fall of the second night,
I came on mine enemy Adam-zad all panting from his flight.
There was a charge in the musket—pricked and primed was the pan—
My finger crooked on the trigger—when he reared up like a man.

"Horrible, hairy, human, with paws like hands in prayer,
Making his supplication rose Adam-zad the Bear!
I looked at the swaying shoulders, at the paunch's swag and swing,
And my heart was touched with pity for the monstrous, pleading thing.

"Touched with pity and wonder, I did not fire then . . .
I have looked no more on women—I have walked no more with men.
Nearer he tottered and nearer, with paws like hands that pray—
From brow to jaw that steel-shod paw, it ripped my face away!

"Sudden, silent, and savage, searing as flame the blow—
Faceless I fell before his feet, fifty summers ago.
I heard him grunt and chuckle—I heard him pass to his den.
He left me blind to the darkened years and the little mercy of men.

"Now ye go down in the morning with guns of the newer style,
That load (I have felt) in the middle and range (I have heard) a mile?
Luck to the white man's rifle, that shoots so fast and true,
But—pay, and I lift my bandage and show what the Bear can do!"

(Flesh like slag in the furnace, knobbed and withered and grey—
Matun, the old blind beggar, he gives good worth for his pay.)
"Rouse him at noon in the bushes, follow and press him hard—
Not for his ragings and roarings flinch ye from Adam-zad.

"But (pay, and I put back the bandage) *this* is the time to fear,
When he stands up like a tired man, tottering near and near;
When he stands up as pleading, in wavering, man-brute guise,
When he veils the hate and cunning of his little, swinish eyes;

"When he shows as seeking quarter, with paws like hands in prayer,
That is the time of peril—the time of the Truce of the Bear!"

Eyeless, noseless, and lipless, asking a dole at the door,
Matun, the old blind beggar, he tells it o'er and o'er;
Fumbling and feeling the rifles, warming his hands at the flame,
Hearing our careless white men talk of the morrow's game;

Over and over the story, ending as he began:—
"There is no truce with Adam-zad, the Bear that looks like a Man!"

HYMN BEFORE ACTION

1896

The earth is full of anger,
The seas are dark with wrath,
The Nations in their harness
Go up against our path:
Ere yet we draw the blade,
Jehovah of the Thunders,
Lord God of Battles, aid!

High lust and froward bearing,
Proud heart, rebellious brow—
Deaf ear and soul uncaring,
We seek Thy mercy now!
The sinner that forswore Thee,
The fool that passed Thee by,
Our times are known before Thee—
Lord, grant us strength to die!

For those who kneel beside us
At altars not Thine own,
Who lack the lights that guide us,
Lord, let their faith atone!
If wrong we did to call them,
By honour bound they came;
Let not Thy Wrath befall them,
But deal to us the blame.

From panic, pride, and terror
Revenge that knows no rein—
Light haste and lawless error,
Protect us yet again,
Cloke Thou our undeserving,
Make firm the shuddering breath,
In silence and unswerving
To taste Thy lesser death.

Ah, Mary pierced with sorrow,
Remember, reach and save
The soul that comes to-morrow
Before the God that gave!
Since each was born of woman,
For each at utter need—

True comrade and true foeman—
Madonna, intercede!

E'en now their vanguard gathers,
E'en now we face the fray—
As Thou didst help our fathers,
Help Thou our host to-day.
Fulfilled of signs and wonders,
In life, in death made clear—
Jehovah of the Thunders,
Lord God of Battles, hear!

THE CONUNDRUM OF THE WORKSHOPS

1890

When the flush of a new-born sun fell first on Eden's green and gold,
Our father Adam sat under the Tree and scratched with a stick in the mould;
And the first rude sketch that the world had seen was joy to his mighty heart,
Till the Devil whispered behind the leaves, "It's pretty, but is it Art?"

Wherefore he called to his wife, and fled to fashion his work anew—
The first of his race who cared a fig for the first, most dread review;
And he left his lore to the use of his sons—and that was a glorious gain
When the Devil chuckled "Is it Art?" in the ear of the branded Cain.

They builded a tower to shiver the sky and wrench the stars apart,
Till the Devil grunted behind the bricks: "It's striking, but is it Art?"
The stone was dropped at the quarry-side and the idle derrick swung,
While each man talked of the aims of Art, and each in an alien tongue.

They fought and they talked in the North and the South; they talked and
    they fought in the West,
Till the waters rose on the pitiful land, and the poor Red Clay had rest—
Had rest till that dank blank-canvas dawn when the Dove was preened to
    start,
And the Devil bubbled below the keel: "It's human, but is it Art?"

The tale is as old as the Eden Tree—and new as the new-cut tooth—
For each man knows ere his lip-thatch grows he is master of Art and Truth;
And each man hears as the twilight nears, to the beat of his dying heart,
The Devil drum on the darkened pane: "You did it, but was it Art?"

We have learned to whittle the Eden Tree to the shape of a surplice-peg,
We have learned to bottle our parents twain in the yelk of an addled egg,
We know that the tail must wag the dog, for the horse is drawn by the cart;
But the Devil whoops, as he whooped of old: "It's clever, but is it Art?"

When the flicker of London sun falls faint on the Club-rooms' green and gold,
The sons of Adam sit them down and scratch with their pens in the mould—
They scratch with their pens in the mould of their graves, and the ink and
   the anguish start,
For the Devil mutters behind the leaves: "It's pretty, but is it Art?"

Now, if we could win to the Eden Tree where the Four Great Rivers flow,
And the Wreath of Eve is red on the turf as she left it long ago,
And if we could come when the sentry slept and softly scurry through,
By the favour of God we might know as much—as our father Adam knew!

MARY'S SON

1911

If you stop to find out what your wages will be
   And how they will clothe and feed you,
Willie, my son, don't you go on the Sea.
   For the Sea will never need you.

If you ask for the reason of every command,
   And argue with people about you,
Willie, my son, don't you go on the Land,
   For the Land will do better without you.

If you stop to consider the work you have done
   And to boast what your labour is worth, dear,
Angels may come for you, Willie, my son,
   But you'll never be wanted on Earth, dear!

THE PALACE

1902

When I was a King and a Mason—a Master proven and skilled—
I cleared me ground for a Palace such as a King should build.

I decreed and dug down to my levels. Presently, under the silt,
I came on the wreck of a Palace such as a King had built.

There was no worth in the fashion—there was no wit in the plan—
Hither and thither, aimless, the ruined footings ran—
Masonry, brute, mishandled, but carven on every stone:
"*After me cometh a Builder. Tell him, I too have known.*"

Swift to my use in my trenches, where my well-planned ground-works grew,
I tumbled his quoins and his ashlars, and cut and reset them anew.
Lime I milled of his marbles; burned it, slacked it, and spread;
Taking and leaving at pleasure the gifts of the humble dead.

Yet I despised not nor gloried; yet, as we wrenched them apart,
I read in the razed foundations the heart of that builder's heart.
As he had risen and pleaded, so did I understand
The form of the dream he had followed in the face of the thing he had
    planned.

*   *   *   *   *

When I was a King and a Mason—in the open noon of my pride,
They sent me a Word from the Darkness. They whispered and called me
    aside.
They said—"The end is forbidden." They said—"Thy use is fulfilled.
"Thy Palace shall stand as that other's—the spoil of a King who shall build."

I called my men from my trenches, my quarries, my wharves, and my sheers.
All I had wrought I abandoned to the faith of the faithless years.
Only I cut on the timber—only I carved on the stone:
"*After me cometh a Builder. Tell him, I too have known!*"

TOMMY

I went into a public-'ouse to get a pint o' beer,
The publican 'e up an' sez, "We serve no red-coats here."
The girls be'ind the bar they laughed an' giggled fit to die,
I outs into the street again an' to myself sez I:
    O it's Tommy this, an' Tommy that, an' "Tommy, go away";
    But it's "Thank you, Mister Atkins," when the bands begins to play—
    The band begins to play, my boys, the band begins to play,
    O it's "Thank you, Mister Atkins," when the band begins to play.

I went into a theatre as sober as could be,
They gave a drunk civilian room, but 'adn't none for me;
They sent me to the gallery or round the music-'alls,
But when it comes to fightin', Lord! they'll shove me in the stalls!
    For it's Tommy this, an' Tommy that, an' "Tommy, wait outside";
    But it's "Special train for Atkins" when the trooper's on the tide—
    O it's "Special train for Atkins" when the trooper's on the tide.

Yes, makin' mock o' uniforms that guard you while you sleep
Is cheaper than them uniforms, an' they're starvation cheap;
An' hustlin' drunken soldiers when they're goin' large a bit
Is five times better business than paradin' in full kit.
    Then it's Tommy this, an' Tommy that, an' "Tommy, 'ow's yer soul?"
    But it's "Thin red line of 'eroes" when the drums begin to roll—
    The drums begin to roll, my boys, the drums begin to roll,
    O it's "Thin red line of 'eroes" when the drums begin to roll.

We aren't no thin red 'eroes, nor we aren't no blackguards too,
But single men in barricks, most remarkable like you;
An' if sometimes our conduck isn't all your fancy paints,
Why, single men in barricks don't grow into plaster saints;
    While it's Tommy this, an' Tommy that, an' "Tommy, fall be'ind,"
    But it's "Please to walk in front, sir," when there's trouble in the wind—
    There's trouble in the wind, my boys, there's trouble in the wind,
    O it's "Please to walk in front, sir," when there's trouble in the wind.

You talk o' better food for us, an' schools, an' fires, an' all: —
We'll wait for extry rations if you treat us rational.
Don't mess about the cook-room slops, but prove it to our face
The Widow's Uniform is not the soldier-man's disgrace.

> For it's Tommy this, an' Tommy that, an' "Chuck him out, the brute!"
> But it's "Saviour of 'is country" when the guns begin to shoot;
> An' it's Tommy this, an' Tommy that, an' anything you please;
> An' Tommy ain't a bloomin' fool you bet that Tommy sees!

THE WIDOW'S PARTY

> "Where have you been this while away,
>   Johnnie, Johnnie?"
> Out with the rest on a picnic lay.
>   Johnnie, my Johnnie, aha!
> They called us out of the barrack-yard
> To Gawd knows where from Gosport Hard,
> And you can't refuse when you get the card,
>   And the Widow gives the party.
>   (*Bugle*: Ta—rara—ra-ra-rara!)

> "What did you get to eat and drink,
>   Johnnie, Johnnie?"
> Standing water as thick as ink,
>   Johnnie, my Johnnie, aha!
> A bit o' beef that were three year stored,
> A bit o' mutton as tough as a board,
> And a fowl we killed with a Sergeant's sword,
>   When the Widow give the party.

> "What did you do for knives and forks,
>   Johnnie, Johnnie?"
> We carries 'em with us wherever we walks,
>   Johnnie, my Johnnie, aha!
> And some was sliced and some was halved,
> And some was crimped and some was carved,
> And some was gutted and some was starved,
>   When the Widow give the party.

> "What ha' you done with half your mess,
>   Johnnie, Johnnie?"
> They couldn't do more and they wouldn't do less.
>   Johnnie, my Johnnie, aha!

They ate their whack and they drank their fill,
And I think the rations has made them ill,
For half my comp'ny's lying still
        Where the Widow give the party.

"How did you get away—away,
        Johnnie, Johnnie?"
On the broad o' my back at the end o' the day,
        Johnnie, my Johnnie, aha!
I comed away like a bleedin' toff,
For I got four niggers to carry me off,
As I lay in the bight of a canvas trough,
        When the Widow give the party.

"What was the end of all the show,
        Johnnie, Johnnie?"
Ask my Colonel, for I don't know,
        Johnnie, my Johnnie, aha!
We broke a King and we built a road—
A court-house stands were the Reg'ment goed.
And the river's clean where the raw blood flowed
        When the Widow give the party.
        (*Bugle:* Ta—rara—ra-ra-rara!)

THE 'EATHEN

The 'eathen in 'is blindness bows down to wood an' stone;
'E don't obey no orders unless they is 'is own;
'E keeps 'is side-arms awful: 'e leaves 'em all about,
An' then comes up the Regiment an' pokes the 'eathen out.

   All along o' dirtiness, all along o' mess,
   All along o' doin' things rather-more-or-less,
   All along of abby-nay,[1] kul,[2] an' hazar-ho,[3]
   Mind you keep your rifle an' yourself jus' so!

The young recruit is 'aughty—'e draf's from Gawd knows where;
They bid 'im show 'is stockin's an' lay 'is mattress square;
'E calls it bloomin' nonsense—'e doesn't know, no more—
An' then up comes 'is Company an' kicks 'im round the floor!

---

   [1] Not now.   [2] To-morrow.   [3] Wait a bit.

The young recruit is 'ammered—'e takes it very hard;
'E 'angs 'is 'ead an' mutters—'e sulks about the yard;
'E talks o' "cruel tyrants" which 'e'll swing for by-an'-by,
An' the others 'ears an' mocks 'im, an' the boy goes orf to cry.

The young recruit is silly—'e thinks o' suicide.
'E's lost 'is gutter-devil; 'e 'asn't got 'is pride;
But day by day they kicks 'im, which 'elps 'im on a bit,
Till 'e finds 'isself one mornin' with a full an' proper kit.

    Gettin' clear o' dirtiness, gettin' done with mess,
    Gettin' shut o' doin' things rather-more-or-less;
    Not so fond of abby-nay, kul, nor hazar-ho,
    Learns to keep 'is rifle an' 'isself jus' so!

The young recruit is 'appy—'e throws a chest to suit;
You see 'im grow mustaches; you 'ear 'im slap 'is boot.
'E learns to drop the "bloodies" from every word 'e slings,
An' 'e shows an 'ealthy brisket when 'e strips for bars an' rings.

The cruel-tyrant-sergeants they watch 'im 'arf a year;
They watch 'im with 'is comrades, they watch 'im with 'is beer;
They watch 'im with the women at the regimental dance,
And the cruel-tyrant-sergeants send 'is name along for "Lance."

An' now 'e's 'arf o' nothin', an' all a private yet,
'Is room they up an' rags 'im to see what they will get.
They rags 'im low an' cunnin', each dirty trick they can,
But 'e learns to sweat 'is temper an' 'e learns to sweat 'is man.

An', last, a Colour-Sergeant, as such to be obeyed,
'E schools 'is men at cricket, 'e tells 'em on parade;
They sees 'im quick an' 'andy, uncommon set an' smart,
An' so 'e talks to orficers which 'ave the Core at 'eart.

'E learns to do 'is watchin' without it showin' plain;
'E learns to save a dummy, an' shove 'im straight again;
'E learns to check a ranker that's buyin' leave to shirk;
An' 'e learns to make men like 'im so they'll learn to like their work.

An' when it comes to marchin' he'll see their socks are right,
An' when it comes to action 'e shows 'em how to sight.
'E knows their ways of thinkin' and just what's in their mind;
'E knows when they are takin' on an' when they've fell be'ind.

'E knows each talkin' corp'ral that leads a squad astray;
'E feels 'is innards 'eavin', 'is bowels givin' way;
'E sees the blue-white faces all tryin' 'ard to grin,
An' 'e stands an' waits an' suffers till it's time to cap 'em in.

An' now the hugly bullets come peckin' through the dust,
An' no one wants to face 'em, but every beggar must;
So, like a man in irons, which isn't glad to go,
They moves 'em off by companies uncommon stiff an' slow.

Of all 'is five years' schoolin' they don't remember much
Excep' the not retreatin', the step an' keepin' touch.
It looks like teachin' wasted when they duck an' spread an' 'op—
But if 'e 'adn't learned 'em they'd be all about the shop.

An' now it's " 'Oo goes backward?" an' now it's " 'Oo comes on?"
And now it's "Get the doolies," an' now the Captain's gone;
An' now it's bloody murder, but all the while they 'ear
'Is voice, the same as barrick-drill, a-shepherdin' the rear.

'E's just as sick as they are, 'is 'eart is like to split,
But 'e works 'em, works 'em, works 'em till he feels 'em take the bit;
The rest is 'oldin' steady till the watchful bugles play,
An' 'e lifts 'em, lifts 'em, lifts 'em through the charge that wins the day!

The 'eathen in 'is blindness bows down to wood an' stone;
'E don't obey no orders unless they is 'is own.
The 'eathen in 'is blindness must end where 'e began,
But the backbone of the Army is the Non-commissioned Man!

Keep away from dirtiness—keep away from mess,
Don't get into doin' things rather-more-or-less!
Let's ha' done with abby-nay, kul, and hazar-ho;
Mind you keep your rifle an' yourself jus' so!

THE BALLAD OF BOH DA THONE

This is the ballad of Boh Da Thone,
Erst a Pretender to Theebaw's throne.
Who harried the district of Alalone:
How he met with his fate and the V.P.P.
At the hand of Harendra Mukerji,
Senior Gomashta, G.B.T.

Boh Da Thone was a warrior bold
His sword and his Snider were bossed with gold,

And the Peacock Banner his henchmen bore
Was stiff with bullion but stiffer with gore.

He shot at the strong and he slashed at the weak
From the Salween scrub to the Chindwin teak:

He crucified noble, he sacrificed mean,
He filled old women with kerosene:

While over the water the papers cried,
"The patriot fights for his countryside!"

But little they cared for the Native Press,
The worn white soldiers in Khaki dress,

Who tramped through the jungle and camped in the byre,
Who died in the swamp and were tombed in the mire,

Who gave up their lives, at the Queen's Command,
For the Pride of their Race and the Peace of the Land.

Now first of the foemen of Boh Da Thone
Was Captain O'Neil of the "Black Tyrene,"

And his was a Company, seventy strong,
Who hustled that dissolute Chief along.

There were lads from Galway and Louth and Meath
Who went to their death with a joke in their teeth,

And worshipped with fluency, fervor and zeal
The mud on the boot-heels of "Crook" O'Neil.

But ever a blight on their labors lay,
And ever their quarry would vanish away,

Till the sun-dried boys of the Black Tyrone
Took a brotherly interest in Boh Da Thone:

And, sooth, if pursuit in possession ends,
The Boh and his trackers were best of friends.

The word of a scout—a march by night—
A rush through the mist—a scattering fight—

A volley from cover— a corpse in the clearing—
The glimpse of a lion-cloth and heavy jade earring—

The flare of a village—the tally of slain—
And . . . the Boh was abroad "on the raid" again!

They cursed their luck as the Irish will,
They gave him credit for cunning and skill,

They buried their dead, they bolted their beef,
And started anew on the track of the thief

Till, in place of the "Kalends of Greece," men said,
"When Crook and his darlings come back with the head."

They had hunted the Boh from the Hills to the plain—
He doubled and broke for the hills again:

They had crippled his power for rapine and raid,
They had routed him out of his pet stockade,

And at last, they came, when the Day Star tired
To a camp deserted—a village fired.

A black cross blistered the Morning-gold,
And the body upon it was stark and cold.

The wind of the dawn went merrily past,
The high grass bowed her plumes to the blast.

And out of the grass, on a sudden, broke
A spirtle of fire, a whorl of smoke—

And Captain O'Neil of the Black Tyrone
Was blessed with a slug in the ulna-bone—

The gift of his enemy Boh Da Thone.
(Now a slug that is hammered from telegraph wire
Is a thorn in the flesh and a rankling fire.)

*   *   *   *   *

The shot-wound festered—as shot-wounds may
In a steaming barrack at Mandalay.

The left arm throbbed, and the Captain swore,
"I'd like to be after the Boh once more!"

The fever held him—the Captain said,
"I'd give a hundred to look at his head!"

The Hospital punkahs creaked and whirred,
But Babu Harendra (Gomashta) heard.

He thought of the cane-brake, green and dank,
That girdled his home by the Dacca tank.

He thought of his wife and his High School son,
He thought—but abandoned the thought—of a gun.

His sleep was broken by visions dread
Of a shining Boh with a silver head.

He kept his counsel and went his way,
And swindled the cartmen of half their pay.

*   *   *   *   *

And the months went on, as the worst must do,
And the Boh returned to the raid anew.

But the Captain had quitted the long-drawn strife,
And in far Simoorie had taken a wife.

And she was a damsel of delicate mould,
With hair like the sunshine and heart of gold,

And little she knew the arms that embraced
Had cloven a man from the brow to the waist:

And little she knew that the loving lips
Had ordered a quivering life's eclipse.

And the eye that lit at her lightest breath
Had glared unawed in the Gates of Death.

(For these be matters a man would hide,
As a general rule, from an innocent Bride.)

And little the Captain thought of the past,
And, of all men, Babu Harendra last.

* * * * *

But slow, in the sludge of the Kathun road,
The Government Bullock Train toted its load.

Speckless and spotless and shining with *ghee*,
In the rearmost cart sat the Babu-jee.

And ever a phantom before him fled
Of a scowling Boh with a silver head.

Then the lead-cart stuck, though the coolies slaved,
And the cartmen flogged and the escort raved;

And out of the jungle, with yells and squeals,
Pranced Boh Da Thone, and his gang at his heels!

Then belching blunderbuss answered back
The Snider's snarl and the carbine's crack,

And the blithe revolver began to sing
To the blade that twanged on the locking-ring,

And the brown flesh blued where the bay net kissed,
As the steel shot back with a wrench and a twist.

And the great white bullocks with onyx eyes
Watched the souls of the dead arise,

And over the smoke of the fusillade
The Peacock Banner staggered and swayed.

Oh, gayest of scrimmages man may see
Is a well-worked rush on the G.B.T.!

The Babu shook at the horrible sight,
And girded his ponderous loins for flight,

But Fate had ordained that the Boh should start
On a lone-hand raid of the rearmost cart,

And out of that cart, with a bellow of woe,
The Babu fell—flat on the top of the Boh!

For years had Harendra served the State,
To the growth of his purse and the girth of his *pêt*—

There were twenty stone as the tallyman knows,
On the broad of the chest of this best of Bohs.

And twenty stone from a height discharged
Are bad for a Boh with a spleen enlarged.

Oh, short was the struggle—severe was the shock—
He dropped like a bullock—he lay like a block;

And the Babu above him, convulsed with fear,
Heard the laboring life-breath hissed out in his ear.

And thus in a fashion undignified
The princely pest of the Chindwin died.

*   *   *   *   *

Turn now to Simoorie where, lapped in his ease,
The Captain is petting the Bride on his knees,

Where the *whit* of the bullet, the wounded man's scream
Are mixed as the mist of some devilish dream—

Forgotten, forgotten the sweat of the shambles
Where the hill-daisy blooms and the grey monkey gambols,

From the sword-belt set free and released from the steel,
The Peace of the Lord is with Captain O'Neil.

Up the hill to Simoorie—most patient of drudges—
The bags on his shoulder, the mail-runner trudges.

"For Captain O'Neil, *Sahib*. One hundred and ten
Rupees to collect on delivery."

Then
(Their breakfast was stopped while the screw-jack and hammer
Tore wax-cloth, split teakwood, and chipped out the dammer;)

Open-eyed, open-mouthed, on the napery's snow,
With a crash and a thud, rolled—the Head of the Boh!

And gummed to the scalp was a letter which ran:
"In Fielding Force Service.
"*Encampment*,
"10th Jan.

"Dear Sir,—I have honor to send, .. *you said*,
"For final approval (see under) Boh's Head;
"Was took by myself in most bloody affair.
"By High Education brought pressure to bear.

"Now violate Liberty, time being bad,
"To mail V.P.P. (rupees hundred) Please add

"Whatever Your Honor can pass. Price of Blood
"Much cheap at one hundred, and children want food.

"So trusting Your Honor will somewhat retain
"True love and affection for Govt. Bullock Train,

"And show awful kindness to satisfy me,
"I am,
"Graceful Master,
"Your
"H. Mukerji."

*   *   *   *   *

As the rabbit is drawn to the rattlesnake's power,
As the smoker's eye fills at the opium hour,

As a horse reaches up to the manger above,
As the waiting ear yearns for the whisper of love,

From the arms of the Bride, iron-visaged and slow,
The Captain bent down to the Head of the Boh.

And e'en as he looked on the Thing where It lay
'Twixt the winking new spoons and the napkins' array,

The freed mind fled back to the long-ago days—
The hand-to-hand scuffle—the smoke and the blaze—

The forced march at night and the quick rush at dawn—
The banjo at twilight, the burial ere morn—

The stench of the marshes—the raw, piercing smell
When the overhand stabbing-cut silenced the yell—

The oaths of his Irish that surged when they stood
Where the black crosses hung o'er the Kuttamow flood.

As a derelict ship drifts away with the tide
The Captain went out on the Past from his Bride,

Back, back, through the springs to the chill of the year,
When he hunted the Boh from Maloon to Tsaleer.

As the shape of a corpse dimmers up through deep water,
In his eye lit the passionless passion of slaughter,

And men who had fought with O'Neil for the life
Had gazed on his face with less dread than his wife.

For she who had held him so long could not hold him—
Though a four-month Eternity should have controlled him—

But watched the twin Terror—the head turned to head—
The scowling, scarred Black, and the flushed savage Red—

The spirit that changed from her knowing and flew to
Some grim hidden Past she had never a clue to,

But it knew as It grinned, for he touched it unfearing,
And muttered aloud, "So you kept that jade earring!"

Then nodded, and kindly, as friend nods to friend,
"Old man, you fought well, but you lost in the end."

*   *   *   *   *

The visions departed, and Shame followed Passion,
"He took what I said in this horrible fashion.

"*I'll* write to Harendra!" With language unsainted
The Captain came back to the Bride . . . who had fainted.

* * * * *

And this is a fiction? No. Go to Simoorie
And look at their baby, a twelve-month old Houri,

A pert little, Irish-eyed Kathleen Mavournin—
She's always about on the Mall of a mornin'—

And you'll see, if her right shoulder-strap is displaced,
This: *Gules* upon *argent*, a Boh's Head, *erased!*

THE GODS OF THE COPYBOOK HEADINGS

1919

As I pass through my incarnations in every age and race,
I make my proper prostrations to the Gods of the Market-Place.
Peering through reverent fingers I watch them flourish and fall,
And the Gods of the Copybook Headings, I notice, outlast them all.

We were living in trees when they met us. They showed us each in turn
That Water would certainly wet us, as Fire would certainly burn:
But we found them lacking in Uplift, Vision and Breadth of Mind,
So we left them to teach the Gorillas while we followed the March of
    Mankind.

We moved as the Spirit listed. *They* never altered their pace,
Being neither cloud nor wind-borne like the Gods of the Market-Place;
But they always caught up with our progress, and presently word would come
That a tribe had been wiped off its icefield, or the lights had gone out in
    Rome.

With the Hopes that our World is built on they were utterly out of touch.
They denied that the Moon was Stilton; they denied she was even Dutch.
They denied that Wishes were Horses; they denied that a Pig had Wings.
So we worshipped the Gods of the Market Who promised these beautiful
    things.

When the Cambrian measures were forming, They promised perpetual peace.
They swore, if we gave them our weapons, that the wars of the tribes would cease.
But when we disarmed They sold us and delivered us bound to our foe,
And the Gods of the Copybook Heading said: *"Stick to the Devil you know."*

On the first Feminian Sandstones we were promised the Fuller Life
(Which started by loving our neighbour and ended by loving his wife)
Till our women had no more children and the men lost reason and faith,
And the Gods of the Copybook Headings said: *"The Wages of Sin is Death."*

In the Carboniferous Epoch we were promised abundance for all,
By robbing selected Peter to pay for collective Paul;
But, though we had plenty of money, there was nothing our money could buy,
And the Gods of the Copybook Headings said: *"If you don't work you die."*

Then the Gods of the Market tumbled, and their smooth-tongued wizards withdrew,
And the hearts of the meanest were humbled and began to believe it was true
That All is not Gold that Glitters, and Two and Two make Four—
And the Gods of the Copybook Headings limped up to explain it once more.

*   *   *   *   *

As it will be in the future, it was at the birth of Man—
There are only four things certain since Social Progress began:—
That the Dog returns to his Vomit and the Sow returns to her Mire,
And the burnt Fool's bandaged finger goes wabbling back to the Fire;
And that after this is accomplished, and the brave new world begins
When all men are paid for existing and no man must pay for his sins,
As surely as Water will wet us, as surely as Fire will burn,
The Gods of the Copybook Headings with terror and slaughter return!

FOUR-FEET

"THE WOMAN IN HIS LIFE"

I have done mostly what most men do,
And pushed it out of my mind;
But I can't forget, if I wanted to,
Four-Feet trotting behind.

Day after day, the whole day through—
Wherever my road inclined—

Four-feet said, "I am coming with you!"
And trotted along behind.

Now I must go by some other round,—
Which I shall never find—
Somewhere that does not carry the sound
Of Four-Feet trotting behind.